Carl Merz und Helmut Qualtinger · Der Herr Karl

EINE BIBLIOTHEK DER ÖSTERREICHISCHEN
ZEITGENÖSSISCHEN LITERATUR

CARL MERZ UND
HELMUT QUALTINGER
DER HERR KARL

HERAUSGEGEBEN
VON TRAUGOTT KRISCHKE

Deuticke

Keller einer Delikatessenhandlung, Stellagen, Ki-
sten, auf den Regalen Konserven, Flaschen, Behälter
aller Art. Karl ist damit beschäftigt, Waren zu ord-
nen. Er ist im Begriff, eine größere Kiste aufzuhe-
ben, hält aber, bevor er Kraft anwendet, inne und
läßt sie stehen.

HERR KARL *spricht in die Kamera wie zu einer an-*
  wesenden Person: Mir brauchen Se gar nix erzählen, weil i kenn das ... die Art von Ge-
  schäften kenn i scho, do ... Se san a junger
  Mensch ... da war ich schon ... ich war auch
  ein junger Mensch ... aber damals, das war
  eine andere Zeit ... da war ein junger Mensch
  noch ein junger Mensch ... wenn er do de
  Kistn ... *Laut:* Ja! I waaß eh, Wermut rechts ...
  de Dings ... de, was? Wia haaßt des Mineral-
  wasser? Ja, i waaß, des is doch eh alles das-
  selbe ... Wasser is Wasser ... *Nach oben:* Bitte,
  ja? Jawohl, Frau Chefin! Ja, ich verstehe!
  Wieder zur Kamera: De Alte keppelt scho wieder ... Chefin ... Des war vor vierzig Jahren
  aa ka Chefin gewesen. A Chef is heit aa nimmer desselbe, ... na ja, wenn man damals so

'gangen is mit de Kartons ... oder de Flaschen oder was da war ... zustellen, da hat's nur zwei Möglichkeiten 'geben: entweder war der Hausherr z'haus ... anständiges Trinkgeld ... oder er war n e t z'haus ... *Lacht*. Na, was glauben S'? De Hausfrau – allein. Man war ein junger Mensch damals, fesch ... das Äußere ...... net? Nach aner Viertelstund' hat ma a Trinkgeld kriegt ... A Trinkgeld hat ma auf jeden Fall kriegt ...

I war damals in an G'schäft ... des war a Begriff: Feinkost-Wawra ... Für Ihnen natürlich net ... De haben sich dann in der Krise ... hat er sich derschossen ... der alte Feinkost-Wawra ...

A Erbe hat dann des G'schäft ... er hat's weiterg'führt als Reform-Wawra ... aber des war scho nix mehr ... Aber: Feinkost-Wawra – hat ma g'wußt: Wann i beim Feinkost-Wawra was bestell', dann kommt der Herr Karl. I bin immer der »Herr Karl« g'wesen. Se – san a junger Bursch. I war in Ihrem Alter scho der »Herr Karl«.

Damals hat man auf Formen was gehalten.

De Kunden. Des warn Herren! Herren und Formen!

Des müssen S' Ihnen vor Augen halten. Auch wann Se mich da anlernen sollen.

Es war a schreckliche Zeit. Inflation. Millionen san g'schwommen ... i maan, g'habt hat ma nix ... aber Formen.

Nimmt eine Zigarette heraus, zündet sie sich an. Blickt Richtung Kamera.

Rauchen verboten ... des hab i gern. Wie soll denn da a Unterhaltung zustande kommen? Was? Ah, sie riecht des oben? Ah so ...

Er tötet die Zigarette ab.

Wann geht s' denn Mittagessen? *Er bietet eine Zigarette an.* Wollen Sie? Se rauchen aa net? Is eh besser, is eh besser ... i sag Ihnen, furchtbar ... was i da mit den Rauchen allein an Geld ... was ma sich da ... wann i des in de Bausparkasse 'geben hätt ... i hätt ja immer a Häusel wolln, net? Aber des Rauchen ...

Sonst hab i ja keine Leidenschaften. Auch als Junger ... i maan scho ... Se wissen ... de Hausfraun ... aber sonst: nix. I hab mir damals geschworen in dieser Zeit, daß ich aus meinem Leben etwas machen werde, und ich hab es getan. Ich war immer bescheiden, ich hab ein bescheidenes Leben geführt, aber ich habe es genossen.

Das war eine furchtbare Zeit damals. So unruhig. De Menschen waren zornig. Verhetzt. Fanatiker. Man hat nie gewußt, welche Partei die stärkere ist. Man hat sich nie entscheiden können, wo man sich hinwendet, wo man eintritt ...

Und dann is das historische Jahr sechsundzwanzig gekommen mit den Brand vom Justizpalast.

Sechsundzwanzig war es ... des waaß i ganz genau. Da is a Onkel von mir g'storben ... er hat mir eh nix hinterlassen ... und da war des mit den Palast ... siebenundzwanzig war's.

Und da san s' also marschiert ... i waaß ja net genau, w a s los war ... es war jedenfalls a Feuer ... a Mordsfeuer war ... a schöner Brand ...

I hab ja an sich Feuer gern. Mir san alle hing'rennt und haben g'schaut ... i siech gern Feuer ... wann i a Feuer siech und hör »tatü«, renn i hin. I hab des gern, wann so de Leit umanandastehn.

Auch Unfälle. Wann wo a Unfall is ... und de Leit ... da hör ich scho: »Heerst, da pickt aner, da liegt aner ... des Bluat ...«, da renn i hin ... glei bin i dort. Weil i bin hart. Weil: I war beim Luftschutz. I hab viel g'sehn ...

Nach oben: Ja, Frau Chefin, ja! Selbstverständlich!

Zur Kamera: De Alte soll sich net aufregen ... soll froh sein, daß s' mi hat ... so leicht kriagt ma heit niemand ... Des is ja auch ein Mangelberuf ... Wer steht auf ihr Geld?

In die Dreißigerjahr – bitte – da habn mir kans g'habt ... traurig war's ... Österreich hat sich aus den Wunden, die ihm der Erste Weltkrieg geschlagen hat ... sich langsam erst von die Wunden erholt.

Aber sonst habn mir a Hetz g'habt ... manchesmal ... i maan ... mit de Katzen ... mit de Madeln ... de waren vielleicht net so anzogen wie jetzt ... aber sonst ... hat sich was abg'spielt im Freien ... a Hotel hat ma sich damals net leisten können ... andere Leit vielleicht scho ... aber i net ... bei mir war immer das Herz dabei ... immer a bisserl das Herz dabei ... mein ganzes Leben ...!

Und i kann Ihnen sagen: Ich bin bitter enttäuscht worden! I bin durch alle Höhen und Tiefen ... gegangen ... i maan, durch alle Höllen und Himmeln des Liebeslebens ... aber eines Tages steht ma do und fragt sich: Was is dir geblieben ... innerlich?

Wissen S', i war nie ein Materialist ... bei de Madeln. Schmäh habn mir g'führt ... Mandoline g'spielt ... Harmonika ... g'sungen ... de Schlager aus de Tonfilme, »Weiße Chrysanthemen schenk ich dir zur Hochzeitsnacht«, »Du schwarzer Zigeuner, ach spiel mir was vor, denn wenn deine Geige weint, das geht mir ins Ohr ...« Da waren im Inundationsgebiet, Überschwemmungsgebiet, so Standeln ... san mir g'sessen mit de Madeln ... Ribiselwein abig'stessen ... dann hab i g'sagt: Geh mer schwimmen, meine Damen? San mir abi zum Wasser, habn si um'zogen ... i hab s' a bissel einkocht ... Gebüsch is eh überall. De Donauauen sind ja wunderschön ...

Nexten Tag hab i Gelsentippeln g'habt ... frage nicht ... Sunst war's ja traurig. Wia alt san Se? Hören Se, i kennt ja Ihner Vater sein! *Lacht.*

Ernst: I hab ja nie Kinder wollen. I hätt ja a haben können ... Aber die Verantwortung? I bin ein verantwortlicher Mensch ... bei solche Zeiten ...!

I maan ... der Schilling hat scho an Wert g'habt ... das muß man ihm lassen ... aber er war net zum derwischen. Man hat sich ja bemüht, de Bundeskanzler ... wia s' alle g'haaßn ham, na helfen S' mir, na, müssen Sie ja g'lernt ham in der Schul – na der Seip... der Bur... der Scho... is ja Wurscht ... aber bein Heirigen – da hat's Persönlichkeiten gegeben!

Der Petzner-Masl, de Woitschkerlbuben, der Korschinek-Vickerl, der Nezwerka-Pepi. Is Ihnen des a Begriff? Ah naa – Se san ja jung ... Sie wissen ja nicht, was Heiterkeit war, echte Fröhlichkeit! So a Hetz wie damals habn mir nie mehr g'habt ...! Im Prater ... an der Donau ... mit de Madeln ... bein Wasser ...

I bin ja nie eini'gangen ... I hab net schwimmen können ... I hab Ihnen ja eh derzählt, wia i s' mit'n Schmäh ein'kocht hab. I hab nie ins Wasser gehn müssen ... I maan scho: I wasch mi. I hab scho z'haus a Waschmuschel, aber des genügt mir eigentlich. I brauch net ans Meer ... weil i hab kan Bedarf für viel Wasser ... da krieg i a bledes G'fühl, wann i viel Wasser siech. Das ängstigt mich. So a bissel in ana Waschmuschel oder an Lawur is grad g'nug ... net?

Oder a See. I waaß, es gibt herrliche österreichische See-e. Aber i hab des net gern. Mir traamt oft von an See ... I lieg auf aner Luftmatratzen ... Auf amal kummt aner und ziagt de Stepseln aussi ... Oiweh! ... I hab manchmal furchtbare Träume ... ich sag Ihnen, ich habe im Traum ... den Zweiten Weltkrieg vorausgesehen! I hab traamt ... 's Schießen ... Rennen ... wie de Häuser z'samm'fallen ... den ganzen Krampf ... jetzt traam i scho wieder so ... naja ...

Nach oben: Jawohl, Frau Chefin, selbstverständlich ... Es san genug Oliven da.

Zur Kamera: Wo san de Oliven? Is ja Wurscht. Von der Alten traam i aa no ... Jaja, i wer scho was machen. Ihnen kann's ja egal sein. Se san murgen eh weg ...

De Dreißigerjahr! Da war i sehr oft arbeitslos. Hackenstad. War immer dazwischen arbeitslos. Ein Leben, junger Mensch! Dazwischen arbeitslos, dazwischen hab i was g'habt, arbeitslos ... was g'habt ... oft meine Posten gewechselt. I war unbeständig ... i war ein Falter.

Bis Vieradreißig war ich Sozialist. Das war aa ka Beruf. Hat ma aa net davon leben können ... heit wann i war ... aber heit bin i ja darüber hinaus ... hab eine gewisse Reife, wo mir die Dinge gegenüber abgeklärt sind ...

Na – im Vieradreißigerjahr ... wissen S' eh, wie des war. Naa, Se wissen's net. Se san ja z' jung. Aber Se brauchen's aa net wissen ... Das sind Dinge, da wollen mir nicht dran rührn, da erinnert man sich nicht gern daran ... niemand in Österreich ...

Später bin i demonstrieren 'gangen für de Schwarzen ... für die Hahnenschwanzler ...

für de Heimwehr ... net? Hab i fünf Schilling kriegt ... Dann bin i umi zum ... zu de Nazi ... zu de damaligen Nazi ... da hab i aa fünf Schilling kriegt ... naja, Österreich war immer unpolitisch ... i maan, mir san ja keine politischen Menschen ... aber das Geld is z'sammkommen, net?

Naja – ma hat ja von was leben müssen ... des kennen S' Ihnen gar net vurstellen, was? Se kennten lernen von mir ... den Lebenskampf, wie mir ihn habn führen müssen! Sogar g'heirat hab i ... I maan – im Leben eines jeden Mannes kommt der Zeitpunkt, wo er ein Zuhause braucht. I hab mi kirchlich trauen lassen ... Damals war des ... eher günstig. I maan, i bin ja katholisch. Net sehr. Aber doch. Wie's halt bei uns is ...

Ich glaube an ein höheres Wesen. An eine Macht, die uns leitet. Schaun S' mi an, was i alles überstanden hab ...

Also se war – meine erste Gattin – se war nimmer so jung. A Witwe, net? Der Mann hat si versoffen ... Er war a Wirt. I hab ihn eh kennt ... Er ist immer g'standen bei seine alten Fleischlaberln und hat ka Luft net kriegt ... so hat er g'macht ... *Er atmet schwer.* Zum Schluß hat er net amal mehr so machen können ... An ganz roten Kopf hat er g'habt und de Fiaß voller Wasser. Sei einzige Freid war, wann er einbrennte Suppen hat essen kennen. Aber der Löffel hat s o stecken müssen. Asthma hat er g'habt ... Überg'wicht ... a fett's Herz, net? Amal kumm i ins Wirtshaus, hat sie, de Frau, ganz rote Augen. Der Poldi is nimmer ... hab i s' ang'schaut ... hab mir denkt: Scheen is s' net, aber eigentlich noch a ganz fesche Frau ... i maan, stattlich ...

I hab damals nix z' tun g'habt ... bin i vül im Wirtshaus g'sessen ...

Amal ... de Gäst' warn scho weg ... kummt s' mit an Papier und Bleistift ... was se schreiben soll: »Der teure Verblichene« oder »Mein unvergeßlicher Poldl« ... für de Parte ...

Hab i ihr g'holfen ... Und wie mir so sitzen ... I hab ja scheene Augen ... i kann scheen schauen ... damals ... heit nimma. I hab a nimmer den Blick, den was i damals g'habt hab ... des verliert si alles mit'n Alter ...

Auf amal sagt sie: »Lassen S' mi anschauen, was Se g'schrieben haben ...« Sie beugt si zu mir ... da hab i g'spiert, daß s' zidert ... da hab i alles g'wußt.

I kennt Ihnen Details erzählen ... aber Se san a junger Mensch ... Wann i Ihnen einmal meine praktischen Erfahrungen auf dem Gebiet da derzähl' ... da hätten S' was fürs Leben ... aber ich will Ihnen ja nicht verderben ... I bin glei ein'zogen ... hat sie g'sagt: »Karl, alles muß sei Ordnung haben ...« Na – da habn mir g'heirat ...

Sie hat ja a scheenes Wirtsgeschäft g'habt. Jetzt – natirlich – hab i die Gäst' dort animiert. An jeden Tisch war ich gern gesehen ... dort a Viertel, dort a Achtel trunken ... was hätt ich machen sollen? Das G'schäft muß ja rennen, net? 's war ja alles stier damals ... Dreißigerjahre ... bei mir is scho was z'sammkommen ... Wir habn a gemeinsames Sparbuch g'habt ... Kennwort hab i eh g'wußt ... verstehn S'?

Aber dann ... *Sich entschuldigend:* Natirlich hab i hie und da was aus der Kassa g'nom-

16

men ... naja, warum nicht? I war ja gegen sie
ein junger Mensch – verhältnismäßig.

I bin umeinanderzogn mit meine Spezi ... Sie
war ja eh den ganzen Tag im G'schäft. I bin
damals sehr aufs Rennen g'standen. Es war
eine furchtbare Zeit – lauter Arbeitslose ...
viele Menschen haben gelitten damals in
Österreich. I hab mir's halt ... i hab mir's
g'richt g'habt. Auf d' Nacht bin i eh ins
G'schäft 'gangen und hab mi um de Gäst'
bemüht ... Schmäh g'führt, Witz g'rissen ... i
hab Witz g'wußt, i sag Ihnen ... Da war
aner ... von an Handwerksburschen und aner
Wirtstochter. Er klopft an, und sie liegt scho
im Bett. Naa ... Es liegen alle zwaa im Bett,
und der Wirt klopft an. Falsch. Alle drei
liegen im Bett. Jetzt waaß i's nimmer ... Aber
Witz' hab i g'wußt ... Wann i Ihna des derzähl'n mecht, da hätt'n S' was fürs Leben ...

Er entkorkt eine Cognacflasche.

Es is vom G'schäft, aber Se sagen's eh net der
Chefin, was? Es ist ja ganz a bülliger. Was? A
französischer? Des is mer aa Wurscht. I kenn

ja net den Unterschied ... I hab ja an ganz andern Gschmacken ... I hab bei mir z'haus guate Sachen, Likörkompositionen, Eiercognac, Kaiserbirn, Glühwürmchen ...

Er trinkt.

Na, so hab i mi halt manchmal a bissel ang'soffen. Eines Tages wird de Alte, mei Gattin, frech. Schmeißt mi auf vur meine Freund, vur meine Haberer, vur de Gäst' ... »Der Poldl mecht scheen schaun, wann er abaschauen mecht, wier's zugeht in sein Wirtshaus ...«

Na, mehr hab i net 'braucht! »Was dei Poldl mi kann, des waaßt eh«, hab i ihr g'sagt. Hab alles hing'schmissen ... Schürzen ... hab meine Sachn aus der Wohnung g'holt ... Anzug ... alles ... Servas ... gemma ... Na, dann hat s' bled g'schaut ... Meine Freiheit aufgeben – das könnte ich nie!

Öffnet eine mitgebrachte Thermosflasche und gießt einen Großteil des Cognacs hinein.

Mei Tee ...

Er hält die Cognacflasche Richtung Kamera.

Wollen S' net den Rest? Es fällt sonst auf.

Die Cognacflasche wird ihm aus der Hand ge-
nommen.

Ich siech – Spezialitäten aus allen Ländern.
Spezialitäten aller Länder vereinigt euch! *Er*
lacht. Das ist mir so eing'falln – jetzt.

Er entnimmt derselben alten Tasche, in der sich
auch die Thermosflasche befand, ein zusammen-
gelegtes Jausenbrot und beginnt es zu essen.

Wissen S', des is mir immer no des Liebste ...
Blickt auf die Stellagen. I wer mir scho amal a
Konserven mitnehmen ... aber net für mi ...
mit aner Konserven können S' mi jagen ... i
bin ein Feind der Konservennahrung.

Stellen S' Ihnen vor – in dieser Zeit steh i
plötzlich da ... I maan, a Gemeindewohnung
hab i ja g'habt ... i hab s' ja net aufgeben
g'habt ... natirlich ... Aber des war ja scho
damals nix ... aber ich hab mich nie vom Leben unterkriegen lassen.

I bin damals einen Sparverein beigetreten ...
zum Sparen hab i ja nix g'habt ... aber ich
habe meine Arbeitskraft zur Verfügung ge-
stellt ... i maan, man hat mi drum ersucht.
Weil mi habn de Leit ja kennt, vom Wirts-

g'schäft, net? I hab das mehr so vom Organi-
satorischen geleitet. An scheenen Namen er-
funden: »Eichkatzerln vom Grund«, bin zur
Konkurrenz von meiner Gattin 'gangen und
hab g'sagt: »Was krieg i, wann i Ihnen an
Sparverein bring?« Na, mir haben jedes Jahr
vor Weihnachten a Ganslessen g'habt – *mit
Bedeutung* – in der Systemzeit, Arbeitslosen-
zeit! ... Schöne, fette Ganseln ... am nächsten
Tag is uns allen schlecht g'wesen ... Aber es
hat si auszahlt ... So bin i Kassier g'worn ...
Aber des war a Leichtsinn. I sag Ihnen,
fangen S' Ihnen nie was mit an Sparverein
an ...

Wissen S', daß de mi fast einsperren hättn
lassen? Da san Sachen g'red't worn ... da
habn s' mir vorgeworfen, mit de Konten ...
Wissen S', was des is, a Konto? Wann ma von
an Konto auf a anders transferiert ... des is a
Bankangelegenheit ... des kann i Ihnen als
Laien net so erklären ... »Herr Vorsitzender«,
hab i g'sagt zu den Richter, »des Gansl war
jedes Jahr da ... aber bitte, es wird mir eine
Lehre sein ...«

Immerhin konnte ich auf einige Erfolge zurückblicken in diesem Fach, und so haben s' mi in an Sterbeverein mit offenen Armen aufgenommen ... Der hat si aber leider nicht als ausbaufähig erwiesen, weil de Leit san g'storben und habn si net an mei Kalkulation g'halten. Und wier s' den Präsidenten von unserem Verein, den alten Herrn Kommerzialrat Krisper, begraben habn, da hab i g'wußt: 's Sterbn haaßt aa nix mehr ... Und dann is eh der Hitler kummen ...

Naja – des war eine Begeisterung ... ein Jubel, wie man sie sich überhaupt nicht vorstellen kann – nach diesen furchtbaren Jahren ... die traurigen Jahre ... Endlich amal hat der Wiener a Freid g'habt ... a Hetz ... ma hat was g'sehgn, net? ... Des kennen S' Ihnen gar net vurstellen. Wann san Se geboren? ... Achtadreißig? Naja ... Also mir san alle ... i waaß noch ... am Ring und am Heldenplatz g'standen ... unübersehbar warn mir ... man hat gefühlt, ma is unter sich ... es war wie bein Heirigen ... es war wie a riesiger Heiriger ...! Aber feierlich. Ein Taumel. *Lacht.* Na, drum

san Se ja achtadreißig geboren ... Wann? ...
Dezember? ... Hab i ma eh denkt.

Die Deitschen sein einmarschiert ... de Polizei
is g'standen mit de ... also mit de Haken-
kreizbinden ... fesch ... es war furchtbar ... das
Verbrechen, wie man diese gutgläubigen
Menschen in die Irre geführt hat ... der Führer ... hat geführt ...

Aber a Persönlichkeit war er ... vielleicht ein
Dämon ... aber man hat die Größe g'spürt ...

I maan, er war net groß. I bin ja vor ihm
g'standn – bein Blockwartetreffen im Rat-
haus. So wie i jetzt mit Ihnen sitz, bin i vor
ihm g'standen ... Er hat mi ang'schaut ... mit
seine blauen Augen ... i hab eahm an-
g'schaut ... hat er g'sagt: »Jaja.« Da hab i alles
g'wußt. Wir haben uns verstanden ...

Da bin i Illegaler g'worn ... I maan, i war
scho ... des wissen S' no gar net ... Illegal ...
des war damals jeder in Österreich ... Illegal ... des war so wie heit, wenn ma bei einer
Partei is ... bei uns im Gemeindebau alle ...
wir waren eh alle bis vieradreißig ... dann
warn mir illegal ...

I maan, schaun S', was ma uns da nachher vorgeworfen hat – des war ja alles ganz anders ... da war ein Jud im Gemeindebau, der Tennenbaum ... sonst a netter Mensch – da habn s' so Sachen gegen de Nazi g'schmiert g'habt auf de Trottoir ... und der Tennenbaum hat des aufwischen müssen ... net er allan ... de andern Juden aa ... hab i ihm hing'fiehrt, daß er's aufwischt ... und der Hausmaster hat halt zug'schaut und g'lacht ... er war immer bei einer Hetz dabei ...

Nach den Krieg dann is er z'ruckkommen, der Tennenbaum. Hab i ihm auf der Straßen getroffen, hab i g'sagt: »Habediehre, Herr Tennenbaum!«, hat er mi net ang'schaut. I grüaß ihm noch amal: » – 'diehre, Herr Tennenbaum ...« Er schaut mi wieder net an. Hab i mir denkt ... na bitte, jetzt is er bees ... Dabei ... irgendwer hätt's ja wegwischen müaßn ... I maan, der Hausmaster war ja aa ka Nazi. Er hat's halt net selber wegwischen wollen.

Alles, was man darüber spricht heute, is ja

falsch ... es war eine herrliche, schöne ... ich möchte diese Erinnerung nicht missen ...

Dabei hab i ja gar nichts davon g'habt ... Andere, mein Lieber, die habn sich g'sundg'stessn ... Existenzen wurden damals aufgebaut ... G'schäften arisiert, Firmen, Häuser ... Kinos!

I hab nur an Juden g'führt. I war ein Opfer. Andere san reich worden, i war a Idealist. Was war i? Bei der NSV ... nationalsozialistische Volkswohlfahrt. Da hat si kaner was denkt, wann er dazu'gangen is. Heit is ma ja aa überall ... bei der Gewerkschaft und so ...

Schaun S', de Leit in so an Gemeindebau waren jahrelang unbetreut ... hat si ja ka Mensch um sie gekümmert ... I hab ja nur versucht, de Leit zu erziehen ... i hab eben net nur de Beiträge kassiert ... des hab i so nebenbei g'macht ... des hab i ja kennen vom Sparverein her. I hab ihnen Sprüche gebracht – Sinnsprüche – von Goethe und von Hitler ... »Gesundheit ist Pflicht« und solche aufbauende Sachen, net? Zum Aufhängen hab i s' ihnen 'bracht ...

Und das war die Zeit, wo ich auch eine zweite Ehegemeinschaft eingegangen bin. Natirlich nur standesamtlich ... Sie war a moderner Mensch ohne Vorurteile ... mir waren in an Kino ang'stellt. Wir waren Billeteure ... I war Billeteur, net, sie war Billeteurin ... a gute Billeteurin, wirklich ...

Wir haben sehr viel Gemeinsames g'habt ... den gleichen G'schmack. Wann man so viele Filme miteinander siecht ... da kriegt ma scho a Urteil ... der Besitzer vom Kino hat aa was drauf geben ... Er hat si nur nach uns g'richtet ...

Uns hat ka Schauspieler was vurmachen kennen ... Wenn S' so a Gfrieß, so a G'sicht zehn oder fuffzehnmal segn ... da kennen S' jeden Schmäh. I brauch des alles net ... von mir aus brauchet's ka Theater gebn, ka Kino, ... a bissel a Musi, des is alles, was i brauch.

Drum bin i ja eigentlich auch für de Ehe net so geeignet ... Na ... es war im Krieg, net ... Sommer ... I hab manchmal Dienst g'habt, dann hat wieder sie Dienst g'habt ... so abwechselnd ...

Natirlich hab i manchmal so a Gelegenheit benützt ... es war ja a moderne Ehe ... a Mann is a Mann, wann er a richtiger Mann is ... im Krieg war's ja leicht mit de Weiber. I hab net einrücken müssen. Die Frau is der gebende Teil, und der Mann is der herrschende. Des hab i ihr ja aa klargemacht, bevor mir g'heirat habn ...

Aber i bin bitter entteischt 'worn. Weil sie hat sich dann Sachen herausgenommen, de was tief unter der Würde des Mannes liegen ...

Mir habn a Kasern' in der Nähe g'habt ... und da hab i immer scho g'heert, daß so viele Soldaten ... also deutsche Soldaten, aus und ein gehen im Gemeindebau ... Na – dann hab i erfahrn ... daß se bei m i r aus und ein gehen ... in m e i n e r Wohnung! M e i n e Zigaretten habn s' g'raucht! Mit m e i n e r Rasierseif habn s' si die Händ g'waschen ... die Piefke ...!

Jetzt ... ma hat ja nix machen kennen ... net? Deutsche Soldaten ... Krieg und so ... hab i g'wart ...

Einmal kummt aner, sagt ...: »Wissen S', wer oben war? A Fremdarbeiter! A Ausländer! A Tschusch!« Na, jetzt war alles leinwand. Weil des is ja kriegsrechtlich strafbar g'wesen ...

I bin eini in die Wohnung ... leise de Tür zug'macht, hab ganz ruhig zu ihr g'sagt: »Schleich di.« Sie hat mi sofort verstanden. Hat alles dag'lassen – Möbel, Wäsch', Lebensmittel ... nur damit i s' net anzag ... weg war s'.

So ist auch dieses Kapitel in meinem Leben vorübergegangen.

Ruft hinauf: Ja? Bitte, gnädige Frau? – Bitte a bissel später ...!

Wieder zur Kamera: Zigaretten holen soll i ihr! I kann do jetzt net weggehn ... mitten in der Arbeitszeit ...

Ich hab mich dann mehr für die Gemeinschaft eingesetzt. I hab alles gemacht. Bein Winterhilfswerk war i ... wann i mit der Büchsen g'scheppert hab', mei Lieber, da hat si kaner 'traut, sich auszuschließen ... an jeden hab i derwischt ... i bin ihm nachg'schlichen ... aufgelauert hab ich eahna ...

27

mit der Büchsen ... wann s' des Scheppern g'heert habn, hat jeder g'wußt: Jetzt muß er parieren!

Es war eine furchtbare Zeit ... Se können Ihnen ja davon kan Begriff machen ... Se warn a Kind ... Was wissen Se, was mir damals alles mitgemacht haben!

I maan, i hab ja alles g'habt. I bin dann Aushilfskellner gewesen ... was damals alles durch meine Händ' 'gangen is ... aber i war ja großzügig ... und freigiebig ... die Frauen ...! Die Feste! Was sich da in meiner Wohnung abgespielt hat ...! I sag Ihnen: Orgien im Gemeindebau ...

Sonst hab i mi dem Luftschutz gewidmet. I hab die Laienhelferausbildung unter mir ghabt ... Laienhelferinnen aa ... Mein Spezialgebiet war Abwehr von Giftgas ... Das Gebiet hab ich völlig beherrscht. Da hamma so an Raum g'habt, da sind s' eini mit die Gasmasken – mir ham an Gas eini'lass'n – dann ham s' mit die Gasmasken rennen müssen und singen ›Oh du schöhöhöner Westerwald‹ – und dann ham s' die Gasmasken g'wechselt alle – ich hab zugeschaut, de ham g'hustet alle – das war a Hetz – aber ich muß sagen, wenn die Alliierten a Giftgas g'schmissen hätten, wär ja nix passiert ... natürlich, wann s' mit die Bomben anfangen ... Das war ja unfair ...

Zur Kamera: Warum i net eing'ruckt bin? Das is a traurige G'schicht. I hab a Herzklappen, wo ma nix Genaues waaß. Dann hab i an Pancreas. Und der ane Lungenflügel is aa net ganz durchsichtig ... und dann – vor allem – meine Füß ...

Außerdem – a paar Leit habn ja die Heimat aufrecht erhalten müssen. Es war a schwere Zeit ... Da hat man Männer gebraucht! I hab ja damals gestrotzt! ... I maan ... auch heit noch. Schaun S' mi an! Sechzig Jahr! Und nie krank gewesen ... immer pumperlg'sund ... wann de Bombenschädlinge kommen san ... de Bombengeschädigten ... I hab die Verteilung von die Marken und die Lebensmittel überg'habt ...

Da hab i damals gute G'schäfte g'macht damit. So a G'schäft – *er deutet in den Laden* –

hätt i mir aufbauen können ... den Bombenopfern war des eh Wurscht. Wann aner grad sei Haus verloren hat, denkt er net ans Fressen. Da is er froh, daß er lebt.

Wann aner si aufg'regt hat, den hab i nur ang'schaut ... des hab i vom Führer g'lernt ... I hab kane blauen Augen, aber des kann i aa ... Na, dann san eh scho bald de Russen kummen ... Also, i bin sehr gut mit ihnen ausgekommen. I hab ja g'wußt, wie ma mit ihnen umgeht ... die Asiaten ... die Slawen ...

De Nachbarn san alle g'rennt mit ihre Hitlerbilder und habn s' am Misthaufen g'schmissen ... I hab meins hängen lassen. Dann hab i de Russen extra in mei Wohnung g'führt – kumm, Kamerad, dawai, Towarisch – hab 's Hitlerbild packt, um de Erd g'haut ... drauf herumtrampelt ... Haben s' g'sagt »Karascho« und san 'gangen ...

Ruft hinauf: Was is denn, Frau Chefin?

Zur Kamera: Na also – jetzt geht s' Mittagessen. Endlich ... *Hinauf:* Kennen S' Ihnen da net de Zigaretten glei selber mitnehmen? Was?

Zur Kamera: »Na schön«, hat s' g'sagt ... hätt aa freindlicher sein kennen ... Ma kommt si dann immer bleed vor. Ma is nett – höflich – von der alten Art – und ...

Na – dadurch, daß i Tschechisch kann – a bissel – hab i immer Zugang gefunden zu der Mentalität von de Russen ... Rußki ... mir is nix a'gangen ...

A paar Monat später – was glauben S', wer 'kommen is? – De Ameriganer. Des war eine Erlösung ...

Da hab i mi gleich beworben ... weil man steht doch dem Westen ... weil ich doch schon die ganze Zeit die Arbeit gemacht hab für die Gemeinschaft ... net? ... um den We-sten zu verteidigen ... Luftschutz und des ... hab i mir denkt, es muß doch a Meglichkeit geben bei de Ami ... und mit'n Essen war's aa ganz gut ... was i so g'heert hab von an-dere Parteigenossen ... und von de Kamera-den von der NSV ... da habn s' mi eingestellt als Tschiwilien Gard ... san mir g'standen ... so ... ältere Männer mit Helme ... haben Park-plätz' bewacht von de Ami ... und waren praktisch sozusagen a Militärpolizei ... a gefährlicher Posten ...

Na – mir haben aufpaßt! Wann a Österreicher 'kommen is – glei habn mir ihm verjagt ...! »Weg da! Go away! You!« ...

Des is mir dann sehr zugute gekommen, wie i später g'arbeit hab am Cobenzl als Parkwächter. Als Autoeinweiser, net? Da hab i a Regiment g'führt! Wie bei der Gemeinschaft ...

Ich war ja ka gewehnlicher Parkwächter ... I hab mir viel Sprachen angeeignet in der Besatzungszeit ... wann a Autobus mit aner russischen Reiseg'sellschaft 'kommen is ... bin i glei dag'standen, hab g'sagt »Towarischi ... sdrasdfudje!« Na habn s' mir auf de Schulter 'klopft und g'lacht ... da hab i scheen kriegt ... Und de Amis ... wann de kommen san, hab' i sogar 's Wagentürl aufg'macht, hab g'sagt »Hello Sör!« Des heern s' immer gern. Des is scho a Sache, was de auslassen ... ka Vergleich mit de Deitschen. Weil Deitsch kann ja eh a jeder.

Natürlich – es war eine harte Zeit ... man hat

ein befreites Volk hungern lassen ... mi net. I hab scho immer was derwischt. G'schäfter g'habt ... Wann i damals in a Nachtlokal kommen bin, habn s' alle 'glaubt, i bin a Lord ...

Dann is de Währungsreform 'kommen ... da hab i wieder alle Lust verloren zum Leben ...

Da hat man sein Leben aufgebaut ... mindestens zwanzigmal hab i mein Leben auf'baut im Lauf von mein' Leben ...

Was is 'blieben? Und wann ma dann scho ölter is und nicht mehr den Schwung hat und den Charme, da ...

I hätt ja net arbeitslos sein müssen ... i hätt in einer Garderobe arbeiten können ... oder als Portier ... sogar in einer Sauna hätt i den Aufguß machen können ... den besten Leuten ... aber wann's so weit war, hab i immer des Gefühl gehabt, es gibt mir innerlich keine Befriedigung.

Z'letzt bin i 'gangen mit deformierte Luftballöner ... ballone. De hab i kriegt ... bülliger ... weil s' zweite Wahl warn ... Sie waren nimmer ganz rund ... haben so Dippeln g'habt ...

manche waren aa a bissel eing'schrumpelt. Ma hat aufpassen müssen, daß s' net zerplatzen, bevur man s' verkauft ...

Bin i 'gangen zum Heirigen ... wann de Leite scho b'soffen waren ... de hätt'n mir eckige Ballons aa o'kauft ...

Na, so hab i s' g'halten, de Luftballöner, und hab mir denkt: eigentlich is's traurig, daß ma so a Leben führen muß ... nach allem, was man geleistet hat ...

Amal hab i nur no an Ballon g'habt ... kumm i zu aner Gesellschaft, was sehr animiert war ... fragt mi ane – se hat so an klan Steirerhut aus Papier aufg'habt ... per Hetz natirlich – originell, net? Fragt s' mi: »Was kost der Ballon?« I sag mein' Preis. Sie lacht bled und sagt: »I gib Ihna a Bussel dafier!« Hab i ma denkt: Ah was! Er kann eh kaum no fliegen, der Ballon ... Bin i pickn blieben ... Bis in der Fruah ...

Se hat am Laaerberg g'wohnt. Bin i mitg'fahrn. Am Weg hab i ihr dann von meine unglücklichen Ehen derzählt ... in gleichen Alter warn mir aa – bitte, sie war Brillenträgerin, aber eine fleißige Person. Aa schlecht behandelt vom Leben ...

Na, bin i zu ihr 'zogn ... Sie war Bedienerin. Aber sonst sehr reinlich. Sie hat in an Biro g'arbeit, und i hab den Haushalt g'führt, 'kocht ... alles in Ordnung g'halten ... i hab gut kocht ... na klar ... i hab ja aa mit'gessen ... da hab ich so meine Stärke gekriegt ... ich bin ja ein stärkerer Herr heit!

Gelesen hab ich sehr vül in dieser Zeit ... so wissenschaftliche Sachen ... sonst interessiert mich ja nix ... Ärztebücher ... ›1x1 des täglichen Lebens‹ ... Aufklärung ... weil, ich mein, praktisch hab ich ja eh alles beherrscht – aber das interessiert einen ja, wie sich das alles abspielt, innerlich ... Dann hab ich noch g'lesen ›Strahlenmeer Weltenraum‹ ... alles, was uns angeht ... mi wundert gar nix mehr, was im Weltall g'schiecht, weil i kenn mi durt genau so aus wie im Gemeindebau ...

Am Sonntag sind mir manchesmal ins Piestingtal g'fahren – sie hat dort so a Siedlungshäuserl g'erbt g'habt von ihre Eltern ... da san mir g'sessen ... habn in Regen aussi-g'schaut ... und habn uns denkt: andere Leite haben das nicht ...

Im Sommer, wann's haaß war, habn mir das Essen ins Papierl packt, Milchkaffee in a Bierflaschen, san zum Donaukanal abi ... i hab mir 's Hemd auszogen, sie war in der Kombinesch ... schön war s' net ... aber i hab da vor kurzem meine zweite Gattin g'sehn ... de fesche Billeteurin ... i kann Ihnen sagen ... De hat ausg'schaut ... schiach ... fett ... ungustiös ...

I bin ja aa net scheen. Aber ein Mann halt' sich immer noch besser. Ein Mann hat noch immer einen gewissen Anwert. Aa so wie i heit bin ...

Wir haben in unserer Gassen viel Witwen und Ledige ... wier de mi anschauen: »Wann S' amal Fernsehen kommen wollen, Herr Karl ...« Fernsehen! I bin ja net interessiert ...

Aber auch diese Lebensgemeinschaft war nicht von Dauer. Sie is leidend geworden ... ins Spital hat s' müssen ...

Na – hab i g'sagt: Du mußt einsehn – jetzt muß i weg. I maan – i hab eh mei Arbeitslo-

sen g'spart g'habt de ganze Zeit. Hat s'
g'fragt: Besuchst mi einmal im Spital? Hab i
g'sagt: I waaß net.

Mei Gemeindewohnung hab i ja net aufgeben. I bin ja net bled.

Na – von da ab is es eh wieder aufwärts
'gangen ... i hab sozusagen meine Lebens-
freude wieder gewonnen ... I hab gute Posten
g'habt ... schlechte Posten g'habt ... g'arbeit
hab i nie vül ...

Net, weil i's net k a n n ... Aber des ... des is
eine gewisse Reife ... da genießt man gern –
wissen Sie – das Leben ...

Man wird überlegen ... man erinnert sich:
Wie man sich geplagt hat ... für die Gemeinschaft ... für die Gattinnen ... für den Beruf ...
für den Wiederaufbau ... und was ist geblieben? Erfahrung ... Lebensklugheit ... immerhin. Aber sonst? Zuviel Herz, zuviel Arbeit ...
zuviel Aktivität.

Natürlich ... es gibt auch schöne Momente.
Und auf die hab ich mich immer konzen-
triert.

G'freut hab ich mich schon ... an dem Tag,

wo mir den Staatsvertrag bekommen haben ... Da san mir zum Belvedere zogen ... san dag'standen ... unübersehbar ... lauter Österreicher ... wie im Jahr achtunddreißig ... eine große Familie ... a bissel a klanere ... weil 's Belvedere is ja klaner als der Heldenplatz. Und auch die Menschen waren schon reifer geworden ...

Und dann is er herausgetreten auf den Balkon, ... der ... der ... Poldl und hat die zwa andern Herrschaften bei der Hand genommen und hat mutig bekannt: »Österreich ist frei!«

Und wie ich das gehört hab, da hab ich gewußt: Auch das hab ich jetzt geschafft. Es ist uns gelungen – der Wiederaufbau ...

Ich mein, nicht daß ich blind wär gegen die Fehler der Regierung ... i war ja immer kritisch. Ich hab immer alles durchschaut ... auch a Regierungsmitglied, wann i mir's so anschau ... der is aa net anders wier i. Und i kenn mi.

So san de alle. Aber bitte – es geht mich nix an. Ich mache meine Arbeit, ich kümmere mich nicht um Politik, ich schaue nur zu und behalte es für mich.

I red ja net vül. I bin ja ein eher verschlossener Mensch ... Schauen Sie – daß i jetzt so mit Ihnen red ... i hätt's ja nicht notwendig. I kennt ja auch arbeiten ... Aber Sie – Sie müssen es ja auch einmal lernen. Und wenn man die Erfahrung hat, dann hat man auch die Pflicht, es weiterzugeben. Denn lernen kann man nur aus der Erfahrung ... Wolln S' an Schoklad? Schweizer. Naja – Sie san a junger Mensch. Vor Ihnen liegt das ganze Leben. Aber so in mein' Alter ... da is ma oft auf was Süßes. Man steckt es in Mund, und es vergeht die Zeit ...

Na – i hab an Schofför kennt, der war mir sozusagen verpflichtet. Der hat g'sagt: »Paß auf, Karl, i fahr jetzt über die Länder – privat – weil i mecht einmal unser schönes Österreich kennenlernen – jetzt, wo es wieder uns g'heert. Willst mitfahren?« Da hab i g'sagt: »Geh – i kann des ja gar net zahlen, was du an Benzin verfahrst ...« – »Naa, naa, Karl, i kenn di – du machst eh nie an Urlaub ...

komm ruhig mit.« – »Naja, aber du verdienst dir ja dei Geld a net so leicht ...« – »Also bitte«, sagt er, »ladst mi halt manchesmal ein und so ...«

Na – san mir g'fahren ... Was mi des kost hat! I hab alles zahlen kennen. Wär' bülliger kommen, wann i mit einer G'sellschaftsreise mit an Autobus g'fahrn war ...

I hab des nämlich an sich gern, mit'n Autobus ... Da san immer vül Leit, mit denen man sich unterhalten kann. Ältere Frauen, net? Sie wissen ja. I hab halt noch die Art von früher ...

So bin i amal sogar nach Italien kummen ... Vüle Städte ... so genau hab i mir's net g'merkt ... der Wein kost' dort fast nix. De andern habn s' in der Hitz umananderzaht – i hab mi ang'soffen ...

Scheen war's in Italien. I hab net vül g'segn. Aber der Autobus is sehr guat g'fahrn.

Aber Österreich ist natürlich auch herrlich ... Großglockner, der Pasterzengletscher ... ewiges Eis durt oben ... die Majestät der Bergriesen ... warn aa viel Leit durt ... nette Leit. Da kummt ma glei ins Gespräch. Weil da steht aner neben an und sagt: »Schaun S', is do eigentlich schön: Österreich. Und ma kennt's gar net ...« Und i sag: »Ja, ja, wirklich. Des mecht ma gar net glaubn, wann ma so in Wien is ...« Unwillkürlich hat ma da was Gemeinsames ... wann ma da steht, net? Herrlich, sag i Ihnen, die Franz-Josefs-Höhe. Achtzig Schülling hat mi des kost! Fünf Bier, fünf Schnäpse hab i eahm zahln müssen, dem Schaffeer. Na gut, i will ja nix drüber ... irgend amal muß ma sich ja etwas leisten ...

Dann warn mir am Semmering. Des is aa schön. Sehr schön. Wann man bedenkt, daß ma das so in der Nähe hat und eigentlich nie ausnützt ... ma kann überall auffifahrn mit an Sessellift ... weil i brauch ja net z'fuß gehen. In Inundationsgebiet, Überschwemmungsgebiet, wann i da spazierengeh, das genügt mir. Was brauch i da auffisteigen, irgendwo? Des is eh net g'sund. I muß eh ... i hab eh kan Aufzug im Gemeindebau ... i wohn ja im dritten Stock. I m u ß steigen ...

I maan ... ich liebe die Berge ... wann i

fahr ... San mir nach Mariazell kummen. Der Gnadenort. Hat mich sehr beeindruckt. Obwohl i also ka so absolut gläubiger Mensch bin. Aber ma denkt sich, es könnt doch was dran sein ... wann ma so de Kirchen sieht und ... de scheenen Hotels. Und de herrlichen Reiseandenken. I hab ma kauft so an Stöpsel, so an Zierkorken mit an Bauernkopf. Scheen, wirklich! Österreichische Heimatkunst!

Auf der Rückfahrt san mir durch de Wachau g'fahren. Da war ich überwältigt von den steinernen Zeugen unserer Vergangenheit ... Melk, Dürnstein, Göttweig ... Da hat er si ang'soffen, mein Freind ... I hab ihm g'sagt: »Achte auf deinen Alkoholgehalt ...« Da is er ordinär worden ... Hab i eahm erklärt: »Leider ... meine Barschaft is nicht so, daß ich mir was leisten kann.« Na, hat er was g'matschkert von Benzin und so ... Dabei is er eh an Diesel g'fahrn ...

Ich hab das dann abgebrochen. Hab g'sagt: »I bin dir net bös, aber i geh jetzt ...« und bin mit der Donau-Dampfschiffahrts-Gesellschaft von Krems nach Wien g'fahren ...

Oben bin i g'standen, am G'lander ... angenehm kühl war's ... die Ufer sind an mir vorbeigezogen, und i hab mir denkt: du kannst allan nach Wien schaffieren ... in dein' alten, miesen, haaßen Kübel.

I maan ... mir hat's ja sehr gut gefallen, unser Österreich. Aber in an gewissen Alter braucht man nicht mehr davon zu sehen ... man interessiert si nimmer so ... Es läßt alles nach ... zum Beispiel das Atomzeitalter ... I war mein ganzes Leben von Gefahren umgeben ... Revolution, Hungersnot, Krieg, Giftgas ... fast ... ich hab keinen Kontakt mit der Atombombe. Es ist außerhalb meines Interessengebietes ... Ich überlaß das anderen Menschen. Ich bin nur ein kleiner Österreicher innerhalb einer unabhängigen Nation ... mi fragt ja niemand ... bitte, sollen sich die anderen den Kopf zerbrechen.

Wann i mi zerstreuen will, brauch i ka Wasserstoffbomben ... i geh spazieren im Überschwemmungsgebiet ... Inundationsgebiet ...

Da geh i gern hin! Oft! Wann's haaß is. Da san so Bombentrichter. Und da liegen s' drin ... de jungen Leit. Madeln und Burschen. I maan, i bin ka Voyeur ... wier's viele gibt, was da so spazieren gehn. Aber mit so junge Leit is's halt a Hetz ... mir haben damals ja noch Hemmungen g'habt ... aber heit ... die kennen nix ... die G'fraster!

I siech s' ja net ... i bin kaner, der zuschaut ... aber was i so heer ... wissen S', da kumm i mir ganz jung vor ... und da werd ich ganz traurig. Und wann i traurig bin, muß ich was fressn ...

Da is aa no des Standel von de Dreißiger-jahr ... und de Alte – i maan, des is scho de Tochter von der Alten von damals – de kennt mi scho. Da kann i essen. Sehr gut ... sehr ausgiebig. Net teier ...

Neilich hab i a Schlachtplatten 'gessen, Schweinsbraten, Blutwurst, Bratwürstel, Le-berwurst, Kraut, Knedel; Bier dazu. Es war leider warm, denn es war furchtbar haaß. *Lacht.* Naja – drum war i ja da.

Leider hab i kan Hut g'habt ... De Sunn hat de ganze Zeit auf mein' Kopf g'scheint ...

Wier i zur Straßenbahn 'gangen bin, is mir

schlecht worn. I fall auf an Sitz z'samm, kummt de Schaffnerin: »Is Ihnen was?« I muß ausg'schaut habn wie der Tod.

I hab grad no sagen können: »Ich wohne Grösslgasse 15, Stiege 6, Tür 12, wann was sein sollt ...«

Na – es war eh nix. I hab mi no mit letzter Kraft z'haus g'schleppt ... man will ja niemand Scherereien machen. Bin z'haus, hab 's Fenster aufg'macht ... dann is mir schlecht worn ... net am Fenster ... scho, wie sich 's g'heert ...

Dann hab i mi aufs Bett g'legt und bin ohnmächtig g'worn ... Am nächsten Tag bin i abigangen ins Wirtshaus ... a klans Gulasch, a klans Bier ... alles wieder leinwand ... Na – jetzt so wie ich leb' ... ich kann mich nicht beklagen. Es geht mir eigentlich sehr gut. Ich hab meine Wohnung ... eingerichtet ... sauber alles ... den Radio ... Eiskasten hab i ... I brauch ihn ja eigentlich net. I hab ja nix drin. I eß eh net z'haus ... I kumm aa kaum zum Radioheern ...

Früher, mit meiner zweiten Frau ... der Bille-

teurin ... da habn mir immer 's Radio auf-
draht g'habt ... es war ja aa Krieg ... Da san aa
viel Leit kummen ... jetzt ...

Wissen S', de Leit in Haus san ma aa zu bled.
I kenn sie jetzt scho fünfazwanzg Jahr ...
Frauen gegenüber bin i ja mein Leben lang
bitter enttäuscht worden ... des mecht i nimmer ...

I hab no an Verwandten in Stuttgart ... i kenn
ihm persenlich net ... aber wir schreiben uns
einmal in Jahr ... zu Weihnachten. De Marken
heb i immer auf ... sind Sie vielleicht Mar-
kensammler? Naja – ahso ... hätt mir gedacht,
daß Sie dafür vielleicht Verwendung hätten ... und sonst ... eh ... i bin ja sehr zufrie-
den. I hab Krankenkassa, i bin völlig gesi-
chert ... i hab alles zuhaus: Schlafmittel,
schmerzstillende Tabletten, wann was is ...
daß 's mi net unvorbereitet trifft ... und so ... i
kennt sagn, es geht mir zum ersten Mal in
meinem Leben wirklich gut. I kann mir's
leisten, heite auch amal wo hinzugehen ...
besser auszugehen ... i hab aa an scheenen
Anzug ... an dunklen. Der is kaum ge-

braucht ... naja, wann geh denn i scho aus? Eigentlich schad drum ... i hab kan Erben ...

Mit mein' Geld kumm i immer aus. I hab keine Bedürfnisse. Lesen tu i aa nix. Damit muß ma frieher anfangen ... Oder Kunst oder solche Sachen ... i hab mei ganzes Leben ka Zeit g'habt fir sowas. I hab Wichtigeres zu tun g'habt ... ich habe Aufgaben zu erfüllen g'habt.

Wann i was sehen will, geh i an de Ecken zum Wirt. Der hat an Fernseh ... man muß net hinschauen, aber man kann. Da sitz i da und schau zu ... Mir is Wurscht, was ge-spielt wird. Wann i miad bin, zahl i und geh furt.

Manchesmal, wann's am Sunntag scheen is, fahr i nach Mödling oder Klosterneuburg ... Da schau i mir de Häuser an und denk mir: De hätten s' dir in der Russenzeit nach-g'haut. Da is a Villa, an der geh i immer vorbei ... de kennt heit mir geheeren ... wer weiß, zu was es gut is ...

Dann steig i in die Stadtbahn, fahr wieder heim und leg' mi schlafen ...

I schlaf ja gut. Net immer, natürlich ... manchmal, wann i so lieg, hör ich die Rettung vorbeifahren ... tatüüü ... dann denk i mir nur: Karl, du bist's net ...

Schaun S', wann i mich von der Arbeit zurückziehen will, hab i meine Rente ... wann i mir nimmer meinen Haushalt führen will, geh ich nach Lainz ... ich kann ruhig in die Zukunft blicken ... na und so wart mer halt ab, was noch kommt, wie's wird ... wie's weitergeht ...

Was si a'spült ... I bin ganz pickert wurn vo dem Schoklad. *Er geht zur Toilette, öffnet die Tür nochmals kurz.* Holn S' ma das Handtuch, ja? De Saaf a. *Schließt die Tür wieder. Man hört ihn weiterreden:* Ich weiß heute eins, daß ich mein Leben nicht umsonst gelebt hab ... und das ist vielleicht das, worauf es ankommt ... Das werden Se als junger Mensch vielleicht no net so begreifen ... aber Se werdn no oft an mi z'ruckdenken. *Er kommt zurück, sieht, daß er allein ist.* Weg is er.

Jaa ... de Kisten ... *Er schickt sich, wie zu Beginn, an, die Kiste aufzuheben, hält inne, blickt*

auf die Uhr. Zwei Uhr ... ahso ... es is ja Samstag ... Arbeitsschluß ... *Er läßt die Kiste sinken
und stellt sie wieder hin.* Geh ma ...

Abblenden.
*Eventuell Kamerafahrt über enge eiserne Wendel-
treppe, durch Laden, Zusperren des Geschäftes mit
Herunterziehen des Rollbalkens.*

Anmerkungen

Mit der Figur des Herrn Karl setzten Carl Merz und Helmut Qualtinger eine Wiener Tradition fort, die bis zu Eduard Pötzls (1871–1914) Herrn von Nigerl und Vincenz Chiavaccis (1847–1916) Herrn von Adabei zurückreicht. Ende der zwanziger Jahre setzte der Zeichner Ladislaus Kmoch (1897–1971) im »Kleinen Blatt« mit der Figur des Tobias Seicherl diese Tradition fort. Während des Exils war es Friedrich Torberg (1908–1979), der mit seinem Herrn Neidinger in der Pariser »Österreichischen Post« folgte, und in den vierziger Jahren in London war es Robert Lucas (1904–1984) mit seinem Herrn Adolf Hirnschal in der BBC. Und schließlich kann auch noch Ferdinand Korbers Herr Haslinger in der kommunistischen »Volksstimme« in den Wiener Nachkriegsjahren als Vorläufer des Herrn Karl gelten.

Über die Entstehung des *Herrn Karl* gibt es mehrere, zum Teil widersprechende Versionen. Ein junger Schauspielkollege, Nikolaus Haenel, der in der »literarisch-musikalischen Revue« von Bronner, Merz und Qualtinger *Dachl überm Kopf* mitgewirkt hatte, war der eigentliche Entdecker. Nikolaus Haenel schreibt: »Vor der Vorstellung *Dachl überm Kopf* im Neuen Theater am Kärntnertor trafen Qualtinger und ich uns öfter im ›TOP – Spezialitäten aus aller Welt‹. Das ›TOP‹ befand sich Ecke Führichgasse-Tegethoffstraße im 1. Bezirk. Es war ein kleines, dreistöckiges (Keller, Laden, Stockwerk)

Geschäft, in dem seltsamerweise Delikatessen (Konserven, Schnäpse, Gewürze, Weine, Biere, aber keine ›Frischware‹) und Einrichtungsgegenstände (Vasen, Gardinen, Nippes) verkauft wurden. Geschäftsführer der Delikatessenabteilung zu ebener Erde war ein alter Freund Qualtingers, Helmuth Hoffmann, den anderen Teil des Geschäftes führte die ›Chefin‹ selbst, Baronin Gerhardus. Im Keller, durch eine eiserne Wendeltreppe zu erreichen, war das Lager.

Am späteren Nachmittag fanden sich also dort im Laden, sehr zum Unwillen der Baronin, mit großer Regelmäßigkeit Qualtinger, Haenel und andere Leute vom Fach, vom Funk, Journalisten, Musiker, Autoren, in unregelmäßiger Anzahl, meistens nur zwei oder drei, zum Gespräch über Whisky, Tagesgeschehen, seltene Delikatessen (Ameisen in Schokolade aus Mexiko) und zur Vorbereitung der Extempores ein.

Übrigens: Später ging diese Funktion auf das ›Gutruf‹ über, damals ebenso Delikatessengeschäft, später Club, schräg gegenüber der Peterskirche. Daher das Gerücht, der *Herr Karl* sei dort entstanden, denn auch dort gab es ein Lager im Keller und eine ähnliche Treppe und ähnliche Gespräche und Zusammenkünfte.

Nun, als das Programm *Dachl überm Kopf* abgespielt war, hatte ich eine kleine Rolle im Volkstheater, dann hatte ich einen Zeitraum von etwa drei Monaten bis zum nächsten Engagement in der Schweiz als Arbeitsloser zu überbrücken. Helmuth Hoffmann suchte einen Geschäftsdiener, ich sagte, das könne ich doch machen, alle lachten, später auf der Straße sagte ich zu Qualtinger, es sei mein Ernst, wir gingen zurück, Qualtinger vermittelte, und so wurde ich Geschäftsdiener.

Als der Zeitpunkt der Abreise in die Schweiz nahte, wurde mein Nachfolger eingestellt, den ich eine Woche lang in die Arbeit eines Geschäftsdieners einzuweisen hatte. Dieser Nachfolger hieß Herr Max. Herr Max war an der Arbeitseinteilung (Lagerbestände prüfen, Nachfüllen der Regale, Boden aufwischen, Bestellzettel ausfüllen, Bestellungen in zwei riesigen Leinentaschen austragen) nicht sehr interessiert und begann dem jungen Studenten, der ihm all dies beibringen sollte, also mir, lieber sein Leben zu erzählen. Er tat dies in einer sehr anschaulichen, theatralischen Weise, wobei er die beiden Stühle, die sich im Keller befanden, immer wieder als Bühnenbild verwendete. Mal waren sie Bett und Waschtisch, für die Schilderung des Mordversuches an seiner Gattin, weil sie sich mit seiner Rasierseife die Hände gewaschen hatte, mal die Schilderhäuser des Wachposten in Norwegen. Ich wußte, daß Qualtinger auf der Suche nach einer Figur war, die man als Nazi hätte bezeichnen können. Herr Max erzählte, daß er NS-Parteigenosse gewesen war. Seine Geschichten waren so ein-

drucksvoll, daß ich Qualtinger anrief, wir uns am nächsten Tag kurz vor Geschäftsschluß trafen, ins ›Halali‹ gingen, einem einer Snackbar ähnlichen Stüberl am Neuen Markt, gleich um die Ecke, und ich dort nacherzählte und nachspielte, was mir Herr Max tagsüber im Keller erzählt und vorgespielt hatte. Qualtinger wiederum begab sich am nächsten Nachmittag zu Carl Merz, der im selben Haus wohnte, in dem das ›TOP‹ war (oder war es das Nachbarhaus?), und Merz schrieb die Geschichten auf. Zur nämlichen Zeit spielte und erzählte Herr Max im Keller des ›TOP‹ den weiteren Verlauf seines Lebens. Kurz vor Geschäftsschluß holte mich Qualtinger wieder ab, wir gingen ins ›Halali‹ – das ging so vier Tage lang. Am letzten Tag meiner Anstellung, dem Samstag, wollte Qualtinger Herrn Max kennenlernen, ich rief ihn aus dem Keller, er solle heute früher als sonst das Geschäft fegen, Herr Max kam, ich versuchte ein Gespräch zu beginnen, aber er war, ich glaube, weil er Qualtinger erkannt hatte, jedenfalls ›vor Publikum‹, sehr verschüchtert und war zu keiner Äußerung, außer zwei verkicherten, witzlosen Bemerkungen, zu bewegen.
Wie er mit Familiennamen hieß – ich weiß es nicht mehr.
In der Mitte der Woche hatte er mich beim Mittagessen in einem Beisl in der Krugerstraße seiner Schwester vorgestellt. Warum? Jedenfalls blieb diese Begegnung folgen- und pointenlos.

Wenige Wochen später erreichte mich in Luzern ein Brief eines Schulfreundes, der Nachfolger des Herrn Max als Geschäftsdiener geworden war und mir berichtete, daß der Herr Max fristlos entlassen wurde, als sich herausstellte, daß die Wermutbestände rapid abgenommen hatten und eine Überprüfung seines Köfferchens, in dem er sein Frühstück mitzubringen pflegte, drei Flaschen Martini zutage förderte. (›Des is nur heite, weil mei' Schwesta so Schädelweh hat.‹)

Es gibt aber noch einen Menschen, der als Vorbild des Herrn Karl diente: Herr Jerschabek. Herr Jerschabek stand meist am Schanktisch im ›Falstaff‹ gegenüber der Volksoper. Qualtinger sagte, als ich zu Besuch in Wien war, das Stück sei fast fertig, es fehle nur noch der Schluß. Ursprünglich sollte es ein Zweipersonenstück werden, wobei die Rolle des Zuhörers nicht nur undankbar zu werden versprach, sondern auch sonst nicht zu Leben kam. Erich Neuberg, Oberspielleiter des Österreichischen Fernsehens, schlug vor, daraus einen Monolog zu machen, mit der Kamera als Zuhörer.

Herr Jerschabek also stand an der Pudel und durfte die Reste aus den zurückgehenden Gläsern in seinem Glas vereinen, bestellte wohl hin und wieder ein Achtel oder ein Seidel. Es hieß, er erzähle sehr merkwürdige Geschichten. Qualtinger bat mich, mich zu Herrn Jerschabek zu stellen, vielleicht käme ich in ein Gespräch. Herr Jerschabek war ein pensionierter Friseur und beklagte sich bitter über einen Verwandten, ich glaube, es war sein Schwiegersohn, und wie dieser ihn auf einer Autoreise durch Österreich alles habe bezahlen lassen. Ich stellte ihn Qualtinger als Rechtsanwalt vor, der vielleicht juristischen Rat wisse, und Herr Jerschabek erzählte seine Geschichte auf die gleiche Weise noch einmal. Er hatte wohl schon Routine darin. Ob er einen juristischen Ratschlag bekam, weiß ich nicht mehr. Jedenfalls gab diese Geschichte den Anstoß für die Österreichreise des Herrn Karl.« (Nikolaus Haenel am 22. 3. 1995 an den Hg.)

Nikolaus Haenel war schon 1962, damals von Martin Morlock (1918–1983), für den »Spiegel«, zur Entstehungsgeschichte befragt worden. »Das Interview fand nur kurze Zeit nach den tatsächlichen Geschehnissen statt und entspricht sehr genau dem, was ich damals zu berichten hatte«, sagt Haenel heute. Damals beschrieb er das Vorbild des Herrn Karl als »mageres Männchen mit graumeliertem Schnauzbart, Glatzenansatz, einer Nickelbrille, die er nur in bedeutsamen Momenten aufsetzt, und ›seltsam kontrollierten‹ Bewegungen«. Für das Interview hatte Herr Max aus Gründen des Persönlichkeitsschutzes den Namen Josef erhalten. »NS-Parteimitglied war er, der Herr Josef. Und NSV-Betreuer und Teppich-Auflader und Katzenvertilger in einem Tierasyl. (›Ganz steif woarn s', die Viecherl, nach aaner Stund' hat ma s' richtig zerbrechen können, die Hax'n.‹) Josef war Norwegen-Kämpfer. ›Zur Illustration dieses Lebensabschnitts stolzierte er mit geschultertem Besen durch den Lagerkeller und fragte: ›Bittä, was bemerken Sie an mir?‹

Haenel: ›Sie tragen den Besen auf der falschen Schulter.‹

Herr Josef: ›Seh'n S', da siecht man's. Sie ham studiert!‹

›Bitter enttäuscht‹ wurden sie – im Privatleben – alle beide. Nur: dem authentischen Josef ist, im Gegensatz zum ersonnenen Karl, wirklich Herzeleid geschehen; seine erste Frau brannte ihm mit dem gemeinsamen Sparbuch nach Südamerika durch, und die zweite Josephsehe endete ungleich dramatischer als irgendeine ›Lebensgemeinschaft‹ des gefilmten Karl.

Erzählte der Herr Josef: ›Meine zwaate Gattin hatte die Angewohnheit, sich mit meiner Rasiersaaf die Händ' zu waschen. Eines Tages kumm i z'haus, wascht sie sich wieder damit. Ich pack' s' bei der Gurgl, druck' zua, sie wird erst rot, dann gölb, dann blau – i lauf' 'naus auf die Gass'n, sag' zu an Taxichauffeur: ›Hör zua, i hab' grad mei Frau um'bracht‹ – in aaner solchenen Situation ist ma schnöll per du mit an Taxler –, ›i pack' jetzt meine Koffer‹, sag' i, ›und du füast mi aussi zu meiner Mutter nach Hernals.‹ Er sagt ›Ja‹, i lauf' z'ruck, kommt mir die Frau, die was i g'würgt hab, auf der

Trepp'n entgegen, waant, bitt' mich um Verzeihung, schreit, ›Joschi, i tu's nimmer‹ – aber i bin hoat geblüben.‹

Qualtinger: ›Den echten *Herrn Karl* hätte uns kein Mensch geglaubt.‹« (Martin Morlock im »Spiegel« vom 21. 3. 1962).

Die Ursendung des *Herrn Karl* war am 15. November 1961 im Österreichischen Fernsehen zu sehen. Helmut Qualtinger spielte den Herrn Karl, Regie führte Erich Neuberg. Die Ausstrahlung löste eine ungeheure Protestwelle aus, auf die Fernsehdirektor Gerhard Freund mit einem offenen Brief reagierte: »Sinn und Aufgabe war es, die Jugend zu informieren. *Der Herr Karl* wurde – meiner Meinung nach – von einigen Zuschauern mißverstanden. Wir wollten keine Generalisierung des Österreichers mit dieser Sendung erreichen. Die Sendung sollte eher zum Nachdenken anregen ... Es war bewußt eine negative Zusammenfassung. Auch Nestroy, der Österreich sehr liebte, hat mit seinen Stücken den Österreichern einen Spiegel vorgehalten ... die Diskussion beweist, wie wichtig die Sendung war ...«

Der Kritiker Hans Weigel (1908–1991), der auch einführende Worte zur Sendung gesprochen hatte, faßte in dem Satz zusammen: »*Der Herr Karl* wollte einem Typus auf die Zehen treten, und ein ganzes Volk schreit ›Au!‹« (Kronen-Zeitung, Wien, 2. 12. 1961).

Hans Weigel war es auch, der dem Regisseur

Friedrich Kallina den *Herrn Karl* als Bühnenstück für das »Kleine Theater der Josefstadt im Konzerthaus« empfohlen hatte. Vierzehn Tage nach der Fernsehsendung war Premiere: am 30. November 1961. Eingeleitet wurde der Theaterabend durch zwei Szenen aus Jean Cocteaus *Taschentheater*: *Das Phantom von Marseille* und *Der schöne Teilnahmslose*. Im Februar 1962 übersiedelte *Der Herr Karl* in die ebenfalls zum Theater in der Josefstadt gehörenden größeren Kammerspiele (Wien 1, Rotenturmstraße 20). Premiere war am 28. Februar 1962. Anstelle der Cocteau-Szenen wurde diesmal Ferenc Molnárs Einakter *Eins, zwei, drei* mit dem Komiker Ernst Waldbrunn (1907–1977) in der Hauptrolle gespielt. Im Programmheft der Wiederaufnahme war ein fiktiver Brief der Autoren Merz und Qualtinger abgedruckt, mit dem sie bereits am 9. 12. 1961 im »Neuen Kurier« satirisch auf die Resonanz, die ihr Stück in der Wiener Öffentlichkeit gefunden hatte, reagierten. Es war zugleich der 250. Beitrag innerhalb ihrer Kolumne *Blattl vorm Mund*.

»An die
Herren Merz und Qualtinger
Wien

Betrifft: Mich

Geehrte Herren!
Ich habe lange überlegt, ob ich Ihnen schreiben soll
oder nicht – weil ich bin an sich ein Stiller im
Lande. Aber die Leserzuschriften von soundso viel
Herrschaften, die ganz auf meiner Seite waren, haben es mir leichtgemacht, diesen Entschluß zu
verwirklichen – das heißt, ich hab's diktiert (mei
zweite Gattin, die fesche Billeteurin, die kann ja gut
schreiben – fließend Maschinenschrift ... Sie war
übrigens empört über die Behandlung, die den
Frauen von Ihnen angetan wurde ... die hat das für
mich getippt), und ich möchte Ihnen vollinhaltlich
bestätigen, daß Sie unrecht haben.
I war in an Kaffeehaus, bin da g'sessen und hab'
mir des ang'schaut: Erstens einmal bin ich nicht so
unförmig und fett und schwitz aa net immer. Vor
allem aber: Diesen Menschen traut man ja nie zu,
daß er das Leben hinter sich hat wie ich ... Ich
meine mit Frauen und auch im Beruf ... und vor allem politisch. Weil, ich meine, solche Menschen
sind einen ja eh gleich verdächtig.
Schauen Sie – gegen an guten Witz hab i ja nix ...
gegen a Hetz oder a Remasuri ... aber wenn sowas

gemacht wird, wie was Sie gemacht haben – da verliere ich den Humor.

Es war, darf ich Ihnen das sagen, meine Herren, eine Frechheit. Sie haben mich treffen wollen, obwohl ich Ihnen nie etwas getan hab'. Und wen haben Sie getroffen? Das Volk der Tänzer und der Geiger! Was unsere Fußballer in mühseliger Beinarbeit gutgemacht haben, das haben Sie im Fernsehen mit einem Schlag zunichte gemacht. Und überhaupt diese ordinäre Ausdrucksweise, die ich nie in meinen Leben gehabt habe, das alles lehne ich ab. Es ist ein Verbrechen, wenn Sie mich so hinstellen, wie wir Österreicher uns nie bemüht haben zu sein ...

Eines hat mich gefreut: Daß auch die Jugend Ihnen ihre Meinung gesagt hat. So etwas wie mich, hat sie gesagt, gibt es nicht. Und daran können Sie ersehen, wie Sie nicht nur mir, sondern auch unserer Jugend unrecht tun. Weil ich war auch einmal ein junger Mensch, und die Jugend, die mutig und rein ihren Weg geht und noch glaubt an was, die soll man mit solchen Sachen in Ruhe lassen: Sie soll froh sein, daß sie von diesen Sachen verschont wird.

Damit habe ich mir alles von der Leber diktiert und überlasse das Wort jenen, die es gleich von Anfang an in meinen Sinne erhoben und mir aus der Seele gesprochen haben: »... kaum ist Gras über die Geschichte gewachsen, kommt so ein Kamel und frißt es wieder ab ...« (Ein hoher Funktionär der AUA)

»Nehmen Sie sich ein Beispiel an O. W. Fischer und Grace Kelly!« (M. Richter, Wien XIX)

»Für Wien war der illegale Nazi typisch, der für seine jüdischen Freunde Leben und Freiheit riskiert hat ... Und daß sich die Wiener so viele Ritterkreuze verdient haben, kommt nicht daher, daß sie so begeisterte Nazis waren, sondern daher, daß sie es ›denen Großgoscheten‹ zeigen wollten, daß ein schlapper Österreicher auch dreinhauen kann, und besser als sie ...« (Otto Friedländer)

»Auch wenn Sie vielleicht Ihr Beruf, Ihr M i l i e u mit solchen obskuren Gestalten in Berührung bringen mag, dürfen Sie daraus keine gezielte Typisierung mancher Schwächen unserer Bevölkerung – welche hätte solche nicht – ableiten.« (Hans Kolland, Wien)

»Ein Dreckfink, wer sein eigenes Nest beschmutzt!« (Alwine St., Wien III)

»Unter meinen Bekannten befindet sich kein Zuhälter, kein ›Strizzi‹ und auch kein charakterloser Opportunist, der von den Sozis über Heimwehr und Nazis bis zu den Russen und Amis überall ›dabei‹ war ...« (Rudolf B., Wien I)

»Man kann den Fernsehteilnehmern nicht so einfach über das Gesicht fahren ...« (Professor Rudolf Henz)

»In Österreich ist man duldsamer. Da darf man vieles, wofür man anderswo mit Zuchthaus oder Sibirien bestraft würde ...« (Brigitte Posselt, Wien XII)

»Wenn wir Wiener so schlecht wären, wie es der Herr Karl ist, dann wären wir wohl heute nicht so weit ...« (Ernst M., Wien I)
Dem habe ich nichts mehr hinzuzufügen.
Ergebenst Ihr
Herr Karl (Wien I, II, III, IV, V, VI, VII, VIII, IX, X, XI, XII, XIII, XIV, XV, XVI, XVII, XVIII, XIX, XX, XXI, XXII, XXIII sowie Graz, Linz, Salzburg, Innsbruck usw. usw.)«

Eine Reihe von Gastspielen in München, Berlin, Köln und anderen Städten folgten und brachten Helmut Qualtinger ungeheuren Erfolg und Popularität. Eine Folge davon war, daß alle seine weiteren Leistungen, als Schauspieler und als Autor, ausschließlich am *Herrn Karl* gemessen wurden.

Der Abdruck folgt dem Wortlaut des 23seitigen Typoskripts zur Fernsehfassung, das sich von der im Band 1 der Helmut Qualtinger-Werkausgabe abgedruckten Bühnenfassung u. a. dadurch unterscheidet, daß anstelle des Wortes »Publikum« das Wort »Kamera« verwendet wird.
Ein Vergleich dieses Typoskripts mit der Fernsehaufzeichnung zeigte, daß Qualtinger offensichtlich nach der Abfassung des Typoskripts noch einige Textpassagen eingefügt oder bei der Aufzeichnung selbst extemporiert hat. Diese Passagen wurden – soweit sie umfangreicher waren – in diesen Abdruck stillschweigend eingefügt. Geringfügige Änderungen, die durch die schauspielerische Wiedergabe bedingt sind, wurden nicht berücksichtigt.

Kommentar

S. 5   *keppelt:* zankt, schimpft.

S. 7   *Inflation:* 1921; sie konnte drei Jahre später durch die Einführung der Schilling-Währung gestoppt werden.

S. 8   *Brand vom Justizpalast:* Am 30. 1. 1927 war in Schattendorf (Burgenland) eine Gruppe von Schutzbündlern beschossen worden. Zwei Menschen kamen dabei ums Leben. Als die Täter am 14. 7. 1927 freigesprochen wurden, kam es am 15. 7. zu spontanen Demonstrationen vor dem Wiener Justizpalast, der gestürmt und in Brand gesteckt wurde. Polizeipräsident Johannes Schober (1874–1932) erteilte Schießbefehl. Es gab 89 Tote und mehr als 1000 Verletzte.

S. 10   *»Weiße Chrysanthemen ...«:* Von Fred Bertelmann (geb. 1925) kreiertes Lied von K. Ujivitri nach dem Text von M. Rebner.

»Du schwarzer Zigeuner«: Schlager von K. Vacek; Text von Beda (eigentl. Fritz Löhner; 1883–1942).

Ribiselwein: Johannisbeerwein.

abig'stessen: getrunken.

S. 11   *Gelsentippeln:* Gelsenstiche.

der Seip... der Bur... der Scho...: Ignaz Seipel (1876–1932), von Mai 1927 bis Mai 1929 zum vierten Mal österr. Bundeskanzler; Karl Buresch (1878–1936), von 1931 bis Mai 1932 Bundeskanzler; Johannes Schober (1874–1932), von September 1929 bis September 1930 zum dritten Mal österr. Bundeskanzler.

S. 12 *Waschmuschel:* Waschbecken.

Lawur: Nach dem franz. lavoir für: Waschschüssel.

Krampf: Verwicklung, Verwirrung.

S. 13 *arbeitslos:* Die große Arbeitslosigkeit in Österreich erreichte mit 402.000 Arbeitslosen im Februar 1933 den höchsten Stand der Ersten Republik; mit den sog. »Ausgesteuerten« waren es rund 600.000 Arbeitslose.

hackenstad: Dialektausdruck für arbeitslos; zusammengesetzt aus Hacken für Arbeit und stad für still, ruhig.

Vieradreißigerjahr: Mit dem Jahr 1934 werden in erster Linie die Februarkämpfe assoziiert, die mit Polizeigewalt niedergeschlagen wurden und mit zahlreichen Verhaftungen und dem Verbot der Sozialdemokratischen Partei endeten.

de Schwarzen: Gemeint sind die Anhänger der Christlichsozialen Partei.

die Hahnenschwanzler: eine umgangssprachl. Bezeichnung für Angehörige der Heimwehr; benannt nach den Hahnenfedern, mit denen sie ihre Kopfbedeckungen schmückten.

S. 14 *Heimwehr:* Gemeint sind die sogenannten

»Selbstschutzverbände« in Österreich, die ab 1927 mehr und mehr zu einem politischen Instrument der christlichsozialen und großdeutschen Parteien gegen die Sozialdemokraten wurden.

S. 15 *Fleischlaberln:* Fleischlaibchen aus gehacktem (faschiertem) Fleisch.

einbrennte Suppen: Suppe mit Mehlschwitze.

Parte: Traueranzeige

S. 16 *stier:* Ohne Geld, pleite.

Haberer: Freunde; nach dem gleichbed. jidd. chavver.

S. 19 *Ich siech – Spezialitäten aus allen Ländern. Spezialitäten aller Länder vereinigt euch!* Damit spielte Qualtinger auf die Schlußworte im »Kommunistischen Manifest« von Karl Marx (1848) an: »Proletarier aller Länder vereinigt euch!«

Gemeindewohnung: Das erste Wohnbauprogramm der Gemeinde Wien, das im September 1923 beschlossen wurde, sah die Errichtung von 25.000 Wohnungen innerhalb von fünf Jahren vor; das 1927 beschlossene zweite Wohnbauprogramm sah den Bau von 30.000 Wohnungen und die Errichtung zahlreicher Großhöfe (z. B. Gartenstadt; d. i. der heutige Karl-Marx-Hof u. a.) vor.

S. 20 *Systemzeit:* Zeit des parlamentarischen Systems während der Weimarer Republik, von den Nationalsozialisten abwertend verwendet.

S. 21 *der Hitler kummen:* Der Einmarsch der dt. Truppen in Österreich erfolgte am 12. 3. 1938. Hitler traf, aus Linz kommend, am 14. 3. in Wien ein.

am Heldenplatz: Dienstag, den 15. 3. 1938 »meldete« Hitler im Rahmen einer »Befreiungsfeier« den von Hunderttausenden bejubelten »Eintritt meiner Heimat in das Deutsche Reich«.

S. 22 *achtadreißig geboren:* Anläßlich des Gastspiels in München Anfang 1962 fügte Qualtinger folgende Passage ein, weil sich, wie er formulierte, »die Münchner nicht ungetrübt darüber freuen sollen, wie mies wir Österreicher sind« (»Spiegel« vom 17. 1. 1962): »Die Deitschen san einmarschiert – mit klingendem Spiel sans kummen, mit'n Bayerischen Hilfszug ... Die haben so Gulaschkanonen gehabt, wie man sagt ... Gulasch war kans drin ... Erdäpfeln, Kartoffeln ... Uns is ja schlecht gangen ... aber sowas hab'n mir nie gessen. Na ... die haben uns g'holfen ... wie die Heischrecken haben s' uns g'holfen ... Auf amal war nix mehr da ... in die G'schäfter und so ... Aber Schwamm drüber – es waren deitsche Brüder ... im süddeitschen Raum ... Altreich ... Neureich ... «

Illegaler: Bezeichnung für Mitglieder der NSDAP in Österreich vor deren Zulassung; wie sich 1945 herausstellte, hatten sich 1938 viele Österreicher aus opportunistischen Gründen rückwirkend als »illegale Parteimitglieder« registrieren lassen.

S. 23 *Trottoir:* Gehsteig.

hat des aufwischen müssen: Ausschreitungen gegen die jüdische Bevölkerung Wiens, die von österr. Nazis gezwungen wurde, Parolen zu Schuschniggs Volksabstimmung (13. 3. 1938) von den Straßen zu waschen.

Hetz: Vergnügen, Belustigung; nach den von Karl VI. (1685–1740) aus Spanien eingeführten Tierhetzen, die zu Volksfesten wurden.

S. 24 *NSV:* Abkürzung für »Nationalsozialistische Volkswohlfahrt«; seit 1935 der NSDAP angeschlossener Verband, durch den »bedürftige Volksgenossen« betreut wurden.

S. 25 *Billeteur:* Platzanweiser.

Gfrieß: Gesicht.

S. 26 *Piefke:* Süddt. und österr. Bezeichnung für die Bewohner Preußens und für die Deutschen im allgemeinen.

S. 27 *Fremdarbeiter:* Meist in den vom deutschen Heer besetzten Gebieten zwangsrekrutierte Arbeiter, die in der Landwirtschaft und in der Industrie im Reichsgebiet eingesetzt wurden.

A Tschusch: Abwertende Bezeichnung für (jugoslawische) Ausländer; während des Baus der Südbahnstrecke (1860–1880) riefen sich die aus dem Südosten Europas stammenden Gastarbeiter »čuješ« (hörst du?) zu.

leinwand: ausgezeichnet, gut, prima.

Winterhilfswerk: Eine 1931/32 entstandene Organisation zur Unterstützung Hilfsbedürftiger und Erwerbsloser. Unter der NS-Herrschaft gab es 1933/34 das erste WHW. Bei Straßen- und Haussammlungen erhielten die Spender kleine Abzeichen aus Metall oder Holz.

g'scheppert: Geklappert.

S. 29 *Pancreas:* Bauchspeicheldrüse.

S. 30 *dawai, Towarisch:* Los, Genosse.

Karascho: Gut.

S. 31 *Tschiwilien Gard:* Civilian Gard für: Zivilstreife.

S. 32 *sdrasdfudje!:* Guten Tag!

S. 33 *Währungsreform:* Gemeint ist die zweite Währungsreform, als vom 11. bis 24. 12. 1947 pro Kopf der Bevölkerung nur 150 österr. Schilling im Verhältnis 1 : 1 umgetauscht wurden, während weitere Beträge um zwei Drittel abgewertet wurden. Schon zwei Jahre früher hatte es eine Währungsreform gegeben, als der österr. Schilling wieder als Zahlungsmittel eingeführt wurde. Auch damals wurden pro Kopf nur 150 Reichsmark 1 : 1 umgetauscht; weitere Beträge kamen auf ein Sperrkonto.

S. 34 *pickn blieben:* kleben geblieben.

Laaerberg: Im 10. Wiener Gemeindebezirk.

S. 35 *Piestingtal:* In Niederösterreich gelegene Fluß-niederung.

S. 36 *Kombinesch:* Unterwäsche, nach dem franz. combinaison für: Unterkleid.

S. 38 *Staatsvertrag:* Am 15. 5. 1955 wurde im Wiener Belvedere der österr. Staatsvertrag unterzeichnet.

Poldl: Leopold Figl (1902–1965), österr. Bundeskanzler von 1945 bis 1953; dann bis 1956 österr. Außenminister.

die zwa andern Herrschaften: Der »Neue Kurier« vom 15. 5. 1955 berichtete: »Figl nimmt mit der rechten Hand die Hände von Pinay und Molotow, mit der linken die von Dulles und MacMillan und hebt sie empor.«

S. 40 *Großglockner:* Mit 3797 m der höchste Berg Österreichs.

Pasterzengletscher: Größter ostalpiner Gletscher auf dem Ostabfall des Großglockner.

S. 41 *Franz-Josefs-Höhe:* Aussichtspunkt an der Großglockner-Hochalpenstraße.

S. 42 *Mariazell:* Bedeutender österr. Wallfahrtsort in der nördl. Steiermark.

steinerne Zeugen unserer Vergangenheit: Benediktinerstift Melk (1702), Burgruine Dürnstein (1731), Benediktinerstift Göttweig (1718).

g'matschkert: gemurrt, geschimpft.

Donau-Dampfschiffahrts-Gesellschaft: Die 1829 gegr. DDSG war 1945 als »deutsches Eigentum« beschlagnahmt worden und wurde 1955 durch den Staatsvertrag wieder an Österreich zurückgegeben.

S. 43 *Kübel:* Abwertend für Auto.

da liegen s' drin ... de jungen Leit: Die Bombentrichter im Überschwemmungsgebiet der Donau waren ein beliebtes Ausflugsziel für Paare. In den Bombentrichtern glaubten sie sich unbeobachtet.

S. 44 *Voyeur:* heimlicher Zuschauer (bei sexueller Betätigung).

G'frast: derbes Schimpfwort.

S. 45 *den Radio:* In Österreich umgangssprachl. auch der Radio.

S. 47 *Mödling, Klosterneuburg:* romantische Kleinstädte mit zahlreichen Villen, am Rande des Wienerwaldes, unweit von Wien gelegen.

Stadtbahn: 1863 wurde in Wien mit dem Bau einer Stadtbahn begonnen; am 9. 5. 1898 wurde sie mit der Wiental-Gürtel-Linie eröffnet.

S. 48 *Lainz:* Gemeint ist das 1904 erbaute Altersheim der Gemeinde Wien, das »Lainzer Versorgungsheim« im 13. Bezirk.

S. 70 *wie die Heischrecken haben s' uns g'holfen:* Spöttische Anspielung auf die biblischen Heuschreckenplagen.

Altreich: Bezeichnung für das deutsche Reichsgebiet vor dem Anschluß Österreichs.

S. 62 *Remasuri:* Trubel, ausgelassenes Vergnügen,
nach dem ital. rammassare für: häufen.

S. 63 *Das Volk der Tänzer und der Geiger:* Charakteri-
sierung des österreichischen Volkes mit Hin-
weis auf die Strauß-Ära.

unsere Fußballer in mühseliger Beinarbeit: Gemeint ist wohl, daß die österr. Nationalmann-
schaft bei der Fußballweltmeisterschaft 1954
in der Schweiz den 3. Platz errungen hatte.

AUA: Austrian Airlines, Bezeichnung für die
1957 gegründete österr. Luftfahrtgesellschaft.

S. 64 *O. W. Fischer:* Otto Wilhelm Fischer (geboren
1915), österreichischer Schauspieler, der zu
einem der beliebtesten Stars des deutschen
Nachkriegsfilms wurde.

Grace Kelly: (1929–1982), beliebter amerik.
Filmstar.

Großgoscheten: Großmäuligen.

Otto Friedländer: (1889–1963), österr. Schriftsteller; publizierte vor allem Novellen, Essays
und Feuilletons.

Professor Rudolf Henz: (1897–1987), österreichischer Schriftsteller. Von 1932 bis 1945 Programmdirektor des RAVAG (Radio Verkehrs
AG); ab Mai 1945 Radiosendeleiter in Wien,
Mai 1954–1957 Programmdirektor des Österreichischen Rundfunks, dann bis 1971 zu-

nächst Aufsichtsrat, später im Programmbei-
rat des Österreichischen Rundfunks tätig.

Sibirien: Synonym für Straflager in der So-
wjetunion.

Qualtinger Werkausgabe in fünf Bänden

Herausgegeben von Traugott Krischke

Band 4

»Heimat bist du großer Zwerge« und andere Texte für die Bühne

Inhalt: Der letzte Aufsichtsrat, Die Rose von Gumpendorf, Um die Zeit schon im Café?, Das Ärztecafé, Die längst fällige Kur, Gynäkologendämmerung, Ein großer Mann tritt ab, Die Taschenambulanz, Brief aus Wien u. v. m.

Band 5

»Blattl vorm Mund«. Satiren für den *Kurier* und andere Texte

Jeder Band ca. 400 Seiten, Hardcover mit Schutzumschlag.

Deuticke
A-1010 Wien, Hegelgasse 21

Alle Rechte vorbehalten.
Abdruck, fotomechanische Wiedergabe bzw.
Vervielfältigung,
Speicherung auf Datenträgern jeder Art,
auch auszugsweise,
nur mit Genehmigung des Verlages Deuticke.
© Franz Deuticke Verlagsgesellschaft mbH, Wien 1996
Alle Aufführungs-, Sende- und Übersetzungsrechte
liegen bei:
Thomas Sessler Verlag GmbH
Bühnen- und Musikverlag
A-1010 Wien, Johannesgasse 12, Tel. 0222/512 32 84
Umschlaggestaltung: Robert Hollinger
Druck: Wiener Verlag, Himberg bei Wien
ISBN 3-216-30260-1

HIM

HIM

SARINA BOWEN
USA TODAY BESTSELLING AUTHOR

ELLE KENNEDY
NEW YORK TIMES BESTSELLING AUTHOR

PRAISE FOR HIM

ONE

APRIL

Wes

The coffee shop line is a little long, but I know I'll make it to the rink on time. Some weeks just *click*.

Over the weekend, my hockey team clinched the first two rounds of the NCAA playoffs, and now we're headed to the Frozen Four. I somehow got a B-minus on a history paper I wrote in an exhaustion-induced coma. And my spidey sense tells me the guy in front of me won't order a complicated drink. I can tell from his clothes he's a simple man.

Things are going my way right now. I'm in the zone. My skates are sharp, and the ice is smooth.

The line advances so Dull Guy can order. "Small breakfast blend. Black."

See that?

It's my turn a minute later, but when I open my mouth to order, the young barista lets out a fangirl shriek. "Omigod, Ryan Wesley! Congratulations!"

I don't know her. But the jacket I'm wearing makes me a rock star, at least for this week. "Thanks, doll. Could I please get a double espresso?"

"Right away!" She barks out my drink order to her colleague, adding, "Make it snappy! We've got a championship to win here!" And wouldn't you know? She refuses my five-dollar bill.

I shove it in the tip jar, then haul my ass outside and head for the rink.

I'm in a stupendous fucking mood as I stroll into the screening room at the team's top-notch facility on the Northern Mass campus. I love hockey. Fucking love it. I'm heading for the pros in a few short months and I can't frickin' wait.

"Ladies," I greet my teammates as I flop into my usual seat. The rows are set up in a semi-circle facing the massive screen at the head of the room. The chairs are padded leather. Yup, Division I luxury at its finest.

I shift my gaze to Landon, one of our freshman D-men. "You're looking kinda green, man." I smirk. "Does your tum-tum still hurt?"

Landon flips me the finger, but it's a half-hearted gesture. He looks sick as hell, and I'm not surprised. Last I saw him, he was sucking on a bottle of whiskey like he was trying to make it come.

"Dude, you should have seen him when we were walking home," a junior named Donovan pipes up. "Stripped down to his tighty whities and trying to dry-hump that statue in front of the south library."

Everyone around us breaks out in laughter, including me— because either I'm wrong, or the statue in question happens to be a bronze horse. I call him Seabiscuit, but I think it's just a memorial for some filthy-rich alumnus who made the Olympics equestrian team a hundred years ago.

"You tried to ride Seabiscuit?" I grin at the freshman.

Red splotches rise in his cheeks. "No," he says sullenly.

"Yes," Donovan corrects.

The cackling continues, but I'm now distracted by the smirk being aimed in *my* direction, courtesy of Shawn Cassel.

I guess you could call Cassel my best friend. Of all my team-mates, I'm closest to him, and yeah, we chill outside hockey, but "best friend" isn't exactly a term I throw around often. I've got friends. I've got a shit ton of friends, actually. Can I honestly say any of them really *know* me? Probably not. But Cassel comes damn close.

I roll my eyes at him. "What?"

He shrugs. "Landon isn't the only one who had a good time last night." He's lowered his voice, but it doesn't really matter. Our teammates are too busy riding Landon about last night's horse shenanigans.

"Meaning?"

His mouth twitches. "Meaning I saw you disappear with that meathead. You guys were still AWOL when Em finally dragged me home at two."

I raise one eyebrow. "I'm not seeing the problem."

"Isn't one. Just didn't realize you were corrupting the straight ones now."

Cassel's the only guy on the team I ever discuss my sex life with. As the only gay hockey player I know, I walk a fine line. I mean, if someone brings it up, I'm not gonna clam up and scurry into the closet, but I don't volunteer the information, either.

Honestly, my sexual orientation is probably the worst-kept secret on this team. The guys know. The coaches know. They just don't care.

Cassel cares, but in a different way. He doesn't give a shit that I like to fuck dudes. Nope, what he cares about is *me*. He's told me on more than one occasion that he thinks I'm wasting my life moving from one anonymous encounter to another.

"Who says he was straight?" I say mockingly.

My buddy looks intrigued. "Seriously?"

I arch a brow again, which makes him laugh.

Truth is, I doubt the frat brother I hooked up with last night is gay. Bi-curious, more like it, and I won't lie—that was the appeal. It's easier to mess around with the ones who are gonna pretend you don't exist in the morning. One night of no-strings fun, a BJ, a fuck, whatever their liquid courage allows them to try, and then they disappear. Act like they didn't spend the hours leading up to it eyeing my tats and picturing my mouth around their dicks. Like they didn't run their greedy hands all over my body and beg me to touch them.

Hook-ups with gay guys are potentially more complicated. They might want *more*. Like commitment. Promises I'm unable to make.

"Wait," I demand when I register what he'd said before. "What do you mean Em dragged you home?"

Cassel's jaw tightens. "Exactly what it sounds like. She showed up at the frat house and dragged me out." His features relax, but only slightly. "She was just worried about me, though. My cell died so I wasn't answering any of her texts."

I say nothing. I've given up on trying to get Cassel to see the light about that chick.

"I would've gotten trashed if she hadn't shown up. So...uh, yeah, I guess it was cool of her to come get me before I got too wasted."

I bite my tongue. Nope, not getting involved in the man's relationship. Just because Emily happens to be the clingiest, bitchiest, *craziest* chick I've ever met doesn't give me the right to interfere.

"Besides, I know how she feels about me partying. I shouldn't have gone in the first place—"

"You're not fucking married," I blurt out.

Shit. So much for keeping my mouth shut.

Cassel's expression goes stricken.

I hastily backpedal. "Sorry. Ah...forget I said that."

His cheeks hollow, jaw working as if he's grinding his molars to dust. "No. I mean, shit. You're right. We're not married." He mumbles something I can't make out.

"What?"

"I said...not yet, anyway."

"Not yet?" I echo in horror. "For fuck's sake, man, please, *please* tell me you aren't engaged to that girl."

"No," he says quickly. Then he lowers his voice again. "But she keeps saying how she wants me to propose."

Propose? The thought makes my skin crawl. Goddamn it, I'm gonna be the best man at their wedding, I just know it.

Is it possible to make a wedding toast without acknowledging the bride?

Luckily, Coach O'Connor marches into the room before this insane conversation with Cassel can make my mind spin any harder.

The room falls silent at his entrance. Coach is...commanding. Nah. Make that *terrifying*. Six-five, perpetual scowl, and a head he shaves not because he's balding, but because he just likes looking like a scary motherfucker.

He starts off the meeting by reminding us—one by one—what each of us did wrong in practice yesterday. Which is completely unnecessary, because yesterday's criticism still burns in my gut. I screwed up one of the faceoff drills, dropped passes I had no business dropping, missed on goal when I had an easy shot. It was just one of those crappy practices where nothing goes right, and I've already vowed to get my shit together when we hit the ice tomorrow.

The post-season is down to just two fateful games, which means I need to stay sharp. I need to be *focused*. Northern Mass hasn't won a Frozen Four championship in fifteen years, and as the leading scorer, I'm determined to seal this victory before I graduate.

"All right, let's get to it," Coach announces after he's finished telling us how much we suck. "We're starting with this Rainier-Seattle game from last week."

As a frozen image of a college arena fills the huge screen, one of our left wings wrinkles his forehead. "Why are we starting with Rainier? We're playing North Dakota in the first round."

"We'll focus on North Dakota next time. Rainier is the one that worries me."

Coach touches the laptop on the desk and the image on the big screen unfreezes, the sound of the crowd echoing in the viewing room.

"If we meet these guys in the final, we're in for a world of hurt," Coach says grimly. "I want you to watch this goalie. The kid's sharp as a hawk. We need to find his weakness and exploit it."

My gaze focuses on the game in progress, resting on the black-and-orange uniformed goaltender manning the crease. He's sharp, all right. Steady eyes assessing the field of play, his glove snapping shut as he stops the first goal slapped in his direction. He's fast. Alert.

"Watch the way he controls this rebound," Coach orders as the opposing team takes another shot at goal. "Fluid. Controlled."

The longer I watch, the more uneasy I get. I can't explain it. I have no clue why the hairs on the back of my neck are tingling. But something about the goalie makes my instincts hum.

"He angles his body perfectly." Coach sounds thoughtful, impressed almost.

I'm impressed, too. I haven't followed any of the west coast teams this season. I was too busy concentrating on the ones in our conference, studying the game tapes to find a way to beat them. But now that post-season is underway, it's time to assess the teams we might face in the championship if we make it to the final round.

I keep watching. Keep studying. Damn it, I like the way he plays.

No, I *know* the way he plays.

Recognition dawns on me at the same moment Coach says, "Kid's name is—"

Jamie Canning.

"—Jamie Canning. He's a senior."

Holy shit.

Holy fucking shit.

My body is no longer humming, but trembling. I've known for a while that Canning goes to Rainier, but when I checked up on him last season I found out he'd been relegated to backup goalie, replaced by some hotshot sophomore who was rumored to be unstoppable.

When did Canning get the starting job back? I ain't gonna lie —I used to keep tabs on the guy. But I stopped once it started to feel like borderline stalking. I mean, there's no way he was keeping tabs on *me*, not after I torpedoed our friendship like an asshole.

The memory of my selfish actions is like a fist to the gut. Fuck. I'd been a terrible friend to him. A terrible *person*. It was so much easier to deal with the shame when Canning was thousands of miles away, but now...

Dread crawls up my throat. I'm going to see him in Boston during the tournament. I'll probably even face off against him.

It's been nearly four years since I've seen or spoken to the guy. What the hell will I even say to him? How do you apologize to someone for cutting them out of your life without so much as an explanation?

"His game is flawless," Coach is saying.

No, not flawless. He retreats too quickly—that was always a problem for him, scrambling back to the net when a shooter approached the blue line, giving them a better angle to shoot from. And he was always too pad-reliant, creating easy rebound opportunities for the offense.

I have to bite my lip to keep from offering the information. It feels...*wrong*, I guess. Telling my teammates about Canning's weaknesses. I should, though. I really should, because this is the Frozen fucking Four at stake here.

Then again, it's been years since I was on the ice with Canning. He could have tightened up his game since then. He might not even have those particular weaknesses anymore.

I, on the other hand, do. I have the same damn weakness I've always had. It's still there as I stare up at the big screen. As I watch Jamie Canning stop another dizzying slap shot. As I admire the grace and deadly precision with which he moves.

My weakness is *him*.

TWO

JAMIE

"You're awfully quiet this morning, even for you." Holly's fingers drift down my back, ending their journey on my bare ass. "Thinking deep thoughts about the Frozen Four?"

"Yeah." And it isn't *exactly* a lie. I can guarantee that Friday's trip to Boston is in the forefront of two dozen other players' minds this morning. And about a zillion fans'.

I have more than winning on my mind, though. Now that we were actually headed for the championship, it was time to come to terms with the idea that we might face Northern Mass. The star player of their team? None other than Ryan Wesley, my ex-best-friend.

"What is it, sweetie?" Holly props herself up on an elbow to study me. She doesn't usually stay over, but last night's sex marathon had lasted until four a.m., and I would've felt like an ass hustling her into a cab that late.

I'm not sure how I feel about having her curled up in bed beside me, though. Spectacular morning sex aside, her presence makes me uneasy. I've never lied to Holly about what this is—and what it isn't. But I've had enough experience with chicks to know that when they agree to a friends-with-benefits arrangement, a part of them hopes one of those benefits will somehow be landing a boyfriend out of the deal.

"Jamie?" she prompts.

I push aside one set of troubling thoughts and replace them with another. "Have you ever been fired by a friend?" I hear myself ask.

"What? Like...someone you worked for?" She has wide blue eyes, which always take me seriously.

I shake my head. "No. The leading scorer on Northern Mass was my best friend in high school. And junior high, too. You know that hockey camp where I work in the summer?"

"Elites?" She nods.

"Yeah, good memory. Before I was a coach there, I was a camper. So was Wes. He was *crazy*." I chuckle to myself just picturing his scruffy face. "The dude would do anything. There's this toboggan chute in the center of town—in the winter you can sled down onto the frozen lake. But in the summer it's closed, with a twelve-foot fence around it. He's like, 'Dude, after lights out we're climbing that thing.'"

Holly massages my chest with one of her soft hands. "Did you?"

"Naturally. I was sure we were going to get busted and thrown out of camp. But nobody caught us. Wes was the only one smart enough to bring a towel to slide on, though. So I had burns on the backs of my thighs from sliding down that fucker."

Holly grins.

"And I still wonder how many tourists had to delete the pictures they took of Mirror Lake. Whenever Wes saw a tourist lining up a shot, he would always drop his pants."

Her grin turns into a giggle. "He sounds like fun."

"He was. And then he wasn't."

"What happened?"

I fold my hands behind my head, trying to appear casual

despite the wave of discomfort sliding down my spine. "I don't know. We were always competitive. Our last summer he challenged me to a contest..." I stop, because I never tell Holly the really personal stuff. "I don't *know* what happened, exactly. He just cut off contact with me after that summer. He stopped responding to my texts. He just...*fired* me."

She kisses my neck. "Sounds like you're still mad."

"I am," I surprise myself by saying.

If you'd asked me yesterday whether there was anything in my past that bothered me, I would have said no. But now that Ryan Wesley has parked his nutty ass back in my consciousness, I'm all churned up again. Goddamn him. I really don't need this going into the toughest two games of my life.

"And now you have to play him," Holly muses. "It's a lot of pressure." She's rubbing my hip now. I'm pretty sure she has some plans for the two of us involving a different kind of "pressure." She's looking for round two, but I don't have the time.

Catching her hand in mine, I give it a quick kiss. "Gotta get up. Sorry, babe. We're watching tape in twenty minutes." I swing my legs over the side of the bed and turn for an eyeful of Holly's curves. My friend-with-benefits is sexy as hell, and my dick gives a little twitch of gratitude for the fun we already had.

"Shame," Holly says, rolling onto her back invitingly. "I don't have class until this afternoon." She runs her hands up her flat stomach and onto her tits. With her eyes locked on me, she gives her nipples a flick then licks her lips.

My dick does not fail to notice.

"You are evil and I hate you." I grab my boxers off the floor and look away before I get all boned up again.

She giggles. "I don't like you at all, either."

"Uh-huh. Keep telling yourself that." But then I clamp my lips together. Six weeks before graduation, it's unwise to start even a playful conversation about how much Holly and I like each other.

We're strictly casual, but lately she's been making noises about how much she'll miss me next year.

According to Holly, it's only forty-three miles from Detroit, where I'll be next year, to Ann Arbor, where she'll be in med school. If she starts wondering aloud whether there are any apartments for rent halfway between those cities, I don't know what I'm going to say.

Yep. Not looking forward to that conversation.

Sixty seconds later I'm dressed and heading for the door. "Are you cool letting yourself out?"

"Yeah, it's fine." Her laughter stops me before I can turn the knob. "Not so fast, stud."

Holly gets up to kiss me goodbye, and I make myself stand still for a second and return it.

"Later," I whisper. It's my standard goodbye. Today, though, I find myself wondering if there are other words she's waiting to hear.

But when the door closes on her, my head is somewhere else already. I sling my backpack over one shoulder and slip out into a misty April morning. Five days from now I'll be on the east coast, trying to help my team clinch the national championship. Man, the Frozen Four is such a rush—I've been once before. It was two years ago, and I was the backup goalie instead of the starter.

I didn't play, and we didn't win. I like to think those two things are related.

This time it'll be different. I'll be waiting between the pipes, the last line of defense between the other team's offense and the trophy. That's enough pressure to freak out even the chillest goalie in college sports. But the fact that the other team's star center is my ex-best friend who abruptly stopped talking to me?

That is whack.

I meet a handful of my teammates on the sidewalk as we all approach the rink. They're laughing about somebody's antics on the bus last night, joking and shoving each other through the glass doors and into the gleaming hallway.

Rainier did a massive rink renovation a few years ago. It's like a temple to hockey, with conference pennants and team photographs lining the walls. And that's just the public area. We pause in front of a locked door so that Terry, a junior forward, can swipe his ID past the laser eye. The light flashes green and we push through to the opulent training area.

I haven't said a word to anyone yet, but I've never been as much of a smack-talker as the rest of them, so nobody calls me on it.

In the team kitchen, I pour myself a cup of coffee and grab a blueberry muffin off the tray. This place makes me feel like a spoiled brat, but it's useful when I've overslept.

Ten minutes later we're watching tape in the team video room, listening to Coach Wallace's analysis. He's at the podium wearing a little mic that amplifies his voice all the way to the back row. But I can't hear him anyway. I'm too busy watching Ryan Wesley dart across the ice. I see clip after clip of Wes passing through the line of defense like smoke, creating scoring opportunities out of nothing but ice shavings and quick wits.

"The number two offensive scorer in the nation, the kid has balls of steel," our coach admits grudgingly. "And enough foot speed to make his opponents look like my ninety-seven-year-old granny."

Shot after unlikely shot flies into the net. Half the time the on-screen Wes doesn't even have the good manners to look surprised. He just glides onward with the grace and ease of someone who'd practically been born with steel blades under his feet.

"Like us, Northern Mass woulda made it to the finals last year, but they were hampered by injuries in the post-season," Coach says. "They're the team to beat…"

The footage is mesmerizing. I'd first seen Wes skate the

summer after seventh grade. At thirteen we all thought we were hot shit just for attending Elites, the world-class hockey training camp in Lake Placid, New York. Hear us roar—we were the best of the ragtag players on our club teams back home. We were the kids to beat during pond-hockey pick-up games.

We were mostly ridiculous.

But even my punk-ass junior-high self could see that Wes was different. I was a little in awe of him from the first day of my first summer at Elites. Well, at least until I discovered what a cocky bastard he was. After that, I hated on him for a bit, but being assigned as roommates made it difficult to keep up my hatred.

Six summers in a row, the best hockey I played was against the sharp-eyed, steel-wristed Ryan Wesley. I spent my days trying to keep up with his quick reflexes and his flying-saucer slapshots.

When practice was over, he was even more of a challenge. Want to race to the top of the climbing wall? Ask Wes. Need a partner in crime to help you break into the camp freezer after hours? Wes is your man.

The town of Lake Placid probably heaved a sigh of relief each August when camp was through. Everyone could finally go back to living normal lives that didn't include seeing Wes's bare ass in the lake every morning for his daily skinny-dipping sesh.

Ladies and gentlemen: Ryan Wesley.

Coach drones on at the front of the room while Wes and his teammates do their magic on-screen. The most fun I ever had at a rink was with him. Not that he never pissed me off. He did that hourly. But I can honestly look back on his challenges and taunts and see he'd made me a better player.

Except for the last challenge he issued. I never should have accepted that one.

"Last day," he'd taunted me, skating backward faster than most of us could skate forward. "You're still afraid to take me on in another shootout, huh? Still whimpering over the last one."

"Bullshit." I wasn't afraid to lose to Wes. People usually did. But it was hard to shut out a shootout, and I already owed Wes a six-pack of beer. Trouble was, my bank account was drained. As the last of six kids, sending me to this fancy camp was all my parents could do for me. My lawn-mowing money had already been spent on ice cream and contraband.

If I lost a bet, I couldn't repay.

Wes skated a backward circle around me so fast that it reminded me of the Tasmanian Devil. "Not for beer," he said, reading my thoughts. "My flask is full of Jack, thanks to the beating I gave Cooper yesterday. So the prize can be something different." He let out an evil laugh.

"Like what?" Knowing Wes, it would involve some sort of public display of ridiculousness. *Loser sings the national anthem while hanging brain on the town dock.* Or something.

I set up a row of pucks and prepared to shoot them. *Whack*, went the first one, just missing Wes as he went by in a blur. I set up my next shot.

"Loser gives the winner a blowjob," he said just as I swung.

I missed the fucking puck. Actually missed it.

Wes cackled, skidding to a stop.

Jesus Christ, the guy was good at fucking with my head. "You're hysterical."

He stood there breathing hard from all that fast skating. "Think you can't win? Shouldn't matter what the prize is if you're confident."

My back felt sweaty all of a sudden. He had me in an impossible position, and he knew it. If I refused the challenge, he won. Yet if I accepted, he had me rattled before the first puck even flew my way.

I'd stood there like a moron, unsure what to do. "You and your mind games," I muttered.

"Oh, Canning," Wes had chuckled. "Hockey is ninety percent mind games. I've been trying to teach you that for six years."

"Fine," I'd said through clenched teeth. "You're on."

He'd hooted through his facemask. "You look terrified already. This is gonna be rich."

He's just fucking with you, I'd told myself. I could win a shootout. Then I'd turn the mind games back on him—I'd refuse the prize, of course. But then I could hold the fact that he owed me a BJ over his head. For *years*. It was as if a cartoon light bulb went off over my head. Two could do mind games. Why had I never realized this before?

I'd lined up one more puck and shot it with great force right past Wes's arrogant smile. "This is going to be a piece of cake," I said. "How about we have this shootout, wherein I kick your ass, right after lunch? Before the end-of-camp scrimmage?"

For the briefest moment his confidence slipped. I'm sure I saw it—the sudden flash of *holy shit*. "Perfect," he said eventually.

"'Kay." I scooped up the last puck off the ice and flipped it in my glove. Then I skated away whistling, as if I didn't have a care in the world.

That had been the last day of our friendship.

And I never saw it coming.

At the front of the room, a new reel is playing, this one highlighting North Dakota's offensive strategy. Coach is no longer thinking about Ryan Wesley.

But I am.

THREE

WES

Boston's skyline comes into view from my bus window well before I'm ready.

It's a mere ninety minutes from Northern Mass to TD Garden. The Frozen Four is always played at a neutral rink, but if anyone has a home-ice advantage this year, it's me. I'm from Boston, so playing in the Bruins' arena is my childhood fantasy come to life.

Apparently it's my jackwad of a father's fantasy, too. Not only is he pumped up to invite all his asshole colleagues to my game, he can look like a hero on the cheap. He only has to spring for a limo, not a charter flight.

"You know what I like best about this plan?" Cassel asks from the seat next to me as he flips through the itinerary our team manager passed out.

"That this event is like the puck bunny world headquarters?"

He snorts. "Okay, sure. But I was just going to say that they're putting us up at a nice hotel, not some sleazepit off the interstate."

"True." Although the hotel, whatever it is, won't be nearly as grand as my family's Beacon Hill mansion a few miles away. I'd never say that, though. I'm not a snob, because I know opulence doesn't stamp out ignorance and unhappiness. Just ask my family.

We spend the next half hour snarled in traffic, because that's just how it is in Boston. So it's almost five o'clock by the time we're finally unloading the bus.

"The gear stays!" our student manager shouts. "Take only your luggage!"

"We don't have to schlep our gear?" Cassel yelps. "Baby, I've *arrived*. Get used to this treatment, Wes." He elbows me. "Next year in Toronto you'll probably have a personal assistant to carry your stick around for you."

It feels superstitious to talk about my NHL contract before the Frozen Four. So I change the subject. "That's awesome, dude. I love it when another guy holds my stick."

"Teed that one up for you, didn't I?" he asks as we grab our duffels off the sidewalk where the red-faced driver has tossed them.

"Sure did." I let Cassel enter the revolving door first just so I can grab the door by its handle and trap him inside.

Stuck now, Cassel twists around to give me the finger. When I don't let go, he turns away and reaches for his belt buckle, setting up to moon me and whatever slice of Boston happens to be walking past the hotel on a windy April Friday.

I let up on the door and give it a shove, smacking him in the not-yet-bare ass.

Ah, hockey players. You really can't take us anywhere.

Then we're in the shiny lobby. "How does the bar look?" I ask.

"Open," Cassel answers. "That's really all that matters."

"Truth."

We find an out-of-the-way place to stand while we wait for the team manager to sort out the hotel rooms. But it's going to be a while. The lobby is busy and getting busier. Our end of the room has a distinctly green-and-white color scheme, with our Northern Mass jackets everywhere.

But on the other end of the room another color catches my eye. It's orange. Specifically, the orange and black of another team's jackets. They're filing through the same doors we just entered, shoving each other and generally acting like testosterone hounds. It's all very familiar.

And then the room tilts a little as my gaze locks onto a sandy-blond head. I only need the oblique view I've got to recognize the shape of his smile.

Fuck me. Jamie Canning is staying at this hotel.

My entire body tenses as I wait for him to turn his head. To look right at me. But he doesn't. He's too engrossed in conversation with one of his teammates, laughing at something the guy has just said.

He used to laugh with me that way. I haven't forgotten the sound of Jamie's laughter. Deep and husky, melodic in a carefree kind of way. Nothing ever kept Jamie Canning down. He was the epitome of go-with-the-flow, probably because of his laidback California upbringing.

I hadn't realized just how much I've missed him until this very moment.

Go talk to him.

The voice in my head is persistent, but I silence it by wrenching my gaze off Canning. With the colossal amount of guilt lodged in my chest, it's now become even more evident that I need to apologize to my old friend.

But right this second I'm not ready. Not here, with all these people around.

"It's fucking Grand Central Station in here," Cassel mutters.

"Dude. There's an errand I need to run. Come with me?" I form this idea on the fly, but it's a good one.

"Sure?"

"Back door," I say, nudging him toward a nearby exit.

Outside, I realize how close we are to Faneuil Hall and all the touristy crap they sell there. Perfect. "C'mon." I give Cassel a tug toward the first row of stores.

"Forgot your toothbrush?"

"Nah. I gotta buy a gift."

"For who?" Cassel hefts his duffel higher on his shoulder.

I hesitate. I've always kept my memories of Canning to myself. Because they're *mine*. For six weeks every summer, *he* was mine.

"A friend," I finally admit. "One of the Rainier players."

"A friend." Cassel's chuckle is low and dirty. "Trying to work out how to get laid after tomorrow's game? What kind of store are you taking me to?"

Fucking Cassel. I should have left him in the crowded lobby. "Dude. It's not like that." *Even if I wish it were.* "This guy—Canning, their goalie—we used to be tight." I reluctantly add, "Until I wrecked it by being an ass."

"You? Who woulda guessed."

"I know, right?"

I scan the row of storefronts. They're full of the Boston tourist crap that is usually invisible to me: toy lobsters, Bruins pennants, Freedom Trail T-shirts. Something here would definitely fit the bill for what I have in mind.

"C'mon." I wave Cassel into the cheesiest store and start scanning the shelves. Everything is garish as hell. I pick up a bobblehead doll of Paul Revere and then put it down.

"These are funny," Cassel says. He's holding a box of Red Sox condoms.

I laugh before I think better of the idea. "True. But that's not what I'm looking for." Whatever I choose, it cannot have anything to do with sex. We used to send each other all sorts of gag gifts—the dirtier the better.

But not this time.

"May I help you?" The sales girl is dressed in colonial garb, complete with the bosom-squishing flouncy dress.

"Sure you can, doll." I lean against the counter in the cockiest way possible, and her eyes open a little wider. "You got anything with kittens on it?"

"Kittens?" Cassel chokes back a laugh. "What the hell for?"

"His team is the *tigers*." Duh.

"Sure!" Miss Betsy Ross perks up at the request, probably because this job is boring as fuck. "One sec."

"What's the deal?" Cassel tosses the condoms down onto a table. "You never buy me prezzies."

"Canning and I were summer camp friends. Tight, but we only saw each other for six weeks a year." A very intense six weeks. "You have friends like that?"

Cassel shakes his head.

"Me neither. Not before, and not since. But we didn't speak during the year. We texted, and we sent the box."

"The box?"

"Yeah…" I scratch my chin. "I think it started on his birthday. He must have been turning…fourteen?" Christ. Were we ever that young? "I sent him this obnoxious purple jock strap. I put it in one of my dad's Cuban cigar boxes."

I could still remember wrapping the box in brown paper and taping it all to hell so that it would get there in one piece. I'd hoped he'd open it in front of his friends and get embarrassed.

"Here we go!" Betsy Ross returns to spread several things on the counter in front of me. She's found a Hello Kitty pencil box, a big plush cat wearing a Bruins T-shirt, and white boxers covered with kittens.

"These." I push the boxers to her. Underwear hadn't been my goal, but the kittens are even the right shade of orange. "Now, for bonus points, I need a box. Cigar-shaped, if possible."

She hesitates. "Gift boxes cost extra."

"I'm good for it." I wink at her and she blushes a little. She's checking out my tats where they peek from the V-neck of my T-shirt. Can't blame her. Most women do. Better yet, men like 'em, too.

"Let me see what I can find." She scurries off.

I turn to Cassel, who's chewing his gum, watching me like I'm not making sense. "I still don't get it."

Right. "So, a couple of months later I get the box in the mail. No note. It's just the box I sent him but it's filled to the top with purple Skittles."

"Gross."

"No, man. I fucking *love* purple Skittles. Took me a month to eat them, though. That's a lot of Skittles. And eventually I sent the box back."

"With what?"

"No idea. Don't remember."

"What?" yelps Cassel. "I thought this story had a punchline."

"Not so much." Huh. I didn't realize until right this second the gift inside wasn't that important. It was the act of sending it. I'd been just like every teenage kid going through the grind of school and practice and homework, communicating only by email and text and grunts. When that box showed up unannounced it was like Christmas, but better. My friend had thought about me and gone to the trouble.

As we got older, the jokes got even more ridiculous. Fake poop. Whoopie cushions. A sign that prohibited farting. Stress balls shaped like boobs. The gift wasn't nearly as important as the fact that something was given.

Now Betsy Ross is back with a gift box that's roughly the right size, even if it doesn't flip open at the top like our box used to. "That will do," I say, even though I'm disappointed.

"So…" Cassel looks around the store, bored now. "You're sending him this one?"

"Yeah. Our old one is probably at my house somewhere." If I weren't an asshole, I'd know where. "I broke the chain a few years ago. So this'll have to do."

"I'm gonna text the manager and see if he's got hotel keys for us yet," Cassel says.

"You do that." I'm watching Betsy Ross wrap the kitty boxers in some tissue paper, then tuck them in the box.

"Need a card?" she asks, flashing me a smile and a better view of her cleavage.

Those don't work on me, sweetheart. "Please."

She passes me a sturdy square of cardstock and a pen. I write exactly one word on it and drop it into the box. There. I'll send this gift to Jamie's room in the hotel as soon as we get back.

Then, when I can pull him aside somewhere quiet, I'll apologize. There's no way to undo the wreckage I'd wrought four years ago. I can't take back that ridiculous bet I'd forced on him or the very awkward result. If I could go back in time and restrain my stupid eighteen-year-old self from pulling that bullshit, I would do it in a heartbeat.

But I can't. I can only man up and shake his hand and tell him it's good to see him. I can look into those brown eyes that always killed me and apologize for being such a dick. And then I can buy him a drink and try to go back to sports and smack-talk. Safe topics.

The fact that he'd been the first guy I ever loved and the one who made me face some terrifying things about myself…well, all that will go unsaid.

And then my team will kill his in the final. But that's just the way it is.

FOUR

JAMIE

We're looking at a quiet night in the hotel—a fact I'm sure half my teammates are extremely unhappy about. Particularly the freshmen and sophomore players, who are at the Frozen Four for the first time and were expecting to party like crazy this weekend. Coach squashed that notion pretty quick, though.

He laid down the law before anyone could even pick up their menus at the team dinner—ten o'clock curfew, no alcohol, no drugs, no shenanigans.

The upperclassmen know the drill, so none of us are especially bummed as we ride the elevator up to our block of rooms on the third floor. Tomorrow is game day. That means tonight is about taking it easy and getting some sleep.

Terry and I were assigned room 343 near the stairwell, so we're the last ones in the hallway as we head for our door.

The moment we reach it, we freeze.

There's a box on the carpet. Pale blue. No wrapping except for a white notecard stuck to the top reading *Jamie Canning* in flowery cursive.

What the shit?

My first thought is that my mom shipped something from California, but if she had, there'd be an address, postage, *her* handwriting.

"Um…" Terry shuffles before planting his hands on his hips. "You think it's a bomb?"

I snicker. "I don't know. Go put your ear on it and tell me if you hear ticking."

He snickers back. "Uh-huh, I see how it is. Such a great friend, Canning, putting *me* in the line of fire. Well, forget it. That's *your* name on the fucking thing."

We both stare at the package again. It's no bigger than a shoebox.

Beside me, Terry scrunches his face in mock terror and wails out, "*What's in the box?*"

"Dude, nice *Seven* reference," I say, genuinely impressed.

He grins. "You don't know how long I've been waiting for an opportunity to do that. *Years.*"

We take a moment to high-five each other, and I squat down and pick up the box because as entertaining as this convo is, we both know the thing is harmless. I tuck it under my arm and wait as Terry swipes his keycard to open the door, and then the two of us stride into the room. He flicks the light and heads for his bed, while I flop down on the edge of mine and lift the box's lid.

Wrinkling my forehead, I unwrap the white tissue paper and pull out the soft bundle of fabric inside.

From across the room, Terry hoots. "Dude…what the fuck?"

I have no idea. I'm staring at a pair of white boxers with bright orange kittens all over them, including an ill-placed tabby right at the crotch. When I hold them up by the waistband, another card flutters out. This one has one word on it.

MEOW.

And holy shit, I recognize the handwriting this time.

Ryan Wesley.

I can't help it. I snort so loud it sends Terry's eyebrows soaring up his forehead. I ignore my friend's reaction, too amused and bewildered by the significance of this gift.

The *box*. Wes has resurrected our old joke box. Except for the life of me, I have no idea *why*. I had been the last one to send it. And I remember feeling pretty damn smug about my choice of gifts—a package of Blow Pops. Because, well, how could I resist?

Wes hadn't sent anything back. He also hadn't called, texted, snail mailed, or courier pigeoned. Not a single word from him for three and a half years.

Until now.

"Who's it from?" Terry is smirking at me, visibly entertained by the ridiculous gift in my hands.

"Holly." Her name leaves my mouth so smoothly it surprises me. I don't know why I lied. Easy enough to say the boxers are from an old friend, a rival, whatever. But for some reason, I can't bring myself to tell Terry the truth.

"Is this an inside joke or something? Why would she send you kitten boxers?"

"Uh, you know, because she calls me kitten sometimes." Oh, for *fuck's* sake.

Terry pounces on that in a heartbeat. "*Kitten*? Your girlfriend calls you *kitten*?"

"She's not my girlfriend."

But the point is moot because he's doubled over in laughter, and I want to kick myself for giving him embarrassing ammo he'll no doubt use against me until the end of time. I should've just told him it was from Wes.

Why the hell didn't I?

"Uh, excuse me," he says, still chuckling as he marches to the door.

I narrow my eyes. "Where are you going?"

"Don't worry about it, kitten."

A sigh gets stuck in my throat. "You're going to knock on every door and tell the guys, aren't you?"

"Yup." He's gone before I can protest, but honestly I don't care all that much. So the guys will ride me about the kitten thing for a few days. Eventually one of my teammates will do something ridiculous and it'll be his turn to take the heat.

After the door swings shut behind Terry, I stare at the boxers again, an unwitting smile reaching my lips. Fuckin' Wes. I'm not sure what this means, but he must know I'm in town for the championship. Maybe this is his way of apologizing? Extending an olive branch?

Either way, I'm too curious to ignore the gesture. I reach for the phone and dial the front desk, then wait on the line to an awesome elevator rendition of Katy Perry's "Roar." Which only makes me chuckle, because, you know, roar. Meow.

When the desk clerk answers, I ask if there's a room number for Ryan Wesley. I'm pretty sure the sea of green-and-white jackets in the lobby means he's at this hotel.

"I can't provide another guest's room number, sir."

That stops me for a second, because clearly Wes was able to learn *my* room number. But this is Wes we're talking about. He probably offered some woman at the front desk a look at his abs.

"Sir? I could try to connect you by phone."

"Thanks."

It rings, but nobody answers. Shit. But there's one more thing to try. I scroll through my phone to see if his number is still in my contacts. And it is. Guess I was never quite pissed off enough to delete him. I shoot him a text, just three words: *still a smartass*.

When my phone chimes a second later, I expect it to say my message bounced. That Wes changed his number a long time ago, fuck you very much.

Some things don't change, it says instead.

I can't help answering him in my head. *But some do*. Eh. Listen to me getting all bitchy. What's the point of that? So I tap out something else: *So was this a hello present or a fuck you, loser, we're gonna kick your ass present?*

His reply: *Both?*

Sitting there on the hotel bed, I'm grinning at my phone. Seriously, my face is about to crack in two. It's really just nostalgia for a simpler time in my life when the biggest decisions were pizza toppings and what bit of ridiculousness I should mail in a box to my buddy.

But I like it anyway, which is probably why my next text says: *I'm probably heading down to the bar for a bit*.

His reply: *I'm already there*.

Of course he is.

I pocket my phone and open my duffel. Heading into the shower, I take a few minutes to wash the long day off me. I need to regroup. And I could really use a shave.

Or maybe I'm stalling.

I don't know what to expect from Wes. With him, you *never* know what to expect, which was one of the reasons I always liked him so much. Being his friend was a goddamn adventure. He'd drag me into one crazy situation after the other, and I was happy going along for the ride.

I did that so loyally. Right up through the crazy part at the end.

In the hotel shower, I take a deep breath of steamy air. Holly was right. I *am* still mad. Because if Wes and I had had a fight or something, then his turning his back on me would at least have made sense.

But we hadn't fought. He'd just challenged me to a shootout. And that day—the second-to-last afternoon of camp—we'd lined up the pucks with perfect fairness. He shot five times at me, I shot five times at him.

Shootouts are never easy. But when you're defending the net against Ryan Wesley, the fastest skater I've ever played with? It's intense. Still, we'd done this often enough for me to be able to anticipate his flashy moves. I remember cackling after I stopped the first three shots. But then he got lucky, deking me once and then winning one on an unlikely bounce off the pipe.

Maybe another guy would have panicked a little when he realized he'd let in two. But I was a cool customer. Ultimately, it was Wes who'd choked. He wasn't used to the goalie gear, but neither was I used to firing on goal. I sank my first two shots. Then he defended the next two.

It was all down to one shot, and I saw it—fear in his eyes. In my gut, I knew I could do this.

I'd won, fair and square. The third shot went past his elbow and landed with a swish in the back of the net.

For the next three hours I let him twist—all through dinner and the bullshit awards ceremony they held at the end of camp. Wes was uncharacteristically mute through all of it.

I waited until we got back to our room to let him off the hook.

"Think I'll collect my prize next year," I'd said with as much nonchalance as an eighteen-year-old can muster. "June, maybe. Or July. I'll let you know, 'kay?"

I'd wanted some kind of relieved gasp. Making Wes sweat for once had been fun. But his face gave nothing away. He'd pulled out a stainless steel flask and slowly unscrewed the top. "Last night of camp, dude," he'd said. "We'd better celebrate." He took a good gulp and then passed it to me.

When I took the flask, his eyes flashed with something I couldn't read.

The whiskey was rough going down. The first swallow, anyway. Up until now, we hadn't drunk more than a beer or two, squirreled away in our footlockers. Getting caught with alcohol or drugs would have meant real trouble. So I didn't have any kind of tolerance back then. I felt the liquor's warmth slide through my chest just as Wes said, "Let's watch some porn."

Almost four years later, I stand there shivering in a hotel bathroom. I shut the water off and grab a towel off the stack.

I guess it's time to go downstairs and see if our friendship is fixable. What had happened on that night was a little crazy, but not exactly worthy of the record books. I'd shrugged it off easily enough.

But Wes had not. There's really no other explanation for why he'd cut me loose.

God, I hope he doesn't dredge that up. Sometimes it's better to just let shit lie. The way I see it, one night of drunken stupidity shouldn't be the defining moment in a six-year friendship.

Even so, I'm oddly nervous five minutes later as I ride the elevator downstairs, and I hate the itchy feeling in my spine, because I don't get nervous often. I'm probably the most chill person you'll ever meet, which I'm sure has to do with the fact that my family is the walking definition of laidback Californians.

The bar is packed when I enter. No surprise. It's Friday night and the hotel is booked solid because of the tournament. Every table and booth is occupied. I have to turn my body sideways to move through the place, and I can't see Wes anywhere.

Maybe this was a stupid idea. "Excuse me," I say. There's a clot of businessmen blocking the thoroughfare between the bar and the tables. But they laugh at someone's joke, ignoring the way they're making the whole room impassable.

I'm probably seconds from going back upstairs when I hear it.

"Suckers."

It's just one word, but I recognize Wes's voice instantly. Deep, kinda raspy. I'm suddenly transported back to high school, to all those summers I heard that voice mocking me, challenging me, ragging on me.

A communal snort of laughter follows his comment, and I turn my head to search him out in the group of hockey players against the far wall.

He turns his head at the same time, almost as if he senses my presence. And shit, I've traveled back in time again. He looks the same. And different. He looks both different and the same.

He's still got the messy dark hair and scruffy beard growth, but he's bigger now. Solid muscle and broad shoulders, more lean than bulky, but definitely bulkier than his eighteen-year-old self. Still has the tribal tattoo on his right biceps, but now there's a lot more ink on his golden-toned skin. Another piece on his left arm. Something black and Celtic-looking peeking from the collar of his T-shirt.

He's still talking to his friends as he watches me approach. Of course he's surrounded by people. I'd forgotten how magnetic he is. As if he burns with higher test fuel than the rest of us.

A barbell pierced through his eyebrow catches the light as he turns his head, a wink of silver just a shade lighter than his slate-gray eyes. Which narrow when I finally swim through the sea of people to arrive at his side.

"Shit, man, did you get highlights in your hair?"

More than three years since we've been in the same room together, and *that's* the first thing he says to me?

"No." I roll my eyes as I slide onto the stool beside his. "It's from the sun."

"Still surfing every weekend?" Wes asks.

"When I have time." I cock a brow. "Still pulling down your pants and flashing your junk for no conceivable reason?"

His teammates erupt around us, their laughter thundering in my chest. "Shit, he was always like this?" somebody says.

A grin tugs the corner of Wes's mouth. "I've never deprived

the world of my God-given masculine beauty." He reaches out to put a big hand on my shoulder. He gives it a squeeze. It's gone again in a split second, but I can still feel the warm spot on my shoulder. "Guys, this is Jamie Canning, my friend from way back and goalie for those punks at Rainier."

"Hey," I say stupidly. Then I glance around, looking for a waitress. I need a drink in my hand, even if it's just a soda. But the place is mobbed, and the only server in view is nowhere nearby.

I glance at the glass in Wes's hand. He's drinking something fizzy—Coke, from the looks of it. No, root beer. He'd always preferred root beer. And obviously his coach gave him the same no-drinking spiel.

Wes raises his hand in the air, and the waitress abruptly turns in our direction. He points at his glass and she nods as if commanded by God to do his bidding. Wes flashes her a smile, his favorite currency for favors. And I notice another flash of metal.

His tongue is pierced. That's new, too.

Annnd now I'm thinking about his tongue. Jesus fuck. And the last four years of silence between us suddenly make a bit more sense. Maybe there *are* drunken antics capable of wrecking a friendship.

Or maybe that's crap, and if we'd stayed friends we could have gotten past an hour's worth of stupidity a long time ago.

Meanwhile, it's really too warm in this bar. If that waitress brings me a root beer, I'm going to be tempted to pour it all over myself. And the silence between my ex-friend and I is growing longer by the second.

"Crowded," I manage. Just barely.

"Yeah. Need a pull?" He offers me his glass.

I take a greedy gulp and our eyes meet over the rim. His

confidence has slipped a millimeter or two. His gaze asks a question. *Are we going to make it through the next half hour?*

Swallowing, I make a decision. "Shame the Bruins got punished by the Ducks last month."

I see the flash of arrogance return at lightning speed. "That was a fluke. And a *terrible* call in the third. Your wing tripped over his own duck feet."

"With a little help from your D-man."

"Oh, fuck that. Twenty bucks says the Ducks don't make it past the first round this year."

"Twenty is all you're willing to bet?" I gasp. "Sounds like you're afraid. Twenty and a YouTube video proclaiming my greatness."

"Done, but when you lose, you make that video in a Bruins T-shirt."

"Sure." I shrug. And just like that, the night gets easier.

The waitress appears with two glasses of root beer and a hungry smile for Wes. He slips her a twenty. "Thanks, doll."

"Let me know if you *need* anything," she says, overselling it by a shade. *Christ.* Hockey players don't have a lot of trouble getting laid, but my old friend obviously enjoys his pick of the litter. She's hot, too. Great rack and a sweet smile.

He doesn't even spare a glance at her perfect ass as she sashays away.

After she disappears, Wes opens his arms and grins at the group of hockey players standing around him. "Shit, we're just a bunch of pussies, aren't we? Root beer and ginger ale on a Friday night. Someone call the cops. We need a game of darts or something."

"Table hockey!" someone calls out. "Saw it in the game room."

"Cassel!" Wes thumps the guy standing next to him. "Who won our last game, anyway?"

"You did, you prick. Because you cheated during the shootout."

"Who, me?"

Everyone laughs. But my mind snags on "shootout."

Of course it does.

FIVE

WES

The college sprang for an executive suite at TD Garden, a fancy-ass private box with a gleaming floor-to-ceiling window that overlooks the arena below. The celebratory bottles of Dom that had been delivered, however, were courtesy of my shithead father. The prick is riding the high of our win as if it had been *him* out on the ice this afternoon—I even heard him bragging to one of his buddies that he was the one who taught me that triple-deke move I used to score the winning goal in the third period.

Bullshit. The old man hadn't taught me a damn thing. From the moment I was able to hold a hockey stick, he threw money at coaches and trainers and anyone else who could groom his only son into a superstar. The only credit I'm willing to give him is that he's really fucking good at signing his name on a check.

Canning's team is on the ice now, facing the same pressure we did earlier. Coach has allowed us each one glass of champagne. We're playing in the finals tomorrow night, and he wants us sharp. He doesn't have to worry about me, though. I'm sipping on a root beer. Not just as a fuck-you to my dad, but because my stomach is in knots as I watch the game, and alcohol will only make it worse.

I want Rainier to win.

I want to face Canning in the finals.

I want to pretend I still don't have feelings for the guy.

I guess I'll have to be satisfied with two out of three. Because I *can't* pretend I'm not still into him. Seeing him again last night made that impossible.

Fuck, he'd looked good. Really good. All golden-boy California hotness, big and blond and sexy as fuck. With those soulful brown eyes—surprising on a blond guy. It's an understated sexiness, though. Jamie Canning never flaunted his looks in all the time I'd known him. Sometimes I think he's not even aware of how goddamn attractive he is.

"Oooooh *shit*," one of the seniors crows as a Rainier player delivers what might be the hit of the week.

It's a clean check, but it makes the opposing player bounce off the boards like a rubber ball and sprawl face-first on the ice.

Rainier is in it to win it. They're playing aggressively, all offense, all the time. I don't think Yale has taken more than a dozen shots on goal, and it's already well into the third. Canning stopped all but one, and the one he let in was a total fluke of a shot, smacking off the pipe to provide Yale with a rebound the center slapped right back in. I could practically hear the hiss of the puck as it whizzed past Canning's glove, just a nanosecond too fast for him to swallow it up.

The score's tied now. 1-1, with five minutes to go. I find myself holding my breath, willing Rainier's forwards to make something happen.

"Your man Canning is rock steady," Cassel tells me, taking a dainty sip of his champagne like he's the fucking Queen of England.

"Cool under pressure," I agree, my gaze glued to the rink. Yale's left wing just flicked a lazy wrist shot that Canning easily stops, his body language almost bored as he keeps possession of the puck before passing it to one of his wings.

The Rainier players tear past the blue line, going on the attack.

But my mind is still on the last goal attempt, the way Canning faced off with the Yale player. I can't even count how many times I was in that exact position, flying toward my buddy, slapping bullets at him.

Except the last time we faced off, I was the one in the net. The last barrier standing between Jamie Canning and a blowjob.

I like to think I didn't let him win on purpose. I'm a competitor, always have been. Didn't matter how much I wanted Canning's dick in my mouth. Didn't matter that if *I* won, I knew I'd have to let him back out of the bet. I'd defended that net with everything I had. Maybe?

Because when that puck flew past me, I can't deny a part of me had been thrilled.

"With that said, I wouldn't bawl my eyes out if they lose," Cassel says. He turns to grin at me. "I know he's your BFF and all, but I'd feel better going up against Yale's goalie than cool cucumber down there."

Cassel's right. Canning's the bigger threat. Those weaknesses he'd had back in the day? Gone. He's a fucking rock star now. No wonder he got the starting job back.

Even so, I don't want him to lose. I want to see him in the finals. I want to see him, period. And I've experienced crushing defeat before—if his team chokes, I know he won't be up for hanging out, catching up, reconnecting…

Sucking each other off?

I banish the thought. I don't fucking learn, do I? The last time *sucking* entered the equation, I'd lost my best friend.

It's funny—I'm sure everyone has something they regret saying. An insult they'd hurled someone's way. A confession they wished they could take back. Maybe, I don't know, an insensitive joke they wish they hadn't told.

The one sentence *I* regret? "*Let's watch some porn.*"

There was no turning back once I uttered those four words, and I can't even fully blame the alcohol, because a few sips from a flask does not a drunken idiot make. I knew what I was doing. What I was coaxing Canning into. I was collecting on the damn bet, which is so fucking ironic, because *he'd* won. The prize was *his*, except it wasn't. It was *mine*. Because I'd wanted to touch him more than I'd wanted my next breath.

I still remember the shock on his face when I loaded the porn site on my laptop. I chose a tame scene—tame for me, anyway. I set the laptop on the mattress, then sprawled on the bottom bunk as if I had no care in the world.

For a long moment Canning didn't move. I waited, tense, while he decided whether or not he was going to sit next to me on my bed, or climb up to the top bunk. Without looking at him, I passed him the flask. I heard him gulp. He swallowed on a sigh, then parked his ass beside me.

I didn't risk a look at him for several minutes. We lay on our backs, passing the flask back and forth as we watched two dudes double-team a busty blonde on the screen.

"How would you compare your technique to hers?" Canning cracked himself up with this quip, his stomach shaking even as he looked at the laptop.

To him, it was just the latest amusing result of our competitive shenanigans. He was going to lord it over me, the way we always did with each other.

But to me, it was no joke. I'd just spent the last year trying to accept my increasingly obvious attraction to men. The bumbling loss of my virginity to a chick during junior year had been a pretty big red flag. I hadn't been attracted to her, but I'd needed to try it. To be certain. I'd barely been able to get it up, and even then, I'd managed only because I was thinking about...

Canning. I thought about Jamie Canning.

I'd been crushing on my straight best friend for a long time. But I couldn't tell him that. My only move here was to play along.

"Well, I've always been good at stickhandling."

Jamie snorted. "Only you could be cocky even about this."

"I always tell you, Canning. No fear. No matter what."

God, I was such a jackass. Because fear wasn't even part of the equation. All I had was a pure, aching desire as I lay there beside Jamie. Last year I'd enjoyed a couple of drunken make-out sessions and a hand-job exchange with a guy from school. But even then, I hadn't been one hundred percent sure.

Lying in bed next to Canning? I burned with certainty.

On the screen, the blonde was moaning like crazy. Spit-roasted and loving it. Canning went quiet for a while. I lay there, trying to keep my breathing even. But I couldn't resist sneaking a peek at his crotch a minute later. And then my breath hitched, because holy shit, he was hard, a long, thick erection straining beneath his athletic shorts. I was sporting the same visible boner, and I know he saw it. He probably thought it was the porn. Hell, that was the only reason *he* was turned on.

Not me, though. My dick throbbed for *him*.

Beside me, he swallowed roughly. "Interesting pick, Wesley. Considering the stakes. I'm not gonna force you to blow me." He grinned. "I'd rather bask in the glory of knowing you finally wrote a check you couldn't cash." Then he rolled his gorgeous eyes at me, and it only made my skin burn hotter.

"What," I said, hoping he couldn't hear the rasp of lust in my voice, "You think I'm too chicken-shit to blow you?"

He turned his chin to meet my eyes...

"Fuck yeah!"

Our team captain's shout jerks me out of my trip down

memory lane. The whole arena is in an uproar, fans screaming as the scoreboard lights up and the screens mounted all over the place flash the word GOAL! in huge yellow letters.

My stomach drops like a sack of bricks when I realize who scored.

Yale.

Fucking hell. Yale scored, and I'd been too distracted to see it. It's 2-1 now, with a minute and a half to go.

"I spaced out," I tell Cassel. "What just happened?"

"One of the Rainier D-men took the stupidest penalty I've ever seen." He shakes his head in amazement. "Idiot just handed Yale the win."

No, they haven't won yet. There's still time for Rainier to regroup. Still time, damn it.

"Your boy didn't stand a chance on that power play," Cassel adds.

My gut twists harder. Say what you will about Yale, but they lead the NCAA in capitalizing on power plays. Every time we played them this season, Coach uttered one grim sentence before we left the locker room—"You wind up in the sin bin against Yale, you lose."

I pray those words aren't prophetic, that Rainier can come back from this, but my prayers go unanswered.

The final buzzer blares through TD Garden.

And Rainier loses.

SIX

JAMIE

We lost.

We fucking lost.

I'm still dazed as I trudge down the chute toward the locker rooms. The mood all around me is somber. Suffocating. Nobody is playing the blame game, though.

There's no anger directed at Barkov, who tripped the Yale forward for no comprehensible reason—the guy didn't even have the puck.

There's no recrimination toward our defense, who inexplicably fell apart during that power play.

And there's no accusation aimed *my* way, for not being able to stop that last shot from lighting the lamp.

But, inside…I blame myself.

I should've stopped it. I should've dived faster, extended my arm farther. I should've hurled my body on that damn puck and not let it get anywhere near the crease.

Numbness sets in. I'd been bummed my family didn't make the trek from Cali to watch me play. Now I'm grateful they didn't see me lose. Except on television. Along with a few million other people…

Damn.

Back in our hotel room, I find Terry sitting on the bed, clicker in hand. But the TV is off, and he's watching a black screen.

"Um, Terry? You okay?"

He looks up fast. "Yeah. Just…" The sentence dies an early death.

The next several days are going to be just like this. I can see it now. We wanted so badly to be the ones who brought this title home to Rainier. It would have proved to our families and the college that all these years of sacrifice were worth it.

We proved nothing.

"It's still the winningest season in thirty years," Terry says slowly.

I flop onto my bed. "Is winningest a word?"

"Not if you're us." We both laugh. But his laugh ends on a sigh. "That was my *last* game, Canning. My very last one. I'm not an NHL recruit like you. Three months from now I'm wearing a suit and sitting at a desk."

Shit. That's really grim.

"For fifteen years I've been a hockey player. As of a half hour ago, I'm a junior associate in the investment banking division of Pine Trust Capital."

Jesus. And now I'm hoping our hotel room windows aren't the kind that open, because I'm half afraid he's going to step out onto a ledge. Or else I will. "Dude, you need alcohol and a girl. Like, yesterday."

His chuckle is dark. "My cousins are on the way over here to pick me up. There will be drinking and titty bars."

"Thank Christ." I roll over to study the pebbled hotel room ceiling. "You know, there's a very real chance I never play a single NHL game. Third-string goalie? Detroit might as well make a bench to my ass's exact measurements. If I'm lucky they'll let me play backup to their farm-team goalie."

"You'll still have the jersey and the puck bunnies." His phone rings and he swipes to answer. "Born ready," he tells the caller. "I'll be right down." Then to me, "You coming with?"

Am I? I definitely need a drink. But at the moment, my back is plastered to the bedspread. "I'm not ready," I admit. "Can I text you in an hour, see where you are?"

"Do it," he says.

"Later," I call out as the door clicks shut.

For a little while I just stew in my own misery. My parents call my phone, but I don't pick up. They'll be awesome, as always, but I don't want to hear nice, encouraging words right now. I need to feel bad. Get drunk. Get off, maybe.

There's a firm knock on the door and I haul my sorry ass up to answer it. Probably a teammate, ready to help me with the getting drunk part of tonight's activities.

I yank the door open to find Holly standing there, her face smudged with orange and black paint, a bottle of tequila in one hand and limes in the other. "Surprise," she says.

"Jesus, Holls." I laugh. "You said you weren't coming."

"I lied." She gives me a big grin.

I open the door wider. "You've never had better timing in your life."

"Really?" she challenges, pushing past me. "Not even the time I got you off in the bathroom of the train right before our station stop?"

"Okay, maybe then." I am so happy to see her it's not even funny. Distraction is what I need, and that's what Holly and I have always been to one another.

She gets down to business, cutting limes on the hotel table with a knife she's pulled from her purse. Do I know how to pick my friends, or what?

"Glasses," Holly orders over her shoulder.

I think I could go straight for the bottle tonight, but for her sake I look around, finding a pair of them on the console by the TV. I plunk 'em down and she's pouring before I know it.

"Here." She offers me a glass and raises another in the air. "To kicking ass and getting over our disappointments." Her wide blue eyes study me, looking for something.

"That's a good toast, pal," I murmur. "Thank you." When I touch my glass to hers, she grins like she's won something tonight. That makes one of us.

"Bottoms up, hunk. Then I'm stripping you naked."

I like the sound of that. The tequila slides down, and then I let her stick a lime in my mouth. We're both chuckling and sucking down the sour citrus flavor. Then I give her a nudge onto the bed. I'd like to freaking *unleash* all my tensions on this smiling girl, but I take a deep breath. Holly is kind of a peanut and half the time I'm worried about crushing her.

My knees are on the bed now, and she's scooting back, shucking off her shirt. My own shirt hits the floor before I lower myself over her body, taking care to hold most of my weight off of her. Except for my hips. Those sink decadently onto hers, and my dick wakes up and says, *lookee what we have here*.

Holly grabs my head and pulls me down for a kiss. I taste lime and tequila and willing, happy girl. "Mmm," she moans. "I've been waiting all day for this."

So was I, it's just that I didn't know it. My eyes slam shut and I sink down into her mouth and this beautiful place of forgetfulness. There's no game and no goal just before the buzzer. There's no disappointment. There's only a sexy girl beneath me and some more shots to drink.

And a knock on the door.

"Fuck," Holly and I grunt in unison.

"Canning!" a voice calls from the hallway.

Wes's voice. The sound of it pulls me out of the moment.

"Do you *have* to?" Holly pants.

"I kind of do," I whisper. "But only for a minute. I swear."

"Fine," she huffs, pushing on my chest. "But I'm pouring more tequila."

"You are awesome," I insist, reaching down to the floor for her shirt. I ignore mine in the interest of time. The second she's covered, I cross the room and open the door.

"Hey," I greet Wes.

I expect him to launch into a "tough luck" spiel. Wes is competitive as fuck but he'd never kick me when I was down. Oddly, though, he stays silent, blinking at me from the hallway. "Hey," he echoes after a long pause. "I just…"

No more words are forthcoming. He takes in my half-dressed look, and the sight of my fuck buddy pouring tequila.

"That's Holly," I say quietly. "Holly, this is an old friend, Ryan Wesley."

"Shot?" she offers from across the room. She's flushed, and her hair is mussed.

I'm probably in the same state. But Holly doesn't seem embarrassed, so I don't worry. "Wes, you coming in?"

"No," he says quickly, and the word sounds like a chip of stone falling onto a hard surface. "I just wanted to tell you that I'm sorry we're not facing off tomorrow." He shoves his hands in his pockets in a rare display of humility. "Won't be the same now." The corners of his mouth turn up, but the smile doesn't make it to his eyes.

"I know." My voice is full of all the disappointment I'd been hoping to escape tonight. "Not like camp."

"Loved that place," Wes says, reaching up to rub the back of his neck.

"I still coach there, you know." I'd meant to end this conversation already, so I have no idea why I add, "It isn't the same without you." It's true, but this is already the most emotionally loaded day of my life, and I really don't need more to think about.

"I'm going to head out," Wes says, jerking a thumb toward the elevators. "You, ah, take care of yourself if I don't see you tomorrow." He takes a step backward.

That's the moment when I really don't know what to do. My team will head back to the west coast in the morning. We won't stay for the final. I'm not sure Wes and I have more to say to each other right now. But is this really it? I feel a strong urge to add something—to delay his departure.

Except I'm beat and confused and so fucking spent. And he's already turning away from me.

"Later," I say gruffly.

He looks over his shoulder to raise one hand in a wave.

I stand there like an idiot a moment longer, and he turns the corner toward the elevator banks.

"Jamie," Holly says softly. "Here's your drink."

Reluctantly, I shut the door. I cross the room, take the glass from her and pound it.

She slips the empty tumbler from my hand. "Now where were we?"

If I only knew.

SEVEN

WES

"You know we just won the national title, right?" Cassel says for the hundredth time in the past hour. He wears the goofy, king-of-the-world grin he's been sporting all night. Even before the four vodka shots he threw back.

"Yeah, I know." My tone is absent as I sweep my gaze over the crowded, overheated bar we'd chosen as celebration head-quarters. The drinks at the hotel bar are ridiculously overpriced, so we decided to venture somewhere else tonight. And according to Donovan's Yelp search, this tiny dive bar has half-price drinks on Sunday nights and apparently they don't taste like piss.

I don't give a shit how the alcohol tastes, though. I'm only interested in the effects of it. I want to get drunk. I want to get shit-faced out of my mind so I don't have to think about what a total fucking idiot I am.

Cassel's voice drags me out of my bleak thoughts. "Then quit sulking like a bitch," he orders. "We're national champions, man. We *crushed* Yale tonight. We fucking shut them out."

We did. The final score had been 2-0, Northern Mass. We'd wiped the ice with our opponents, and I should be happy about that. No, I should be goddamn ecstatic. It's what we trained all year for, yet instead of savoring the win, I'm too busy bumming out about the fact that Canning has a girlfriend.

Yes, folks, Jamie Canning is straight. Shocker.

You'd think I'd have learned my lesson by now. I spent six years hoping that maybe the attraction wasn't one-sided. Maybe one day a switch would suddenly go off and he'd be like, *hmmm, I'm totally into Wes*. Or maybe he would figure out he swings both ways and decide to take a walk on the dude side.

None of those maybes had panned out, though. And they never fucking would.

All around me, the guys laugh and joke and recap their favorite moments of tonight's game, and nobody notices I'm not saying anything. My mind keeps wandering back to Jamie and his girl and the hook-up I'd interrupted last night.

"We need another round," Cassel announces, searching the main room for our waitress.

When I spot her behind the counter, I abruptly scrape back my chair. "I'll go order it," I tell the guys, and then I dart away from the table before anyone can ask why I've suddenly become so charitable.

At the bar, I order another round of shots for the group, then rest my forearms on the splintered wooden counter and study the liquor bottles on the shelves. I've been drinking beer all night, but it's not getting the job done. I need to be drunker. I need something harder.

My gut tightens when my gaze lands on a gleaming bottle of bourbon. My father's drink of choice. But the bourbon he buys is a thousand times more expensive than the bottle on this shelf.

I shift my gaze to the row of tequila bottles.

Canning had been drinking tequila last night.

My gaze moves again. Jack Daniel's.

Aw hell. It's like every bottle in this fucking bar is full of memories.

Before I can stop it, my mind flashes back to that last day at camp, to the silver flask I'd passed Canning, and the mocking question I'd hurled his way.

"You think I'm too chicken-shit to blow you?"

He'd seemed to consider me for a minute. "I think it's a bad idea to ever say that Ryan Wesley is too chicken-shit to do something."

"True dat."

He chuckled, but his eyes went back to the screen. Again, he let me off the hook. But I didn't want to be let off. I wanted to *get* off. The longer we sat there discussing sex, the more certain I was. Touching my best friend was all I could think about. It wasn't a dare for me, either. It was pure desire.

On the screen, the blonde was on her knees, sucking one of the guys while jacking off the other. Jamie took another sip from the flask before passing it my way. Beside me, he shifted his hips, and I had to suppress a shudder. My heart's desire was sitting beside me.

And now he was horny.

His hand had moved, resting just above the waistband of his shorts. He gave the spot beneath his abs the tiniest of caresses, like he had an itch, but it was obvious he'd been hoping to do some strategic rearranging.

I swallowed a mouthful of whiskey. For courage. Then I put a hand between my legs, just resting it there. "This is killing me," I said. It was the most truthful statement I'd made all day. I took a slow stroke down my hard cock and then back up again. I could feel his eyes on me, on my hand. And that made me even crazier. Forget the screen. I'd rather star in my own solo act right here, with my favorite pair of brown eyes as the only audience.

My heart started to pound, because I knew what I was about to do.

There's this cliff at the swimming hole we liked, a twenty-foot drop into the lake, and that night, it was like I was standing atop it. Like I was creeping toward the edge and pulling him with me. I remember one year when Canning was taking so long to jump I'd lost patience and pushed him off, cackling as I watched him wind-mill down to the water below.

But I couldn't do that this time. I couldn't push him. He had to jump.

I licked my dry lips. "I really need to jerk. You mind?"

His moment of hesitation practically killed me. "Go ahead. We shower in the same room, right? Hell." He chuckled. "We crap in the same room. Though there's walls."

There weren't any here.

I shoved my hand under my waistband and gripped my aching shaft. I didn't whip it out, though. Just gave it a slow tug beneath my shorts.

His eyes had filled with surprise, then flashed with something that sucked the breath right out of my lungs. Not anger. Not annoyance.

Arousal.

Holy hell, he was getting off on seeing me jerk it. And neither of us was looking at the laptop now. Canning's gaze stayed glued to the slow movement of my hand beneath my shorts.

"You can, too." I hated the gravelly sound of my voice just then, because I knew that I had an agenda. "Go ahead. It'll be less weird for me."

Hell. I was like the serpent shoving the apple at Eve. Or rather the banana…

All the bad analogies fled my stupid brain a moment later when Jamie reached into his shorts and pulled his dick all the way out.

My heart shimmied in my chest at the sight. He was pink and thick and perfect. With the fingers of one hand he stroked the underside—up and down. The lightest touch. I envied those fingertips.

I cupped my aching balls and tried to take a deep breath. My chest was tight from wanting him. He was right there—his hip touching mine. I wanted to bend down and take him in my mouth. I wanted it so badly I could taste it.

His eyes went back to the screen. I felt him sink a little further back into the bed. We were both stroking in earnest now. His breathing became shallower, and the sound of it sent another shot of lust up my spine. I wanted to be the one making him pant like that. But then his pace faltered, and I looked up to find out why.

The video had ended. I'd chosen a clip that was only a few minutes long. And now the screen had frozen on a menu of clips, but the thumbnail photo displayed most prominently was this awful shot of a woman's giant ass.

"Um…" Jamie actually chuckled. "That's not getting the job done."

I felt a sort of awareness settle over me then. In hockey, when a shot opens up, a good player has to react immediately. That's exactly what was happening here. A window of opportunity had cracked open a sliver, and I was going to dive through it.

"You could call in your bet," I croaked.

Stroking himself, he let out a hot breath. "You daring me to?"

"Yeah."

His throat worked as he swallowed. His eyes flickered with a parade of emotions I couldn't keep up with. Reluctance. Heat. Confusion. Heat. Irritation. Heat.

"I…" He laughed, his voice hoarse. He stopped, cleared his throat. "Double dog dare you."

His gaze locked with mine again and I almost came right there and then. My cock had swelled in my hand, pulsing. Aching. But somehow I managed to put on a careless tone, my trademark up-for-anything drawl that half the time is a total front.

"Well. This should be interesting."

The faint hint of panic on his face was unmistakable, but I didn't give him time to back out. I wanted him too much. I'd *always* fucking wanted this guy.

Releasing myself, I reached over to cover his hand with mine. He tensed, and for a split second I thought he was going to push me away.

I wouldn't have blamed him.

But then he let go, leaving my hand there alone. And I was holding his dick. *Finally*. He was hot and hard, and the ends of his soft blond pubic hair tickled my fingertips. I squeezed, and all the air seemed to drain out of his body, his torso practically melting into the mattress. My mouth was a desert, my pulse a loud drum in my ears.

I stroked my palm along that hard shaft, acting like what I was doing was no biggie. Then I said, "Fuck, I think I'm drunk." Because that seemed like the right thing to say. Like alcohol was the reason we were doing this. Alcohol was our hall pass.

It worked, because he choked out, "Me too." But his voice was smoky and distracted.

And maybe he *was* drunk. Maybe the flush on his cheeks was all thanks to the whiskey and not from the feel of my other hand yanking his shorts down further. Maybe his breathing quickened because alcohol was surging through his bloodstream and not from my fingers curling around his shaft.

I shifted on the mattress, kneeling in front of him as I pumped him in slow strokes. My entire body throbbed with uncontrollable need, my erection heavy between my legs. I ignored it, though. Jamie blinked twice when I rose above him, and I watched his face, gauging his reaction. He didn't look horrified. He looked turned on.

I'd been fantasizing about this moment for years. Couldn't believe it was really here.

"What are you waiting for, *Ryan*? Suck it already."

Surprise jolted through me. He only called me Ryan when he was taunting me. And right now he was taunting me about sucking his dick.

Jesus.

My bravado faltered, just for a second. Until I saw his pulse hammering in the hollow of his throat, and realized he was as nervous and excited as I was.

I took a breath and lowered my head.

Then I closed my mouth over his swollen tip and sucked.

Jamie's hips snapped up instantly, his breath leaving his throat on a ragged shudder. "Oh Jesus."

I remember wondering if he'd ever been blown before. The shock and awe in his voice had been so raw. *So* sexy. So I'd wondered, but not for long. Not when he started whispering the hottest, filthiest commands at me.

"More," he muttered. "Take more. Take it all."

I sucked him deeper into my mouth, almost to the base, and just when he moaned, I released him, gliding my tongue along the long, hard length of him until his dick was glistening. I lapped at the moisture leaking out of his tip, and the taste of him infused my tongue, making my head spin.

I was blowing my best friend. It was so surreal. It was what I'd dreamed about for so long, and the fantasy was nothing compared to the reality of it.

"Fuck, yeah." Canning's hips began to rock as I took him in my mouth again.

I licked the crown of his cock, teasing, savoring, then taking him deep again. I didn't dare peer up at him. I was too afraid to look him in the eye—afraid he'd be able to see on my face how much I wanted him.

"Jesus, Wes, you're way too good at this."

The praise just lit me up. Holy *hell*. He was thrusting into my mouth because *I* turned him on.

His fingers suddenly tangled in my hair, tightening when I swallowed him as far as I could take him.

"Oh Christ. Keep doing that, man. Let me fuck your mouth."

Every husky thing he said practically made me go up in flames. I knew *I* would enjoy this. But if he was too? Mind bending. I quickened the pace, squeezing his shaft on every upstroke, tighter than I thought he'd like, but he kept muttering *harder*, *faster*.

My eyes squeezed shut as I worked him over, determined to make him lose control, to make him feel the same urgent need wreaking havoc on my body.

"Wes…" A choked sound left his lips. "Fuck, Wes, you're making me come."

His fingers pulled my hair to the point of pain, his abs tightening as his hips rocked faster. A few seconds later, he groaned. The husky sound vibrated against my lips as he went still, thrust deep, and came inside my mouth while I swallowed up every last dro—

"You hoping one of those bottles holds up a little sign for you and says 'order me'?"

A male voice jolts me back to the present. I blink, disoriented. I'm still at the bar, still standing at the counter and staring at the liquor bottles. Shit. I'd totally spaced out. And I'm semi-hard now, thanks to the memory of my last night with Jamie Canning.

Gulping, I turn to find a smiling stranger beside me.

"Seriously," he adds, his smile widening. "You've been eyeing those bottles for almost five minutes. The bartender gave up on trying to ask you what you wanted."

The bartender had talked to me? He probably thinks I'm a total weirdo.

The guy next to me doesn't look like a weirdo, though. He's

really good-looking, actually. Late twenties, wearing faded jeans and a *Ramones* T-shirt, a full-sleeve tattoo covering his right arm. Tribal shit, mixed with skulls and dragons and some other badass imagery. He's skinnier than I usually like, but not anorexic thin. Not entirely my type, but he's not *not* my type, either. He's definitely hook-up material, and from the way he's checking me out, I know he'd be down.

"You with those guys?" He gestures to the table of hockey jackets.

I nod.

"Whatcha celebrating?"

"We won the Frozen Four tonight." I pause. "College hockey championship."

"No shit. Congrats, man. So you play hockey, huh?" His gaze lingers on my chest and arms before sliding back to my face. "It shows."

Yeah, he'd be down.

I glance at the table, where Cassel catches my eye. He grins when he notices my companion, then turns back to the guys, laughing at something Landon just said.

"So what's your name?" my stranger asks.

"Ryan."

"I'm Dane."

I nod again. I can't seem to muster up any charm. No cocky remarks, no blatant come-ons. I won a championship game tonight—I should be celebrating. I should invite this very attractive guy back to the hotel, hang the do-not-disturb sign on the door so Cassel gets the hint, and screw Dane's goddamn brains out.

But I don't want to. I'd just be trying to screw Canning out of my system, and I know I'd feel like shit after.

"Sorry, gotta get back to my boys," I say abruptly. "Nice chatting with you, man."

I march across the bar before he can say another word. I don't turn around to see if he looks disappointed or to make sure he isn't following me. I just tap Cassel on the shoulder and tell him I'm taking off.

It's another five minutes before I'm able to convince him I haven't been abducted by aliens. I plead a headache, blame it on the adrenaline and the beers and the temperature and everything else I can think of, until finally he gives up on coaxing me to stay, and I'm able to leave the bar.

It's twenty blocks back to the hotel, but I decide to walk instead of cabbing it. I could use the fresh air and the time to clear my head. Except now I'm ten blocks into the walk, and my head still isn't clear. It's fogged in with images of Canning.

I can't stop picturing the way he looked last night. His sexed-up hair, the flush on his cheeks. He'd either gotten laid or had been about to. And the chick had been hot, a tiny little pixie of a girl with big blue eyes. He'd always gone for the petite ones.

Gritting my teeth, I force the girl out of my head and think about the goodbye Canning and I shared.

The place isn't the same without you.

It had sounded like he'd meant that. Hell, he probably had. We'd spent the best summers of our lives at Elites. Obviously one BJ hadn't wrecked all the good memories for him.

I shove my hands in my pockets as I stop at a crosswalk and wait for the signal to turn green. I wonder if I'll ever see him again. Probably not. We're both graduating, about to start our post-college lives. He's on the west coast; I'm heading north to Toronto. Our paths aren't likely to cross.

Maybe that's for the best. Two measly encounters this weekend, just *two*, yet somehow they'd managed to erase the *four* years I'd spent getting over him. It's obvious I can't be around Canning without wanting him. Without wanting more.

But this weekend wasn't enough for me, damn it.

I grab my phone before I can stop myself, halting at a newspaper dispenser and leaning against the metal box as I pull up a web browser. The site takes a while to load, but once it does, it takes no time to get to the contact page. I skim the staff directory until I find the phone number for the camp director. He knows me. He likes me. Hell, for the past four years he's been hounding me to come back.

He would do me this favor if I asked him.

I click on the number. Then I hesitate, my finger hovering over the call button.

I'm a selfish bastard. Or maybe I'm a fucking masochist. Canning can't give me what I want, but I still can't stop myself from wanting it. I want whatever I can get—a conversation, a joke gift, a smile, *anything*. I might not be able to have the steak, but fuck it, I'm fine with some scraps.

I just… I just can't let him go yet.

EIGHT

JUNE

Jamie

"Hey, Canning?"

"Yeah?"

Pat, the camp director, has come over to the penalty box to talk to me. I don't take my eyes off the scrimmage I'm coaching, but he won't think I'm rude. "Got you a roommate," he says.

"Really?" That's good news, because every summer Pat scrambles for coaches. And this year is no different. Guys like me keep graduating and moving on. He wants the best coaches at his camp, but the best guys are in high demand.

This year I'm one of those. I'm due in Detroit for training camp six weeks from now, which means Pat will have to find someone to fill in for me when I go. I glance at him for a split second before looking back at the boys' game in progress.

He's sizing me up, and I don't know why. "Be nice to him, okay?"

It takes me a moment to answer, because I don't like the direction the scrimmage is taking. Tempers are about to flare. I can feel the tension mounting. "When am I not nice?" I ask, distracted.

A firm hand lands on my shoulder. "You're the best there is, kid. Although your goalie is about to lose his shit."

"I can see that."

It's like watching an accident. I know what's about to occur, but forces are already in motion and I can't stop them.

My best goalie—Mark Killfeather—has stopped twenty shots in this scrimmage already. With quick reflexes and a big, agile body, Killfeather has all the physical traits a good goalie requires.

He also has, unfortunately, a lightning-quick temper. And the talented French Canadian forward on the other team has been playing him like a fiddle all day—taunting him and teasing him on every offensive push.

I see the play the Canadian is about to make. He passes back to his buddy on the blue line then takes the puck again as the other side's D-men get hung up in the corners. He fakes left, then right…and sends a flying saucer past my man Killfeather. It is a beautiful play until the Canadian kid sprays the goalie with ice shavings and calls him "*un stupide*."

As if it were a boomerang, Killfeather throws his stick with enough force to crack it like a matchstick against the boards. It falls onto the ice, splintered.

Check, please. I blow the whistle. "That's the game, we're out of time."

"*Pourquoi?*" protests the aggressive forward. "Zhere is time on zee clock!"

"Debrief with your offensive coach," I say, waving him off. Then I skate over to Killfeather, who stands panting in the net, helmet yanked off to reveal his sweaty head. He is only sixteen and looks it. While other kids his age are kicking back under the sun or playing video games, he's spent his hours duking it out on the rink today.

I'd been that kid, too. It was a good life and I wouldn't trade it for anything, but it helps to remember these are still kids. So I don't open with, "Hey asshole, you just trashed a hundred dollar stick."

"Who's your favorite goalie, kid?" I ask instead.

"Tuukka Rask," he says immediately.

"Good pick." I'm not a Bruins fan, but the man has an excellent record. "What does his face look like after he lets in a goal?"

Killfeather quirks an eyebrow. "Why? He just takes a drink and puts his mask back on."

"He doesn't lose his shit and throw his stick," I say with a smile.

The kid rolls his eyes. "I get that, but that guy is *such* an ass."

Leaning down, I tug the net off its spike so the ice can be resurfaced. "You did great goaltending today. Truly exceptional."

Killfeather begins to smile.

"But you have to learn to keep your cool, and I'm going to tell you why." His smile fades. "Rask is calm after he messes up. But it's not because he's a better person than you or me, or because he meditates or never gets mad. It's because he knows that putting it all behind him is the only way to win. Seriously—when he's having that gulp of water, he's already moved on. Instead of saying, 'Man, I wish I hadn't done that,' he's saying, 'All right, now I get a brand new chance to stop him.'"

The kid is scowling at his skates now.

"You know that thing they say about goldfish? Their memories are so short that each time they swim around the bowl, it's all brand new again."

The corners of his mouth lift up. "That's deep, Coach Canning."

Aw. It kills me to be Coach Canning for a few weeks a year. I freaking love this job.

"Be my goldfish, Killfeather." I give him a little punch on the chest pads. "Forget every stupid thing that guy says to you.

Because the world is filled with dicks who will rile you up for fun. You've got the moves. You can do the job. But only if you don't let him wreck it for you."

He finally looks up at me. "Okay. Thanks."

"Hit the showers," I say, skating backwards away from him. "Then get your credit card out and buy another stick."

I leave him, unlacing my skates and slipping into my Chuck Ts. When you're the coach, you don't have to gear up. Just skates and a helmet. I'm wearing hiking shorts and a Rainier College sweatshirt. And they feed me three meals a day in the camp dining room.

Did I mention this is a sweet job?

Leaving the rink takes me past every kind of Olympic sports memorabilia. The rink where I stood a minute ago trying to talk some sense into a sixteen-year-old goalie is the same ice where Team USA won Olympic gold in 1980. So there are "Miracle on Ice" pictures everywhere. During the winter months, there are more athletes per capita in this little town than most anywhere. People move here to train for hockey, skating, ski jumping and alpine events.

But when I push open the glass doors, it's a warm June day. Mirror Lake glitters in the distance and I have to shield my eyes. The town of Lake Placid is five hours from New York City or Boston. The closest real city is Montreal, and that's still two hours away. Smack in the middle of nowhere sits this cute little touristy town surrounded by unspoiled lakes and the Adirondack mountain range.

Heaven. Unless you need airport access.

But today I don't. I'm walking past a ski shop and an ice cream parlor, measuring the hours until dinnertime. I have a lot of nostalgia for this town, probably because it's *mine*. When you're the youngest of six kids, nothing is ever just yours. I think that's why I went out for hockey in the first place—my family is all about football. No Canning had ever set foot in the Adirondacks until I was invited to this camp. In fact, leaving the family cuckoo's nest to come here as a teenager felt like venturing to the moon.

It's four o'clock, and there's time for a run or a swim, but I'll need to change clothes.

All the campers and coaches are housed in an old dormitory that was built to accommodate European athletes for the 1980 winter Olympics. The building is a five-minute walk from the rinks. As I jog up the steps I pass a plaque that describes the original occupants and the medals they won, but I don't stop. Spend a few years in this town and you forget to be impressed.

My room is on the second floor, and I always take the stairs instead of the creaky old elevator. The dim hallway smells of floor wax and the lilacs blooming outside. Plus a whiff of old socks. You can't have a building full of hockey players without that.

I am ten feet from my door, keys in hand, when I realize someone is standing stock still beside it. That alone is enough to startle me. And then I realize who it is. "Jesus Christ!"

"I still go by Wes," he says, pushing off the wall. "Or Ryan. Or jackass."

"Are you…" I'm almost afraid to say the words, because he's shut me out for so long now. "My roommate?"

I open the door to my room to give my hands something to do. A surge of joy builds low in my stomach. Just the idea of another crazy summer with Wesley…it can't be true.

"Well…" His voice is uncharacteristically cautious. And since light from my open door spills into the hallway, I can see his face properly for the first time. He's *worried*. That jaunty jaw is tucked low, and his eyes dip when I study him.

Weird.

I push into the room and fling my keys onto my bed. "I'm

about to go running. Feel like a jog? You can fill me in. I assume you're coaching for Pat, or you wouldn't be here."

He nods. But when I strip off my shirt, he jams his hands in his pockets and turns away. "We have to talk, though."

"Okay." *About what?* "We can do that while we're running. Unless you're getting fat since your big victory?"

He snickers. "Fine." From out in the hall he grabs a big duffel bag.

"Pat just said something to me at practice about finding me a roommate. He meant you, right? He was just pulling my chain?"

With his back to me, Wes nods. Then he yanks his faded T-shirt over his head. And Jesus Christ, he's enormous. Tattoos and rippling muscles as far as the eye can see.

I'd forgotten we were really only boys the last time we stood here together. Teenagers. Feels like yesterday.

"Nice room you got here," he remarks as he changes into a wife-beater and gym shorts.

It's true. Instead of bunk beds, we've got twin beds built into the walls. And there's a comfortable expanse of floor between them. "The coaches get a little more breathing room. I've been living it up in here the last three years."

He spins around. "Who do you room with?"

"Whoever." I drop a wicking shirt over my head and then toe into my running shoes. Tying them takes only a few more seconds, and I'm anxious to get out of here and run. Maybe Wes will stop acting like a weirdo and just tell me what's on his mind. "Let's go?"

He gives his bag a kick. "I'm going to leave this here."

"Where else would you leave it?"

He winces, and I don't know why.

NINE

WES

Outside, Jamie heads toward Mirror Lake, and I follow him. How many times have I run this loop with him? A hundred, at least.

"Remember that summer when we said we'd do five miles a day, no matter what?" I ask.

He's put us on an easy pace as we head away from the dormitory. "Sure do."

"Then we had that hot day with two practices and weightlifting. But you said, 'We still have to do the run, or the summer won't count.'" I snort just thinking about it.

"Nobody told you to eat that ice cream cone first."

"I was starved. Of course, I haven't been able to order pistachio since."

Jamie snickers as we turn toward the lake. "Light green puke all over the lawn."

"Good times." They were, though. I'd yarf on the grass every day if it meant I could go back to the easy times. Chasing Jamie's big, blond body around the lake was all I wanted out of life.

Okay, that's a lie. I'd rather tackle him to the ground and strip off his clothing. Seeing him again is killing me right now.

I have something to say, though, and it has to be soon. We run the next mile in silence as I rehearse it again. My big apology. If Jamie is horrified, it's going to sting.

There are kayakers on the lake, their vessels tipping with each stroke of the oar. I feel as steady as they look.

"So what did you want to talk about?" Jamie finally asks.

There's no ducking it anymore. "I'm here just through July." It's best to get the preliminaries out of the way.

"Me too. I'm supposed to be in Detroit before August first. You're heading to Toronto, huh? You pumped?"

"Sure. But listen… I just need to say that if you don't want to room with me this summer, I'll ask Pat to move me. I won't even be offended."

Jamie stops running, and I pull up short to avoid plowing into his back. "Why?" he asks.

Here goes nothing. It all comes out in a rush. "Canning, I'm gay. And yeah—maybe that's not such a big deal in the grand scheme of things. Except that the last time we were here I kind of…pushed you into fooling around with me. It wasn't cool, and I've spent the last four years feeling shitty about it."

For a long moment he just gapes at me. And when he finally speaks, it isn't what I expect him to say. "And?"

And?

"And…I'm sorry."

His face reddens. "You know I'm from Northern California, right? You get that I know a gay dude or ten?"

"Uh, okay?"

Jamie's mouth opens and then closes. And opens again. "*This* is why you didn't call me for four years? Why you ignored my texts?"

"Well…yes." I'm so confused now. I just pled guilty to assholery in the first degree and practically molestation. And he's worried about a few texts.

His face turns another shade redder. Then he takes off running again, and I'm so startled that it takes me a second to chase him.

He's running faster now. He lengthens his long strides and moves his arms with power. The athletic shirt he's wearing hugs each muscle as he moves, and I am jealous of that piece of polyester fabric.

The loop around Mirror Lake is a little under three miles. I don't know what's in his head as he runs the rest of it. I'm a few paces behind, confused and disheartened. On our way back through town, we pass all our old haunts—the fudge shop and the toy store that sells rubber-band guns. A bakery called Miracle on Icing.

I don't see Jamie's face until he slows to a stop in front of the toboggan run, locked up again for the summer. I wish we could go back to a simpler time when climbing some chain-link was my biggest offense.

When he turns his sweaty face to me, there's still anger in it. "You didn't talk to me for four years because you thought I'd freak out about you sucking me off."

"Uh…yeah." But given the resentment in his voice, it's clear I'd fucked up in some other way that hadn't made it into my calculus.

His hands are clenched into fists. "Is that how you see me? Some uptight asshole?"

On a bench nearby I see a young mother scoop up her toddler and walk away from us, frowning.

But Jamie is on a roll. "It was just a little *sex*, for God's sake. Nobody died."

And I'm probably going to swallow my tongue now. "I… It was dishonest."

"Ah. Thanks for punishing me for *your* dishonesty. A four-year sentence. I went off to a strange college where I knew nobody, wondering how I'd been such a shitty friend."

Well, fuck. "I'm sorry," I mumble. It sounds inadequate. To both of us, I'm sure.

Jamie kicks a trashcan. "I need a shower."

My traitorous dick volunteers to join him, but I keep my big trap shut as we walk the last block and climb the stairs. This had *not* gone the way I'd anticipated. My worst-case scenario had involved Jamie recoiling in horror at my gayness and accusing me of manipulating him into fooling around.

I've spent four years riddled with shame over what I'd done, and now it turns out I should've felt ashamed about something entirely different. Jamie didn't care that I'd blown him. He cared that I'd *abandoned* him. And knowing I'd hurt my best friend much more deeply than I'd realized twists me up in knots.

I hesitate at the top of the steps, calling out to his rigid back. "Um, Canning?"

"What?" he mutters without turning around.

"Am I finding somewhere else to sleep tonight?"

He sighs. "No, jackass."

TEN

JAMIE

Twenty-two seems too old to be giving someone the silent treatment. Not that I played those sorts of games when I was younger. I've always been a talk-it-out guy. Face your problems head on, don't freeze the other person out.

That's Wes's specialty, freezing someone out.

Can anyone say "still bitter?"

The two of us haven't really spoken since we went running. At dinner, he'd sat with Pat, catching up on the last few years. Then Pat banged his spoon on a water glass and introduced Wes to the campers. "Frozen Four champion..." and "number two in the nation for points scored," and "guaranteed to see some ice time in Toronto next year."

The eyes of the boys around me grew wider and wider. They'd hung on every word. Meanwhile, Wes had sat there cracking half an "aw, shucks" smile, looking cocky and carefree.

Maybe he's not as carefree as he looks, my conscience suggests.

Fuck off, conscience! I'm busy being mad here.

Now we're in our respective beds, but neither of us is sleeping. I still wear my anger around me like the bedsheet that covers me. But it's a thin layer.

I hear him sigh from the other bed, and I stare up at the ceiling, wondering if I should just get over it already.

His husky voice breaks the silence. "I was afraid."

There's a rustling sound, and from the corner of my eye I see that he's rolled over on his side, watching me in the darkness.

"You?" I ask. "Didn't know that was possible."

"Not often," he concedes, and I snort.

There's more silence, but I finally give in. "Afraid of what?"

"That I'd used you. And that you'd hate me for it."

A sigh rises in my chest. I shift onto my side too, but it's hard to make out his expression in the shadows.

"I could never hate you, dumbass." I consider it. "Well, unless you did something hate-worthy, like run my mom over with a car on purpose or something. But hate you for being gay? Or for giving me a BJ without telling me you were gay?" Fuck, I'm still resentful as hell that he thought I was capable of being so narrow-minded.

"But I wasn't ready to tell you the truth," he admits. "I'm not sure I was ready to tell *myself*. But deep down I knew, and I felt like such a shit afterward. I felt like, I dunno, I took advantage of you."

I can't help but laugh. "Dude, it's not like you tied me to the bed and forced yourself on me. I don't know if you remember, but I came like a motherfucker that night." *Aw shit*. I don't know why I said that. And the flash of heat that travels down to my dick is equally perplexing.

Thinking about that night is something I rarely let myself do. It was easily the hottest sexual experience eighteen-year-old Jamie Canning had ever had. But remembering it always confuses me, because I associate it with getting banished from the friendship I valued most.

"Oh, I remember everything about that night." His voice thickens, and the stirring down below grows stronger.

I quickly initiate an emergency subject change, because talking about BJs seems to be confusing my body. "So are you out now? Like officially? Do your folks know?"

His answering breath is heavy. "Yeah, they know."

I wait for him to continue. He doesn't. Which isn't much of a surprise, since Wes never liked talking about his family. I know his father is some bigshot investment banker and his mother sits on a bunch of charity committees. And the one time Wes's dad had driven him to camp, I remember shaking the man's hand and thinking he was the coldest person I'd ever met.

I'm so curious to hear what they think about having a gay son, but I know he won't answer if I ask. The thing with Wes is, everything is always on *his* terms.

"What about your teammates?" I try. "Toronto?"

"With the Northern Mass guys, I had a don't-ask-don't-tell thing going on. I didn't hide it, but I didn't talk about it, either. They left it alone. But Toronto—" He groans. "Not sure how that's going to work. My plan is just to duck the question as long as I can. I guess I'm slipping back into the closet for a while until I feel like I know those guys. Until I'm so valuable to them they won't care who I screw in my spare time. That should only take three, four years tops."

That sounds unbelievably rough. "I'm sorry."

"No, *I'm* sorry. I'm sorry I fucked up our friendship, Jamie."

Shit, he called me Jamie. He only does that when he's actually being serious, earnest. Regret radiates from his body and rolls toward me in palpable waves, and I feel my anger crumbling like a sandcastle in high tide. I can't stay mad at this guy. Even when I thought he'd thrown our friendship away like a piece of trash, I still hadn't been able to hate him.

I swallow. "Water under the bridge, man."

"Yeah?"

"Yeah." Letting out a slow breath, I crook my arm under my head and glance over at him. "So what's been going on with you? Catch me up on the last four years."

He snickers. "Four years' worth of Ryan Wesley shenanigans? That'll take all night, dude." Then he pauses, his tone going awkward. "I'd rather hear about you, anyway. How's the Canning clan? Still chaos central over there?"

I smile in the darkness. "Always. Mom sold her art gallery and opened up one of those pottery places where you come in and spend the day making vases and ashtrays and shit."

"How many times do you think she's caught people acting out that scene from *Ghost*?" he cracks.

"At least once daily," I answer solemnly. "No joke." I think about what else has happened, but it's hard to sift through four years of events. "Oh, my sister Tammy had a baby, so I'm an uncle now… Um, what else… Joe—that's my oldest brother—he got a divorce."

"No shit." Wes sounds genuinely upset. "Weren't you best man at their wedding?" He suddenly laughs. "Hey, remember that bowtie I sent you to wear for the ceremony?"

I stifle a groan. "You mean the bright red one with pink cocks all over it? Yeah, I remember. And fuck you very much, by the way. Joe was in the room when I opened the box, and he almost had a heart attack when he thought that's what I was wearing."

"So you let my gift go to waste? Asshole."

"Nope, I wore it at the bachelor party."

We both snicker, and something hot and familiar clenches in my chest. I've missed this. Talking to Wes. Laughing with Wes.

"The wedding was fun," I add. "Me and Scott and Brady were the best men, Tammy was one of Samantha's bridesmaids, and my sister Jess got ordained and performed the ceremony. She was hilarious up there."

Wes chuckles. "How have you not gone insane yet, dude? I don't think I'd survive having five siblings."

"Naah, I love it. Besides, I'm the youngest—by the time I came around, my parents just let me do whatever I wanted. They were exhausted from all that disciplining they had to do with my brothers and sisters."

He falls silent, and I can feel the tension in the air again, as if he wants to say something but is too afraid to say it.

"Just spit it out," I order when his silence continues to drag.

He sighs. "Are we good?"

"Yeah, Wes, we're good." And I mean it. It took us four years to get back to this point, but we're here now and I'm happy.

I have my best friend back, at least for the next six weeks.

ELEVEN
WES

So this coaching thing? It's harder than it looks.

At the start of the morning session, it feels easy. I set up some drills for the youngest offensive players and run 'em like crazy. There's a whistle around my neck, and they have to do whatever I tell them. Easy money, right?

Not so fast.

When I take on a scrimmage for the older teens, all the wheels fall off. It's not that the kids are no good. Their skill levels vary from awesome to virtuosic. But they don't work in sync like a college team. They're headstrong and irrational. They listen to what I say, and then they go do the opposite.

They're *teenagers*. And after ten minutes of play I'm basically beating my head against the plexi, praying for my own death.

"Pat," I beg. "Please tell me I wasn't like this."

"You weren't," he says with a shake of his head. "You were three times worse." Then that traitor has the balls to exit the building, leaving me in charge of thirty sweating hormone-crazed teenage hockey punks.

I blow my whistle for the millionth time. "Offsides! *Again*. Seriously?" I ask Shen, an arrogant D-man who's been torturing the goalie for my whole session. The two of them have some kind of vendetta against each other, and it isn't helping the general chaos. "Faceoff."

Play starts again when I drop the puck. I look up to see Canning walking down the chute to assist me with the scrimmage. Thank Christ. His calm face is like a cool drink of water.

I skate over and hop the wall to greet him. "Why didn't you tell me this job was hard?"

He grins, and my heart melts a little in the usual way. "What's hard? You're not even sweating."

I am, though. Because even as I turn my head to watch my players, Shen goes sliding backward into the goalie he's been taunting, knocking him over. It looks intentional, and Canning must have thought so too, because we're both scissoring over the wall to get over there.

"What the—" starts Killfeather, the goalie.

Shen smirks. "Sorry."

"Fucking chink," Killfeather swears.

"Faggot," Shen returns.

My whistle is so loud that Canning claps his hands over his ears. "Two minute penalties!" I roar. "Both of you."

"What?" Killfeather yelps. "I didn't touch his ass."

"For your *mouth*," I snarl. "On my ice you don't use a slur of any kind." I point toward the sin bin. "Get."

But Killfeather doesn't move. "You don't get to make new rules." His sneer is as big as the banner advertisements lining the boards.

All the players are listening, so I can't do this wrong. "Ladies, it *is* a rule. Two minute bench minor for unsportsmanlike conduct. If you'd kept your trap shut after he hit you, your team would have a power play right now. I'm doing this for your own good."

"Sure you are."

In spite of that parting shot, both my troublemakers finally aim their bodies toward the penalty boxes. So I issue *my* parting shot, and I make sure that everyone can hear. "By the way— science has proven the correlation between calling someone a *faggot* and having a really small penis. You do *not* want to advertise that. Think about it."

Canning doesn't say anything. But he skates off, too. I see him take a seat off to the side and then bend over as if he's retying his skates. Whatever, right? But then I see his back shaking.

At least somebody gets my jokes.

The rest of the scrimmage lasts about a decade. When we finally break for lunch, Jamie catches up to me on the way to the locker rooms. "Science has *proven?*" He chuckles.

"I do science on the side."

"Uh-huh. I'm thinking of skipping the dining hall today and grabbing a burger at the pub in town. You down?"

"Fuck yeah," I answer. Then I wince and glance around to make sure none of the kids are lurking around. I don't know if I'm cut out to be an authority figure. I've spent four years surrounded by Northern Mass hockey players who drop F-bombs in every sentence, and I keep forgetting I need to censor myself while I'm at Elites. The teenagers here swear like sailors—at least when Pat and the other coaches aren't around—but I refuse to corrupt the younger ones with my filthy mouth.

"*Fudge* yeah," I correct.

Canning gestures at the emptiness around us. "We're the only ones here. You can say *fuck*, dumbass. You can say anything, really." With a grin, he unleashes a string of expletives. "Fuck, shit, cock, pussy—"

"For the love of Christ!" a loud voice booms from behind us. "Do I need to wash your mouth out with soap, Canning?"

I choke down my laughter as Pat appears. He shakes his head in disbelief as he stares at Jamie, then narrows his eyes and turns to me. "Actually, what am I saying? Canning wouldn't even know those words if it weren't for you, Wesley. Shame on you."

I flash Pat an innocent smile. "I'm pure as the driven snow, Coach. Canning was the one who corrupted *me*."

They both snort. Pat claps me on the shoulder and stalks past us. "Yeah, keep telling yourself that, kid," he says over his shoulder. "And both of you, watch your mouths around the campers or I'll kick your motherfucking asses."

Jamie and I are still laughing as we duck into the locker room to ditch our skates and change into our sneakers. When we exit the building a few minutes later, I feel like I've just left an icy pool and stepped into a sauna. The humidity in the air is stifling, causing sweat to roll down my back. My T-shirt sticks to my chest like plastic wrap.

Shrugging, I yank it over my head and tuck the fabric in the waistband of my gym shorts. The atmosphere in Lake Placid is as casual as it gets—nobody's gonna care if I walk through town rocking a bare chest.

Canning keeps his shirt on. I think I might prefer it that way, because his shirt is paper-thin and doing the same clinging thing mine had done, which gives me a decadent view of every hard ripple on his broad chest. Fuck, I'm yet again jealous of his shirt. I want to be the one plastered to his chest, and the ache I feel for him brings a spark of guilt.

We're good now. We're *friends* again. So why can't my traitorous body just be cool with it? Why can't I look at him without imagining all the dirty, dirty things I want to do to him?

"So what's the deal with you and that girl?" I hear myself ask. I don't particularly want to hear the answer, but I need the wake-up call it'll bring, the reminder that lusting over this guy is a disaster waiting to happen.

"Holly?" He shrugs. "Nothing, really. We just hook up. Or rather, we used to hook up. I don't think I'll be seeing much of her now that we've graduated."

I arch a brow. "Just a hook-up? Since when are you into a friends-with-bennies arrangement?"

Another shrug. "It was convenient. Fun. I don't know. I'm just not looking to settle down with anyone right now. Holly understood that." His voice takes on a note of challenge. "What, you disapprove?"

"Nah, I'm all about fuck buddies."

We pass the toy store and duck out of the way of two moms pushing strollers. Both women swivel their heads in my direction and stare at my tats. Not with contempt, but intrigue. It happens again on the next block when a group of teenage girls stop in their tracks at the sight of me. The words "tattooed hottie" tickle our backs as we walk past.

Jamie chuckles. "You sure you don't want to go the bisexual path? 'Cause I'm pretty sure you won't have any trouble in the chick department."

"S'all good. Wouldn't be fair to the straight guys if I threw my hat in the pussy ring. They wouldn't stand a chance."

His expression turns thoughtful. "I've seen you fool around with girls before. You *seemed* interested."

I know he's thinking about all those nights we snuck into town and flirted with the locals. But we were fifteen, maybe sixteen then, and I was still experimenting, figuring things out.

"Were you just pretending to enjoy it?" he asks curiously.

"Not so much pretending as *trying* to enjoy it," I admit. "And it wasn't awful. I didn't go home afterward and scour my skin off in the shower. Making out with those girls was... I don't know... it just *was*. I did it, it was all right, but it's not like I was dying to rip their clothes off and get inside them."

The way I'm dying to rip your clothes off and get inside you.

I clench my teeth, annoyed with myself. Christ, enough. It's not going to happen with Canning. I need to stop this.

"Got it." He nods, then tips his head. "Who does it for you, then? Like, what's your type, looks-wise?"

You. "Ah, I'm not picky."

We reach the corner pub, but he doesn't make a move to open the door. He just lingers on the sidewalk and chuckles. "Really. So you'll just stick your dick in anyone?"

"No," I concede. It feels so fucking weird discussing this with him. "I'm not crazy about twinks, I guess. I don't like the whole scrawny, young boy vibe."

"So you like 'em big." A broad grin fills his face as he winks at me. "So to speak."

I roll my eyes. "Yeah, big's a nice bonus. Tall, athletic, not too hairy—" That makes him snicker. "—and, I don't know…" I start to laugh. "You seriously want to hear all this?"

His eyes flash with hurt. "Why, because you're talking about guys instead of girls? I already told you, I'm not some uptight prude who—"

"That's not what I meant," I cut in hastily, and he relaxes slightly. "It'd be weird even if I was describing a chick. Like, what two guys stand around describing their perfect sexual partner?" I widen my eyes and look around. "Did we wander onto the set of *Sex and the City*? If so, I'm Samantha. Called it."

The tension diffuses instantly, as Canning's lips twitch uncontrollably. "You know actual character names from *Sex and the City*? Shit, if you hadn't told me you were gay, I would've figured it out just now."

"That was an extremely insensitive case of stereotyping, Jamie," I say primly. "Just for that? You're springing for lunch. Asshole." But I'm grinning to myself as I flip him the bird and stride into the bar.

TWELVE

JAMIE

Sunday is the day the coaches have off. Pat's wife usually takes the kids on an outing. They're all going fishing on East Lake tomorrow morning. Meanwhile, the coaches usually have a drunken Saturday night followed by a sleep-in on Sunday.

We've just eaten a six o'clock dinner with all our teenage charges, so we're officially free. Wes has been at camp for four days now, but we're usually too beat at night to do anything but chill in our room. So I'm going a little stir-crazy.

"What should we do tonight?" I ask Wes, who is lying on his bed. "You have a car, right? Let's put 'er to use."

"My car is a dude," he says, swiping through some app.

"Of course it is. What are you doing, anyway?" The app keeps making a strange notification sound that's unfamiliar to me.

"Checking out Brandr. Pretty entertaining in a small town."

That shuts me up for a moment. Brandr is a gay hook-up app. I'm suddenly ornery because I just assumed we were going out tonight. Together. Maybe that was a stupid assumption, but that's how it always was before.

"So…" I clear my throat. "How does that work?"

He chuckles. "Come here and see. It's hysterical. All the worst traits of humanity on display in one place."

Intrigued now, I sit down on his bed, and he props himself on an elbow to show me. We're leaning over the phone together, the same way we did when we were teenagers. Except we haven't been on a bed together since...well. *That* night. And I'm conscious of the fact that we don't fit so well. We're taking up most of the surface, but I'm still practically sitting on top of him. I can feel the crinkle of his leg hair brushing mine when he leans in to show me the screen.

"It's like a menu board. Each picture is a dude."

Some of the pictures are close-ups but some are impossible to see. There's a number tagging each one, too. *0.7 mi.* and *1.3 mi.* "It tells you how close everybody is? That's a little creepy."

"That's part of the fun. If someone acts creepy, you can just block them forever. One click and they're history. The bios are the funny part. Check this out." He taps one of the tiles and some dude's picture fills the screen. It says: *Online now, 0.9 mi away.*

"He's too old for you," I say immediately. "And what's with the socks?" The guy has gray hair and leans against a red convertible. He's in decent shape, but nobody should wear socks that tall with shorts. That's just wrong.

I won't lie. This is weirding me out—the idea that this man is staring down at his screen somewhere on the other end of town, tapping Wes's picture...

Wes just laughs. "Looking at Brandr in a small town is always amusing. The odds are good, but the goods are odd." He scrolls the picture to the bottom where the guy has added his 140 characters or whatever. The headline is "Looking 2 get naked with muscles." And below that: *If I'm online then I'm lkng to get naked. Kissing, body contact & more just ask. No fems. Sorry only attracted to whites.*

"What the fuck?" I stutter.

"Sounds like a charmer, doesn't he? That's the internet for you." Wes bails out of that jerk's profile. But then his phone makes a noise and a little window pops up.

"Hey," it says, and there's a thumbnail of some other guy beside it.

"Someone's talking to you," I mutter. And now I hate this app more than I thought possible. Competing for my friend's attention isn't fun. So I stand up and shuck off my Elites T-shirt. I'm getting out of here tonight whether Wes comes along or not. I pull on a polo shirt, which is as dressy as a guy ever gets in Lake Placid.

"You want to head out?" he asks from the bed.

"Yeah." When I turn around, he's changing his clothes, too. Thank Christ.

"To think that we can be out after dark without climbing out of the windows," Wes cracks. "That's just weird." He's dressed in hiking shorts and boots, and pulling a black wife-beater over his head, leaving his arms bare.

"You can jump off the fire escape if you want," I tell him. "But I'm taking the stairs."

"Where are we headed?"

I grab my keys and phone. "If your manly car is available, let's go to Owl's Head."

He stops in the middle of tying his shoelaces. "Yeah? I thought we'd go to a bar."

"We're going to do both," I say. "But only if you can move your ass out that door."

Wes drives a newish Honda Pilot with a sweet stereo and leather seats. But it's a mess. I have to move several copies of *USA Hockey* off the passenger's seat and throw away an old McDonald's bag. "This is...nice," I tease as I chase an empty cup off the floor.

"I'm not going to gay up my ride for you, Canning. Let's go. We're racing the daylight."

Owl's Head is a short hike we used to do with the group as campers. It's a few miles out of town, and there aren't any other cars at the trailhead when we arrive. Wes bleeps the locks, and then we're scrambling uphill over rocks and tree roots.

I love this. Hockey is great, but it keeps you indoors. My summer sport is surfing, but I've always loved a good hike.

Did I mention I'm from California?

"Slow down," Wes pants at one point.

I stop, holding on to a sapling to wait for him. "Too much for Toronto's recruit to handle? I'd better call my bookie. Who are you playing first?"

He smacks me on the ass. "I stopped to take a picture, asshole. Carry on."

The views really are intense. We're climbing up a ledge, basically, and Adirondack peaks stand out all around us, dark against the early evening sky. "It's just two more turns," I promise.

It takes us thirty minutes to reach the bald, rocky outcroppings at the top just as the sun prepares to set behind a distant peak. Panting a little from the climb, I plop down on a sun-warmed rock and take it in.

"What a dump," Wes jokes, sitting beside me.

"Right?"

I've probably climbed this hill every summer for the last nine years. When we were fourteen, it was fun to scare each other by sitting way out on the ledge. When we were seventeen, we probably came all the way up here without really seeing it. Wes and I would have been arguing about hockey. Or football. Or some dumbass movie. We climbed because that was the activity on the day's itinerary.

It had startled me this past year to realize everything I did from here on out I did for myself. College graduation is the end of the road map. It's all uncharted territory from this point, and I'm the one in the driver's seat.

The distant clouds turn orange-pink while I watch. My friend sits beside me, lost in his own thoughts. "We're going to lose the light," he says eventually.

"We still have time." Another beat of silence goes by before I ask, "What are you thinking about, anyway?"

He chuckles. "Freshman year of college. What a dick I was to everyone."

"Yeah?" I'm surprised Wes is going all introspective like me. I would have thought he was sitting there trying to figure out the best way to prank Pat and blame it on the kids.

"Yeah. Rough year. Lots of hazing."

I sneak a look at him for the first time since we sat down. "Same here. Those seniors were psycho, seriously. Never seen anything like it." I clear my throat. "That fall I kept thinking, Wes is not going to believe this shit when I tell him…" I let the sentence die. That was probably too harsh. If we're friends again, I shouldn't let my anger bubble back to the surface.

He makes an irritated sound in the back of his throat. "Sorry."

"I know," I say quickly.

"But I spent that first semester just praying those assholes didn't figure out I liked dick. And since I wasn't so comfortable with that idea myself…" He sighs. "I wasn't very good company that year, anyway."

Something goes a little wrong in my stomach at the idea of Wes being scared. My whole life I'd thought of him as fearless. Nobody is. Intellectually I know that. But even the other night when he'd told me he had struggled with being gay. I don't think I really got it.

"That sucks," I say softly.

He shrugs. "Didn't kill me. Just made me work twice as hard. Maybe I wouldn't have ended up as a first liner if those jackasses hadn't put the fear of God into me every fucking day."

"That's looking on the bright side."

"Canning, we're going to lose the daylight," he reminds me.

He's right. The sky has already faded to a soft purple in some places. I hastily stand up. "Let's go, then."

It's counterintuitive, but on a steep hike the way down is much harder than the way up. Every step threatens to sweep your feet out from under you. We don't speak at all during our descent. We're too busy concentrating on where to place each foot and which branches will make a steadying hand-hold.

The dark is coming on fast. We're almost there when the path becomes truly difficult to see. I can hear Wes's footfalls behind me, and the skittering sound of the pebbles he displaces with each step. I'd bet cash money that Wes is in the zone like I am right now, thinking only of the task at hand. When the body is busy, the mind shuts up for a while.

It's almost totally dark, but I know we're just yards from the trailhead. That's when I hear Wes stumble. There's a grunt and the sound of feet sliding on dirt. My heart catches as I hear him go down a few paces behind me. "Fuck," he grumbles.

I turn around and find him splayed out on the ground. Shit. I've dragged Toronto's new forward up a fucking mountain in the dark. If he's sprained something, it's all on me. "You okay?" Feeling sick, I make my way uphill again to where he is.

"Yeah," he says, but that's not proof. A hockey player always says that, even when it's not true. But then Wes sits up from the shadows.

I stick out a hand and he closes his fingers around it and squeezes. The pressure of his grasp calms me down. With a tug from me he's on his feet again, and the warmth of his hand leaves mine. But I don't turn around and head down yet. "Seriously, did you twist anything?"

The shadow of Wes shifts his weight from one foot to the other and back again. "Nope. Banged my knee on a rock. But it's nothing." He scrapes his hands together to dust them off.

Letting out a breath I don't even know I'm holding, I turn around and pick my way even more slowly down the hill.

Wes's car waits for us in the dark. I hop into the passenger seat, relieved that my hike hasn't injured anyone. The dome light shows me a smiling Wes, but there's dirt on his shirt. I reach over and brush it off, undoing the damage.

He gives me a wink. "You copping a feel?" Laughing at his own joke, he cranks the engine. "Where are we headed?"

"Anyplace. Your pick."

Wes turns the car around and heads back to the main road. "We passed a bar before this turnoff. Lou's, or something. You ever been there?"

I shake my head. "Never have wheels, so I always drink in town."

"We'll give it a try," he says.

THIRTEEN
JAMIE

There are a million cars outside Lou's because the place shares a parking lot with a Dairy Queen. We park on the road and walk through the cricket-filled darkness to the decently sized roadside bar.

Lou's has an Adirondack theme, and they're working it pretty hard. The requisite old wooden paddles hang from the paneled walls. An inverted canoe is suspended on hooks from the ceiling. The drink specials are named for nearby peaks.

Of course they are.

"Okay, so you'll have the Nippletop, and I'll have the Dix Mountain." Wes is already enjoying himself.

"Dude, if the Nippletop has peach schnapps in it, I will hurt you."

He grins, and it's wicked. "How do you feel about elderflower vodka?"

"Not funny." I wave down the bartender. "I'll have a Saranac IPA. Thanks."

Wes flips the drink menu onto the bar. "Make that two, please." He puts a twenty down, and when I reach for my wallet, he waves me off. "I'll get these."

We take our beers to a high table, both of us doing a little people watching. I don't see any girls I want to chat up, but that's fine because that's not what I came here for, anyway.

Wes fishes his phone out of his pocket. "Should have shut this thing off," he says. Then he squints at the screen.

"What?"

"It's a Brandr notification. Somebody's trying to chat me. And it says 'less than 100 feet away.'"

I almost choke on a swallow of my beer. "Some guy in here?" Then I'm swiveling my head in every direction, wondering who it is.

Wes kicks me under the table. "Cut that out."

But it's too late. At the far end of the room, there's a guy in a Fugees T-shirt looking this way. He's watching me. Then he *smiles*.

"Oh, fuck," I hiss out.

Wes is laughing. "Dude, you just picked up a guy."

"What?" I'm sweating now. And I can't beat the crap out of my best friend because the guy has almost reached our table.

"Hey," he says, giving me a grin. Then he looks at Wes. "Wait." He chuckles. "Which of you…?"

Oh my fucking God.

"It's my profile," Wes says, and I can tell he's trying very hard not to bust a gut. "You like?"

"You fishing for compliments?" The guy winks. He's a few years older than us, with dark, shiny hair. "I need another beer. Can I buy a round?"

"I'm good," I say quickly.

"One for you, then," he says, pointing at Wes. Then he slips away to the bar.

When he's gone, Wes puts his face in his hands and laughs. "Jesus, the look on your face!"

Ugh. "Why did he think it was me, anyway?"

"My face isn't in my profile pic." Wes can hardly speak for laughing.

I realize something. "You didn't show me your profile."

"No kidding," he says, getting a hold of himself finally. "Not showing you that."

"Why?" When he shrugs, I suddenly wonder if... "Is it a *dick pic*?"

Another burst of laughter shudders out of his mouth. "Abs," he croaks. "It's my abs."

Of course it is.

Wes's new "friend" drifts back to our table, sliding a bottle in front of Wes, who's barely made a dent in his current one. We spend the next few minutes chatting. Well, *they* chat. I just listen, feeling uneasy. There's something kinda...*sleazy* about the whole thing, about this *guy*, but maybe I'm just grumpy. I wanted to hang out with my best friend tonight, not watch him eye-fuck some other dude.

"I teach second grade at the public school," the guy's telling Wes. His name is Sam, and it's a little hard to hate him now that I know he works with kids. He seems decent. And he's really good-looking. Not Wes good-looking or anything, but—Jesus. Am I seriously sitting here comparing the level of attractiveness of the two guys beside me?

I take a deep gulp of my beer. Screw it. If I'm going to be the third wheel tonight, I might as well get wasted.

"Pool table's available," Sam says, gazing across the room. "You guys up for a game?"

"Sure," Wes answers for us, and I swallow down my irritation with another swig of beer.

"I'll just watch," I mutter as we reach the table. "Not in the mood to shoot pool."

Wes eyes me for a moment. "All right."

Sam racks the balls and flashes Wes a grin. "Looks like it's you and me. For the sake of full disclosure, I'm about to kick your ass."

This guy doesn't know Wes, though. I used to watch my buddy hustle every unsuspecting sap who'd ever challenged him to a game.

Wes smiles sheepishly. "Yeah, you might be right about that. I'm not very good."

I stifle a snort.

"You want me to break?" Sam offers.

Wes nods. His gaze meets mine briefly, and I see the twinkle in his eye before he turns away.

I lean against the wood-paneled wall as Sam bends over at the far end of the table, the pool cue positioned skillfully in his hands. His opening shot sends the balls scattering in a dizzying whirl, but he only lands one—solid red in the side pocket. He sticks with solids, sinking one more before missing the next shot.

Wes is up. He studies the table with a frown, as if he can't decide which shot to take. Bullshit. Like his shrewd brain hasn't already planned out every single shot all the way up to the sinking of the eight ball.

Sam sidles up to him, lightly resting his hand on Wes's shoulder.

I narrow my eyes. Handsy motherfucker, ain't he?

"Go for the eleven," Sam advises. "Corner pocket."

Wes bites his lip. "I was thinking the thirteen." Which would require a combo shot that would make even the most advanced billiards players sweat.

Sam chuckles. "That might be a bit too difficult considering you're not—"

Wes takes the shot before Sam can finish the sentence. He sinks the thirteen. And the nine. And the twelve. In one impressive combo that makes Sam's jaw hit the floor.

I can't help it. I start to laugh.

"You're not very good, huh?" Sam sighs heavily.

Wes's mouth twitches. "I may have underplayed my level of proficiency."

A part of me hopes Sam is one of those sensitive egomaniacs who can't handle losing, but Mr. I-Teach-Second-Grade seems delighted by Wes's awesomeness. He simply stands there and whistles as my buddy circles the table like the pool shark he is, even breaking out in applause after Wes cleans the table without once letting Sam take another shot.

Sam accepts his defeat by chugging the rest of his beer, then slamming the empty bottle on the ledge behind the pool table. "Another one?" he asks Wes.

Wes glances at me as if to check if I'm cool with it. I just shrug. I know there's no prying Sam away from Wes right now. He's too fucking enamored with my buddy.

They play another game.

I order another beer.

They play a third game.

I order a third beer.

The drunker I get, the handsier *they* get. Sam's palm grazes the small of Wes's back as he leans in to line up his next shot. Wes glances over his shoulder and winks at Sam, his gray eyes gleaming.

Eventually I wander back to the table, alcohol buzzing in my bloodstream as annoyance builds in my gut. Fuck this Sam guy. I take it back—he's not decent. He seems to have no problem monopolizing my best friend's time. Doesn't even give a shit that they're both ignoring me.

And he won't stop touching Wes.

My fingers curl around the beer bottle. When Sam steps closer to Wes and whispers something in his ear, my knuckles turn white as my grip tightens. Is he asking Wes if he wants to get out of here? Telling him how much he wants to screw him right now? Offering to blow him in the bathroom?

I drain the rest of my beer. Yeah, I'm buzzing hard now. And the alcohol has done something to my brain. Short-circuited it somehow, flooded it with memories I don't usually allow to surface.

The soundtrack of that last day at camp four years ago runs through my mind.

"What are you waiting for, Ryan? Suck it already."

"Fuck, Wes, you're making me come."

It bothers me that I remember every word I said to him. I've been on the receiving end of some pretty phenomenal blowjobs these past four years, but can I tell you what was said during them? Can I repeat, verbatim, every single word I uttered to those chicks? To Holly? Every dirty command that left my mouth?

No, I can't.

My gaze shifts back to the pool table, locking on Wes's mouth. My dick stirs, remembering that mouth wrapped around it.

Shit, maybe I'm more drunk than buzzed.

Sam and Wes's laughter wafts toward me. Looks like Sam finally won a game, and knowing Wes, he's taunting the guy about it being a fluke. Or hell, maybe Wes let him win. Maybe he decided to throw the guy a bone before he...*throws the guy a bone.*

My chest goes rigid. The thought of Wes hooking up with someone tonight pisses me off.

Jealous? a little voice mocks.

Screw that. I'm not fucking jealous. I don't care what Wes does—or *who* he does—but we were supposed to hang out tonight. Me and him. Not him and some random guy he met through a hook-up app.

I abruptly hop off my stool and make my way back to the pool table. They're not even playing anymore, just standing close together, chuckling about something. Sam's hand rests on Wes's hip. A casual gesture. Light, harmless.

But it sparks resentment in my gut. Why the hell is he touching him? He doesn't even know him. Presumptuous asshole.

"Ready to go?" I raise my voice, because neither of them notices me standing there.

Wes blinks. "Now?"

I answer through clenched teeth. "Yes. I want to take off." I can't help but offer a cool look. "You're my ride, remember?"

Wariness floats through his expression. Then he gives a quick nod and turns to Sam. "Thanks for the games, man. Looks like we're taking off now."

The other guy's disappointment is impossible to miss. He glances at me, then back at Wes. "Uh, yeah…sure. Let me just grab your number before you go?"

Asshole.

I grind my molars as I watch them exchange numbers. Well then. I guess they're going to meet up again. So much for getting to spend the summer reconnecting with my best friend.

Wes doesn't say anything as we head for the exit. The music in the bar had been too loud to hear what was happening outside, but when we step out the door, we find ourselves in the middle of a torrential downpour.

A cold gust of rain slaps me in the face, soaking my clothes in seconds. "Shit. Run to the car?" I shout over the deafening pounding of the rain hitting the pavement.

Wes stays put. His expression is as thunderous as the weather. "What the hell was that?"

I can barely hear him over the wind and rain. "What?"

"You acted like a total douchecanoe in there." Then he stalks away, his boots splashing the puddles forming on the asphalt.

The little awning spanning the side of the building does nothing to protect us from the rain. Our clothes are plastered to our bodies. Water clings to my hair and drips down my face as I hurry after him.

"*I* was the one acting like a douchecanoe?" I yell after him.

He stops, spins around to face me. "Yes. Jesus, dude, the way you treated that guy, you'd think he was carrying the Ebola virus."

"Maybe I just didn't appreciate the way he was pawing you right in front of me!" I shoot back.

Wes's mouth falls open. "What?"

My mouth slams shut. Jesus fuck. Why did I say that?

"I mean…" I swallow. "It was rude."

Wes stares at me. Droplets run down his chiseled face, catching in the beard growth shadowing his jaw. His lips are slightly parted. I can't stop looking at them.

"What is happening right now?" he asks slowly.

Misery lodges in my throat. I don't know. I honestly don't know what's happening. The rain falls harder. A flash of lightning slices through the black sky. I should be cold, but I'm not. My body feels like a furnace. Three beers shouldn't be having this effect on me.

Maybe it's him? Maybe *he's* making me hot?

Wes's tongue darts out to lick at the raindrops on his bottom lip, and I catch a glimpse of his tongue ring. It wasn't there when we were eighteen. It wasn't there when his tongue had circled the head of my cock the night he gave me the best BJ of my life.

And there it is.

Ryan Wesley had given me the best BJ of my life.

"Canning…" He trails off, watching me again. He looks uneasy, but…there's something else in his gaze. A flicker of confusion. A hint of interest.

I take a step closer, but I'm not sure why. My heart is pounding harder than the rain. My eyes are glued to his mouth.

"Jamie." A note of warning this time.

I suck a gulpful of oxygen into my lungs.

Then I ignore the warning.

His eyes widen as I shove my fingers through his hair and tug his head closer. "What—"

He doesn't get to finish that sentence, because I'm smashing my mouth against his.

FOURTEEN
WES

Jamie is kissing me.

Jamie is *kissing* me.

Jamie is kissing *me*.

Nope, no matter which way I run it through my head, it still doesn't make sense to me. The pressure of his mouth? Makes no sense. The shocking sweep of his tongue over my bottom lip? No sense.

But holy fucking shit, I want it.

Rain pours off the awning and slides over our heads as my best friend's lips latch onto mine. I taste the rain, beer, something addictively masculine. His mouth brushes mine, over and over again, and when I part my lips to draw a shaky breath, he takes full advantage and slides his tongue inside.

It's like a cattle prod to the spine. Desire surges through me and spirals down to my balls, drawing them up tight. When his tongue touches mine I damn near keel over. I have to grab the front of his shirt and bunch it between my fingers to keep from being swept away by the storm. Not the storm that's lighting up the sky, but the one that's roaring inside me.

I know the moment he feels my tongue ring, because his

tongue curls around the metal stud and he moans against my lips. Deep and husky.

It's that lust-drenched sound that snaps me back to reality. This might *feel* right, but it's wrong. He's drunk again. Not thinking clearly. For some reason he decided shoving his tongue down my throat was a good idea, but it fuckin ain't. At the end of the day, I'm still gay—and he's still straight. Even worse, I'm still *in love* with him.

With a tortured groan, I wrench my mouth away. I can't fucking do this again. I can't let myself want him or get my hopes up about the two of us. He's my friend. He'll always be my friend and nothing more.

His eyes, hazy with passion, absolutely wreck me. He blinks as if disoriented, as if he can't understand why I broke the kiss.

"Your tongue ring…" His voice is hoarse with excitement. "I want to feel it on my cock."

Oh sweet Jesus.

Okay, he's drunker than I thought. I hadn't seen him pound back more than a couple beers, but he must have snuck a few more in when I wasn't looking.

"Yeah…" I manage a hasty laugh. "That's not gonna happen, man."

Jamie narrows his eyes.

The rain slows a bit, making it easier to speak without having to raise my voice. "We're not going down this road again, Canning." I swallow hard. "The last time we did, it ruined our fucking friendship."

He slants his head, those big brown eyes gleaming with challenge. "You're saying you don't want me?"

Aw hell. "No, I'm saying this is a bad idea."

Jamie steps closer, backing me into the wall until my back bumps the wet bricks. Now he's got me pinned in place. There's a hard wall behind me and an equally hard one in front of me.

Emphasis on *hard*, because holy hell, he's rocking one hell of a boner. It presses against my thigh as he eases even closer, until his lips are inches from mine.

"You're the king of bad ideas," he reminds me. "At least this one ends with both of us feeling good."

He's going to kill me. The role reversal melts my brain, because I'm the one who's usually in charge, who calls the shots, sets the limits.

Jamie shifts his hips, a breath panting out as his erection brushes my leg. If he were sober, he'd probably be horrified. When he sobers up, he *will* be horrified. He'll apologize for coming on to me, and we'll end up having that awkward conversation we should've had after I blew him four years ago. He'll tell me he's straight, he was just fucking around, he's not into me.

And I'll be crushed.

I know all this, but it doesn't stop me from stealing one more taste. I mentioned I'm a masochist, right? It's the only explanation for why I curl my hand around the back of his neck and tug him toward me again.

Our mouths meet in another kiss. Soft this time. Agonizingly slow. It's not enough. I'll stop it soon, any second now, but not yet. Not until he gives me more.

Groaning, I push my chest against him and spin us around so he's the one against the wall, and *I'm* the one grinding up on him. He makes a surprised noise, but it turns into a husky rumble when I deepen the kiss and drive my tongue into his mouth.

I'm greedy now. Desperate. I fuck his mouth with my tongue the way I want to fuck him with my cock. Deep, hungry strokes that leave us both breathless, and now he's the one clutching *my* shirt.

To my right, the door of the bar bangs open. A female shriek rings out. She's probably screaming about the weather, not the two guys against the wall trying to eat each other's faces. Either way, her scream brings me back to my senses. Stumbling backward, I'm panting like I've just run three marathons.

I'm under the downpour now, but Jamie's not. So I can see his expression perfectly—the wide-eyed panic on his face. The disbelief.

Fuck. My straight-as-a-blue-line friend is about to freak out. An hour from now, he'll probably have one hell of an identity crisis, and for what? The best kiss of my life wasn't worth screwing up *his* life.

I've lived confusion. It ain't pretty.

Now I have to look away. If I don't, he'll see my eyes and know I'm dying inside. I want him more than anything in the goddamn world. It takes all my willpower, but I turn and walk off in the rain toward my car.

The rain is coming down in sheets, so I start to run for it. I don't even know he's followed me until he slides into the passenger seat opposite me and slams the door.

In less than thirty seconds I've got the engine cranked. We're cruising back up 73 toward Lake Placid before a whole minute has passed. There's a terrible silence in the car. If it weren't raining I'd probably double the speed limit trying to get Jamie back to town.

He still hasn't said a word.

"I'm sorry," I croak. "Didn't mean to let that happen."

He makes an irritated noise. I'm dying to know what it means, but too chicken-shit to ask. We are never speaking of this night again. Never. Even if we're wasted the night before Jamie's wedding. Even if we're trapped in a mineshaft with thirty minutes of oxygen. Not even then.

Earlier, I told him he'd acted like a douchecanoe. But that's crap. I'm the one who's in love with my best friend and pretending I'm not.

The rain lets up. A few minutes later (even though it feels like hours) I pull up in front of the dormitory building and step on the brakes. Jamie doesn't move.

"I'm going to find a parking spot, and then take a walk," I tell him. There is no way I can go back to our room right now. We need a time-out. I hope he understands.

Later, when he's asleep, it might be possible to breathe the same air as Jamie Canning again.

He doesn't move.

Please, I beg him inwardly. *Please go up to bed.* It's hard enough to look at his face each day and not feel heartbreak. I can't be close to him right now. I'm afraid I'll give in and kiss him again. The way his hard body had aligned so perfectly with mine is burned in my consciousness. I'll be trying not to remember that for weeks.

I wait, and I ache.

Finally the door clicks open. I hear him exit the car. When the door slams shut, I feel it like a sledgehammer to the heart. *Don't look*, I coach myself.

But my self-control isn't infinite. His fair hair glints under the streetlight as his long legs eat up the walkway in just a few paces. Seeing him walk away from me splinters something inside me.

FIFTEEN

JAMIE

I pound up the steps of the building, my heart thumping, my skin wet from the rain and sweat and nerves.

"Jamie."

Shit, I'd almost made it inside. But Pat is sitting in stealthy darkness in one of the rocking chairs on the front porch. He's probably on stakeout, watching for teenagers sneaking out. Instead he's caught me sneaking in. And at the sound of his voice I feel at least as much terror as an escaping kid.

Stumbling, I stop before reaching the door. "Hey," I say, trying to sound normal. At least it's dark. I don't trust my face right now.

"Got a minute?"

Do I? What I need is to be alone for several hours to bang my head against a wall. To try to figure out what on God's green earth just happened. But Pat is like a second father to me, and being rude to him isn't something I can do.

I don't answer, but I do take the rocking chair right next to his. My hands are shaking so I curve them around the chair's arms. A couple of very slow breaths help me calm down.

Across the road, the lake is a dark void. Lights from the Lake

Placid restaurants twinkle in the misty night air. Everything looks so calm and ordinary. The world would make more sense to me if the buildings were falling into the lake, or the fudge shops were on fire. But the only thing quaking is me.

"You okay, son?"

"Yeah," I grind out, my voice like a chainsaw. "Got caught in the rain."

"I can see that." He's quiet for a moment. "I just wanted to ask you how Wesley is holding up. Did the first week treat him okay, you think?"

Just the sound of his name makes my gut clench.

Well, Pat, I just threw myself at him. We made out like porn stars up against the side of a bar. Then he gave me the brush-off. And I don't have any idea what any of it means.

"He's, uh, okay," I stammer. I don't really even remember the question he'd asked.

"If he's struggling out there, I hope you'll tell me. I won't fire him—I'll just get him some backup."

I pull myself together and try to focus on the conversation. "Coaching takes practice."

Pat smiles. "That's very diplomatic of you. Coaching takes practice, yes, but not everyone is a natural at it the way you are."

"Thank you." The compliment is unexpected.

"And I think the kids will get a lot out of their time with Wes —I wouldn't have hired him if I wasn't sure of that." Pat's chair squeaks as he rocks it gently. "It surprised me, though, getting that call from him. It was a few hours after the Frozen Four victory. I'd watched the game—it makes my year anytime I get to watch you boys on my television. But it's funny—when I saw who was calling, I had this moment where I thought he was going to say, 'I owe it all to you.'" He chuckles to himself. "That's not Wes's style, so I don't know why I expected to hear that. But yeah, when he said, 'I'm calling to take that job you offer me every year,' I really was surprised."

So am I. In fact, many things about this information surprise me. "You've been recruiting him all these years?"

"Sure. All my boys who become successful college players get a call from me. Wes never said yes, though. Then I get *this* call…" He pauses. "Took a lot of guts, really. He says, 'I want to coach for you this summer. But you need to know I'm gay. Nobody knows, but if it bothers you—running a camp and all—I understand.'"

A drop of sweat runs down my back. "What did you tell him?" Even though I know Pat hired him, my breath still catches for the Wes on the other end of that phone, waiting for someone to pass judgment on him.

Maybe it takes more balls to be Wes than I'd realized.

"I said that was his business, and I didn't give a shit as long as he showed up every morning ready to coach. Later I asked him if he wanted to room with you again after all these years. He said, 'Sure, but I gotta come out to Jamie, too. If he has an issue, you might have to trade things around.'"

An *issue*. I have one all right. My *issue* is the giant boner he gave me tonight. God, it's a struggle not to bury my head in my hands and scream from confusion.

Weirdest night of my life. Right here. Winner!

And Coach Pat is still waiting for me to say something. "Um, I just told him I'm from Northern California."

Pat laughs. "I see. Didn't think you'd have a problem. You two were inseparable all those years."

Inseparable. A while ago my tongue was inseparable from his. And it was all my doing. I mauled my best friend. His taste is still on my lips.

I need to eject from this conversation before I lose my mind.

"No problem at all," I say gruffly. "I think I gotta hit the hay, though."

"Good night, coach."

"Good night."

I climb the stairs and walk down the hall toward our room. None of the doors have light leaking from underneath, but I can hear the sound of voices and male laughter as I pass by. Wes and I had been the same at their age—talking 'til all hours.

Now? I'm not sure we're talking at all.

I make a stop in the bathroom to brush my teeth. When I catch my face in the mirror, it looks the same as it always does. Same square jaw. Same brown eyes. My skin is a little pale under the fluorescent bathroom lights. There's nothing to see here, but like an idiot I stare a little while, looking for who knows what. A change. A sign.

What does a guy who's not as straight as he thought look like, anyway?

"Like you, apparently." My lips move with these words, and I'm no closer to understanding what happened.

But now I'm talking to myself. *Awesome*.

I can't avoid it any longer, so I head into our room. Flipping the lights on only makes me squint, so I shut 'em off again. I strip down to my briefs and climb into bed. I'm sober now, which is a bummer. That's not going to help me sleep. But at least I'm not shaking like a leaf anymore.

Wes is not here, but I feel his presence. And I'm just lying awake, waiting to hear his rough, cocky voice in the hallway. It's not an exaggeration to say I've always felt a little more alive when he's around. Life is just a little brighter, a little louder wherever Wes is.

But now it's tempting to reexamine my impressions of him. I'm *mostly* sure I've always loved him as a friend and that tonight's impulse was just a new craving born of beer, ordinary jealousy, horniness and some kind of friendly emotional overload. The perfect storm. My desire is a strange creature of the night, brought to life by a strike of lightning in exactly the right place.

Right?

Sigh.

I'm not a navel gazer. I don't sit around inventing complex theories to explain my behavior. But tonight it's impossible not to lie here and wonder... All those times I watched him fly down the rink with the puck under his command—was that simple admiration? All those times I watched his flashy skating with a warm feeling in my chest. Or when he'd smile at me from across the table. Was I hiding something from myself? Or was there nothing to suppress?

Fuck, does it even matter?

Desire is chemistry. And in a biochem class I took once, they taught us that all chemistry is just electricity. We're all just bags of charged atoms walking around bumping into each other.

My electrons went seriously haywire for his tonight, though. Particles *collided.*

Pushing my hips into the mattress, I wish I could feel it again —the press of his body. The scrape of rough hands on my forearms.

I don't know why I want it. I don't know if the craving will disappear with tonight's rain shower. But right this moment it's here. And it's real.

The night now feels endless. And tomorrow will be an awkward eternity.

Yay.

I can't even begin to imagine what Wes is thinking right now. He wanted me—I felt it. But he stopped because it would ruin our friendship. This man who fucks strangers off an app.

I'm still lying there face down in my pillow when his key finally turns in our lock. I freeze, of course. He tiptoes in. I hear the thud of his hiking boots hitting the floor, and the soft swish of clothing coming off.

My dick hardens against the mattress. I'm actually hard, and all he's done is walk in and undress. *Interesting.*

His sheets rustle as he gets into bed. And then there's silence. A minute passes, then two. I'm not sleeping, and he can probably tell. Which means we're like two teenage girls after a catfight at a sleepover—ignoring each other.

I roll over to face him. "If you're trying to avoid me, you might have to do another seventeen laps around town. I'm still awake."

Wes sighs. "How are you feeling?"

"Horny."

He snorts. "That's the beer talking. Did you know you go gay when you're drunk?"

When I hear the word "gay," I almost argue. But that's not really the point. "I'm not drunk, Wes."

What I am is very, very curious. Wes thinks he did me a favor tonight by heading us off at the pass, but now I have this giant question inside me, and I don't think it will fade in the morning. But it *will* make things awkward. I'll be watching him in the mirror while we both shave, wondering what it would have been like. Wondering whether it's something I could really get into, or just a weird moment of happenstance.

"I don't want to fuck with your head," he whispers. "I wish I hadn't ever done that."

But it's not my head that needs fucking.

"Come over here," I say. "Please."

"No fucking way," he replies.

"I can make you."

He laughs. "Did you smoke some pot while I was out, Canning?"

I laugh, too, and it's such a relief. Because it means I haven't wrecked everything. But then I lift my hips, peel off my briefs, and throw them at his head. He bats them away, smiling in the dark.

Kicking the sheet off, I put my hand on my dick. And he stops laughing.

SIXTEEN

WES

Fuck me. I'm a strong guy. I'm a tough guy. But I was not built to withstand the sight of Jamie Canning stroking himself.

The shred of moonlight shining through the gap in the curtains shows him reclining on his back, his far knee cocked wide. His body is perfect—strong and lean on the bed. His palm is cupped over his dick, the fingertips just brushing the cockhead. He takes a deep breath and then pushes it out slowly, his back arching a little ways, his hips rolling a few degrees.

And I am dying a quiet death. My mouth actually waters, and I have to swallow hard. He's *right* there. In two paces I could have him in my mouth. It's like Jamie Canning looked into my filthy mind and extracted my fantasies. Well, the opening reel, anyway.

He doesn't turn his head to look at me, because he doesn't have to. We both know where my attention lies. He squeezes his shaft once. Twice. Then he opens his hand, letting the fingers drift down. He cups his balls, his thumb skimming the delicate skin.

I hear a hot gasp, and realize it's come from me.

Then? The fucker *smiles*.

That wakes me up, at least a little. "What the fuck are you doing?"

"I really need to jerk. You mind?"

Holy...! I *rue the fucking day* that I said those same words to him. I was eighteen, and I thought I was so smooth. But I was only setting in motion some serious pain for everyone. And it's *still* happening. There's blood pounding in my ears now.

And other places.

My hand creeps down into my boxers without my approval. Jamie is pumping himself now. Slowly, up and down. He pauses to rub his thumb over the head, and my throat constricts.

"Wes," he says, his voice like gravel. "I need your help."

It's a miracle I'm able to answer in an almost-normal voice. "Looks like you're doing fine on your own."

That's when he finally turns his head to look at me. As he rubs himself, he swallows, and I see his Adam's apple bob roughly. "I need to know."

Know what? I almost ask. But he's studying me now. His eyes are trailing across my chest and down my arm. He's watching the hand in my shorts. And I get it. He wants to know why he's feeling this way, if it's attraction or beer or temporary insanity.

Earlier tonight I was telling him the truth when I said I didn't want to help him make this discovery. I'm not sure I'd survive it.

This is, of course, all my fault.

We lock eyes. His are heavy-lidded. I've always wanted another chance to see his lust-filled face. Now his lips part on the upstroke, and it's almost enough to get me across the room. But still I hesitate, and not because I'm afraid he'll regret this tomorrow.

Because I know I will.

"Please," he says.

That one word is enough to get me off my bed. I'm standing

in the center of our room now, hands on the waistband of my boxers. I yank and let them drop to the floor.

And now he's staring at my cock, stroking his.

"What do you want?" I ask. And I need him to be specific. This is a very dangerous game we're playing. It will probably end in disaster. But if there's any way I can prevent that, I will.

He moves further onto the bed, making room for me. Then he beckons. And there isn't enough money, fame or fortune in the world to keep me from obeying. I'm on that bed a second later. His arms reach for me, pull me in.

We're side by side, chest to chest. And Jamie Canning is kissing me again.

He doesn't taste like beer anymore, but toothpaste. There's no way either of us can blame this on alcohol tomorrow. His tongue is in my mouth and I take greedy pulls on it, loving every second of it.

Our lower bodies grind together, and he lets out a soft moan, rocking harder into me. His cock slides over my belly, lines up with my own aching shaft. That bit of friction brings stars to my eyes.

"*Fuck*," I choke out.

His eyes slit open, searching my face as his tongue comes out to lick his bottom lip. "If you stop right now, I'm going to kick your ass."

Stop? Is that a word? What does it mean? Probably the opposite of what I'm doing when I slide my hand between our bodies and grasp both our cocks in my hand.

Jamie's spine arches on another husky moan. "Oh shit. That's good."

I jack us slowly, squeezing on each upstroke. His mouth finds mine again. His stubble scrapes my cheek as he angles his head to deepen the kiss. That magic tongue slides between my lips again, hungry and eager. I can't believe we're doing this. I can't believe he's *letting* me do this.

We're both leaking, making it so fucking easy for my fist to slide over our slick cocks. My balls are heavy, tingling with the need for release. A few more strokes and I'll probably blow, but Jamie doesn't let it happen.

He wrenches out of my grip and plants both palms on my chest to shove me onto my back. My dick sails up and slaps my navel, and he groans at the sight before wrapping his fingers around my shaft.

"Can I..." His voice comes out in a rush. "Can I suck you off?"

Holy mother of God. I'm caught in some kind of fever dream. I *have* to be, because there's no other explanation for why my best friend is offering to put his mouth on my dick.

I figured this exploratory I-need-to-know-if-I-like-dudes session would involve me doing all the work, ravaging him the way I've always fantasized about doing. But one thing about Jamie Canning? He's full of surprises. Every time he used to accept one of my crazy challenges, my eyebrows would soar, my mind unable to comprehend how this laidback Cali boy who always followed the rules could be so willing to follow me down whatever rabbit hole I was leading him into.

I'm not leading him into anything tonight, though. This is all Jamie. It's Jamie's fingers skimming along my hard length. Jamie's breath hot on the tip of my dick as he slides down and brings his mouth within inches of me.

"Have you ever..." I swallow past the gravel in my throat. "Done this before?"

"No." His lips are hesitant as they graze my cockhead. "I might suck."

A laugh chokes out. "Sucking is kind of the point."

He lifts his head, brown eyes twinkling. "I might be *bad* at it," he corrects.

"You won't be." Because there's no way he can be. I'm too close to coming already, just from being in the same bed as him. He doesn't need skill—he just needs to be here. Him. Here. With me.

I almost lose my mind when his tongue touches me. Every inch of me is hot, tight, prickling with need. He licks a slow circle around my tip, then kisses his way down my shaft. He's *kissing* my dick, light, open-mouthed caresses that blow my fucking mind. Holy shit. Jamie Canning is a cocktease. Who woulda thought?

"You trying to drive me crazy?" I growl after he kisses another path up my cock.

His chuckle vibrates through me. "Is it working?"

"Yes." I slide both hands through his hair, cupping his head. "What about you? Enjoying your first taste of dude?"

He laughs harder now, broad shoulders quaking as he crouches between my thighs. "It's…" His tongue finds me again, tickling the underside of my shaft. "Different."

He wraps his hand around my base and closes his mouth around my cockhead, giving a slow, decadent suck. "It's…"

He sucks again, taking me deeper this time, and my cock pulses uncontrollably. He must feel it on his tongue because he groans, loudly, desperately. He lifts his head, his expression foggy with lust, cloudy with confusion.

Joy surges through me. And apprehension, because I don't know what to do with his bewilderment. Do I assure him it's no big deal? That it's perfectly cool for a straight guy to love blowing another man?

But he doesn't give me the chance to say *anything*. He just dips his head and his hot, wet mouth surrounds me again.

My hips shift on the mattress, pure lust sizzling in my cock and balls as my best friend works me over. I keep one hand tangled in his hair. The other claws at the sheet, bunching it tight between my fingers. My heart is pounding. It's all I can hear, a frantic *thump-thump* rattling my ribcage. That and the sounds Jamie is making. Husky groans, wet *pops*, a deep growl as he takes me almost all the way to the back of his throat.

Jesus Christ. This man is wrecking me. I'm *wrecked*. I'm—

"Going to come," I ground out.

The climax seizes my balls and shoots up my shaft, hot jets spurting out of my cock just as Jamie's mouth releases me. He strokes me through the release, his breathing heavy and eyes gleaming as he watches my come land on my abs, my chest.

I can't breathe. I'm a gasping, shuddering mess, and he just keeps watching. And then the fucker does it again—he *smiles*. He fucking smiles as he lowers his head and licks one pearly drop off my stomach.

"That was so hot," he tells me.

Hot? Try scorching. Blistering. A goddamn inferno.

I'm unable to do anything but lie there like a sack of potatoes. Struggling to breathe. Blinking like an owl as I watch the most beautiful man grab my discarded shirt from the floor and clean me up. Once he's done, he tosses the shirt away and bends down to kiss my collarbone. Then my shoulder. My other shoulder.

He keeps kissing my feverish flesh, licking, nibbling, and I just let him explore, offering myself up as his sexual guinea pig. He's tasting every inch of me, his mouth moving tentatively over the ripples of my abs, my hips, my pecs. I moan when he licks one of my nipples, and he peeks up at me, his lips curving.

"You like that."

I manage a nod.

He does it again, this time closing his lips around the tiny nub and sucking on it. I can feel his erection against my thigh, leaving streaks of moisture against my skin. Drawing a breath, I reach down and grasp him, and now *I'm* smiling, because his tongue freezes on my nipple as his entire body tenses.

He thrusts into my hand, and it's all the invitation I need. "On your back," I mutter.

Jamie rolls over so fast it makes me laugh. He props his arms behind his head, one brow cocked as he nudges his hips up, all but taunting me with his perfect dick.

"Let's see if you've still got it," he teases.

My laughter is muffled against his stomach. "You know, you're a cocky bastard when you're gay."

"Guess I am."

I slowly crawl up his body, propping my elbows on either side of his head. Our gazes lock. He parts his lips, peering up at me with hazy eyes. Swallowing, I lower my mouth to his in a soft kiss. Fuck, I taste myself on his tongue, and it's enough to send my mind spinning. This guy…goddamn it, this guy. I've never wanted anyone the way I want Canning. The way I *crave* Canning.

Four years' worth of meaningless sexual encounters flash through my head as I break the kiss and slide down his body again. All those guys I hooked up with in the past…they're a blur. They're faceless. Sometimes they were faceless even when I was *with* them. I got off, they got off, but I wasn't fully present. I always held something back from them.

Not with Jamie. I can't hold back with him, and never could.

"Trust me, I've still got it," I whisper as my mouth descends toward his cock. And I'm going to prove it to him. Show him how much I fucking love him, because I sure as shit can't *tell* him.

I take a breath. His erection is millimeters away and it's mine. Tonight, *he's* mine. I grip his shaft and give it a light squeeze. He shudders in response, watching me. Waiting.

Licking my lips, I bend down and swipe my tongue over the little slit at his tip. He teased me before, and now it's time for some payback. I'm going to worship every inch of Jamie Canning's cock. I'm going to torment him with my tongue until he can't remember a time when my mouth wasn't on his dick bringing him pleasure. I'm going to—

Jamie comes the second I wrap my lips around him.

Yup, he fucking *comes*, and I don't know whether to laugh or groan as he starts to shake with release. In the end I do neither—I suck him all the way down to the base, drawing a strangled cry from his lips as I swallow the salty drops that shoot down my throat.

When he finally goes still, I raise my head with a sigh. "Really, dude? That was like *two* seconds. You have the stamina of a pre-teen."

His shoulders tremble as he rolls over on his side in hysterics. "I guess you've still got it," he chokes out between laughs.

Climbing up the mattress, I ease in behind him, yanking his big body toward me. He stiffens for a second, then relaxes, his taut ass nestling against my groin, his back flush to my chest.

I wrap an arm around his waist. If I'm honest, I wanted this as much as the blowjob—the right to just touch him. To lean on him, skin to skin.

But he's silent. Too silent, probably. "Jamie," I murmur in his ear, before planting a kiss on his shoulder. "Are you going to freak out now?"

The pause before he speaks cuts me in half. "Do you want me to?" There's humor in his voice.

"No." It's my turn to pause. "Do you want me to go back to my bed?"

He snuggles even closer, plastering himself to my body like a warm blanket. "No." He sighs in contentment. "Night, Wes."

A lump rises in my throat. "Night, Canning."

SEVENTEEN
JAMIE

Wes isn't beside me when I open my eyes the next morning. I roll over and study the room. His bed is empty. It doesn't look like it's been slept in, and I don't remember him climbing out of mine during the night. What I do remember is waking up at six in the morning to find Wes's arm wrapped tightly around me. Then I'd fallen back asleep, so he must've left some point after that.

Probably makes me a jerk, but I'm relieved. I'm not sure what I would have said if I woke up to find us snuggling.

According to the alarm clock on the end table, it's almost eleven-thirty. Dining hall stops serving breakfast at eleven. I'd slept right through it, but that's okay. It's our day off, so I'm not needed at the rink.

On the other hand, *it's our day off*. That means hours and hours of free time. Time I'll probably be spending with Wes. Who I hooked up with last night.

I don't feel any different, though. I fooled around with a guy yesterday—shouldn't I feel different?

Feel gay, you mean?

A laugh bubbles in my throat. Does one *feel* gay?

And damn it, I'm bewildered to discover I'm rocking a boner, and it's more than just a case of morning wood. It's Wes-wood, a result of thinking about us messing around.

I...think I might want to do it again. And how screwed up is *that*? I'd been fully prepared to view last night as a chemistry experiment. A test. I hadn't expected to *ace* the damn thing.

The door suddenly swings open and Wes trudges inside, red-faced and breathing hard. He's in running gear, the front of his sleeveless shirt drenched in sweat. He peels it off his muscular chest and throws it aside.

"It's fucking hot out there," he mumbles without glancing my way.

Oh shit. He's going to make it awkward. He can't even look me in the eye.

"Why didn't you wake me?" I ask. "I would've come running with you."

He shrugs. "Figured I'd let you sleep in." He kicks off his shoes and socks, then strips out of his shorts.

Now he's naked. And I'm even harder.

He's still averting his gaze, so he has no idea I'm admiring his lean, sculpted muscles and the black ink winding around his heavy biceps. I realize this is the first time I've seen him naked in the light of day, and his skin gleams in the sunlight peeking through the curtains. He's all muscle. All man.

And all those questions I'd asked myself last night—*Am I really attracted to him? Would I like it if we hooked up? Am I totally crazy?*—I know the answers to them now. Yes, yes, and maybe.

But I didn't expect to wake up with *more* questions.

I slide out of bed and notice he's making an even greater effort not to look at me now. Because...yep, I'm naked, too. We'd fallen asleep naked. In each other's arms.

His back is to me as he stalks over to the dresser.

"Wes," I say quietly.

He doesn't react. He grabs a pair of blue gym shorts from the top drawer and tugs them up to his hips.

"Wes."

His shoulders tense. Very slowly, he turns around, and his gray eyes focus on my face. There's an unspoken question flickering there—*what now?*

Fuck if I know.

What I *do* know? I'm not equipped to have this conversation right now. Not until I've given it some thought and figured out what I want from this. From *him*.

So I put on a careless tone and ask, "What are we doing today?"

He's silent for a beat. I can tell he expected me to go all chick on him and demand we talk about last night. I can also tell he's relieved I decided to choose the dude route and ignore it.

His lips quirk slightly. "Well, we need to get some food in you and then hike over to the soccer field. The kids came back from the fishing hole already because nothing was biting except the mosquitoes. So Pat's organizing a game."

And just like that, we're cool again. Sure, we're pretending we didn't blow the shit out of each other last night, but for now, I'm happy to pretend. I'm not ready to deal with this yet.

I wrinkle my forehead. "For the kids?"

"Nope, the coaches. But a bunch of the boys are already there taking bets on which team will win."

"There are teams already?" How long had I been asleep?

Wes grins again. "Pat's calling it boys versus men. Him and the older coaches against us young'uns."

"Sweet." I'm not a soccer enthusiast, but any sort of competition gets my adrenaline going.

"PS—losers have to perform a song for the campers in the dining hall tonight," Wes says.

I narrow my eyes. "Which song?"

"Winners' choice." He snickers.

"Just out of curiosity—who came up with these stakes?"

My best friend blinks with the utmost innocence.

That's what I thought.

"You know if we lose, Pat's gonna make us sing Mariah Carey or some shit," I grumble as I look for my shorts.

"Which is why we're not going to lose," he says cheerfully.

We stop at the bakery in town so I can grab a coffee and something to eat, and I scarf down two banana muffins as we head to the soccer field. It's another gorgeous day and the tourists are out in droves, bustling down the sidewalk and filling the outdoor patios we pass on our way.

Two chicks stop in their tracks as Wes and I walk by. They're in their early twenties, both blond, both incredibly attractive. One girl is wearing a top that's cut so low her tits are practically hanging out of it, and a spark of heat ignites my groin. Shi-it. That rack is spectacular.

Wes winks at them and keeps walking. I match his strides, trying not to glance over my shoulder to see if the girls are watching us.

Okay, just one peek. I flick my chin back for a quick look, which causes one of the girls to nudge her friend.

Whoops.

"See something you like?" Wes asks.

I feel a slap of discomfort that wouldn't have been there twenty-four hours ago. "Just thinking things over," I mumble.

"I'll bet." His voice is low.

We don't speak of it anymore, because I don't need to involve Wes in my confusion. But I'm pretty sure that my dick is an equal-opportunity player. Because I love women. I love how soft they are and the way they smell and how they feel in my arms. I love fucking them and going down on them, and I'm never faking it.

Last night, I wasn't faking it, either. And now I have no idea what it all means.

Wes nudges me, then points at a street sign we're passing. *Cummings Road.*

"Like that joke has never been made before. Now who's the pre-teen?"

He stiffens for a beat, as if he didn't expect me to make a reference to last night. Then he snorts. "Let's play some soccer, Canning."

Indeed.

First, Pat gathers everyone around. You can't ask a bunch of highly competitive athletes to play a friendly game of soccer without going over a few rules first. There will be two twenty-minute periods. And will the offsides rule count? Yes it will. Is slide tackling legal? No. "Because I will fucking kill anyone who injures himself," Pat adds.

Good to know.

We're playing five on five, and I'm in the goal, of course. I can see Killfeather over on the side, watching me with a grin on his face. He's not a bad kid when he forgets to be stressed out.

I'm not stressed, either. I'm bored to tears, because Wes and the other guys are giving 'em hell at the other end of the field. We're up 1-0 by the time I have to make my first save. A soccer net is a lot bigger than a hockey goal, so saving the net seems more haphazard. But I stop Pat's shot in my hands and my team cheers.

I set the ball down on the line, back up and kick it downfield. Before it reaches Wes, he gives me a little smile, then traps the ball with his chest. It drops to the ground between his muscular legs and then he's off running, controlling the ball, masculine beauty in motion.

Suddenly I'm thinking about sex again. In the middle of a game.

That's never happened before.

The next time the ball threatens our goal, things don't go so well. Our defense falls apart when Pat is able to deke my team-mate Georgie, leaving the most senior coach unguarded. The old man promptly fires a flying saucer right at me.

I leap, but it sails past my thumb and into the corner of the net.

Wes makes an ornery noise, and I can see he's about to lay into Georgie for leaving us wide open.

Meanwhile, Killfeather and the rest are watching. I walk over to Wes and put a hand on his shoulder. "Hey," I say, holding my hand up for a high five. "We'll get the next one."

Wes is a quick study, so it's no surprise to me that he catches on. He smacks my hand. "Yeah, man." Then? He reaches around behind me and gives my ass a quick squeeze.

Holy...!

I can't help that my eyes dart around, checking everyone's face for a reaction. But there isn't one, because nobody saw. And even if they had, it's such a Wes move that nobody would think twice about it.

But I do. Because even if I'm not freaking out about what we did last night, I don't want anyone else to know.

If Wes was a girl, I wouldn't care, though.

And why is that, exactly? my conscience wonders. It's a good question, and not one that I'm prepared to answer. And anyway, there are ten more minutes of soccer to play.

We hold at 1-1 until there are only two minutes remaining. Then Wes gets lucky with Georgie's corner kick, heading the ball into the top of the net. And we've won. I collapse on the grass and yell for Killfeather to bring me a bottle of water.

He does, but he pours some of it on my face before handing me the rest.

"You are such a punk," I complain, and he laughs.

The walk home takes longer than it should, because the coaches are sweaty and tired. "So who do you room with?" I ask Killfeather.

"Oh, with Davies."

"Really? How's that working out?"

"It's all right," he says. "He's not bad when he's not on the ice."

I file that away to think about later. And I let my eyes linger on Wes. His gait is so familiar to me. The way he carries his shoulders hasn't changed in the nine years I've known him. The way his hamstrings tighten with each step is as familiar as my own hand.

There's a warm feeling in my belly when I look at him. And it's not just sexual. It's...*comfortable*. Like we're close even when he's twenty yards ahead. I wear a consciousness of him like a second skin.

Okay, that sounds a little creepy. A little too *Silence of the Lambs*. Sunshine and sexual confusion have gone to my head.

Just before he reaches the dormitory, I see Wes answer his phone. And when I arrive in our room a minute or so behind him, he's frowning out the window while he talks.

"What if I don't want to do an interview?" he asks. His tone is recklessly belligerent if he's talking to a PR person. *Careful*, I feel like saying.

"This isn't a good idea. Why set me up just to lie?" There's a pause on Wes's end. He kicks off his shoes with more force than is necessary, and they fly with an angry thunk into the desk we never use. "Dad, if I tell them there's a girlfriend, they're going to ask her name. And *then* what would you have me say?"

Ah. The conversation makes more sense now. Wes never got along with his father. Every phone call home had always ended with Wes red-faced and irritated. The one time I met Wesley Sr., I found him to be awfully arrogant and demanding for someone who sits at a desk all day.

The fact that Mr. Wesley isn't happy about his son's sexuality comes as no surprise to me at all.

In front of me, Wes hunches his shoulders. Without thinking too hard about it, I step forward and put both hands there, squeezing the muscle between his neck and shoulders. I dig my thumbs into his traps and push.

At first he goes rigid. Then he makes an effort to relax. And when he shoots me a little glance over his shoulder, it's grateful.

"I gotta go," Wes is saying, his voice still grumpy. "I'll think about it. But don't you dare schedule anything without my permission."

He ends the call and drops the phone on the desk. Then he drops his head and leans into my touch. "Thanks, man," he says gruffly.

"What does he want from you?" I work my hands up onto the back of his neck. Would I have touched him this way yesterday? Maybe? Probably not. But it isn't sexual. He feels good under my hands, though. Warm and alive.

Wes groans. "He's got a buddy at *Sports Illustrated*. You know him—he's got a buddy *everywhere*. My dad came out of the womb with business cards in his hands. He's convinced the guy to interview me about my rookie season. Like—following the ups and downs."

I'm horrified. "That's a terrible idea." In the first place, rookie seasons are wildly unpredictable. Wes could end up as a healthy scratch for two dozen games before suddenly seeing tons of play.

And who wants the pressure of speaking to a reporter all the damn time? "You don't want to be *that* rookie on the team—the one a reporter follows around all fucking day."

Wes sighs, his back rising and falling under my hands. "You think?"

I feel a rush of...*something* for him. Solidarity. Affection. Maybe it doesn't need a title. But I wish his father hadn't meddled. "What are you going to do?"

"Lie," he says, his tone flat. "I'll tell him I spoke to the Panthers' PR team, and they vetoed the idea."

"Will he believe you?"

"Does it matter?"

"Yeah," I say quietly. "Because you don't want to piss off *Sports Illustrated* before you've even sharpened your skates in Toronto."

Wes makes a frustrated sound as I work my hands down his spine. "My fucking father, sticking his nose where it doesn't belong again. He thinks he's helping, too. He wants his buddy to write an all-American-kid kind of story. Apple fucking pie and all that. Like if it's printed in a magazine, he can make it true."

Wes turns around suddenly, interrupting the killer massage I'd been giving him. I'm oddly disappointed. I enjoyed having my hands on him. I know he enjoyed it too, but his expression is shuttered again, just like it was this morning.

I open my mouth. Then close it. Nope, I'm still not ready to have this conversation.

Neither is he, apparently. "Let's grab some lunch," he suggests.

I hesitate, then shake my head. "You go ahead. I think I'll take a nap for a bit. I'm...tired after that game."

It's a lame-ass excuse, and I know he sees right through me. But he just nods. "Yeah. Sure. I'll catch up with you later."

A moment later, he's gone.

EIGHTEEN

WES

I don't end up grabbing lunch. Instead, I walk around aimlessly for almost an hour, then plant my ass on a park bench and do some people-watching.

Canning is freaking out. I don't need to be a mind reader to know that. But fuck, I wish I *could* read his mind. I want to know just how badly I screwed up our friendship again.

Or had I? I don't even fucking know. A part of me assumes that yes, I've lost him again. But another part keeps saying, *dude, he just gave you a MASSAGE.* That means we're still friends, right? Except…do friends really give each other back rubs? The one time I had a kink in my neck and asked Cassel to knead it out for me, he nearly bust a gut laughing.

And speaking of Cassel, there are two text messages from him on my phone, both from earlier in the week. I've been too busy settling back into the Lake Placid routine to answer him.

I type a quick response: *Camp's good. Some real talent here. How's ur sis? Make friends with any lobsters?* I chuckle to myself. Cassel's spending the summer with his older sister in Maine, busing tables at her seafood restaurant.

He responds faster than I expect: *All good here. Sis says hi.*

There's a long delay, and then a second message pops up: *Broke up with Em*.

Sitting there on the bench, I let out a whoop of joy. About fucking time. This is too important for texts, so I pull up his number and call him.

He answers on the second ring, his familiar voice sliding into my ear. "Yo."

"So how'd she take it?" I demand.

"As expected."

"Freaked out and slapped you, you mean?"

A heavy sigh echoes on the line. "Pretty much. She accused me of stringing her along for four years. I reminded her we were only going out for one, and then she called me an insensitive fucktard and stormed out."

"Shit. Sorry, man. You doing okay?"

"Oh yeah. Never realized how high maintenance that chick was until I set her loose. Just enjoying my freedom now, taking a page out of the Ryan Wesley playbook and screwing anything that walks."

"Next year that won't be my playbook."

He's silent for a second. "You going to try to keep your extracurriculars on the DL?"

"I think I have to keep it zipped up instead. A rookie can't afford rumors. At school... That was just different. The stakes were lower."

"Yeah. I guess so. Sorry, man. Sounds lonely."

I try to laugh it off. "Sounds *horny*."

"You'd better have some fun this summer, before you're all famous and shit." Cassel laughs at his own humor.

"I'll get right on that."

"How is the pickup scene in Lake Placid? Can't imagine there's a gay bar there. You'll have to turn a jock or two."

My stomach shimmies. *If only I hadn't already tried that.* "I'd better go," I say. Because I'm really not fit for conversation today.

"Good talking to you, man."

"Stay strong if Em calls," I warn.

"Don't worry." He sighs. "I will."

NINETEEN

JAMIE

I glance at the door for the hundredth time in ten minutes. Just, you know, to make sure little gremlins didn't crawl out of some air vent and unlock it. But nope, still locked.

It feels like I'm doing something wrong. Like I just dipped my hand in the cookie jar when my mom turned her back to me. But maybe I'm being too hard on myself. There's nothing wrong with looking at porn. I'm a red-blooded, twenty-two-year-old man. I'm not a virgin. I'm not a prude. Just a guy trying to figure out what his kinks are.

Sighing, I lean back against the pillows, my laptop positioned on my thighs as I scroll through the thumbnails on the screen. I hover over one of the images, which shows a preview of what I can expect. All right. Seems okay.

I click on the title: *Hot jocks suck 'n fuck*.

Did I mention I'm browsing gay porn?

Yep, I'm a filthy liar—I told Wes I was taking a nap, and look at me now.

A breath shudders out of my chest as the video loads. It's a short clip, and it starts splat in the middle of a scene from whatever movie the site pulled the clip from. I've got the sound turned down low, but I can hear every word loud and clear. Well, just one of the dudes is *talking*. The other guy is only capable of wet slurps and deep moans as he goes to town on the first guy's dick.

"Fuck yeah…oh fuck yeah…suck that big cock…"

Okay, that's just cheesy. I laugh as I imagine myself ordering Wes to "suck that big cock".

Next clip. This one's not doing it for me.

I click on something labeled *Poolside fuck*. Sounds promising. I like pools and I like fucking. Can't go wrong with that, right?

"You like that big dick in your hole, boy? That's it, boy, take it—"

Annnnnnd I press stop. Nope. Just nope.

I hit the jackpot on my next selection. Two very attractive guys are making out on a bed, grinding their hard cocks together.

My dick says hello.

Interesting. There's something about the grip they have on each other that turns me on. It's not gentle. There's a hungry, forceful energy to their kissing that I appreciate. That my dick appreciates.

Shit, like *seriously* appreciates. I'm hard now, my gaze fixed on the screen as I watch one guy kiss his way down the other one's stomach. When his mouth engulfs his partner's erection, a jolt of heat shoots up my spine.

Sucking in a breath, I reach down and grip my aching cock. Oh fuck, that feels good.

I keep watching. Keep stroking.

And the messed up thing is, I'm not even mentally replacing the guy's face with Wes's. That had been one of the reasons for this little experiment, to find out if it's just Wes who turns me on, or dudes in general.

The guy receiving the blowjob releases a husky moan. The masculine sound of it does something to me. His partner sucks him harder.

I'm literally five seconds away from coming.

Chillax, I order my dick. *We're just getting started.*

But the little goalie's got a mind of his own. He won't quit throbbing, so I hit the fast forward button to skip to the *real* test.

The anal.

And holy shit, that's some serious pounding. I wince as the sound of flesh slapping flesh bursts out of the laptop speakers. Jesus. How is that guy not screaming in pain?

He is screaming, though. Well, moaning. And there's grunting. They're not careful with each other, but all that graceless enthusiasm looks like fun. I keep staring at the guy who's taking it. His biceps bulge as he jacks himself, his eyes slammed shut, his neck taut with pleasure.

And then he's coming, and I'm not far behind. The computer falls off my lap as I stroke faster, cupping my balls with my other hand. I gasp for air, my eyes glued to the screen, to the sight of two *men* screwing. My spine arches as my cock twitches in my hand, spilling all over my stomach.

Holy…shit.

It takes almost a full minute for my heartbeat to regulate. Once my limbs no longer feel like spaghetti noodles, I reach for the tissue box next to me and clean myself up. Then I stare up at the ceiling for a while.

I'm not done, though. That was just the first part of the experiment. I pick up the laptop again and click on a new category. Good ol' fashioned lesbian porn.

I'm too spent to jerk it again, but I still click on a thumbnail, one that shows two smoking hot brunettes tangled together on a white couch. I hike my shorts back up, one hand resting on my crotch as I settle in to enjoy the view.

And enjoy it I do. I'm hardening again. The lust isn't as strong as before, but that's because of the orgasm I just had, not because the girls aren't doing it for me. They are. Big-time. Their soft curves and pretty pussies and those sweet whimpers.

I'm attracted to women, no doubt about it.

I'm also attracted to men, apparently.

Wonderful. Complicated fellow, my dick.

When footsteps thud in the hall, I slap the laptop shut, nearly clipping my fingers off. Then I shove the computer aside and stand up, quickly tossing the used tissue in the wastebasket near the dresser.

A second later, a key jingles in the lock and Wes strides through the door. He sees me standing in the middle of the room, lifts an eyebrow, and says, "How was the nap?"

I get the feeling he knows exactly what I've been up to, but I simply shrug. "Just what I needed. How was lunch?"

"Didn't have any. I ended up walking around."

"You hungry?" I swipe my T-shirt off the floor and throw it on. "'Cause I am."

When my head pops through the neck hole of the shirt, I find Wes eyeing me warily. "You okay, Canning?"

"Yep." I walk to the door, glancing at him over my shoulder. "So...lunch?"

His brows knit, drawing my attention to the barbell in his left eyebrow. It gives him this whole bad-boy vibe that makes me kinda...horny.

"Wes?"

He snaps out of whatever thoughts had just preoccupied him. "Uh, yeah. Lunch sounds good."

I leave the room without checking if he's following me. I know he is. I can feel his perplexed gaze tickling my back.

After the way I spent the afternoon, I'm pretty sure he's nowhere near as perplexed as I am.

TWENTY

WES

We buy burritos and eat them by the lake. After that, we go for ice cream at one of the many places on Main Street. Jamie wants to talk about coaching, apparently. So we do.

"A lot of these kids still don't understand 'first touch,'" he theorizes. "If there was one thing I could have 'em take back home, it would be that. In a high-level game, you only get one chance at the puck. If they waste time repositioning, it's over."

"Uh-huh." But every time he says "first touch" my mind is on an entirely different kind of touching. He's talking a lot with his hands, and I'm fixated on his biceps, and the fine blond hair on his arms, which I now know is very soft to the touch. I think about removing that T-shirt to kiss his chest, and my dick begins to grow heavy.

Wearing these nylon athletic shorts? Not smart. And horniness isn't even my only problem.

Last night I'd asked Jamie if he was freaking out. Funny, I've now spent an entire day doing just that.

The guy is fucking with my mind. First he acts like nothing happened. Then he ditches me so he can take a "nap." But no way was he doing that. I mean, I wasn't born yesterday. When I got back to our room and saw him standing there all guiltily, it was obvious what he'd been doing. The fucker had jerked off.

I would have been happy to help him out with that, but clearly he'd rather go solo than let me touch him again.

Except…then he'd checked me out. Again, not born yesterday. I saw the way he was looking at me before we headed out.

Jesus. Good thing he's not a traffic cop, because he's sending enough mixed signals to cause a ten-car pileup.

I've played it cool, but inside I'm a wreck. Because once was not enough, and yet I haven't a clue what Jamie's thinking.

No clue.

Shoving the last of my ice cream cone in my mouth, all I want is to drag him back to our lair and do very dirty things to him. But is that even in the cards? I know two things so far. First, Jamie Canning can get hot for me. I saw it last night. And second, he's not horrified by what we did.

That's amazing, and I feel like pinching myself that I had even one awesome night with the love of my life. But it doesn't guarantee me a fucking thing. He owes me nothing. He could tire of this little experiment. He probably already has.

It's terrifying. Because I want another taste. Hell, I want to gorge myself on him. I'm a glutton for Jamie Canning.

"Wes?"

"What?" Oh, shit. I've been staring at him, and I have no idea what we're talking about.

"I asked if you wanted to swim. It's still hot."

"Uh." I really just want to go home and get very, very naked. "I'm not wearing a suit."

His eyes narrow. "Who are you?"

Right. When you spend your life giving zero fucks about appropriate attire, people notice. "Okay," I concede. "Let's swim."

Jamie's phone makes a trilling noise. "Oh. Hang on two

minutes? If I don't answer, they'll keep calling." He swipes the screen, but holds the phone away from his body. "Hey guys!"

A chorus of voices pours from his phone, which is on Skype or some shit. "Jamie!" "Jamester!" "Hi baby!"

I'd forgotten about this. Jamie's whole family has a big meal together on Sunday every single week, and apparently it's a family sacrilege to miss one. So while their youngest was away at camp, he got these calls every week. Probably when he was away at college, too.

"You need a haircut," a female voice pipes up.

"Yeah," he concedes, running a hand through his golden hair. I'm jealous of that hand. "What's new in Cali?"

I listen while his family all tries to talk at once. "Guess who's knocked up again?" a male voice asks.

"Language!"

Apparently Jamie's sister is pregnant again. And one of his brothers got a promotion. Another brother broke up with his long-time girlfriend.

"I'm sorry about that," Jamie says.

"We're not!" a sister cries.

"Fuck off!"

"Language!"

Suffice it to say that Jamie's call from home is nothing like mine.

"So, son," an older voice booms. Jamie's dad always manages to sound commanding without coming off like an asshole. My father could take a few pointers. "What have you been up to this week?"

I snort so hard that Jamie's eyes flick over to me before quickly moving back to the screen. "The usual," he says, giving me a kick under the table. "Lots of ice time. Went hiking."

Sucked off my gay friend Wes.

He keeps his eyes firmly on the screen so I can't really tell whether he's sweating this part of the conversation or not.

"Sounds good," his father rumbles. "Your mother is busy in the kitchen, but she said to tell you to make sure you come home before you head for Detroit."

"I'll try," he promises. "It depends on whether Pat can replace me for that week."

"Your mother also reminds you to try to get enough fiber and eat organic."

There's a boom of laughter from the phone at that.

Jamie grins. "I'll get right on it."

"Be good, Jamie!" "Love you!" "Wear your cup!" More snickers. More endearments.

And then Jamie ends the call, tucking his phone into his shirt pocket, shaking his head. "Sorry about that."

"No big. Still want to swim?" *Please say no.*

"Yeah. Let's do it."

The town beach is at the southern end of Mirror Lake, really close to the dormitory. Everything in Lake Placid is close to everything else. This town was a summer resort for rich people well before it was a winter sports destination. So we pass all manner of attractive old buildings on the short walk to the little beach.

Jamie kicks off his flip-flops and strips off his shirt. He walks into the water, where his shorts start to cling to his body even before he's submerged himself.

I follow him, of course. He could lead me anywhere right now, and I wouldn't argue.

The cool water feels great, though. When I'm up to my thighs I dive under, chasing Jamie out past the sandy area. There's a floating raft a hundred yards out, and we swim to it.

Jamie is smiling at me when I break the surface. With one

palm I splash him a good one, then dive under again to escape retribution. Passing him, I make for the far side of the raft.

When I come up to take a breath, a big hand pushes me under again. So of course I'm coughing when I bob up a second later. "Fucker," I sputter, even though we spent the better part of our summers trying to drown each other every afternoon after practice.

He's got an elbow on the raft now, too, which prevents me from dunking him. Figures. So I do the same, coming to perch beside him.

Our shoulders are touching. All he has to do is turn his head and his mouth would be inches from mine. And then all I'd have to do is lean forward and his mouth would be *on* mine.

But he doesn't turn toward me. He just stares straight ahead.

Fucking hell. I can't take this anymore. I need to know where we stand. Because the thought of spending even another minute guessing what this guy wants from me is absolute torture.

Under water, I reach out and touch his belly with my fingertips.

Jamie's eyes widen. But he doesn't say anything. I hitch myself over to be a little closer. Then I flatten my palm on his cool, wet skin, my pinkie finger breaching the elastic of his shorts. I don't think anyone can see what I'm doing. But Jamie's eyes do a circuit of the lake. He's worried.

Fuck, I don't want to freak him out. "Feel like going home now?" I ask. It's code for, *are we going to fool around again?* If we're not, I wish he'd just tell me. Put me out of my misery.

He licks his lips. "Yeah," he says. Then he knocks my hand away. "But cut that out, or I won't be able to get out of the water."

I obey immediately.

Five minutes later we're walking into the dormitory, our clothes dripping on the old tile floors. But that's how people roll around here in the summertime. The place is mostly quiet, which means the kids are all at dinner.

Without a word we walk into our room and shut the door. The first thing I do is drop my shorts and boxers to the floor where they make a wet slap. Jamie follows suit. Then we're both just standing there, starkers, staring at each other. His eyes are startled, and my heart quakes with the fear that he's about to say, "I can't do this again."

"We have to be quiet," he says instead.

My smile is the size of Mirror Lake. "You can bite the pillow when I make you scream."

He takes a stuttering breath when I move closer to him, and I instantly freeze.

"Are you sure you wanna do this?" I gnaw on the inside of my cheek. "You've kinda been running hot and cold on me all day."

He nods. "Needed to get some things straight in my head."

I snort at his choice of words. "Straight, huh?" I offer a pointed look at his very noticeable hard-on.

His mouth twitches. "My dick and I reached an understanding."

"Yeah? And what's that?" I ask curiously.

He shrugs. "We both like you."

Fuck yeah.

I erase the rest of the distance between us. I'm hardening already, which is no surprise, because I've been thinking about this all day. My hands land on skin cool from the water. I brush his nipples with my fingertips, and they stiffen immediately. His ear is right beside my mouth, so I stick my tongue in it, making him gasp.

"Get on my fucking bed," I whisper.

Two seconds later, he's there. And I'm stretching out on him like a blanket, and jamming my tongue into his mouth. Jamie moans, but I'm too wrapped up in the taste of him to worry about it. I have my fingers in his hair and his hot, hard body under mine and it's everything I've ever wanted.

He's not hating life, either. His hips roll beneath me, his cock bumping and scraping against mine. It aches. My balls are tight already. Rubbing off on him feels amazing, and I love that his sweet mouth is a prisoner of mine. But I don't want to come yet.

So I force myself to pull back. When I look down at Jamie, his eyes are glazed with lust, and his lips are swollen and red. I make the sign for "time out." He tips his head back into the pillow and sighs, and I can't help dipping down to kiss his exposed throat.

I love you. The words are always right there on the tip of my naughty tongue. I swallow them back like I need to and say something much more practical instead.

"Have you ever been acquainted with your prostate?"

He shakes his head.

"Do you trust me?"

Jamie nods immediately, and my heart constricts. I must be insane to push him like this, but the things I crave are at war with my better judgment. So now I'm getting off the bed to dig in my duffel for the bottle of lube I keep in there.

His eyes follow the bottle when I sit back on the bed. He's probably seconds away from saying, "Hang on, that's just too gay for me." So I lean down and take the tip of his erection in my mouth.

"Fuck," he gasps, arching his back.

Once again I am socked with the certainty that I'm the world's most manipulative bastard. But I'm trying to blow his mind, and I'm hoping that's enough justification. I torture him with my tongue until he's practically levitating off the bed.

"Lift this leg," I whisper.

Drunk from my teasing, he hikes his knee without complaint, and I position him so I can reach his crease easily. I dribble some lube onto the fingers of one hand. Then I drop my head and take his cock in my mouth. When I start sucking, he gasps. But when I slide my fingers between his ass cheeks, he goes silent.

For a moment I don't know what he's thinking. I release his dick and place a kiss on its tip. "You okay?"

He takes a slow breath. "Yeah," he says as I tease his hole. "It's strange."

"Can you take more?" If he says no, I'll drop it.

"Okay."

I apply some more lube and then penetrate him with the tip of my finger. "Relax for me, baby."

He tries. So I reward him with some kisses right where he wants them. "Mmm," he says. "*That* I like."

I give him some more. Since I've weirded him out with the ass play, he's not teetering on the edge anymore. I lean down, sucking and licking and just generally bringing out my A game. And at the same time, I'm working a finger slowly toward his prostate.

When I finally get there, everything changes.

"Ohfuckohfuck," Jamie whispers, his thigh muscles trembling.

I rub his prostate again and give another good suck.

He moans, and I reach up with my free hand to cover his mouth. "Shh," I remind him. "Don't make me stop."

He shakes my hand off his mouth. "It's... You're... My feet are tingling."

That's a good sign.

Smiling, I resume my wicked ministrations, my finger sliding inside him in time to the long, lazy strokes of my mouth. Jamie begins to shift his hips, thrusting into my mouth. And it's not just his dick he's thrusting. It's his ass, too. He's bumping it toward me, seeking me out. Jesus. He's trying to fuck my finger.

"You doing okay?" I murmur.

"More than okay." His voice is a choked whisper.

He's squeezed his eyes shut. A flush rises in his cheeks, his brow drawn together as if he's in pain. But I know pain is the last thing he's feeling right now. His dick grows impossibly hard in my mouth, and I groan when his ass bears down on my finger.

"Wes…" He breathes out my name, his thighs quivering as he lifts his hips again. "You're making me crazy."

That's what I like to hear. His arousal surrounds us like a thick mist, pulsing in the air, in my cock. I slide the pad of my finger over his prostate again, and he croaks out a curse, and I'm loving it. "Has anyone ever told you before that you're sexually adventurous?"

One eye opens. "All the time," he mumbles, and I experience a jolt of jealousy, wondering which lucky girl helped him discover it. Jamie groans again. "Keep doing that. Please…don't stop…"

This guy is under the impression that stopping is even an *option*. I would, of course, if he asked me to, but as long as he's begging for my mouth? For my finger? Nothing short of dying will stop me from giving it to him. I'll give him every fucking part of myself, serve it to him like a feast at a banquet.

Jamie Canning has no idea the kind of power he has over me.

TWENTY-ONE

JAMIE

I thought I had sex down to a science. I mean, it's not difficult. Kissing, foreplay, intercourse. I've tried almost every sexual position known to man, even the crazy ones you see in porn, where the chick pulls some exorcist-contortionist maneuver while I pound into her.

But my ass was never part of the deal.

Right now, it *is* the deal. Because even though Wes's mouth engulfs my cock like it's trying to swallow me whole, the arousal humming in my blood is centered solely on the pressure between my ass cheeks. It's good pressure. A slight burn that turns into a mind-melting rush of pleasure each time he hits this one spot inside me.

He's destroying me. He's bringing to life nerve endings I didn't know existed. It's unfamiliar. It's new. And experiencing it is a million times hotter than watching it happen to some other guy in a porn clip.

"*So* good," I choke out. "Jesus, don't stop...baby." He called me that before and I test it out now. It feels weird leaving my mouth. As weird as the new sensations coursing through me and tingling in my ass.

I wasn't sure I'd like this, but I do. God, I do. When his tongue ring scrapes the underside of my dick, I shiver, my breath catching. His finger is lodged inside me, and I wonder what it would feel like if he slipped another one in there. Or if he used something other than a finger...

I suddenly think of the porn I watched earlier, the husky moans of the guy who was being drilled, and the dirty memory makes me clamp harder around Wes.

He lifts his head abruptly, his finger stilling but not withdrawing.

Uneasiness circles my gut as I meet his eyes. Lust has darkened them to stormy silver, and his throat works as he swallows.

"Why did you stop?" I swallow, too. "Are you going to...fuck me now?"

The question brings a jolt of panic. As hot as it was to watch on a screen, I don't think I'm ready to experience that for myself yet. I'm not sure I'll ever be ready—

"No." He's quick to reassure me, his gaze softening when he sees my face. "Not unless you want me to."

"I..." I bite my lip. "I...don't know. Maybe another time."
Maybe another time? God, when I go gay, I *really* go gay.

Wes's lips quiver. "We'll put a pin in that."

I shudder out a laugh. "Why'd you stop then?"

"Just wanted to do *this*," he says roughly, and then his finger disappears as he slides up and brushes his mouth over mine.

The kiss goes from sweet to molten in a matter of seconds. His tongue fills my mouth in deep, hungry strokes that make me gasp. I'm eager for more, desperate for it, but he's gone again before I can blink, crawling back between my legs.

This time when his finger slips past that puckered ring of muscle, I welcome the burn. I crave it. Wes licks a hot line from the tip of my cock to my aching balls, teasing the delicate sac while his finger toys with me. When I try to push my ass against it, he retreats, a dark chuckle fanning over my shaft.

Jesus. I can't take it anymore. I need to come before I self-combust.

"Stop being a cocktease," I growl. "Give me what I want."

His tongue ring teases my slit. "Yeah, and what do you want, baby?"

"For you to suck me dry."

Wes pushes his finger in deeper, rubbing that spot that makes me see stars. My prostate. Why hasn't anyone ever told me the prostate was some kind of magical pleasure zone? Are there unicorns and orgasm fairies dancing around in there?

"Ask me nicely and I'll consider it." He grins up at me.

I narrow my eyes at him. "Make me come, jackass."

His laughter sends my heart soaring. Which is the most confusing thing of all, because it adds an element to the sex I didn't expect. I'm comfortable with him. I have fun with him. I'm not trying to impress anyone. It's...easy. Like splashing in the lake. But with orgasms.

"You're a bossy bastard, Canning." His lips tickle the head of my cock. "I fucking love it."

And I love what he's doing to me. The sucking, the blunt fingertip rubbing inside me. It's not long before the tension gathers again. A knot of pleasure that coils tighter and tighter until finally I cup the back of Wes's head and bear down on his finger as the orgasm shoots through me. Out of me.

Wes drinks me up like he can't get enough, humming around my cock, and I have to tug on his hair to get him to stop once my dick has had enough.

I lie there panting. When my breathing finally slows to an almost normal rate, Wes is straddling my thighs, his hard dick in two hands. He jacks himself slowly. My gaze rests on his erection, long and proud, the engorged head making my mouth water. It's the same response I have when a girl parts her legs for me, offering that sweet paradise to my mouth or dick. I never thought another guy's package could look appealing too, and I really wish I knew what it meant.

Now's not the time to dwell on it, though.

"Give it to me," I say roughly, beckoning to his erection.

His eyebrows go up, the barbell catching the light. "You feel like returning the favor?"

When I nod, he moves closer and straddles my shoulders, then grabs the second pillow on the bed and tucks it under my head. The added height brings my mouth to cock-level. I swallow, then flick my tongue around the head.

"I'm almost there," he admits.

"Yeah?" I tip my gaze up, but keep my mouth on him, lightly scraping my teeth over his dick.

A soft groan escapes his lips.

I release him with a chuckle. "Didn't we have a whole convo about stamina last night?"

"That was before I spent twenty minutes fingering your ass."

I shiver at the memory. Jesus, I'm getting hard again. It's like I can't get enough of this guy.

"Turned you on, huh?" I drawl.

"Oh yeah." He nudges his cockhead forward, and I open my mouth, letting him slide inside.

My hands drift around his body to cup his ass. I squeeze and he groans again, pushing in a bit deeper. With my hands occupied, it's hard to control how much of him I take, but he's not a jerk about it. He doesn't plunge deep and force any deep-throat action on me. He seems to sense my limits, the same way he senses shit on the ice—when to pass the puck, when to take his time until that perfect opening reveals itself so he can slap one in.

He fucks my mouth in fast, shallow strokes that match his

fast, shallow breathing. I taste his pre-come on my tongue. It's a heady flavor that makes me wonder how it would feel flooding my mouth, sliding down my throat. Never in a million years did I think I'd be contemplating that. Or that I'd be kneading another man's ass cheeks, urging him to orgasm while I clamp my lips around his dick.

"Coming," he warns.

I stick with him until the end this time. The first hot spurt hits my tongue, the second goes to the back of my throat, triggering my gag reflex. I breathe through my nose and swallow, my heart pounding as my best friend gasps through the orgasm.

That wasn't…bad. The taste of him is strangely appealing.

I indulge in one more lick before allowing him to pull out. He collapses beside me, his head resting on my shoulder. We both release a sated sigh, then laugh.

Silence stretches between us, but it's not an awkward one. We're both relaxed. My mind drifts in a post-sex haze, where thinking is overrated.

"We should probably head to the dining hall before dinner ends," Wes says. "Don't want to miss the big show."

Right. The song. Someone—ahem, *Wes*—had decided the coaches should serenade the kids with some good ol' Britney Spears. Pat had griped and complained, claiming he didn't know the words to any of her songs. Wes, of course, had promptly whipped out his phone and emailed the older coaches the lyrics to Britney's entire catalogue. Very resourceful, my best friend.

I'm too relaxed to move, though. "Five more minutes," I tell him, wrapping my arm around his shoulders to prevent him from getting up.

His cheek nuzzles my left pec. "You're a cuddle whore, huh?"

I am. Absolutely. Just never dreamed I'd be cuddling with another *guy*.

"I watched porn earlier," I blurt out.

He snickers. "Yeah, I figured. You had that guilty, I-just-tugged-one-out look when I walked in."

I pause. "*Gay* porn."

He tilts his head up to look at me, his gray eyes twinkling playfully. "Uh-huh. I see. Did you enjoy it?"

Another pause. Then I puff out a breath. "Yeah."

Wes lowers his head again, rubbing a soothing hand over my stomach. "Freaked you out, huh?"

"Well…" It's not easy to explain. "I'm a little freaked out about not being freaked out. If that makes sense."

We go silent again. I can tell he's absorbing what I just told him.

"Can I ask you something?" I murmur.

"Hit me." His breath tickles my nipple, and it hardens. Instantly.

"Have you ever…" I'm not sure how to phrase it. "Bottomed? Is that the right word?"

His shoulders tremble as if he's trying not to laugh. "As good a word as any. 'Been fucked' also works. 'Taken it up the ass', also a goodie."

"Okay. Well?"

He shifts a bit. "Yeah. I have. Once."

"Just once?" I guess I'm not surprised. Wes has "top" written all over him. "Did you like it?"

He considers it. "Not at the beginning. And definitely not at the end. But it was pretty good in the middle."

Classic Wes answer. I burst out laughing, my palm sliding over his bare arm before I give his biceps a pinch. "Um…what happened at the beginning and end?"

"The beginning, it hurt." His tone is rueful. "But that's probably 'cause we were both eighteen-year-old morons and neither one of us thought to bring lube."

Eighteen. For some reason that makes me bristle. I wonder if it was before or after our last night at camp. Before, I'd be okay with. But after… Not sure why, but the thought of Wes cutting me out of his life and then going off to lose his virginity to some dude pisses me off.

"Spit'll only get you so far," he's saying, oblivious to my turbulent thoughts. "So it took a while for him to…yeah."

I force a casual tone. "But then it got good?"

He pauses again. Then nods, his chin bumping my shoulder. "Yeah, it got good."

A hot rush travels up my spine. I'm stunned to realize it's jealousy.

"And at the end?" I prompt, in the hopes that hearing how the sex got sucky again will ease the tightness in my chest.

Wes sighs. "He wasn't anyone I need to see again. He got off on making it degrading for me. Kind of soured me on the whole experience."

I stroke the top of his head. I can tell he feels awkward talking about it, but I appreciate that he told me. It's rare for Wes to shed his fuck-the-world attitude and let himself be vulnerable.

"So that was it? You didn't let anyone else…uh…stick their flag in there after that?"

He chokes out a laugh. "Nope. I decided I'd leave the flag-sticking to me."

I chuckle, stroking his hair again. It's silky-soft beneath my palm, a contrast to the stubble scraping my shoulder.

"I…" He clears his throat. "I'd let you do it, though."

My hand freezes in his hair. "You would?"

Wes nods. "I'd let you do anything to me, Canning."

When his voice cracks, something inside of me does, too. I have no clue what's going on here or what we are to each other.

Friends. We're friends. Except that doesn't feel like the right label.

Friends with benefits? Doesn't feel right, either.

I must have stayed silent for way too long, because Wes suddenly sits up, the warmth of his body abandoning me. "Come on," he says gruffly. "We should get going."

TWENTY-TWO

WES

Our coaching schedule picks right back up again the next morning, and I hit the ice ready to coach the hell out of these kids. I had a rough start last week, letting their hot-headedness and inability to follow my instructions get to me, but I'm determined to take a page out of Jamie's book and exercise some patience.

Don't get me wrong, I know how to be patient—when I'm *playing*. But watching other guys play? Seeing the mistakes they're making and then watching them make them all over again instead of correcting them based on my advice? It's maddening.

The kids are listening better today, though. I'm running some basic passing drills with my forwards, switching up the lines every so often to let them get a feel for their teammates' style and technique. For the most part, it's going okay, but one kid—Davies —hogs the puck no matter what line he's playing on.

I blow my whistle, tempted to rip my hair out by the roots. Davies has just ignored my instructions *again*, snapping a weak wrist shot at Killfeather instead of passing back to Shen like he was supposed to.

I call him over, and he skates up to me, red-faced and surly.

From the corner of my eye, I see Jamie watching us carefully, as if he's assessing my coaching prowess. Pat's watching too, from the bench, and I'm gratified to see he's finally quit scowling at me. Last night Canning and I had shown up too late at the dining hall to catch the live performance, but luckily, Georgie filmed it on his iPhone. And trust me, I'm never going to forget the sight of Pat and his four coaches shuffling around and singing the most off-key rendition of "Oops, I Did It Again."

I don't think Pat will forget it, either. Or stop hating me for choosing the stakes of that soccer game.

Focusing on Davies, I cross my arms over the front of my Northern Mass hoodie and ask, "What kind of drill are we running?"

"Um…?"

"Passing," I clarify.

He nods. "Right."

"Which means you need to *pass* the puck, kid."

"But last practice you gave us that whole speech about not hesitating. You said if you have a shot, you take it." His chin juts out defensively. "I had a shot."

I mock gasp. "Wait—the puck made it past Killfeather? I must've missed that goal."

His expression goes sheepish now. "Well, naw, I missed, but…"

"But you *wanted* to score. I get it." I offer a gentle smile. "Look, I'm with you, kid. There's no sweeter feeling in the world than watching that lamp light up. But lemme ask you something —how many forwards are usually on the ice?"

"Three…"

"Three," I confirm. "You're not playing alone out there. You've got your teammates with you, and it's not so they can skate there and look pretty."

He cracks a smile.

"Shen had a shot. If you'd passed to him, he would've one-timed that baby right in, top left corner. And you would've gotten the assist. Instead, you got nothing."

Davies nods slowly, and a burst of pride goes off inside me. Holy fuck, I'm reaching him. I can see him absorbing the words —*my* words—and suddenly I understand why Canning has such a hard-on for this coaching thing. It's…rewarding.

"You need to trust your teammates," I tell Davies.

But for some reason, that wipes the smile off his face, a dark scowl taking its place.

"What is it?" I ask.

He mumbles something I can't make out.

"Can't hear you, kid."

He meets my eyes. "It's kinda hard to trust them when I know they want me to fail."

"That's not true." Except even as I voice the protest, I know on some level he's right. Some players do have the tendency to be cutthroat, to only look out for themselves. It suddenly makes sense why Davies is always looking to be the star—because he thinks that's what everyone else is doing.

"It *is* true." His gaze strays toward the net, where Jamie is talking to Killfeather. "Especially with Mark. He fuc—frickin'," he corrects. "He frickin' loves watching me screw up. And then he lists everything I did wrong the next day at breakfast, or dinner, or when I'm trying to fall asleep. He's all about the mind games."

I stifle a sigh. "You're roommates, right?"

"Unfortunately," he mutters.

"You guys ever hang out outside of practice? Talk about something other than hockey?"

"Not really," he says with a shrug. "I mean, he talks about his dad sometimes. I don't think they get along. But that's pretty much it."

"You want my advice?"

His expression is earnest as he nods again.

"Try getting to know him. Develop some trust off the ice." I jerk my head toward Jamie. "The first day I faced off against Jamie—uh, Coach Canning, I mean—I was a total a-hole. Cocky, full of myself. I taunted him every time I took a shot at goal, did a little victory dance every time I scored. I swear, he wanted to murder me by the time practice was over. He told Coach Pat he hated my guts and suggested they send me back to whatever jackass planet I came from."

Davies snickers. "But you guys are bros now."

"Yup. And we were roommates back then, too. We were in our room after that first practice and he just sat there glaring at me for a good hour."

"So what'd you do?" Davies asks curiously.

"I suggested we play a game of 'I Never'. Took a while to convince him—he was still pretty annoyed with me—but I wore him down eventually."

I smile at the memory. We'd passed around some cans of Red Bull I'd stolen from one of the coaches and gotten to know each other by saying the craziest things. *I never pissed my pants at a Bruins game. I never mooned a bus full of nuns during a school trip to a gum factory.* Those were mine, of course.

Jamie's had been more serious—*I'm not an only child. I don't want to play for the pros one day.* Yeah, he hadn't quite mastered the "never" part of the game, but I hadn't minded. My thirteen-year-old self was having too much fun getting hopped up on sugar and caffeine. We stayed awake until four a.m. and could barely get up the next morning.

"After that, we were inseparable," I say with a chuckle.

Davies chews on his lip. "But Coach Canning is cool. Mark is...kind of a dick."

I swallow a laugh. "You never know, he might end up being the coolest guy you've ever met."

"I don't know…"

I give him a good-natured slap on the shoulder. "Just give him a chance. Or don't. Do with that advice what you will." Then I snap into Coach Wesley mode, blowing my whistle loud enough to make him jump. "Now get back out there and share the wealth, kid. Hog the puck one more time and I'll bench you for the rest of the practice."

The week goes fast.

When Jamie and I were teenagers, everything took forever. A summer was a lifetime. But I'm already two weeks into my six-week stay in Lake Placid, and I can't figure out where the time went.

After dinner with the kids on Friday night, Jamie and I have dorm duty. That just means counting heads and yelling "lights out" when ten o'clock comes. Then yelling it again when they fail to follow through.

By eleven it's totally quiet. Jamie is lying on his bed texting someone. And I don't like it. Not at all. So I climb onto his body, straddling his ass, my chest to his shoulders. "Hi."

"Hi," he says without looking up.

I drop my nose into his hair and take a deep breath of him. He smells like summertime, and I can't get enough.

"Dude, are you sniffing my head?"

"Just checking to see if you were paying attention."

"Mhm," he says, tapping away on his phone.

I settle in a little further, my dick waking up to the fact that I'm *this* close to Jamie's ass. Funny how he thinks it's weird when I sniff his hair, but he's perfectly fine that I'm about two seconds from dry humping his backside.

Times they are a changin'.

We've been going at it every night like puck bunnies in heat this week. Pinch me. It's like a blowjob relay race around here. And we've gotten really good at passing the *baton*.

But my favorite thing is just to make out while we rub off. Kissing Jamie Canning is mind-blowing. I'm greedy for it, because I know in my gut it won't last. The summer ends for me in four weeks, and Jamie's interest in me may be even shorter. So I'll take all I can get.

It's one hundred percent honest to say I've never been happier. But of course I can't say it aloud.

Trouble is, it's harder every day to express any of the fuck-it-all attitude I'm famous for. And I'm *not* going to look over his shoulder and read the text. That would be an asshole thing to do, right?

I look. The screen says HOLLY.

The next instant I feel a fucking tsunami of jealousy. "You want to go to a movie?" Except I don't want to go to a movie, and they've probably started already. "What's at the theater this week, anyway?" I ask. As if I care. I'd rather get naked and make out.

"A chick flick and a kids' movie," he says. "I checked."

"Bummer. Blowjobs, then?"

He snickers. But he's still holding that goddamned phone. I'm not saying a word, though.

Right.

"Whatcha doing?"

"Texting Holly."

I can't help it—even the sound of her name on his lips tenses me up. The first and only time I met the girl, she had sex-tousled hair and a dreamy smile on her face. It bothers me that Jamie was responsible for both of those things.

"What's she up to?" I try to sound casual.

I fail, because he turns his head to roll his eyes at me. "Is that your way of asking if we're sexting?"

I shrug.

Jamie starts tapping on the phone again. "We're not sexting. We don't do that anymore, by the way. And tonight she's stuck babysitting her little cousins on Cape Cod. They keep watching the same movie over and over again, and she's about to quit the family and join a traveling circus." He turns to smile at me. "I suggested fire eating, but she thinks trapeze would be fun." He stops talking, those brown eyes holding a hint of amusement. I think he's this close to calling me on my dickish behavior.

Then he doesn't. Fucking Jamie. Always so easygoing. Some days I'd give up a limb to be more like that. But not a leg, because I need those for skating. And not my arms... God, I'm stuck inside my head tonight.

Do I need a blowjob or what?

Jamie reads the screen again and chuckles, and I want to grab the phone and bash it against the wall. The only thing holding me back is the fact that Cape Cod is like five hours away from here. Maybe six.

So I start kissing his neck instead. That's something Holly can't do.

After a while, it works. He sets the phone down and drops his head onto the pillow. "You feel good up there."

"Yeah?" I thrust my hips downward and feel him pushing back at me.

I slip a hand under his T-shirt, stroking his side. Then I work the shirt upward and kiss his back, and he flattens under my touch, his body lazily shifting on the bed.

"Want you," I whisper. Lately, those two words define me.

"Have me," he says.

My heart stutters in my chest, and my dick hardens into the approximate texture of an iron bar. Does he even mean it the way it sounds? We haven't talked about fucking since the one time. I want him so badly, but only if he wants it.

Only one way to find out.

I climb off him and yank his shorts down. And his briefs. His ass is perfect—strong and round, with a tan line cutting across at his waist. I kiss the tan line, because I have to.

"Mmm," he agrees, his eyes shut. I watch as he pushes his hips into the bed. Like me, Jamie has two speeds: horny and asleep.

I yank off my shirt and then my shorts. The more of my skin that touches his, the happier I am.

Then? His phone rings.

I swear to God, if that's Holly…

Since I'm lying on his body, I swallow my annoyance and ask if he wants me to get it.

"Just check the number," he says lazily. "It's probably nothing."

But Jamie's phone doesn't usually ring at this hour, so I look. It's not Holly. The display says KILLFEATHER.

"Um… It's a camper."

He lifts his head up quickly. "Really?"

I hand over the phone, and he answers.

"Hello?" He frowns. "Where are you? Where?" Another pause. "I'll be right there." He ends the call.

"What's the matter with your goalie?"

Jamie scowls, and I can't help noticing even his grumpy face is hot. "That was Shen using Killfeather's phone. Apparently my goalie is drunk with two of your forwards. They're not far away, but Killfeather won't come home, and they didn't know what to do."

I reach for my shirt. "Let's go. Where are they?"

"Behind the high school."

"That's original. When I got you drunk, it was on the roof of the Hampton Inn."

Jamie laughs, tugging his clothes into place. "They can't all be Ryan Wesley. The town would have to double the size of its police force."

By silent mutual agreement, we leave the dormitory like thieves in the night. If it's necessary to call in reinforcements, I'm sure Jamie will do it. But sometimes it's just better to handle things quietly.

Once outside, we book it toward the high school. There's a fence around the place, but Jamie points to a two-foot gap. When I squeeze through ahead of him, he puts a warm hand on my back, and I shiver slightly.

I'm so gone for him. I hope he can't tell.

We find our charges sitting on their asses in the gravel under a sign that says "The Blue Bombers". It's fitting, because these kids are bombed. Especially Killfeather.

Jamie crouches down to talk to them. "What seems to be the trouble here?"

"We're, like, drunk," Davies says. "Annnnd Killfeather won't go home. But we can't leave 'im here."

"I see." Jamie somehow keeps a straight face. "Why won't you go home?" he asks his goalie.

"Just…sick of it all," Killfeather slurs, his head knocking back against the brick wall. "Tomorrow we gotta just do it all over again."

"I see," Jamie says again. "How much did you all drink?"

Shen makes a face. "A six-pack."

Wait, what? "Each?' I ask sharply.

Killfeather shakes his head. "No." He pushes a six of long-necks into the light. The bottles are empty, of course.

"What else?" I demand.

Looking sheepish, Davies pulls an empty liter bottle of some local beer out from the shadows. Jamie takes it and reads the label. "Okay. Anything else?"

Three heads shake.

"Where'd you get it?" Jamie asks.

"Paid a guy."

Jamie tips his chin up to look at me, and I can see him struggling not to laugh. That's how we got our beer at that age, too. "Sidebar," he says, standing and beckoning to me.

I walk around the corner of the building with him. We're only a few yards away, so he puts his lips right to my ear. "Seriously? They got wasted on less than three beers each?"

Turning to whisper my answer, my chest brushes his shoulder. I let my lips brush his jaw before I speak. "They have zero tolerance and a really fast metabolism. Weren't we the same?"

Jamie chuckles and his breath tickles my ear. "So no hospital."

"Nah," I say quickly. "Nobody ever died from two and a half beers. Let's march 'em around, sober 'em up and then put 'em to bed."

"Sounds like a plan." Jamie stalks back around the corner. "Okay, ladies. Let's go. We're going to make a deal. You three go for a little walk with us, and we'll take you home without turning you in to the authorities."

"Like, the police?" Shen slurs.

"Naw, he means Pat," I clarify.

Shen struggles to his feet. "Okay. Lesh go." Davies rises, too.

That leaves Killfeather still sitting there. Not budging.

Jamie leans over, offering a hand. "Come on now. You have practice in the morning."

"Won't be good enough," Killfeather mumbles.

"You'll be a little hung over," Jamie admits. "But that's never killed anyone."

Killfeather gives an adamant shake of the head. "Won't be good enough for my father. Never will be. Nothing is."

Ah. I could have written that speech myself. "Don't play hockey for your dad, dude. You have to play for yourself." I try putting a hand out, too. This time he takes it. I haul him to his feet, which mostly works. He has to steady himself against the wall for a second, but then he's vertical on his own power. "Seriously. Fuck 'im. It's your life."

Killfeather's head dangles a little in the classic drunken pose. "He needs to chill out."

"But some never do," I tell him. The truth hurts, but he should understand this as soon as he can. "And you still have to live your life. If you don't, then he wins. What a waste, right?"

The young goalie nods with his whole body, like a horse. But he's listening to me.

"Let's go, then."

"Where are you taking us?" Davies asks.

"We're going to have a little history lesson," Jamie replies. "You chose to imbibe about fifty yards away from a legendary spot." He leads the kids across Cummings Road, and I manage not to make a crack about it. They shuffle along behind him until we're standing in a dusty parking area behind the Olympic stadium. "Okay, what's famous about this place?"

"Um," Shen says. "The arena. Where the U.S. beat Russia to win the gold in 1980."

"Ah," Jamie says, raising a finger in the air. "The U.S. did beat the impressive Russian team four to three, with a team of twenty college students. But the gold medal game was two days later, against Sweden. Four to two. But that's not why we're here."

"It isn't?"

Jamie shakes his head. "See that hill?" He points over his shoulder, and we all look up.

"I see another parking lot," Killfeather mutters.

With a closed fist, Jamie cuffs him gently under the chin. "That's not just any parking lot, and it's not just any hill. Herb Brooks was the coach of the U.S. team. That's why the building is named after him now. He put his guys in all their pads and ran 'em up and down that hill."

"Sounds like a party." Davies sighs.

"We're going to find out." Jamie rubs his hands together. "On a count of three, everyone runs up there. We'll go together. You too, Wesley."

"I'm not running," Shen complains. "Too drunk."

"Uh-huh," I say, gripping his shoulder. "Shoulda thought about that earlier. Let's go." I clap my hands.

"One, two, three!" Jamie takes off across the gravel. There's a grassy bit where the hill begins, and he reaches it quickly.

I hang back to make sure the boys follow him. And they do, at a sluggish pace. That's fine, because we really don't need any injuries. The moon is up, though. It's not all that dark, and there are floodlights at the top of the hill.

We're all breathing hard within minutes. The hill is a real bitch, and I'm glad I'm not wearing my pads. The kids make it up to the top eventually, grumbling all the way. Then the five of us are panting in the parking lot, hands on hips, wishing we had water.

"I don't feel so good," Shen mumbles.

"In the bushes if you're going to yarf," I say quickly. This parking lot belongs to a golf club. We're already trespassing.

He lurches off, just making it to a boxwood before there are sounds of retching.

"We'll walk 'em down slowly," Jamie says, stroking his chin. "And buy some water."

"And Advil. I have some in our room."

"Of course you do."

I have to bite back a smile. Another silly, ridiculous night in Lake Placid with Jamie. I hope the next four weeks go slowly.

On our way down, I have a little chat with Davies. "So…

Why'd you guys have to go and get drunk? You could get kicked out of camp."

He sticks out his chin. "You told me to."

"Say what?"

"You said to spend some time with them off the ice. I did that."

I give this some thought. "Okay. It's my job to tell you to quit breaking the rules. But I hear where you're coming from. And I like that you called Coach Canning when Killfeather wouldn't go home."

"I wouldn't just *leave* him there."

He gets a friendly slap on the back for that. "Good man. Stay out of trouble and we can keep these shenanigans private, okay?"

"Okay."

We walk back to the dormitory through the fresh summer air while the moon rises higher over the lake. I can't wait to get home.

TWENTY-THREE
WES

Forty minutes later I have Jamie's dick in my mouth and I'm stroking his prostate like a champion. He's writhing and begging. "Give me more," he pants. "Give me the D. You know you want to."

I release him with a pop, and practically swallow my own tongue. The casual way he's asked me to fuck just blows my mind. "I don't know," I stammer.

He opens one heated eye and looks at me. "Christ. Sometimes it feels like you've got your whole arm up there, anyway. How is it so different?"

Because it just is.

Don't get me wrong—I want inside that fine ass of his more than I want my next breath. But I'm also afraid. It's not a familiar sensation. I never used to care about the consequences of my actions. But if we do this, I won't just be fucking Jamie. It will *mean* something to me. And chances are, it won't to him.

For him, it'll be another little experiment he can take with him before he goes off and settles down with some girl.

He's watching me now, waiting for me to decide. And while he waits he's gently jacking himself and staring into my eyes.

Holy shit, I'm going to do it.

I'm going to fuck the only man I've ever loved.

I can hardly breathe as I reach for the lube. Then I realize I need a condom too, so I climb off the bed in search of my duffel bag. I stashed a whole box of them in there, though I'm not entirely sure why. When I took the job at camp, it was for the sole purpose of spending time with Jamie, not to go on some kind of sex spree with the gay locals.

I never thought I'd be opening this box. With Jamie. *For* Jamie.

"Are you *sure?*" I ask thickly.

He nods. Those brown eyes burn with hunger. They shine with trust. I memorize that expression, the way he looks lying there at my mercy, big and hard and rippling with masculine power.

I take my time with him, more generous than usual with the lube. Fuck, I don't want to hurt him, and I absolutely don't want him to hate this. I can't help but remember my first time, how cheap it made me feel, being used by a guy who didn't give a shit whether I enjoyed myself or not.

I want this to be so good for Jamie.

"One finger won't be enough this time." My voice is so gravelly it stings my throat. "You'll need to get used to more before I…uh…"

He sounds as raspy-voiced as I do. "You'll stop if I don't like it?"

My heart squeezes. "Of course." I lean over him and plant a reassuring kiss on his lips, then wink at him. "Just say *ballsack* if you want me to stop."

A wave of laughter shudders through him. "Oh shit. I totally forgot about that."

I laugh too as I think about the ridiculous code word we made up when we were fourteen. I'm not sure who came up with it—

who am I kidding? It was obviously me—but we'd used it during our wrestling phase. We decided MMA was the *coolest* shit ever and spent hours in the gym practicing our "moves." Except half the time when one of us tapped out, the other wouldn't notice, so we devised a safe word.

I don't think I'll ever forget the day Pat walked into the gym and found us—me, flat on my stomach with Jamie's knee digging into the back of my neck, while I yelled "Ballsack!" over and over again.

"Ready to come harder than you've ever come in your life?" I ask solemnly, lifting one of his knees up.

He smiles. "You sure you want to put that much pressure on yourself, dude?"

"No pressure. Just fact. Science has proven it."

Now he snickers, but the sound dies when the tip of my finger circles his hole. His ass cheeks instantly clench. Not in fear, but anticipation. I see it in his eyes, a raw gleam of heat, before he lifts up his other knee and all but puts himself on display for me.

Jesus. Nope, not gonna survive this.

I tease and caress for several long moments before slipping my finger inside. My other hand grips his erection. I'm selfish, but I don't want him to come until I'm buried inside him, so I don't take him in my mouth or jerk him as hard as I know he wants. Slow, featherlight strokes are all he gets as I work my finger into his tight hole.

When a second finger joins the party, his brows draw together. Beads of sweat break out on his forehead. Mine, too. Loosening him up is one of the hottest things I've ever done. It takes all my concentration. Stroking, teasing, twisting, getting him ready for me.

At three fingers, he moans loud enough to wake the dead, and I release his erection to press my palm to his mouth. "Quiet, baby."

"Wes..." He's squirming now, pushing his ass against my probing fingers. Every time I connect with his prostate, he pants out a breath. "I need more."

He's beautiful. Goddamn beautiful. And I'm so hard it hurts. My heartbeat takes off like it's on a breakaway as I tear open the condom packet with my teeth. I cover myself with one hand, then pour lube on the condom to get the latex even slicker. My fingers continue to torment Jamie's ass.

"You ready for it?" I rasp.

His lips part on a shaky breath. He nods.

Gripping my shaft, I position myself between his big thighs. My breathing is equally unsteady. Hell, my hand is trembling around my cock as if I've never done this before. But I *haven't* done this. Not with someone I love.

The head of my cock nudges his hole. He tenses again, clenching to deny me entrance.

I find his erection and stroke my fist up its length. "Breathe," I whisper. "Relax for me."

His throat dips. Then he lets out another breath.

I push forward again, and this time I'm able to ease in. Just the tip, but holy hell, the pressure is incredible. He's hot and tight, squeezing me into oblivion.

"Ohfuckohfuckohfuck." It's all he seems capable of saying as my cock tunnels deeper. Jamie's cheeks are flushed, his eyes glassy.

If I last more than five strokes, it'll be a miracle. Then again, we *are* in Lake Placid, which just happens to be Miracle Central.

His erection pulsates in my fist, but I don't stroke it. Not yet. Not until he begs me to. "Jamie...you doing good?"

He moans in response.

I'm all the way in now, and my dick is in heaven. *I'm* in heaven. I lean forward and cover his torso with mine, my elbows on either side of his head as I bend down to kiss him. Then I start to move.

"Oh... God..." He whispers the words into my lips and I swallow them up with another tongue-tangling kiss.

I fuck him slowly, letting him get used to the sensation, but Jamie Canning is a master at adapting. It's him who wraps his arms around me, who hooks his legs around my ass. It's him who starts rocking up to meet my every thrust, and him who says, "*Faster*, Wes" as I desperately try to go slow.

"Don't wanna hurt you," I mumble.

"Wanna come," he mumbles back.

I smile when he snakes one hand between the tight seal of our bodies, trying to find his cock. He's burning up, his face and chest flushed with desire. When he bears down on my ass and groans in frustration, I take pity on my man and rise to my knees again, yanking his hips to pull him closer.

The new angle makes him curse. His fingers seek out his erection, but I gently bat them away. "My job, baby. *I* make you come."

I withdraw until just my cockhead remains inside him. Our gazes lock. His breathing quickens.

Then I jack his dick in a long, hard pump at the same time I slam back in.

I have to give him credit—he manages to stay quiet this time. He bites his lip to keep from groaning, his gorgeous features strained. He's close. I can see it in his eyes, feel it in the urgency with which he grinds his ass against my groin.

I'm covered in sweat. My own release is imminent and I want so badly to prolong it, but that's like passing the puck to Gretzky and asking him not to take a shot. There's no stopping the orgasm. It sizzles in my balls and ripples through my shaft, and I come while still jacking Jamie's cock.

My world is reduced to the man beneath me. I nearly act out a scene right out of a chick flick and shout "I love you!" while I shudder in release. But I fight the temptation and focus on getting Jamie where he needs to go. My dick remains rock-hard despite the mind-blowing climax. I keep fucking him, keep thrusting forward as my hand works his erection.

"Oh…yessss…"

Sheer bliss rolls through me when his release soaks my fingertips. He comes on a strangled cry. And keeps coming. And then comes some more.

I guess nobody can say he didn't enjoy himself.

When he finally goes still, I collapse on his sticky chest and growl in his ear. "That was the hottest thing I've ever seen."

He clings to me, his big palms pressed to my damp back.

We lie that way a long time. I'm just drifting on my own happiness. I lead a big life, and it's a hell of a ride. But there aren't many moments like this. I want to bottle it and carry it everywhere I go.

Finally Jamie speaks. "Do you think anyone's still sick?"

"Wha?" There are only two people who exist to me right now, so I have no idea what he's asking.

"I was just hoping they got it all out on the way home."

He's talking about the drunk teens who took half a fucking hour to walk home tonight. We had to keep stopping while they upchucked. "They're fine," I murmur. I kiss Jamie's sweaty neck, and he tastes like heaven.

"Should we clean up?" he asks.

I can't hold on to this moment any longer. It won't stretch and stay with me no matter how badly I want it to. "Yeah. You want to go first?"

"You go ahead."

I take my sticky self into the bathroom for a sixty-second shower. When I get back to the room, Jamie departs for his own shower. I stare at my bed, cursing its size. The twin beds are built into the wall, so the only times I've pushed them together have been in my imagination.

Sometimes we fall asleep together, but it's a really tight fit. I have an idea, though. Actually I've thought of this before, but I'm too chicken to bring it up. Fuck it, though. The summer is half over.

In for a penny, in for a pound.

My mattress slides off the wooden frame when I give it a tug. I drop it on the floor beside my bed. There's just enough room left for Jamie to do the same.

Standing there staring down at my mattress, I feel exposed in a way I haven't ever felt before. Jamie and I fool around, but we don't talk about it. I don't ask him for anything except orgasms.

It has to be that way. I'm heading to Toronto in a month, where I've vowed to keep my head down and play the best hockey those fuckers have ever seen. My rookie year is going to be spotless—no scandals, no shenanigans.

It's shocking, but my dad and I are actually in agreement about something for once in our sorry excuse of a relationship: flashing my sexuality around is not a good idea right now.

Which is why it terrifies me that I'm becoming so attached to Canning.

Says the guy who's already stupidly, disgustingly in love with him...

I am, and always have been. I love everything about him. His quiet strength, his dry humor, his carefree approach to life that contrasts with his controlled manner on the ice. That sexy-as-sin body...

I've made sure to keep my feelings for him under wraps, though. He thinks we're just messing around. Good-time Wes just having some fun. But I've changed the game for myself tonight. And if I let him know how much I want him beside me in bed, that's changing it for him, too...

Which is why I'm just standing here in my underwear, arguing with myself about whether or not I should have thrown a mattress on the floor.

The door opens behind me, and I'm so busted.

Jamie towels off his hair. He looks down at the mattress. "Never thought of that," he says. The towel lands on our unused desk chair, and then he yanks his mattress down, too.

My face heats as I go to switch off the light. It's hard to move around the room with the floor space eaten up with mattresses.

Jamie gets into bed on his side, and I lie down too. I wrap an arm around his waist and stroke his bare belly with my hand. "You okay?" I murmur. As if I've changed our sleeping arrangement to comfort him.

As if.

"I'm going to be sore, aren't I?" he asks.

I hesitate. "Maybe a little. Sorry."

He picks up my hand and kisses the palm. "Totally worth it."

Now I'm grinning in the dark. I hold him as close as I dare. Even if my entire life goes to shit before breakfast tomorrow, I'll always have this night.

TWENTY-FOUR

JAMIE

The kids aren't nearly as hung over as they should be. I'd forgotten how the teenage body can bounce back from anything. All the day's drills are over already, and nobody even looks green.

Now the teens are scrimmaging on the practice rink, and Killfeather is kicking some serious ass. Every time he makes a save I feel like I did something good. This kid is going to be *great* someday. He's scholarship material, and I hope the father Killfeather complains about can appreciate it.

The young forwards Wes has been coaching are finally pulling it together. They've taken quite a few shots on goal already. And Wes is reffing the game. Even the lazy backward circles he skates are fluid and powerful. There's so much talent in this room right now I can hardly believe it. This is why I've made the 2,500-mile trek every year. For this.

There's another attack on the net. Shen makes a tape-to-tape pass to Davies, who doesn't hesitate. He fires it into the goal before Killfeather can stop him.

A small whoop of victory rises up from the scoring team. "Smoked you, Killfeather!" Davies yells. "You're a sieve, sucka!"

Oh, fuck. Here we go. I watch Killfeather push his mask up.

Then he takes his water bottle off the top of the net and pours some into his mouth. I'm half expecting him to spit it into Davies' face, because my boy's face is red. I brace for disaster.

Killfeather tosses the bottle onto the net. Then he locks eyes with me.

Please don't blow like a land mine, I silently beg him.

My goalie actually gives me a small smile before he speaks. "Yeah, Davies. You owned me. Only took you two dozen tries, you big bad thing." He yanks his mask down over his face and picks up his stick.

Wes is grinning when he skates over to retrieve the puck. "Good attitude today, kid," he tells Killfeather.

The teenager looks a little smug when he tosses the puck into Wes's hand.

I'm so engrossed in this little drama I don't notice heads are swiveling to look at someone who's appeared behind the penalty box. "Jamie! Over here!"

I turn around to find Holly standing there, waving her arms. "Holly," I say stupidly. "What are you doing here?"

She rolls her eyes, her hands on the hips of a tiny pair of jean shorts. "That's a heck of a greeting, Canning. You can do a little better than that."

"Holy crap," Killfeather blurts out. "Coach Canning's girl-friend has a great rack."

"Shut it," I mutter, glaring at him.

More than a dozen teenage boys are now eye-fucking Holly in her teeny shorts and skimpy top. My neck is hot all of a sudden. And that's *before* I glance at Wes.

He skates up, a twisted little smile on his lips. "You're having a visitor, Canning?"

"Um." I've lost the ability to speak, because I'm busy sifting through all the uncomfortable conversations coming my way. "Holly, this is my friend Wes."

"I remember you from the hotel," she says with a wink.

Wes keeps his own smile waxed on, and you'd have to know him as well as I do to see the sneer beneath it. Yikes. "Looks like you should quit early, Coach. Take your girl out for drinks. Catch up a little."

"That would be awesome," Holly says. "I stopped at the dormitory first, and Coach Pat said I could probably shake Jamie free."

"Yeah, okay," I say slowly. "Let's head out."

"You kids have fun," Wes drawls. Then he turns his back on me and blows his whistle. "Let's go, ladies! Enough standing around."

That's how I find myself removing my skates and exiting the rink an hour early with Holly.

"God, you look good!" She stops on the steps of the building to hit me with another blinding smile, then stands up on her tiptoes and... kisses me. Her mouth is smaller and softer than I expect it to be. Confusion must be written all over my face, because she says, "Sorry to surprise you, but I thought it would be fun."

"It's... Wow," I stammer. "How did you get here?"

"Well, when I threatened to take up trapeze, my uncle lent me his car. Thought I'd get away for the night."

I do the math. It's got to be a five-hour drive from Cape Cod. "Wow," I say again. Apparently "wow" is now three quarters of my vocabulary.

"Jamie," she says, staring up at me. "Stop freaking out."

"What?"

She tilts her head to the side, and those familiar blue eyes study me. "You're panicking. Why?"

"Um..." I can't tell her. But I can't *not* tell her. Because Holly is almost certainly planning to stay with me tonight. In fact, last summer I told her she could visit and I'd make it work, but she hadn't been able to swing it then.

Fuck.

"Honey." She reaches up to cup the side of my neck. "Is there someone else?"

My heart spasms, because there is someone else. Sort of. Wes and I aren't a couple, exactly. We've never had one word of conversation about it. But there's no way I'm sleeping with someone else right now—that just wouldn't be right.

"There is," I admit.

Her eyes widen. She'd asked the question, but she still seems pretty shocked by my answer. "Who is she?"

I shake my head. "You don't know her. I'm sorry," I say quickly.

She takes her hand off me and steps backward. "Okay." She bites her lip. "I should have called."

"I'm sorry," I repeat.

And I am. Holly has only been good to me. But after graduation, we'd had a little talk. She'd said, "I want to see you when you're in Detroit," and I'd said, "That's probably not going to work."

She'd said, "We'll see." And now here she is, her face turning red.

"Look," I tell her. "Let's go have ice cream. Or tequila, if you prefer. I want to catch up with you."

"We're still friends," she says softly.

"Always."

Her eyes wander away from me and over toward the lake. She takes a slow breath and lets it out again. "Okay, Jamie Canning. Show me Lake Placid. You always talk about how much you love it here." Her gaze returns to mine. "Show me why."

For a moment, my mind goes straight into the gutter, because Lake Placid means something a little different to me this summer than it ever has before. But I clobber that thought and hold out a hand for her. "How do you feel about waffle cones?"

She closes her fingers around mine. "I feel pretty good about waffle cones."

We spend the afternoon together walking all over town. Holly likes to poke around in the little touristy shops, and this gets old pretty fast. But since I've ruined her day once already, I just go along with it. I show her the toy store with the awesome rubber band guns, and she buys one for her brother. They have targets set up inside the store, so we stand there for a long time trying to outshoot each other.

A few doors down there's another kitschy shop, and I hold back my sigh when she leads me inside. She stops to look at a bunch of Miracle on Ice coffee mugs, while I wander over to the back aisle where they have a bunch of candy for sale in bulk. And when I take a closer look, I let out a bark of disbelief.

"What is it?" Holly asks.

"Purple Skittles!" I grab a bag and hold it under the chute. "Pull the lever," I tell Holly. She does, and I don't say "stop" until the bag is full. Then I chuckle all the way to the checkout counter.

"What's so funny?"

I toss my wallet onto the counter. "I have this friend," I begin. I feel like a heel describing Wes that way, but it's the best I can do at the moment. "We used to send this box back and forth with, like, gag gifts inside."

"That's fun. And he likes purple Skittles?"

"Yeah. Except the last time I sent him purple Skittles in the box, you had to buy all the colors at once. I bought four giant bags at BJ's..." Holy God, the name of the store causes an inappropriate bubble of laughter to rise in my chest. "I sorted them myself and sent him only the purple ones. Then I shared, like, five pounds of the other ones with my high school buddies at a party. It was a kegger, and when they did the Technicolor yawn, it was *really* Technicolor."

She hip-checks me. "Thanks for that visual."

"My pleasure."

When we step outside, she clears her throat. "Jamie, I need to find a place to stay tonight. Can we sit down somewhere so I can use my phone?"

I don't answer right away, because I'm wracking my brain for a solution. Which doesn't come easy, because the dormitory is always plenty full. "Let me find you a hotel room," I suggest.

"I've got it," she says quickly. "Seriously. It's no big deal."

Still. "Let's sit on the porch at the dorm. You can use the wi-fi. And if everything is booked up, I'll ask Pat for help."

"Thank you." Her voice is low.

Another apology is on the tip of my tongue. But I don't say it, because I don't think she wants to hear it.

There's nobody in the rocking chairs, so I set Holly up with the wi-fi password and tell her I'm going to get us a couple of drinks. "I'll be right back," I promise. Then I shoot up the stairs and drop by our room, hoping that Wes is there.

The room is empty.

Before I leave again, I dig out that gift box Wes had sent me in Boston. I'd brought it all the way to Lake Placid, because I was trying to decide whether I should restart our meme. But then he showed up here, and I forgot about it entirely.

Now I dump a motherlode of purple candy into the box and close the cover. Setting it on his pillow, I wonder if I should leave some kind of note. But what the hell would it say?

Before Holly showed up, it didn't seem to matter that Wes and I were hooking up without any sort of discussion about it. We didn't need a label. This room was like our private bubble—

everything that happened here was just between us. The rest of the world didn't matter.

And that was fine. Except the rest of the world still exists, whether I remember it or not. Suddenly this whole thing has gotten all kinds of tricky, and not because of Holly—that was just an awkward moment with a friend. In a few short weeks, though, he and I would land on two different NHL teams in two different cities. We were heading for an upset regardless, and I just hadn't realized it.

Hurrying back downstairs, I grab two sodas and take them to the porch where my ex-fuck-buddy waits. "I found a place just outside of town," she says. "It wasn't even expensive."

"Are you sure? I don't want you to—"

She holds up a hand, silencing me. "It's fine, sweetie. And in the morning I'm going to drive back to Massachusetts, okay?"

"We could—"

Holly shakes her head. "You have a job to do. And it's not your *fault*, Jamie. I didn't… I wasn't being smart." The words are firm, but her eyes water a little, and it kills me to see it.

"I'm sorry," I whisper. "I do care about you but…"

Once more she waves me off. "You were never dishonest, Jamie. Don't start now."

Well okay then.

We go out to dinner together. I pick a nice seafood restaurant right on the water, but as we eat our crabcakes, the mood is subdued.

"Will you tell me about her?" she asks at one point.

I shake my head. "Let's not do that."

Holly gives me a rueful grin. "I was just trying to be a big girl about it."

I take a long look at her. "Can I tell you something *I'm* trying to be a big girl about?"

Holly giggles, and I'm happy to have made her do that. "What?"

"The idea of moving to Detroit depresses the hell out of me." I haven't said that to anyone yet, and it feels good to get it off my chest.

She stirs her drink with her straw. "I know it's not the prettiest city in the world, but you can find a nice place there, I bet."

I shake my head. "Urban decay isn't the problem." Although it isn't helping me picture a life there. "I don't know a soul. And I'm not getting any playing time next year. Let's be honest."

"Oh, honey." She sighs. "The first year could suck. But you're good at what you do."

"See, I know that. It's not that I lack confidence. But the odds of really making it as a goalie are awful. It isn't just the first year that might suck. It could be five years where they play me twice a season, and I'm just waiting around for my big chance. Or they send me to the minors, and I play seven games instead of two."

"Or someone could get hurt, and your number could come up." She puts her hand over mine. "But I know what you're saying. It's a long shot. And it won't be your fault if it doesn't work out."

A waiter comes over to take our plates out of the way, and Holly orders a piece of blackout cake. "And two spoons."

I've never been a fan of blackout cake, but now is not the time to point that out.

"I don't like feeling ungrateful," I tell her. "Everyone is so excited for me—they hear 'NHL' and get stars in their eyes. I'm not sure what to do."

"I guess you show up and try it. Give it a year?"

"Maybe." That's the easy choice. But I can see how I could end up waiting forever. You could keep telling yourself, *just a little longer!* "Maybe there's something else I could do with that year, though."

"What does your friend Wes think?" she asks suddenly.

"What?" The mention of his name startles me.

"What does he think about Detroit?" She waits for my answer.

"I, uh, haven't asked his opinion," I confess. "He wants to be in the pros so badly. I'm not sure he'd understand. But it's different for him. There's more demand for centers. And he's got that Frozen Four win..."

"Should have been yours," Holly says firmly. She's loyal to the core.

I look across the table at her wide-set eyes and wish things were different. If I was in love with Holly, life would be less confusing.

But I'm not. And it isn't.

When the dark chocolate cake arrives, I tell her I'm too full to have any. Then I pick up the check on my way to the men's room, so she can't get to it first.

TWENTY-FIVE

WES

It's past midnight when I stumble back to the dorm. Luckily Pat isn't sitting guard in one of the rocking chairs, because there's no way I can carry on a normal conversation right now. Walking in a straight line is also a challenge.

Yeppers, I might be a *wee* bit drunk.

I approach mine and Canning's door and stare at it for a good minute. Fuck, what if his girl is in there? I stayed away for as long as I could, but a man's gotta sleep sometime. And I'm not fucking doing it on the porch.

He would've texted me if she was crashing here and told me to stay away.

Right?

The thought is like a hot blade to the gut. I can't believe his fucking *girlfriend* showed up at camp. He spent the whole day with her. Whole night too, probably.

My hands curl into fists as a parade of unwelcome images marches through my head. Jamie's big hands roaming Holly's feminine curves. His cock sliding inside her. His lips lifting in that dirty grin he always gives me right before he puts his mouth on my dick.

I'm such a goddamn moron. I shouldn't have started anything with him. It was going to end once I left for Toronto, anyway. So hell, maybe it's better if it just ends now.

I finally suck it up and turn the doorknob. It's unlocked. And when I enter the room, I see Jamie's mattress is on the floor again, just where it had been last night. But mine is on the bed frame where I'd put it this morning. Jamie is the only one in the room, too. My blood pressure eases, but just a bit.

He's asleep. Good, because I'm not in the right frame of mind to talk to him right now. I can feel my temper pulsing through my veins along with all the alcohol I drank.

The room's annoyingly dark. I stumble forward, bumping my arm on the side of the dresser as I reach down to unbutton my jeans. I kick 'em off, then tackle my shirt. There. I'm in my boxers now. I just need to make it to the bed without waking Canning, and then we'll both be sound asleep and the Big Talk can be dealt with in the morning.

I ease my body onto the mattress as quietly as possible. Hell yeah. I did it. My drunken ass is now in bed and Jamie is still sleepi—

My head collides with something hard, and then an explosion of sound blasts through the room. A cacophony of *pings* and *dings* and *clangs* assaults my ears. It's as if someone took a sledgehammer to a gumball machine and unleashed a wave of candy.

I stagger to my feet, cursing loudly when I step on something hard and round. "Son of a motherfucking *bitch*!" I hop around on one foot as I use my hand to rub away the pain shooting through the other foot.

Jamie bolts into a sitting position, his panicked voice slicing through the darkness. "What the *hell*?"

"Seriously? You're asking *me*?" I squawk. "What did you put on my pillow?"

"Skittles."

He says this as if it's supposed to make sense. "*Why?*"

I kneel down, fumbling for the box I'd just conked my head on. I hear Jamie's footsteps heading for the door, and then a switch flicks and light floods the room.

Jesus. A sea of purple Skittles covers the floor and Jamie's mattress.

And a lump rises in my throat as I realize the significance of what I'm seeing. Canning kept the box I'd given him in Boston, filled it with my favorite candy and left it on my pillow.

As an apology for spending the day with his ex?

Or is it an apology for something else? Something worse... like *fucking* his ex.

Jamie squats beside me. "Help me clean this up."

He sounds pissed. Looks it, too. Which only pisses *me* off, because what the hell does he have to be angry about? I'm the one who got ditched today.

We don't speak as we start picking up Skittles. His jaw is set in a tense line, and he's tossing the candy back in the box with more force than necessary.

"What?" I mutter when I catch him scowling at me.

"You're back late." His voice is tight.

"It's our night off. I grabbed a drink at Lou's." I stick a hand under my bed and gather up more Skittles.

"I'd say you had more than one. Your breath smells like a brewery." His tone suddenly sharpens. "You didn't drive, did you?"

"Naw. I got a ride."

"With who?"

"What's with the Twenty Questions?"

Jamie whips a Skittle into the box but it bounces right back out, skidding under the desk. "None of the other guys have cars, Wes. Please don't tell me you hitched with some random stranger."

Guilt pricks my insides. But why the fuck am I feeling guilty? Unlike some people, I didn't spend the day gallivanting around with an ex.

"Who drove you home?" he demands when I don't answer.

I meet his gaze head-on. "Sam."

Jamie's breath hitches. There's no mistaking the cloud of hurt in his eyes. "Are you kidding me? The guy from that hook-up app?"

"I met him for a drink," I say with a shrug. "What's the big deal?"

He doesn't answer. He just kneels on his mattress, gathering up more candy.

"Are you seriously pissed off right now?" I fight a burst of annoyance. "Because you're not the one who got ditched today, Canning."

"Like hell! First of all, *you* told me to take off early. And I didn't know she was coming, okay? She showed up out of the blue, and, what, I'm supposed to ignore her? She's my friend."

"She's your fuck buddy," I shoot back.

"Not anymore."

He stands up and rakes both hands through his hair, then grabs the box and slams it on the desk. The floor looks pretty clear, but I know there's no way we managed to pick up all the candy. Canning must've cleaned out that entire fucking candy store.

Either way, the Skittles are all but forgotten as Jamie levels an irritated look in my direction. "But just because we're not fooling around doesn't mean she's not my friend anymore. And she drove all this way to see me. So yeah, I spent the day with her. Went shopping, grabbed some dinner."

I can't control the hot streak of jealousy that races through me. "Bet that was fun. Did you eat some pussy for dessert?"

His mouth falls open. "Did you really just fucking say that?"

I sure did, and I don't even regret it. I'm sick to death of not knowing where I stand. Where *we* stand. Last night, I was *inside* this guy. And the second Holly showed up, he acted like we were strangers. He hadn't even *looked* at me before he'd gone off with her.

Ain't gonna lie—it hurt.

"Am I wrong?" I ask flatly.

Jamie releases a slow, even breath, as if he's trying to calm himself. "I want to punch you right now, Wesley. Like, for real."

I set my jaw. "What, for *daring* to call you out on the fact that you're still into women?"

"You really think I'd just roll out of bed with you and into bed with her? I didn't hook up! Which is more than I can say for you and your precious *Sam*."

"I didn't hook up with him, either." Frustration spirals through me. "We just met up for a drink and talked about *you* the whole time. Jackass."

Jamie blinks. "Then why the hell are we arguing right now?"

I falter. "Uh. I'm not sure anymore."

There's a beat. Then we both let out a tense chuckle. I'm feeling a lot less hostile and a lot more sober as I walk over to shut off the light again. When I turn back toward Jamie, he's beckoning to me in the dark from his mattress on the floor. When I sit on the edge, he tugs me down to his pillow.

We're stretched out on our sides, facing each other. We're both waiting for the other to speak. Then Jamie sighs, his expression flickering with resignation. "I don't like the idea of you messing around with anyone else."

I swallow my surprise. "Right back atcha, babe."

"I told Holly there was someone else," he admits. "Pretty much right when she got here."

My heart soars. "You did?"

His voice is thick. "Yeah. "

"I told Sam the same thing," I confess. "He tried to cop a feel when we hugged hello, and I straight-up said I wasn't there for that."

His eyes narrow. He slides toward me, one arm coming around my waist as his warm palm settles over my ass. "Where did he touch you?" Jamie squeezes one of my butt cheeks. "Here?"

I chuckle. "Yup."

"Fucker."

I lean closer and kiss the tip of his nose. "That's as far as it got, man. I promise."

"Don't have to promise. I trust you."

My stomach churns at his earnest declaration. He trusts me. Fuck, I'm such an asshole. Because *trust* was the last thing I felt today when I was imagining Jamie's hands all over that chick. And the fact that she's rocking a vagina makes it a thousand times worse. I've never had to worry that the guy in my bed might choose a girl over me.

Then again, I've never cared what the guys in my bed did after they *left* my bed. It's different with Jamie. I feel sick when I picture him leaving me. I feel sicker knowing I'm competing with not one, but *two* gender pools for his affection.

Except I won't have his affection for much longer. Once camp is over, we'll be going our separate ways. I hadn't been joking around with Cassel the other day—if I want to succeed in the pros, I need to keep my pants zipped.

"But I think we need some ground rules or something," Jamie says ruefully.

I swallow. Me and rules have always had a love-hate relationship. "Like what?"

"Like as long as we're fooling around, we're exclusive."

Ha. Because I'm *so* interested in screwing anyone else. Still, I nod in agreement, because I happen to be *very* interested in making sure *he* doesn't screw anyone else. "Deal. What else?"

He purses his lips. "Ah…that's all I've got right now. You?"

Reluctance jams in my throat. I know I need to say this, but I don't want to. I've wanted this guy for so fucking long. Forever. And the thought of letting him go in less than a month rips me apart.

But I'm going to have to.

"We end it when we leave for training camp." My voice comes out hoarse, and I pray he can't hear the note of pain in it. "We only have the summer."

Jamie goes quiet for a moment. "Yeah." He sounds equally hoarse. "I figured."

I can't tell how he feels about that. Disappointed? Sad? Relieved? His expression reveals nothing, but I decide not to push for answers. Besides, I'm the one who came up with that rule. I should be glad he's not fighting me on it.

"We should go to sleep," I murmur.

"Yeah." He closes his eyes, but instead of rolling over, he shifts closer and kisses me.

I return his kiss softly. When I put a hand on his hip, the fabric crinkles beneath my fingers in a way that feels unfamiliar. They're not his usual underwear, so I break our kiss to squint at them in the dark. "Canning," I whisper. "Are you wearing your boxer shorts with kittens?"

Even in the dim light I can see the corners of his mouth twitch. "So what if I am?"

For some reason, this makes me unthinkably happy. I lean in to touch my smile to his. But Jamie squirms a little, as if uncomfortable. Then he sticks a hand down the back of the aforementioned boxer shorts and brushes something.

"Everything okay back there?" I ask, wondering if he'd left the tag in them.

"Just, uh, a Skittle in my shorts."

We both chuckle even as our lips meet again. And again.

Finally I'm able to relax. His arms close around me and it feels like coming home.

Our mouths fit together so perfectly. Every time we kiss, I fall even more in love with him, and it has nothing to do with sex or lust. It's *him*. His closeness and his scent and the way he soothes me.

My life has been chaotic for as long as I can remember, and I always dealt with it alone. My parents' criticism, my confusion over my sexuality. But for six weeks every summer, I didn't have to be alone. I had Jamie, my best friend, my rock.

Now I have even more of him. I have his strong arms around me and his lips lazily brushing mine, and it absolutely kills me that I have to give him up when I go to Toronto.

We kiss for a while. There's no urgency to do anything more than that. Our dicks don't even enter the equation. We just lie there making out, while his palms stroke up and down my back in sweet, reassuring glides.

Eventually we fall asleep with my head on his chest and the sound of his steady heartbeat beneath my ear.

TWENTY-SIX
JULY

Jamie

Several days later, I get an email from my agent.

A year ago, I loved saying that. *My agent*. Sounds pretty important, no?

Not so much.

When I was a kid I collected hockey cards. They came in packs of ten with a lousy piece of gum that tasted awful. In every pack there'd be one good player—hopefully not a duplicate of a card I already had—and nine guys you'd never heard of. Those nine went in the bottom of my shoebox, where they waited. Every once in a blue moon one of those guys would rise in the ranks, but usually they didn't.

Fast forward ten years. To my agent, I'm one of those cards at the bottom of the shoebox. In fact, it's unlikely the emails I get from him are even written by him.

This one asks me for the date I'm moving to Detroit. "The club will put you up in a hotel near the rink until you've found housing. Attached you will find the real estate agent's contact information. Please set up an appointment with the realtor once you've arrived in Detroit."

The end of summer crawls closer every day. I'm not going to be able to put off these plans any longer.

Between sessions at the rink on Thursday, I look for Pat in his cramped little office. Since I'd promised my mother I'd try to come home, I need to find out if that's possible.

"Got a second?" I ask from the doorway.

Pat beckons to me, then turns away from his computer screen. "What's up, Coach?"

Still tickles when he calls me that. Campers get *what's up, kid?*

"I'm trying to plan my life, which is always a fun time. So I need to know how you're doing with your personnel shortage at the end of the month."

He gives me a thoughtful stare. "Sit down, Canning."

I drop into a chair feeling like a kid who's been called to the principal's office. And I'm not sure why. But there's something serious in his expression, and I think I'm about to find out what it is.

"I haven't heard you mention Detroit all summer," he says, folding his hands into a tent. "Why is that?"

"Um. Been busy." *And you don't want to know with what.*

Pat smiles at me, cocking his head. "Not buying that. Sorry. A man who's getting everything he wants in life can't stay silent about it. Not even you."

Damn it. Coach is going all head-shrink on me. "It's… I dunno. Not quite sure how it's going to work out, that's all. Maybe in a year I won't be able to shut up about it."

His nod is slow. Thoughtful. I feel like an amoeba under a microscope. "You know I think you're a hell of a goalie. You put your heart into it, and someone is going to notice. Even if it takes time."

It's kind of hard to swallow all of a sudden. "Thanks," I manage.

"But I find myself wondering if you're feeling it. Not everybody wants to get on that treadmill when he could be, say, coaching instead."

Now it's my turn to stare across the desk. "Who would hire me as a coach?"

Pat makes a show of looking up at the ceiling before meeting my eyes again. "Lots of people, Canning. You've been coaching your ass off here every summer since you started college. I'd be happy to tell anyone who'll listen. And you had great stats in college. Best stats on your team. Rainier might even want you."

It's sort of dizzying to allow myself to think about this. Coaching? As a full-time gig? That sounds like a blast. Coaching at the college level would pay me a living wage, too. I'd just never imagined I could have a job like that.

But Pat knows people. A lot of them. All over the country. Where would I want to be?

The idea pops out of my mouth before I can think better of it. "Do you think someone in Toronto might need a defensive coach?"

Pat's bushy eyebrows lift, but only for a split second. "Dunno, Canning. They don't play a lot of hockey in Canada." Then he bursts out laughing. "Lemme see what I can learn."

I leave his office feeling lighter, even though nothing has really changed, except there's a new idea in my head.

But it's a hell of an idea.

It's the Friday of parents' weekend, so coaches have tonight off instead of Saturday because we're required to be at a special dinner with the parents tomorrow.

When Wes and I were campers, neither one of us ever had visitors on parents' weekend. My clan couldn't exactly buy airfare for seven people and drop everything to watch me play a scrimmage in upstate New York. And Wes's parents... They just didn't bother. His father liked the fact that his son sometimes won state championship games, but if there wasn't any way to brag about an event, he didn't see the point of showing up. And Wes's mom? I've never even met the woman. Sometimes I wonder if she even exists.

As coaches, parents' weekend means we have to show up and look attentive. Pat's camp is funded by tuition checks from parents, and when those parents stop by, they want to be sure their kids are getting 24/7 attention.

The kids don't really want 24/7 attention, of course. But that's not our problem.

Wes and I are just back from the rink and trying to sort out our options.

"So tell me about this outdoor concert," he says. "Is that what we're doing tonight?" Wes is scrolling through his messages.

"I think the music could be okay."

He looks up. "Says the man with boy bands on his phone."

"That was a *joke*," I sputter. "We've been over this."

Wes cackles. "Tell you what—let's make a deal. It's been a while since I had a steak dinner. You find me a steak, and I'll subject myself to this concert."

"Here, man." I pretend to unbutton my fly.

He throws a pillow at me. "Feed me, Canning. Bad local music is easier to take after a porterhouse."

I pull out my phone. "We can use your car, right?"

"Sure."

Most of the restaurants in Lake Placid are burger joints, but the Squaw Lodge Boathouse on West Lake looks like the real deal. And since the outdoor concert is in the same direction, I make a reservation and hope for the best.

Then I go over to the closet we share and fish out Wes's one polo shirt.

Dropping it on Wes's bed, I find a button-down shirt for myself, and a clean pair of khaki shorts.

"You want me dressed up?" Wes asks, hoisting the shirt over his head. "Are we going on a date, Canning?"

"Seems so. The steak place looks nicer than swim trunks and flip flops."

"So it's my fault then." His words are grumpy, but he's admiring my chest while I button up the shirt. "You clean up nice, honey."

I flip him off.

Wes heads to the bathroom to brush his teeth, and I watch him go. I even catch myself admiring his ass. Lately I find myself sneaking looks at him, trying to raise some kind of *holy shit* reaction to the idea that I'm involved with a guy.

When I was young I used to try to scare myself walking through the woods alone. I'd peer into the shadows and imagine something terrifying waited there, just to give myself a little thrill. But it never worked all that well, and neither do my attempts to frighten myself over recent events.

Because it's Wes. He's not scary. And the things we do in bed are just plain hot.

As it happens, the lodge *is* a nice restaurant. But we're not underdressed, because the place offers dockage. In other words, some of the dinner guests have arrived on small watercraft, looking wind-tousled and sunburned.

We don't get a table outside, because I only made the reservation an hour ago. But the interior is dark and sleek, with leather upholstery and candles flickering on the tables. We're shown to a comfortable booth in back, and I slide onto the seat feeling like this was a damn good idea. I smell garlic bread, and there's a microbrew beer list a yard long.

"We're going to eat like Vikings," Wes says, giving the hostess his cockiest grin. "Which steak is the best one?"

The girl is all too happy to stay and chat. "The creole is popular," she says with a toss of her hair. "I like the New York strip, though."

"*Do* you now. Thanks for the tip."

She walks away, shaking her hips, and I bite back a grin. "You were *this* close to making a bad *strip* joke, weren't you? Be honest."

Wes reaches across the table to cover my hand with his. He makes a dead-serious face, the kind he only makes when he's pulling my chain. "I was this close to making a *good* strip joke. Duh."

That's when the guy sneaks up on us. "Good evening! I'm Mike, and I'll be your server this evening…"

Calmly, Wes removes his hand from mine and looks up at the waiter.

The man glances from Wes to my hand and back again. "Welcome to the Squaw Lodge Boathouse. Have you dined with us before?" His voice has taken on a slightly different tone. Softer, with a riff of affectation in it.

I'm distracted, but Wes looks him straight in the eye and says, "Actually, it's our first time."

"Oh! Well, you're in for a treat…"

He and the waiter discuss the menu, but I tune out. This is the first time someone has looked at me and decided I was a gay man out on a date, and I'm trying to figure out how I feel about that. Don't get me wrong—I'd be seen anywhere with Wes. Any day of the week. But there's something strange about becoming his dinner date. Like I've shrugged on someone else's costume and I'm playing a role.

I order a beer and a steak when it's my turn, and the guy runs off to put in our order.

"You buggin'?" Wes asks, nudging my foot under the table.

"No," I say quickly. I'm not, either. "I don't give a shit whether we set that guy's gaydar off or not."

Wes actually winces. "Wouldn't blame you if you did. Look, *that* dude is only jealous. But some people are assholes about it. I mean, the things you and I do every night are illegal in some places."

"You're really selling it to me then."

His grin is wry. "There are benefits."

"Yeah? Hit me. What's good about going gay?" I nudge him back under the table.

"Well, *dicks*," he says. "Obvs."

"Obvs."

He smiles. "Okay, now picture this. You wake up on a weekend beside your really hot boyfriend, and fuck like horny hedgehogs for a couple of hours. Then you spend the rest of the day watching sports on television, and nobody ever says"—he pitches his voice high—"honey, you said we could go to the mall!"

Now I'm laughing. "And I guess you can leave the toilet seat up, right?"

Wes spreads his hands. "See? Benefits everywhere. And here's one more—the parents don't nag you for grandchildren."

"I have five siblings," I point out. "They're guaranteed at least a basketball team."

The waiter brings our beers, and I actually give him a wink before he goes.

"Look at you!" Wes crows after he walks away. "You could be good at this."

"Like it's hard?" Wes is grinning at me, and I hate to kill the mood. But I realize that I've got a question for him that's been bothering me. "What did your parents say when you told them?"

His face falls. "Well. At first they didn't believe me. My mother said, 'This is just a phase.' And my father said nothing."

"When was this?"

"Freshman year of college. I decided to tell them on the way to my grandfather's house for Thanksgiving. We were all trapped in the car together."

"Nice timing."

He shrugs. "I didn't even know what to do with that reaction. It never occurred to me they'd just sort of ignore me. Though in retrospect it makes plenty of sense."

His dull admission brings an ache to my heart. It also makes me wonder how my own family would react if they knew I was hooking up with a guy. But no matter how many times I try to picture their expressions filling with horror or disgust, I can't see it. Support is all I've ever gotten from them.

"So what did you do?" I ask, hoping my inner distress doesn't show on my face.

"Well, Canning, this is me we're talking about here. So I got really fucking mad. And next time I was home on break I picked up a guy at a party and blew him in the family room when I knew they were on their way home."

Yikes. "That probably got the point across."

Wes takes a long pull of his beer and I watch his strong throat work. "It did the trick. My dad did all the yelling I expected him to do the first time. He said I was disgusting. And that I was going to fuck up my hockey career. Hell. That's still his biggest concern."

Ouch. "What does your mom say?" He never mentions her. How can a mother not defend her son?

"She's his yes man and pearl-clutcher-in-chief. So she never says much."

Shit, I *really* killed the mood. But luckily our appetizers arrive a moment later, and we're happy again. Sometimes it's just that easy.

TWENTY-SEVEN

WES

I drive us a mile farther up the road to the park where the band is playing. Neither of us has ever been to this place before, but it's nice. A lawn runs all the way down to the water. A band shell has been set up near the shore, and people of all ages are settling down on the grass.

We find a spot easily enough. I sit down, but Jamie doesn't. "Shit. I didn't think this through," he says, eyeing his rather nice pair of khaki shorts.

I look up at him. "And here I thought I was the gay dude."

He smacks the top of my head. "Tomorrow is Pat's parents' weekend. I'm just trying to represent."

"Fine." I stand up. "Wait here a second." I jog to the car and dig an old plaid blanket out of the back. When I rejoin Canning, I give him a cocky smile. "See? It's a *good* thing I never clean my car." I spread it out on the grass and flop down.

Jamie sits beside me. We both lean back at the same time, and my hand comes down on top of his. So I move mine a couple inches to give him space.

But he moves his too, covering mine.

I don't want him to know how much I like that, so I don't look him in the eye. Instead, I stare up at the darkening sky over the lake and wonder how I've made it to age twenty-two without ever going on a date. I'd *teased* Jamie about it earlier, too. But here we are. Dinner and live music. Sitting on a fucking blanket in the park. I've never dated anyone before, and I'm probably not very good at it.

After a while the band starts up. There are four of them—a singer, a guitar, a double bass and percussion. The first song they play is a weak cover of a Dave Matthews song.

"Huh," Jamie says.

"What?"

"I'm worried."

"About the music?" I'm in a mood to be generous. "They're just warming up, right? Every band covers Dave Matthews. It's a law, I think."

Unfortunately, things don't improve.

"Could that be an old tune by Billy Joel?" Jamie asks.

I listen hard for a second. "God, maybe. It sounds like they're trying to play 'New York State of Mind'."

"Not sure they've quite got it."

I flip my hand over and squeeze his fingers as the sky grows darker.

By the third song, it's so bad it's funny. The lead singer looks out into the crowd and announces, "We're going to play an original tune that my friend Buster wrote."

Jamie and I both clap, like we know Buster. *Go Buster.*

"It's called 'Captive Rain,' and we're giving this song its world debut."

The drummer counts them in, and the first four bars aren't so bad. But the lyrics are… awful. I don't know what the guy is singing about. Captive rain is coming at him like a...train.

"Oh my God," Jamie whispers. His hand lands on mine again.

As the song progresses, I can feel him start to shake beside me.

"Shh! I'm trying to hear the music," I say, and he pinches me with his free hand. "Dude, he just rhymed 'chicken' with 'stickin.'"

Jamie snorts and I reach across my body to clamp a hand over his mouth. So he sticks out his tongue and licks my palm. So I wipe that on his shirt. Seeing as we're seconds away from repeating our experiments with MMA, I make a suggestion. "Time to swim?"

His eyes cut over to mine. "I don't have a suit."

"Seriously?"

When the song finally ends, Jamie jumps up and heads for the trees that border the lawn. I wad the blanket under my arm and follow him.

He's waiting a few yards into the woods. "Look out for poison ivy," he says, and I freeze, looking down. "Made you look!"

"Jesus, Canning."

He laughs and picks his way toward the water's edge.

We can't see the people on the lawn from here, but we can still hear the band. It's almost completely dark, which is good for us. There are some rocks at the water's edge, so I toe out of my shoes and put them in a safe spot. Then I strip off my polo.

Jamie is laying his clothes on the rock almost daintily. He's even removing his shorts. I'd forgotten he was trying to keep them clean.

"Dare you to skinny-dip."

"Of course I'm skinny-dipping," he says.

Well then. Can't let him do that alone. I drop every thread of my clothing onto the rocks. It's not a hot night, but when I wade into the water, the temperature isn't too bad. I turn to watch Jamie step toward the water's edge, and I like what I see. The dim light makes shadows in the valleys of his abs.

I wade in deeper, and the water caresses my bare skin. This is decadent. The sound of Jamie's chuckle makes me smile in the dark. When he reaches me, I take his hand, and he lets me. Together we duck under water, swimming out just a little ways. Some of the people on the lawn probably have an oblique sight-line of us by now. Then again, it's awfully dark.

We're in up to our necks, and the lake is both beautiful and a little creepy if your mind works that way. I wonder if Jamie's does. "I think I just felt something brush my foot." I didn't, but Jamie doesn't know that.

He twitches a little. "Probably just a sunfish."

"Uh-huh. You're right." I maneuver my foot under the water, finding Jamie's calf and grazing it with my toe.

He lurches away from me. "You asshole."

That gets me laughing, and Jamie splashes me. "The bottom's kind of sludgy here." And this is true. "I worry about leeches. Did you ever see *Stand by Me?*"

"Ugh," he complains. "Way to ruin it." He moves closer to me. All at once he springs forward, grabbing my shoulders, wrapping strong legs around me. "Now they can only find you."

He kisses me.

Jesus. So sexy. I open for him and our tongues tangle right away. I moan into his mouth, and it doesn't matter, because the music is going again, and the darkness gives us plenty of privacy. Jamie's fingers weave into the hair at the back of my head. He tastes like good beer and sex. I'm standing in a lake with the most beautiful man wrapped around my body, and his dick is hard against my belly already. This must be what heaven is like.

I cup his ass, unable to resist sliding a finger down his crease and teasing his hole. He moans into my mouth. "You are goddamn addictive, Wes."

That's what I like to hear. I've only fucked him one other time since that first night almost a week ago. Our second time, I took him from behind and had to cover his mouth the entire time to stop him from making noise.

I want him again now, but screwing in the lake isn't really an option. No condom or lube, a lawnful of people less than a hundred yards away.

I move my hand to his groin and give his erection a soft stroke as our tongues tangle in a hungry kiss. Then I jump, because *his* hand is on my backside now, *his* fingers traveling between my ass cheeks.

"Gonna fuck you one of these days," he whispers.

Yeah, I know he will. I know I'll let him, too. Maybe one guy soured me on the idea of taking it, but with Canning, I'll take anything he has to give me. I'll take it all.

His finger breaches my hole and I hiss out a breath. Jesus. I'd forgotten how sensitive all those nerve endings are.

"You like that, huh?" Droplets cling to his perfect face as he smiles at me. A filthy, beautiful smile.

"Mmm-hmmm." I jam my tongue in his mouth again, grinding my cock against his as he tentatively plays with my ass.

He kisses me back, just a brief taste, before breaking our mouths apart. He's in the mood to talk. No, he's in the mood to *torment*.

"So tight," he sighs.

The angle allows just the tip of his finger to penetrate me, but even that is deep enough to make me moan.

"My dick's gonna like being in you, Wes." His lips latch onto my neck, dropping greedy kisses on my wet skin. "And you're going to be begging for it."

I shiver. I think he's right.

When his finger disappears, I bite back a disappointed groan. That fleeting tease had turned me on like nobody's business.

"But not tonight." He says it decisively, as if he's carrying out some conversation in his own head. That dirty smile returns as he leans in to nibble on my jaw. "Tonight, I want you to fuck me. I've been thinking about it all day."

I growl. "You need to shut up, Canning. Otherwise I'll do you right now. Bend you over that log over there and take what's mine."

Wet lips place a kiss right under my jaw. "Promises, promises." Then he disentangles from my body and swims backward as if he has no care in the world.

Swimming with a hard-on is extremely difficult. But maybe I should be thinking of my stiffy as a floatation device. Or an oar, because God knows it's long and hard enough to single-handedly propel an entire fucking canoe. We swim side by side for a while, then float on our backs and stare up at the inky black sky.

I laugh when I notice both our cocks slicing upward as if to salute the moon. "Should we do something about those?" I crack.

Jamie chuckles. "Yeah, probably. I'm dying over here."

"Me too."

In unspoken agreement, we swim back to shore, our naked bodies dripping lake water all over the muddy bank. Jamie stares at his pristine clothes, then says, "Fuck it." He puts on only his boxer-briefs, and holds on to the rest.

I do the same, and luckily we don't encounter anyone on the quick walk back to the parking lot. His briefs are black and my boxers are navy-blue, so there's no peekaboo happening with our dicks, but still, traipsing around in our underwear might be a bit too racy for Lake Placid.

A moment later, we're in the car. I put it in drive and breeze out of the lot, tensing when Jamie reaches over and strokes my package over my wet skivvies.

"Won't be able to drive in a straight line if you keep doing that," I warn him.

"Eyes on the road," he teases. "Don't worry, we're not going far."

I wrinkle my forehead. I was planning on driving back to the dorm, but Canning apparently has other ideas. We've traveled no more than five minutes when he nods to a gravel path to our right. "Turn there."

A grin tugs on my lips when I realize what he has in mind. It's the pull-off to one of our old hiking spots. The area is usually deserted even in the daytime, so at night there definitely won't be anyone around.

I park in the small dirt clearing near the trailhead, and before I can even kill the engine, Jamie is climbing into my lap.

TWENTY-EIGHT

JAMIE

I wasn't exaggerating before. I'm addicted to Ryan Wesley. And right now I desperately need a fix. A couple of weeks ago, getting it on with a dude had freaked me out. Now it's as obvious as breathing that everything about this guy turns me on—his raspy voice, his powerful body, the tattoos inked all over his golden skin. My mouth is on his in a heartbeat, my tongue down his throat as I straddle his muscular thighs.

He sighs against my lips. "You're such a horndog."

I totally am. I rock into his lower body, my palms skimming up and down his broad chest. The question now isn't whether I want to fool around with this man. The question is how I'm ever going to give it up. I push that thought overboard, though, because I'm about to combust.

But I might have been too hasty with my choice of hook-up spots, because the front seat is too small to accommodate two horny-as-fuck hockey players. My legs are already starting to cramp, and when I shift around trying to get more comfortable, my back hits the horn and a blast of sound hits the air.

Wes bursts out laughing. Then laughs harder when I make another attempt to reposition myself. "Backseat?" he chokes out.

Much better idea. He climbs over first, his butt cheek smacking me in the face as he heaves himself into the back. I land on him with a thud, and now we're both laughing our asses off. It's just as cramped back here. We can't lie side by side, so I'm on top of him, and when I bend down to kiss him, my forehead slams into the door handle. And when I grab my head in surprise, I manage to elbow him in the eye socket.

"Holy fuck!" Wes yells. "You trying to kill me, Canning?"

"No, but—"

"Abort!" he says between laughs.

Screw that. All this shifting and maneuvering has succeeded in my rubbing my aching dick all over his body. If I don't get off soon, I'm going to lose my mind.

"We've got this," I tell him. Then I sit up and bump my head on the car roof.

"Uh-huh," he says solemnly. "Seems like it."

"Hockey players like it rough," I argue, reaching into the front seat for Wes's shorts. In the back pocket I find his wallet. A second later, I flick a condom at him and order, "Suit up."

"Yes, Coach." He still looks like he's trying not to laugh, but his gray eyes are now glittering with lust. Keeping our gazes locked, he eases his boxers down his hips.

I shuck my briefs as he covers himself, then curl over and take him in my mouth. The medicinal taste of the latex fills my mouth, but I ignore it. This is the first time lube hasn't entered the equation, so I want to make sure the condom is nice and wet before I dare ride his cock.

God, and that's something I never imagined I'd be doing. Riding another man's cock.

"Baby," his voice is low and husky. "I'm loving that, but you don't have to do it. Give me my wallet."

I fumble into the front seat one more time and pass it to him. He removes another packet and tears it open. This one is full of lube. A second later, a deliciously slippery hand slides up my crease, rubs my taint and makes me shiver.

"That's handy," I rasp.

He doesn't answer. He's too busy working me open with his fingers.

When we do this, there's always one awkward moment when he first breaches me. Before my body gets the joke. But now that I know how this works, it doesn't even slow me down. I'm eager for it. And it's only a couple of minutes later when I'm pushing Wes's hand away and straddling his lap again.

The way I handle him is nothing like the way I'd touch a woman. He's as big and strong as I am, and I don't have to worry about hurting him. His broad shoulders make a sturdy place to put my hands. Rising up, I wait for him. He positions himself beneath me, and we both hiss when I slide down over his hard cock.

For a moment I don't move. We're nose to nose, blinking into each other's eyes. Wes's tongue emerges to slick my lower lip. And I dive onto his mouth, jamming my tongue inside. There isn't a lot of space for me to move, but it doesn't matter. I'm riding him in short, fast strokes. The angle is heaven—I can bear down on him just where I need him.

Wes is cupping my ass in strong hands, and with each thrust, he lets out a sexy grunt. Our chests rub together as our mouths lock again. My dick is trapped between our stomachs, slicking us both with pre-come.

My climax takes me by surprise. One second I'm fighting Wes over whose tongue belongs in whose mouth. The next, I'm fighting the urge to explode. And losing. "Fuck. I have to come."

Wes moans into my mouth, and I jam myself down on him one more time. That's when I feel it—the whole-body orgasm. My limbs tingle unpredictably as I slump forward, my face landing in Wes's neck. The world goes fuzzy at the edges, but I feel myself shooting all over him while he bucks beneath me.

He lets loose a growl, and the muscles in his neck tighten all at once. Then he drops his head back and shudders through his release.

Heavy breathing and thudding hearts are all that can be heard in the car afterwards. I'm lazing against his sticky chest, too blissed out to move. His hands trace lazy patterns over my back.

I could get used to this. I really could.

After a bit, Wes slaps me on the ass. "Up, baby. We can't stay here forever."

I hate the way that sounds, but it's hard to argue the truth. So I peel my satisfied body off his, and we begin the ridiculous process of trying to clean up in a confined space without further injury.

We manage, but just barely.

Wes and I drag our bleary selves out of bed the next morning and book it over to the rink, where the other coaches already congregate.

The parents are arriving at nine, the first scrimmage is scheduled for ten, and Pat has a prep list that's a mile long. He begins to bark instructions once Wes and I round out the group, then stops midsentence when he notices Wes's face.

"What the hell happened to you, Wesley?"

I press my lips together to fight a laugh. Our sexual circus act in the car last night left Wes with a nice shiner on his left eye, courtesy of my wayward elbow. It's not black, but definitely purplish, and visibly swollen.

"Canning beat me up," he says gravely.

Pat flicks his gaze to me, then back at Wes. "What'd you do to piss him off?"

Wes mock gasps. "You saying I deserved it, Coach?"

"I'm saying you've got a smart mouth and it's a miracle you don't get wailed in the face every day of your life." But Pat's grinning as he says it. Then he claps his hands and gets back to business. "Maybe you boys can kiss and make up on the trip to the supermarket. You're on ice duty. Make sure you use some of it on that eye."

I feel my neck heat up at Pat's mention of kissing. *Coach, if you only knew...*

Wes lifts a brow. "Ice?"

"Machine in the cafeteria broke down, so I need you to drive to the market and grab a dozen bags." He's already dismissing us, turning to Georgie and Ken. "Check the equipment—we need the extra helmets and pads out of storage for any parents who want to scrimmage with us later."

Wes and I head out while Pat is still playing drill sergeant. I slide into the passenger seat of his car, grinning at him as I remember last night's automotive adventures.

He casts a rueful glance over his shoulder. "I can never look at that backseat the same way again."

"Wait, you're saying you never hooked up in your car before yesterday?"

"Nope. I had a single at Northern Mass, so I usually brought hook-ups home. Or I went to their place." He pauses. "That was the better option. Means I didn't have to kick 'em out when they wanted to spend the night."

I furrow my brow. "You've never spent the night with anyone?" He and I have been sleeping together regularly.

"Nope," he says again.

"Why not?" I'm suddenly curious to know about his love life. Not the sex—the idea of him with anyone else bugs the shit out of me—but the relationship stuff. For as long as I've known him, Wes has been single. Now, knowing he's gay, it makes sense why he never had a girlfriend. But has he had a *boyfriend*?

"I didn't want anyone getting too attached to me," he says with a shrug, his eyes focused on the road.

The response only makes me more curious. "Did you ever get attached to *them*?"

"Nope." This is his go-to answer for the day, apparently.

"Have you ever gone out with anyone?" I ask slowly.

He's quiet for a moment. "No," he admits. "I don't do boyfriends, Canning. It's too messy."

For some reason, my gut clenches. I want to ask him what *I* am, then. An extended hook-up? A summer fling? I knew this thing with us was bound to end eventually, but I at least thought the time we've had together has meant something to him.

Because it means something to *me*. I'm not sure what, or why, but I do know that this isn't just about sex for me.

"And once I'm in Toronto, I won't be doing *anything*," he says glumly. "Celibacy is gonna suck."

An uneasy feeling washes over me. "Did you talk to your dad about the *Sports Illustrated* thing?"

"Haven't told him yet. But I'm not doing the interview. That's not a can of worms I'm interested in opening." He swiftly changes the subject, as he usually does when the conversation is too focused on *him*. "What about you? Have you bought a ticket to Detroit yet?"

Great. He picks the one topic I don't want to discuss. "No."

"Dude, you need to get on that."

Wes parks in front of the supermarket and we hop out of the car. I hope he'll drop the subject now that we're here, but he's still talking about it as we walk into the air-conditioned store.

"You're supposed to report there in three weeks," he reminds me as he grabs a shopping cart. "You thinking of renting a house in the suburbs? Where do the Detroit players tend to live?"

I nod, thinking about my conversation with Pat. He pulled me aside a couple days ago and said he'd put some feelers out in the coaching community. We're supposed to talk again on Monday, but I still haven't told Wes about it.

Deciding to test the waters, I grab another cart and say, "Honestly, I'm not sure how I feel about going to Detroit."

He looks startled. "Meaning what?"

"Meaning…" I take a breath. Screw it. Might as well tell him.

We head for the freezers in the back, and Wes listens with no expression as I pretty much repeat everything I discussed with Holly—how I don't want to play backup my entire career, my lack of enthusiasm about going to Detroit, the possibility of being sent to the minors and not even playing a pro game. The only part I leave out is that I'm toying with taking a coaching job. I'm not ready to talk about that yet, especially when nothing is even official.

Once I'm done, he still doesn't respond. He chews on his lips, thoughtful. Then he opens the freezer and heaves out a bag of ice. "You're really considering not playing this season?" he finally says.

"Yeah." The cold air hits my face as I grab two more bags and load them into my cart. "Do you think I'm fucked in the head for throwing away a chance at the pros?"

"Yes and no." He drops another bag in his cart. "I think all your concerns are valid."

The conversation halts when a woman pushing a cart pops around the corner. Her step stutters when she notices Wes's black eye, and then she continues on with a wary look.

Wes glances at me, chuckling. "She thinks we're hooligans."

I roll my eyes. "She thinks *you're* a hooligan. As she should. I, on the other hand, am a saint."

He snorts. "Should I flag her down and tell her how I got the shiner, Saint Jamie?"

I give him the finger, then grab two more bags. We push our carts side by side and wander over to the checkout counter, where we get in line behind an elderly couple with a shopping cart full of cereal boxes. *Just* cereal boxes and nothing else.

"So my concerns are valid," I prompt as we wait our turn.

He nods. "Goalies have it tough. I can't deny that."

"But?"

"But this is your one chance." His voice softens. "If you don't take it, you could regret it for the rest of your life. Look, if I was in your shoes, I might be questioning my decision too, but—"

"No, you wouldn't. You'd report in a heartbeat, even if it meant spending years waiting for your shot."

"True dat." He rests his forearms on the cart. "But that's because I love the game. Even if I get to play only five minutes in a whole season, it's worth it to me. Hockey is everything to me."

But is it everything to me?

I'm even more troubled as I think of all the hard work that goes into a professional hockey career. The constant training, the rigid diet, the grueling schedule. I love hockey, I really do, but I'm not sure I love it as much as Wes loves it. And if I compare the level of satisfaction I get from stopping a goal to the pride I feel teaching someone like Mark Killfeather to become a better goalie, a better *man*... I honestly don't know which one means more to me.

"I just think you need to give it a shot," Wes says, jolting me from my thoughts. "At least go to training camp, Canning. What if you're there and suddenly they're like, 'We're giving you the starting job, kid.'"

Right, and then I'll fly to work on a Pegasus, befriend a genie, and get paid in leprechaun gold.

Wes notices my expression and sighs. "It could happen," he insists.

"Yeah, maybe," I say noncommittally.

The old couple pushes their cereal cart away, and Wes and I

step forward, charging the ice to Elites' account. Five minutes later, we're loading the bags into Wes's trunk.

I'm no closer to reaching any sort of conclusions about my predicament, and Wes seems to sense that. He nods at the gas station fifty yards from the supermarket. "Let's grab some slushies," he suggests.

"The ice'll melt if we leave it in the trunk for too long," I point out.

He rolls his eyes. "It'll take us all of five minutes. Besides, science has proven that slushies are conducive to the making of important life decisions."

"Dude, you really need to quit quoting 'science' all the time."

Laughing, we lock the car and make the short trek to the gas station, where Wes grabs two empty cups and nudges me toward the slushie station. He fills his cup with the cherry flavor and then waits. But I haven't had a slushie in a long time, and I can't decide. So I put some of each flavor in my cup.

At the counter, the middle-aged clerk chuckles at the sight of my rainbow concoction. "I did that once," he remarks. "Felt sick for days afterward. You've been warned, son."

Wes snickers. "My buddy likes a little bit of everything."

I give him the side-eye for that awful joke. We pay for our drinks and leave the store, but we've barely taken two steps when Wes slaps his forehead. "We forgot the straws. Wait here. I'll grab 'em."

As he ducks back inside, I linger near the door, admiring the sleek, silver Mercedes S-class that pulls up to one of the pumps. A gray-haired man gets out of the Merc and smooths the front of his silky tie. Shit, the guy's rocking a suit that probably costs more than my parents make in a year.

His gaze flicks in my direction. "Are you the attendant?" he barks out.

I shake my head. "It's self-serve," I call back.

"Of course it is." His tone is condescending as fuck, and there's a sneer on his face as he twists off the cap of his gas tank.

Frowning, I turn away from Snobby McSnobbers just as Wes pops out the door. He hands me a straw, his forehead wrinkling when he notices my expression. Clearly he thinks my frown is a result of my Detroit dilemma, because he lets out a quiet sigh.

"You'll figure it out, babe," he says softly. "You've still got time."

Then he leans into me, gripping my shoulders with one arm. He brushes a reassuring kiss over my cheek, and my entire body tenses, because Snobby McSnobbers chooses that exact moment to glance our way.

The look on the man's face cuts through me like a blade.

Disgust.

Pure, malicious disgust.

Jesus. *Nobody* has ever looked at me that way before. Like I'm a piece of dog shit they've just had the misfortune of stepping on. Like they want to wipe my very existence off the face of the earth.

Beside me, Wes stiffens. He's just realized we're being watched.

No, that we're being *judged*.

"Do you know that guy?" he says warily.

"No."

"He looks familiar."

Does he? I'm too stuck on his expression to know.

"Ignore him," Wes murmurs, taking a step toward the car.

My breathing is shaky as I follow him. Unless we walk all the way around the gas station to get back to our car—which I'm unbelievably tempted to do right now—we have no choice but to pass the Mercedes. As we near the man in the suit, I find myself bracing myself the way I do on the ice right before a puck flies toward me. I'm in defense mode, ready to protect myself at all costs, even though I know I'm being ridiculous. This man isn't going attack me. He isn't going to—

"Fucking faggots," he mutters under his breath as we walk by.

Those two words are like a blow to the gut. From the corner of my eye I see Wes flinch, but he doesn't say a word. He keeps walking, and I struggle to match his brisk stride.

"I'm sorry," he says when we reach the car.

"Nothing to be sorry about, man." But I can't deny I'm shaken up. That bubble Wes and I have been living in all summer has just burst. If we somehow managed to keep seeing each other after camp, I might encounter this type of shit all the time.

Unbelievable.

"People are assholes." His tone is gentle as we get into the car. "Not all of them, but some."

My hand shakes as I place my slushie in the cup holder. "This happens to you a lot?"

"Not often. But it happens." He reaches for my hand, and I know he feels it trembling as he laces our fingers together. "It sucks, Canning. Not saying it doesn't. But you can't let jerks like that get to you. Fuck 'em, right?"

I tighten my grip on his hand. "Fuck 'em," I agree.

Still, the drive back to the rink is subdued. We don't say much as we drop the ice off at the cafeteria. I really wish I could just brush off that bigoted comment—that *look*—but it stays with me. Gnaws at me. Yet at the same time, I feel a burst of pride for Wes. No, it's *awe*, because it takes true strength for him to be so unflinching about his sexuality. His own parents refuse to accept it, and even that doesn't keep him down.

"Coach Canning, Coach Wesley!" Davies calls when Wes and I arrive outside the rink. "Come meet my dad."

The front steps are littered with teenagers and their folks, all of whom are eager to meet the coaches who are grooming their kids into champions. Shen is in the middle of an animated conversation with his parents, grinning wildly as he talks about his progress. A few feet away, Killfeather stands alone, his teeth worrying his bottom lip as he looks around.

Wes and I have just reached Davies and his father when a flash of silver catches my peripheral vision.

I shift my head, and my heart drops to the pit of my stomach when the Merc from the gas station suddenly speeds up to the curb. I notice Killfeather take a step forward, looking even more agitated now.

The driver's door opens.

The bigot gets out of the car and addresses Killfeather in an annoyed voice. "Isn't there a closer parking lot?"

My goalie visibly gulps. "No. Only the one behind the building."

"I'll leave the car here then."

"It's a fire lane," Killfeather protests. "Just park in the lot, Dad. Please."

Oh shit. *Dad?*

Dread floods my stomach at the same time Killfeather Senior registers my presence. His head turns sharply, those dark eyes landing on me. Then on Wes.

As his lips curl in an angry sneer, only one thought runs through my head.

Fuck.

TWENTY-NINE

WES

Damn it. I *knew* that fucker at the gas station had looked familiar. I hold my breath as my gaze locks with the man at the curb. But Mr. Killfucker doesn't make me hold it for long.

"No fucking way," he spits. "No *fucking way*. Where is Pat?"

"Right here," says a calm voice. Pat appears in the open doorway, a frown playing on his lips. "Is there a problem?"

"You're damn right there is. *This* is what's costing me thousands? I'm paying a couple of *perverts* to spend hours each day with my kid? That is fucking *bullshit*."

Heads are turning faster than on spectators at Wimbledon. And as I watch, Pat's face pales. His eyes bounce onto me for a fraction of a second, and my heart sinks.

I'm going to be a liability here. A fucking crater for Pat and his business.

Killfucker is also noticing all the other parental attention he's garnered. That's when he goes in for the kill. "I will not keep quiet about this."

Cue his son's involvement. "Dad!" the kid shouts. "What the hell are you saying?"

Pat's jaw hardens until it resembles a granite block. "You'll need to follow me, sir. If you're going to slander my NHL-bound coaching staff, you can do it in the privacy of my office." He turns around and disappears into the building.

I wait until Killfucker passes me. On his way up the steps he gives me an evil glare. Then I follow him inside. Right behind me is Jamie, his eyes downcast.

"I'm going to hear what he has to say," I whisper. "But you don't have to come."

Jamie gives me an exasperated glance and follows me anyway.

Fuck me sideways. I've just fucked up Jamie's final summer at Elites. This job he loves so much? Torpedoed by yours truly. He's going to rue the day he ever met me.

A minute later, the four of us gather in Pat's tiny office, and I flick the door shut.

Killfucker obviously knows not to hesitate before taking a shot. He lets it fly before Pat can speak first. "Don't try to tell me you don't know about these two. How the *fuck* could you hire them to work with impressionable teenagers?"

Pat takes a deep breath, but his face is red. "I have no idea what's set you off. Does someone want to fill me in?"

Jamie opens his mouth to speak, but I hold up a hand. I can feel myself shaking with anger, but my voice sounds reasonably steady. "Let's let Mr. Killfeather tell Coach Pat *exactly* what he saw." I turn to Killfucker. "And don't hold back, man. Tell him every detail."

This parry works, because Killfucker starts to look uncomfortable. I've just managed to use his own homophobia against him. He can't even get the words out, he's so disgusted. "They…" He clears his throat and points at me. "He kissed him."

And now I have to give Pat credit. There's a flash of surprise on his face, but he shuts it down only a nanosecond later.

I jump in again before Pat has a chance. "That's not a good

enough description, man. What *else* did you see? I'm waiting to hear the perversion."

Killfucker shakes his head. "That was plenty, trust me."

"Really?" I snarl. "*Where* did I kiss Coach Canning?"

He's clearly finding my offensive play exasperating, so I know I'm on the right track. "At the gas station!"

"On what part of his body, dude?" Then I almost snicker, because now there's a throbbing vein in the center of Killfucker's forehead.

"Uh, *here*," he says, pointing at his cheek. "But that's not the point."

I keep pushing. "Really? Because I think it is *exactly* the point. I've known Jamie forever, and he'd just told me something important about his career, and I hugged him. With one arm. Don't skimp on the details, okay? I *comforted* my friend in all that gory detail—half a hug and a kiss on the cheek. Slap the cuffs on me, why don't you?" I put my wrists out straight.

Killfucker is about to explode. "But I saw... I think you two *clearly*..."

Pat jumps in now. "It really doesn't matter what you think. *This* is your big problem? A G-rated private moment between friends?"

"Friends who—"

"Not your business!" Pat shouts him down. "Not mine, either. I've never seen my coaches do anything inappropriate. They are *all business* on that rink. And that's what you're paying for, sir."

"No!" counters Killfucker. "I'm paying for good judgment, and I will tell whoever is willing to listen that you don't screen your employees. You're just waiting for disaster, anyway. These two cause a stir and—"

Pat cuts him off. "The only *stir* Coach Canning caused was the day his girlfriend showed up at the rink. And your son made an inappropriate comment about her anatomy."

Killfucker's mouth falls open. "Then it's worse than you know, Coach, because Mr. Canning here obviously gets around. Because I *know* what I saw. And my son and I are out of here."

Shit. Poor Killfeather. He's got this ass for a dad, and he gets yanked from camp?

Pat's face is a stone. "You're free to do as you wish. But if you slander my coaches to anyone I will *not* take it lying down."

"Not like *they* do, huh?"

After issuing this parting shot, Killfucker leaves.

The office is left in a deafening silence. The only sound is Pat's loud sigh, until Jamie tries to say something. "Coach, I…"

Pat holds up a hand. "Just give me a minute to think."

Chastened, Jamie is silent again. He doesn't glance at me, though, and I wish he would.

"Okay," Coach says. "You two can head back to your room, I'll text you when it's clear how this jackass is going to play it. And I want to apologize, Jamie, for bringing up that bit about your female friend…"

"Not necessary," he says quickly.

But Pat is shaking his head. "No. It shouldn't matter! I don't give two fucks if you have a girlfriend or not. But I let him get me flustered. The fact that the situation took me by complete surprise only means you've both behaved impeccably."

Now *that's* not true. Good thing Coach Pat doesn't follow us around when we're skinny-dipping and fucking in the car.

"I've run this camp for twenty years," he adds, looking us each in the eye in turn. "There have been times when I've had to ask staff to be more discreet. But that is not the case here."

And now Jamie is the color of a tomato. He looks like he'd happily activate any trapdoors in Pat's office floor.

My fists finally unclench. "Pat? I apologize if I'm making your day more complicated, but I'm not going upstairs to wait for your text. We're supposed to be scrimmaging, right? I don't run.

My private life is my business. Not many people know my secret. But if some asshole decides to confront me, I *never* duck him. That only looks weak. I have every right to be here. I have every right to coach those kids."

Pat squeezes the bridge of his nose. "Of course you do. I was just trying to shield you from any more ignorant bullshit. Get your skates on, then. Fuck 'im."

THIRTY

JAMIE

Maybe it makes me a pussy, but I take Pat up on his offer to sit this scrimmage out. I'm not afraid of Killfeather's dad. And I'm not afraid to have people whisper about me.

But what I am is *sad*. And I don't want it to show.

Before today I didn't really understand what Wes was up against. I'd never heard anyone give a homophobic rant except in movies. I didn't know that one man in a hundred-thousand-dollar car could wreak so much havoc.

Since everyone is supposed to be at the rink, the second floor of the dormitory sounds deserted as I turn my key in our lock. Inside, I stretch out on my bed.

Sad as I am, I can at least take one heart-lifting thing from this experience. One piece of insight I've been reluctant to give a label to.

I'm…bisexual.

Yep, I know, not exactly a mind-blowing M. Night Shyamalan plot twist over here, but it's the first time I've allowed the word to take root in my consciousness. I'm bisexual, and it's not just a physical connection I feel with Wes.

I can also see myself in a *relationship* with him. I can see myself being happy with him and never feeling like things were lacking.

I'd had this idea I could find a job near Toronto. That Wes and I could keep up... whatever it is we are to each other. But that isn't going to happen. Wes all but told me to go to Detroit. He *needs* me to stay four hours away.

We only have the summer, he'd said the night we argued. He was right. That's all we're going to get.

Some time later I hear a commotion out in the hallway. The place echoes, so even though Killfeather's room is on the opposite end of the building it's easy to hear him. "I don't *want* to leave!" he yells after a door bangs open.

"You *will* get your ass in my car right now."

"You can't make me!" The kid is putting his best effort into the resistance. But I know very well who always wins these fights.

The voice that answers him is low and steely. "If you're not in that car in sixty seconds, you're not playing in the Labor Day tournament this year."

Ouch. Hit the kid where it hurts, why don't you?

I hear the inevitable—the sound of a suitcase rolling across the tile and feet on the stairs. When I look out the window a minute later, I see my goalie slouching toward the passenger seat, and his father heaving suitcases into the trunk. That asshole didn't even get a ticket for parking in the fire lane.

They peel off a minute later, and that's the end of the Killfeathers, both junior and senior.

I blow off the barbecue, too.

Since I've missed the scrimmage, Pat doesn't really need me, and I use the time to regroup. I need to face the fact that summer will end soon.

So I call my mom on her business phone—the one that's always smudged with clay. "Hi baby!" she chirps when she answers. "Are you calling to tell me that you're coming home?" The woman always cuts to the chase. With six kids, she's always had to. There just aren't enough hours in the day for small talk.

"I am, as a matter of fact. Coach Pat hasn't replaced me yet, but I'm going to tell him I need that week off."

"Excellent," she says in the same tone of voice she'd always reserved for good report cards. "We need to see you before you join the NHL. While you still have all your teeth."

"That's uplifting," I complain.

"I don't know why my boys choose dangerous careers," she says. "I always tell your brother to make sure he visits while he still has all his vital organs."

My brother is a cop. "Gross, mom. And Scott has never drawn his weapon in the line of duty."

"Truthfully, bullets aren't his biggest problem right now." She fills me in on the fact my brother has moved back home for a little while. He's the one whose girlfriend recently dumped him. And since they lived together, he needed a temporary place to land.

"So he's in his old room?" I ask, trying to picture it. Scott is twenty-eight years old.

"He is, but rarely. He's picked up a lot of extra shifts lately. I think he's just trying to stay busy."

"Ouch," I mumble.

"*James,*" my mother says sharply. "Why are you blue?"

"I'm not," I try. But bullshitting my mother is impossible. You don't raise six kids without having laser-sharp perceptive abilities.

She clucks her tongue. "If you say so. But I'll be taking a good look at you later this month, young man. I'm going to make lasagna and hold it under your nose while I grill you with questions."

Mom's lasagna is damn good. I'll probably confess everything if she does that. "Can't wait," I say truthfully. Home sounds pretty good right now.

"Love you, Jamie boy," she says. "Buy your plane ticket."

"I will."

Talking to Mom has improved my mood. So I go out and treat myself to a bacon cheeseburger in a bar on Main Street. While I eat it, I watch the Red Sox lose, and think of Wes. He's at the barbecue right now, where parents are probably grilling him about the NHL recruitment process. And he's the best man to answer their questions.

That's not me brooding—that's just a fact. Wes has always wanted to play in the NHL. It's the first thing he told me about himself when we met as teenagers.

Me? I chose hockey because my brothers had already broken every football record our high school had ever recorded. I love hockey. But you can't ever say I love it more than Wes does. Because nobody loves hockey more.

When I get back to the dorm, the place is still empty. I brush my teeth and dig out a military thriller I'd brought with me to camp and haven't had time to read. I slide into bed in my underwear. Maybe Wes will come home in the mood to burn off some tension.

I fall asleep with the book on my chest.

Some time later I wake to the sound of the key turning in the lock. Bleary, I blink at Wes as he walks over to my bed.

"How was it?" I ask, my voice rough from sleep.

Wes doesn't answer me. But he removes the book and sets it on the floor.

"You okay?"

He's still silent, but it doesn't seem weird. Because he's

perched on the side of my bed now, just admiring me. Lifting one hand, he pushes my overgrown hair off my forehead. Then he bends down and kisses the cheek that had caused all the trouble earlier. In the exact same spot.

The brush of his lips makes me shiver and lean in for more.

Soft lips continue to press kisses on my face. On my neck. Their gentleness feels unfamiliar to me now. And the contrast between the size and strength of this man and the softness of his touch makes goosebumps rise on my chest.

A warm hand lands on the juncture between my legs, settling over the thin fabric of my underwear. The gentle pressure encourages me to roll my hips into his hand. A little friction would feel terrific right now. But all I get is the soft sweep of his thumb across my groin.

Apparently Wes is in the mood to torture me with kindness. And I'm in the mood to let him. Sinking into the bed, I close my eyes while he bathes me with soft kisses and even softer touches. When I reach up to put my hands on his chest, he corrects me, gently moving my hands back down onto the mattress.

"Fine. Be that way," I grumble.

He doesn't even chuckle. Instead, he clicks off my lamp and begins to shed his clothing. Every scrap. I lie there on my back while my eyes grow accustomed to the dark, admiring each newly exposed inch of smooth skin and hard muscle. An impressive erection bobs against his stomach. I want to sit up and take him in my mouth, but I wait lazily instead. Whatever Wes has planned, I'm pretty sure I'm going to enjoy it.

Then he's bending over me, kissing the strip of exposed skin between my T-shirt and my briefs. "Mmm," I sigh. I'm so hard, and he hasn't really even touched me yet. His hands slide into the elastic of my shorts and I lift my hips. *Whoosh*, they're gone. The next second, he puts a hand across my mouth and then deep-throats my cock in one gulp.

The heat and pressure are so swift and shocking it's a miracle I don't bite his hand. Wes works me over with his eager mouth, while my stomach quivers and my hips roll. Jesus Christ. I know we have to be absolutely silent, but I may not survive it.

By the time he releases me with a pop, I'm trembling everywhere. Wes disappears from my line of vision for a moment. When he returns with a condom and a bottle of lube, I sigh with relief.

He offers me a hand, and I take it, allowing him to pull me into a sitting position so he can remove my T-shirt. Then he straddles my thighs, crouching there on his knees. For the first time since he walked into the room, we're kissing for real. And I'm so hungry for it. All the softness from a few minutes ago burns off like steam, leaving a brush fire in its wake. These kisses are hard and molten. I capture Wes's tongue in my mouth and suck hard.

He moans—the first real sound I've heard from him tonight—and I swallow the sound down my eager throat. On his knees, he ruts slowly against my body, our chests bumping, our cocks aching. Wanting him hurts so good.

Eventually he sits back a bit, breaking our kiss. I reach for the condom, hoping to move things along. But he takes it out of my hand, tearing the package.

Instead of sheathing himself, he reaches down and rolls it onto my cock.

The breath halts in my chest. "Really?"

Wes kisses me instead of answering. Another tongue-tangling scorcher. Then he pops open the lube and applies some to his own hand. He reaches back, a serious expression on his face. I can tell when he penetrates himself, because he bites his lip.

"Let me do that for you," I whisper. I lube up my hand and reach between his legs. Wes puts both fists on the bed and leans into my body, kissing my jaw.

I caress his taint, and he sighs into my ear. When I finger his crease, he lays his head on my shoulder. "That's it," I breathe. When I penetrate him, he freezes for a second. Then I hear him take a deep breath, and I feel him relax.

He's hot and tight and like nothing I've ever felt. I ease inside. He alternately fights me and then relaxes. I stop to apply a ridiculous amount of lube to my hand. And now I'm able to reach his spot. I move my finger in a beckoning motion, and he shivers against my body.

Wes's face is still buried in my neck. I like it there. I wish he'd never leave.

THIRTY-ONE
WES

I'm struggling.

That's the theme of today, apparently: flat-out struggle. But this is a struggle I've chosen. Letting another man into my body isn't easy for me. I don't know why. It just isn't.

I want to, though. Every time I tense up against the intrusion, I tell myself the same thing: *this is Jamie. It's okay.* And then I'm able to relax. Jamie's taking it slowly. He reads me in the way a talented goalie would. He's firm and gentle in this as in all other things.

Fuck. I love him so much.

Today was another reminder of the way things are. The first time I ever touched Jamie, I pretended to be giving him something when in truth I was *taking*. He forgave me, of course. Unfortunately, this summer has been more of the same. I give him my affection. And in return, I put him at the mercy of assholes like Killfucker.

Today Jamie lost his star player. He'll probably never see that kid again. And it's all my fault.

Jamie's free hand warms my back while his other one preps me. "Baby," he whispers. "Can you take more?"

I nod into his neck. A second finger joins the first one. At first I struggle against the burn. *It's Jamie. It's okay.* Another deep breath and I make myself relax.

"That's it," he urges. "I want you to ride me, okay? And when you come, I want you to shoot all over my chest."

A bolt of lust races down my spine. I bear down on his fingers, and I'm rewarded with a brush against my prostate. Yes. That zing of pleasure makes me shiver, and I can feel Jamie's smile against my cheek.

After a few minutes, he gets me to three fingers. I start riding his hand in small thrusts. He murmurs encouragement while I ask my body for a little more stretch. It's been years since I tried this. I was hoping it would just seem easy, but like everything else in my life, I have to work for it.

But I do it. And it leaves me with yet another reason to appreciate Jamie. My daring, big-hearted man. He does this for me, and he makes it look easy.

He's amazing.

I sit up a little straighter, kissing him hard to let him know I'm ready. Jamie's mouth welcomes me in. I take a few more exquisite sips of him. For courage. Then I rise up on my knees, readying myself for him.

Jamie settles himself so he's propped up on the headboard, pillows at his back. He applies some lube to his cock, and the sight of him rubbing himself makes my mouth water. He positions himself beneath me.

Right then, with those brown eyes looking up, full of lust for me, he's the sexiest thing I've ever seen.

So I do it. I sink down onto his dick. Jamie's mouth opens on a silent groan, and those beautiful eyes go half-mast. The burn returns, but it's nothing I can't handle. I give myself a minute to adjust, and I use the time to take Jamie's gorgeous face in my hands. For a second I just admire the view. He's flushed and sex-tousled, burning up with arousal. I came to Lake Placid hoping we could still be friends. I got much more than that. And I'm so grateful.

The kiss I give him tries to let him know that. He's almost whimpering into my mouth now, so maybe he hears me. I give my hips an experimental thrust, and I like the results. So I brace my hands on Jamie's shoulders and begin to slowly fuck myself on him. I shift my hips until I get the angle just right. And when I do, it's miraculous. Pleasure pulses through my body each time I thrust. It's so, so good.

Beneath me, Jamie takes my weeping cock in hand. His lips are parted, his throat working. I see yearning anywhere I look at him. It's in the set of his jaw and in the ripple of his forearm while he jacks me.

He licks his lips. "If you come, you'll take me with you."

Now that he's said it, I really want to. Closing my eyes, I slow my pace and focus on the pleasure of each stroke. Out and in blur together. There's only the ruffle of bliss I get from him.

When I open my eyes again, it's Jamie's expression that finally takes me there. It's a cocktail of desire and wonder so potent that I feel myself tip over the edge. "Jamie," I gasp, chasing the sensation. Leaning into it.

I shoot and he shudders beneath me. I collapse on his messy chest before it's over. My lips land beside his ear and I moan quietly while my ass clenches around his cock.

"Jesus," he whispers.

Indeed. I wrap my arms around him and hold on for as long as I dare.

I honestly don't know how I'm ever going to give him up when summer comes to an end.

THIRTY-TWO

JAMIE

Camp is almost over. Seriously, these past five weeks have flown by. And now there's one week left and I can't wrap my brain around it. I guess time flies when you're playing hockey every day and getting laid every night.

As the afternoon scrimmage winds down, the kids are in high spirits. Correction—the offensive players are in high spirits. My goalies, on the other hand, are grumpy as hell. It was a high-scoring game for both sides, and there was no stopping Wes's forwards today.

Killfeather's absence is definitely noticeable. He had real talent. *Has*, I correct myself, because it's not like the kid dropped dead. His gay-bashing father decided that pulling his son from one of the most prestigious training facilities in the country was a *smart* move. You know, because Elites is crawling with perverts. Moron.

I skate over to the net, where my fifteen-year-old goalie lingers, scowling as he removes his helmet.

"I was dog shit today," Brighton informs me.

"You had an off day," I say with a smile. "But you weren't dog shit. You stopped more than you let in."

"I let in *seven*."

"It happens, kid. You did everything right out there." I'm not lying—Brighton heeded every piece of advice I gave him today. Just happened that Wes's advice to his forwards was better.

I blow my whistle to signal my other goalie, who looks equally glum as he skates over to us.

"I played like—"

"Let me guess, dog shit?" I cut in, grinning at Bradowski. "Yeah, Brighton and I just went over that. But you guys played hard today, and you played *well*. I don't want you going back to the dorm and sulking all night, okay?"

"Okay," they say in unison, but it doesn't sound too convincing.

I sigh. "Look at it this way. Brighton, you let in seven out of —" I call out to Georgie as he skates by us. "How many shots did Wes's boys take on net?"

"Thirty-five," Georgie calls back without stopping.

"Seven out of thirty-five," I tell Brighton. I do some quick math. "That's twenty percent. And Bradowski, you had eight get by you, but stopped about as many as Brighton. It's not a terrible statistic." I chuckle. "Coach Wesley and I used to challenge each other to shootouts all the time when we were training here. There were days when he'd slap five shots at me and every single one would hit its mark."

Wes's ears must be burning, because he suddenly appears beside me. "Everything okay here?"

"Yep. Just telling the boys about how you used to smoke my ass in shootouts."

When his brows shoot up, I realize he's thinking about the last time we faced off. Awesome. Now I'm thinking about it too, and I hope to God the kids don't see the blush on my cheeks.

"Yeah, Canning didn't stand a chance against me," Wes says, recovering quickly. "On either side of the goal, actually. Didn't matter if I was holding the stick or wearing the goalie pads—he lost every time."

I narrow my eyes. "Bullsh—uh, bullcrap. Are you forgetting who won the last one?"

I have to give Wes credit—he doesn't even blink this time, even though we both know he's remembering the outcome of that last shootout.

The boys snicker. "Rematch," Brighton blurts out.

Bradowski's eyes light up. "Shit! Yes!"

Wes and I exchange a look. We should really be hustling the kids into the showers so they're not late for dinner, but the boys aren't having it. Bradowski and Brighton are already whizzing away, calling out to the teenagers who haven't made it to the tunnel yet.

"Coach Canning and Coach Wesley are having a shootout!"

Well, then. I guess it's time for a shootout.

Wes winks at me and says, "Same stakes?"

"Damn straight."

We both grin at my choice of words.

Ten minutes later, we're suited up and getting in position. Our audience has grown—even the coaches are gathered around the boards, Pat included. I'm wearing full pads, because no way am I leaving myself unprotected while Toronto's new forward fires bullets at me.

Wes shows off his flashy moves as he skates toward the blue line, then stops and looks right at me. The wicked gleam in his eyes makes my pulse race. I can practically hear his unspoken taunt—*get ready to suck my dick, Canning*.

I take a breath and tap my stick against the ice. A whistle blows, and then Wes comes barreling toward me. One lightning-fast slapshot, and a loud cheer echoes in the rink. *Goal*.

Shit. He's not pulling any punches today. I brush it off and focus, defending against his next two shots and drawing my own cheers from the crowd.

Wes grins at me as he lines up the next puck. "Ready for this?"

The asshole has just repeated the same words he'd said to me last night right before he'd shoved his cock in my ass. All about the mind games, my boyfriend.

Wait, *what*?

The puck flies past me and I don't even stand a chance, because my brain is still tripping over that last thought.

My boyfriend? I thought I'd resigned myself to the fact that we weren't going to be together. And now I'm thinking of him as my *boyfriend*?

I shrug the cobwebs from my head and force myself to concentrate on defending the net. When my glove swallows up the last puck, I breathe in relief. I only let in two. Which means I need to score on him twice to tie, three for the win. Considering he's nowhere near as good as me in the crease, I can already taste the victory.

But he looks way too comfortable in front of that net. His gray eyes mock me behind the mask, and when he calls out, "Show me what you've got," there's laughter in his voice.

Cocky bastard thinks he can actually stop me.

Fuck. The cocky bastard *does* stop me. My first shot lands in his glove.

I grit my teeth and try to deke him out with the second attempt, but his hawk-like gaze isn't fooled. He stops this one with his pads, the next one with his stick. Shit. I need to sink the next two to tie.

The kids whoop in delight when my fourth attempt proves fruitful. It flies past Wes's shoulder and hits the net.

"Last shot," he says in a singsong voice. "You're totally gonna blow it, Canning!"

I know exactly what kind of blowing he's talking about.

Brighton gets a drum roll going by tapping his hands on the boards, and the other kids quickly follow suit. The beat matches the steady thumping of my heart. I take a breath, then skate forward. I pull my arm back, assess, and release a slapshot.

The puck hisses in the air.

I miss.

The kids go nuts as Wes leaves the net and skates up and down the boards to accept their high fives. I watch him in suspicion, wondering when he'd gotten so good at defending against the puck. Four years ago he'd been totally inept.

Shrugging the thought away, I accept my condolences from my goalies, who actually look kinda pleased I lost. I guess it made them realize even the best goaltenders suck sometimes.

As the kids file toward the locker rooms, Wes skates his way over to me and raises one eyebrow. "You're either slacking on your shooting drills, or you let me win that."

"Didn't let you win," I say through clenched teeth. Except then a thought occurs to me. That last shootout before college... had *he* let *me* win? Because the guy I saw in the net today was *not* the one I saw there four years ago...

I'm about to ask him point-blank when Pat interrupts us. "Canning," he says, appearing near the bench. "A word."

Wes claps a hand over my shoulder. "I'll see you in the dining hall."

We skate off in opposite directions, but Pat doesn't speak until Wes is well out of earshot.

"I got a call from a friend in Toronto this morning." As usual, Pat gets right to the point.

I tense up. "About the possibility of me coaching?"

He nods. "My buddy's name is Rodney Davenport. He's with the OHL, coaches one of the Junior A teams in the league. He's in Ottawa, but he's tight with the head coach of the

Toronto team—Bill Braddock. He spoke to Braddock on your behalf."

Surprise jolts through me. "He did?"

"I told Davenport all about you. Vouched for you." Pat shrugs. "You've got an interview in Toronto on the twenty-eighth."

"I do?" I'm dumbfounded. A part of me hadn't expected Pat to actually come through for me.

"It's an assistant coach position, defensive coordinator for a major juniors team, so you'd be working with kids ages sixteen to twenty. The interview is just a formality, though. The league was highly impressed with your level of experience."

Well, goddamn. I guess all those years of coaching here at Elites are coming in handy.

"I…" I don't know what to say. But then I realize there's an important question to address. "If I'm in Toronto with…" I clear my throat. I'm not ashamed; it's just that I've never had any practice talking about this. "What if there are other men like Mr. Killfeather?"

Pat yanks a piece of paper from his shirt pocket. "This is the league's anti-discrimination policy. I looked it up. Everything is, uh, covered."

I skim the words on the page. The league has pledged not to discriminate on the basis of race, religion, creed or sexual orientation.

"That's…helpful," I say, and Pat grins. "July twenty-eighth, huh?" Shit. That's next week, and three days before I report to Detroit. *If* I report to Detroit. The thought of showing up at training camp grows less and less appealing the closer it gets to the date.

Do I want to play in the pros?

Or do I want to help young, talented kids *get* to the pros?

"Braddock needs an answer by the end of the week," Pat tells me. "They had another candidate they were considering, so if you decide not to interview for the gig, they'll most likely give it to him."

My mind is still reeling, indecision surging through me. I should really talk to Wes before I do anything. He made it more than clear he won't be dating anyone when he's in Toronto. He *told* me to go to Detroit.

So yeah, I need to talk to him before I make any decisions.

But I have a sinking feeling I know exactly what he's going to say.

THIRTY-THREE
WES

Canning is acting weird. He barely said a word during dinner, and then he vetoed my suggestion about catching a movie in town, saying he just wanted to go back to the room.

As we climb the dormitory steps in silence, I wish I knew what was going on in that sexy head of his. He doesn't seem angry, or even upset. More like worried, which is so unlike Jamie it worries *me*.

"So what did Pat want to talk to you about earlier?" I'm trying to make conversation, but my question has the opposite effect.

"Just some coaching stuff," he answers. And then he clams up again.

I smother a sigh and follow him up to the second floor, admiring the way his faded jeans hug his ass. We've been in shorts and flip-flops all summer, but it's surprisingly cool out tonight, so now I get to experience Jamie in jeans. He looks fucking spectacular.

"Wanna watch something on your laptop?" I ask as I enter our room. "Cassel sent me this hilarious video of—"

His lips are on mine before I can finish that sentence.

Jamie pushes me up against the door and jams his tongue in

my mouth, and I instinctively kiss him back despite the WTF bells going off in my head. He grips my waist and grinds his lower body against mine, groaning roughly.

Jesus Christ. I'm not sure where this sudden onslaught of passion came from, but my dick sure appreciates it. After a minute or two, I'm an iron spike behind my zipper. Jamie notices, and his hands are almost frantic as he fumbles for the button of my jeans.

"Owe you a blowjob," he mumbles.

Right. The shootout. I'd forgotten about the prize. Not that it matters, seeing as we blow each other regularly without needing a shootout to justify it.

He tugs my pants and boxers down my hips, sinking to his knees with damn near desperation. The alarms in my head blare louder.

"Hey." I thread my fingers through his hair to still his frenzied movements. "What's gotten into you?"

"Nothing yet." He licks the head of my cock, and I see stars. "But I'm hoping *this* will get into me pretty soon."

Then he takes my entire length in his mouth, proving without a doubt he's picked up a few new tricks this summer. He can deep-throat like a champ now, and normally I'm all over that.

Tonight, something feels off.

His urgency thickens the air. I lean back against our door and try to give myself over to him, but in spite of his magic mouth, I can't quite focus. Slipping a hand under his chin, I urge him upward. "Come here."

Jamie gives one more good suck, which I feel down to my toes. When he stands, I turn us around so his back is to the door. Cupping his chin in both hands, I examine his gorgeous face. His cheeks are flushed, and his big brown eyes are full of some emotion I can't quite read.

I'm going to find out what's up, but first I kiss him. Once.

Twice. "Canning," I whisper. "We don't fuck until you tell me what's on your mind."

His eyes drop. "I might coach next year," he says, his voice hoarse.

"Really?" That's an idea I didn't know he'd considered. Depending on the job, it might be an interesting solution to his goalie woes. Though a part of me still thinks he'd be nuts to throw away a professional hockey career. "Where?"

"There's a defensive coordinator job for a major junior team..." He swallows. "In Toronto."

In Toronto. The words ricochet through my mind. For the briefest of seconds, my heart takes off like a rocket. I might have gotten around to giving a whoop of inappropriate glee, except I'm still staring into Jamie's wary eyes. He's always been the smarter of the two of us.

But I'm a quick study. So it's only a half-second later when my chest tightens, and my hands slip from his face. He actually flinches when they fall away.

I can't be with Jamie in Toronto. Because if we're found out, there won't be any reason for me to be in that city at all. I'm a fucking rookie, hoping to be lucky enough to make myself valuable to the team.

Another few seconds go by before I can bring myself to point this out to him. Because it's Jamie Canning we're talking about here. The odds of me ever loving anyone else like I love him are about as good as being attacked by a shark.

In Toronto.

But Jamie's odds of moving on are exponentially better. We've had a lot of fun this summer, but it can't possibly mean to him what it means to me. This beautiful man is probably more straight than not. And even if I'm wrong about that, there are now twice as many available partners for him on the planet than there were six weeks ago.

He can have anyone. And I won't ask him to wait around for me.

"Say something," he mutters.

I don't want to. There's heat behind my eyes, and my throat might crack. But I won't pussy out. He deserves my honesty for once.

"We can't be together in Toronto," I say.

Just six little words. But they make his eyes turn red.

"I'm sorry," I add. Sorry doesn't even begin to describe it.

He sidesteps me, moving away from the door. I take a moment to tuck myself back into my jeans. By the time I've done up my zipper, Jamie has made a frantic change into a pair of running shorts. He stuffs his feet into his shoes, not even taking the time to lace them.

"Going for a run," he grunts.

When he moves for the door, I move out of the way. It's precisely the opposite maneuver than I want to perform, and my heart is screaming at me to call him back.

But the door opens and shuts again with a snap, and he's gone.

Panicking now, I hurry over to our window. A minute later he bursts off the front porch and goes running down the street, shoelaces still trailing behind him.

Even after he's out of view, I need a minute of calm breathing to compose myself. I can't believe I just did that. It's not what I want. My thoughts zip around like a pinball while I search my brain for a solution to the problem.

But there isn't one. I've just spent a decade of my life trying to get this job in Toronto. I have a college degree in communications, like every other fucking jock on the planet. And a father who will have me tarred and feathered if I fuck up in Toronto.

Jamie Canning was my first crush and my first love. But he was never mine to have.

There's one silver lining here. Just one. I know Jamie's pissed right now because he's feeling rejected. That's never fun. But I know in my gut he'll move on. The Hollys of the world are waiting to take him back. Some cute girl will catch his eye before the week is through, and a few months from now, today's disaster will be just a bad memory.

As will I.

I swallow that thought down, then look on the closet floor for my suitcase.

THIRTY-FOUR
JAMIE

It's Sunday dinner at my parents' house in San Rafael, California. This time I'm not seeing it on Skype—I'm prepping the pasta course myself. I've minced a mountain of garlic, diced several onions and chopped a mountain of olives. We'll be ten for dinner tonight—the eight of us plus Tammy's husband and Jess's new boyfriend. Mom has had me in the kitchen for an hour and a half, and we're nowhere near ready.

As it happens, cooking is very therapeutic. I've got something to do with my hands, and I don't have to look anyone in the eye.

I've been home for forty-eight hours, and Mom is circling like a shark. She knows something is seriously wrong with me. All I've told her is that I'm having a career crisis. She knows about the interview scheduled three days from now, which conflicts with the fact that I'm supposed to be in Detroit six days from now.

Everything I've told her is true. But it's not *all* the truth. Choosing between two career paths is big stuff, but it's not nearly as painful as what Wes has done to me.

After that awful scene in our room, I went out to run. Three miles later, Wes was gone. I don't mean gone out for a drink—he was gone from camp. All his clothing had disappeared from our closet. His toiletries were gone.

His skates were gone.

I knew without asking that he wasn't coming back. When I went down to breakfast the next morning, Pat's face was full of sympathy. And when I asked Pat if he was sure he had enough coaches on hand the following week for me to take off for Cali, he said yes without even an argument.

I've spent the last two days trying not to mope around my room. Coincidentally, my parents' garden is well weeded. I've lost to my father at chess four times. And I finally finished that book I'd brought to camp.

But I just *ache* from the loss of my best friend / boyfriend / whatever. We never did get around to putting a label on it. And now we never will.

"Fuck!" I curse as the paring knife slices the top of my finger. The knife slips from my hand when I pinch the cut closed.

"James." My mother's voice is gentle. "Maybe you need a break." She doesn't even complain about the F-bomb I just dropped. So I must be acting like a real head case. "Let me find you a bandage," she says instead.

Two minutes later she's covered the wound. "I can sauté one-handed," I offer.

"How about you tell me what's bothering you instead?"

Now, I *could* do that. My parents wouldn't flinch at the idea of me being involved with a man. They're both California hippies all the way to the core. And if Wes and I had stayed together, I'd share it in a heartbeat. But there's no point in telling the story now. I'd just be buying myself a lifetime of teasing from my siblings. ("You need to know which shirt goes with those pants? Ask Jamie. He was gay once for a few weeks.") You can't just give five siblings that kind of ammo unless it's relevant.

And anyway, I'm saved from answering my mother's questions, because the kitchen door bangs open as the first wave begins to arrive.

"Jamester!" my sister Tammy yells. "Here. Hold this."

Before I can argue, there's a toddler in my arms.

"Fresh meat!" my sister cackles. And her husband slips past us both to get himself a beer.

I look down at the baby. "Um, hi," I say to Ty. I haven't seen him in two months, and I swear he's doubled in size.

"Hah," he answers around the four fingers he's got jammed in his mouth. Then he removes his drooly little hand and uses it to grab my nose.

The size of Tammy's smile doubles. "Good to have you back, kid." Tammy is thirty, but she's been calling me "kid" since she was twelve and I was four.

Ty and I fetch a beer from the refrigerator and head out to the deck where there's a sweeping view of the San Rafael bay in the distance. My parents bought this house thirty-four years ago before Joe was born. That's the only reason they can afford this sweet view in a great neighborhood. The house itself received two half-hearted additions as the family grew. We call it the Hodge Podge Lodge. In its current configuration, there are five bedrooms. As the youngest, I had my own room in this house for exactly one year before leaving for college. My life was a series of bunk beds, fights over the best-flavored cereals, and loud family meals.

I fucking love it here.

"I think I need to add a third thing to the list," I tell Ty. When I look down at him, he's staring back with wide brown eyes that are not unlike my own. "Detroit, Toronto or California?" I ask him.

Ty scrunches up his face and appears to consider the question. He's thinking about it *hard*. But then there's a small gassy sound. His face relaxes just as I begin to smell something foul.

"Did you just take a crap on my watch?" I ask the baby.

He gazes back, all innocence.

"There he *is!* Jamie!"

I spin around to find my other sister, Jess. And before she can react, I've walked over and handed her the baby. Then I give her a big kiss on the cheek. "Good to see you, sis."

"Did you just hand me a poopy nephew?"

"Is that what that smell is?"

"You!" Jess sputters. She and I are the youngest of the family. She's twenty-five, and the sibling I feel closest to. Which means we drive each other insane.

"No backsies," I add.

She rolls her eyes. "Fine. I'll go find the diaper bag. Get a beer for Raven, would you? Do something useful." She leaves the deck, walking past a man I've never seen before.

"You're..." Did she say *Raven?* What the hell kind of name is that?

"Raven," he says, and he holds out a fist for me to bump.

Seriously? I bump it, so as not to be rude.

"You're the hockey player," he says. His voice is kind of smoky, I realize.

"Sure," I reply noncommittally. Because who the hell knows what I'll decide to do by the end of the week.

"Cool," he says, sounding rather stoned. My sister sure can pick 'em. But when Raven puts his hip against the deck railing and crosses his arms, I notice the tats peeking out from the sleeves of his T-shirt and the curve of his bicep. Not bad.

Jesus Christ—now I'm checking out my sister's boyfriend. Argh! *Fuck you, Ryan Wesley. You see what you made me do?* But that's a ridiculous thought, and now I have the sudden urge to laugh like a hyena.

"You," I choke back a laugh, "want a beer?"

"Sure," he grunts. He's a real talker, our Raven. If Wes were here he'd…

Right.

Sigh.

Dinner is loud and fun, the way it's always been. Listening to my brothers' smack talk, I forget about Wes for a couple of hours at least.

"We got one professional athlete in the family," Scotty whines, "and he wastes it on hockey."

"It's not too late," his twin Brady argues. "Jamie could take up football. The Niners need defense, too."

"I've got it all figured out," my dad announces. "Jamie's team plays Anaheim in November…"

My stomach drops, because there's almost no chance he would see me play in that game.

"Which means we could all go to a Niners game together!" my father finishes.

Typical. At least if I do give up on the NHL, nobody will be too upset.

We tease Tammy about her round belly. And we tease Joe about his thinning hair. And when it's my turn to be teased, I hardly even hear it.

The day flies by in a whirl of gossip and taunts. Now the dishes are done and the peach pie is eaten up. Most of the clan has gone home, and it's down to me, my parents, Brady, and Scotty, who is staying here right now.

We're on the deck again, feet up on the railing, watching the sun go down as Scotty tells me his tale of woe. "She said, 'I don't want to be married to a cop.' And—honest to God—I tried to figure out how not to be one. I have a degree in criminal justice and seven years of work experience. And I seriously thought of chucking it."

My brother's voice is rough, and I feel a hell of a lot more than a simple pang of sympathy.

"But then I realized that it probably wouldn't matter. If she loved me, the job wouldn't matter. But she didn't. Not enough anyway."

Okay, *check, please*. There's a small but statistically significant chance I'm going to be crying into my beer in a minute. And won't that be fun to explain?

"At least I know I did everything I could," he adds. "I told her that I loved her, that I wanted the real deal. I made my case, and I made it strong. So I have no regrets."

Fuck. It's not like I can say the same thing. Wes pushed me away, and what did I do? I went for a run. I let him sneak off like a thief in the night. I didn't say, "I love you." I did not say it. Instead, I just choked it back.

I am a moron.

"Jamie?" my mother says gently.

"What?" I croak.

"You okay over there?"

Where do mothers get that ability? It's so fucking inconvenient. "I'm fine," I mutter, convincing nobody.

"Whoever she is, honey… If she matters to you, I hope you'll tell her."

Argh. I guess there's someone else I'll need to see after that interview in Toronto.

THIRTY-FIVE
WES

I approach the floor-to-ceiling windows of my potential apartment's living room, gazing at the panoramic view of Toronto's waterfront. It's definitely the best view of all the other apartments I've looked at today, but the calm water of Lake Ontario reminds me too much of Lake Placid. Of Jamie.

But who am I kidding? *Everything* reminds me of Jamie. Last night I couldn't even sit at the hotel bar without remembering the roadside place back at camp, where we shared our first kiss. This morning I walked past a candy shop and thought of the purple Skittles he'd bought me. At the last apartment I toured, I spent ten minutes staring at the futon bed on the floor remembering the two mattresses we slid together at the dorm.

I can't escape Jamie Canning, no matter how hard I try.

"You're not going to find a better deal in this neighborhood," the realtor chirps. She waltzes over and stands next to me, admiring the view. "Rent this low for a two-bedroom Harbourfront condo? It's unheard of."

I turn away from the window to study the huge open-concept room. The apartment isn't furnished, but I can already imagine how it would look with furniture. Leather couch and massive flat screen in the living area. A dining room table. Some tall stools for the eat-in breakfast counter.

I can picture myself living here, no doubt about it. And I have to admit, I'm a lot less likely to break my self-imposed celibacy rule in this neighborhood. The gay scene isn't as prominent here compared to the other areas I visited. One apartment was down the street from not one, but *three* gay bars.

Not that I'm looking to hit up any bars and sample the meat market. The idea of being with anyone other than Jamie absolutely kills me.

"And I'm not sure if this is a plus or a minus for you," the realtor continues, "but the owners told me they're planning on selling in a year or two. If you're already living here and looking to invest in real estate in the city, you'd be in a great position to buy this place."

I frown. "What if they decide to sell earlier and I'm not interesting in buying? Will I have to pick up and move?"

She shakes her head. "You'll be signing a one-year lease. You're guaranteed the place until the lease is up."

Fuck it. "I'll take it," I tell her. Because honestly? I'm tired of apartment hunting. I just need a place to sleep. Doesn't matter where.

Either way, my heart won't be in it. My heart is back in Lake Placid. Or maybe it's in California. It goes wherever Jamie Canning goes.

I feel like such a shit for walking out on him like that. But I've never been good with goodbyes. Which just proves I'm as immature and thoughtless now as I was four years ago. I cut him out of my life back then too. I guess that's my "thing".

I really am an asshole.

Oblivious to my self-hatred, party of one, the realtor's face lights up. "Wonderful. I'll draw up the paperwork this evening."

Five minutes later, I step out of the glass lobby onto the sidewalk, breathing in the warm July air. There's a streetcar stop a block away, so I shove my hands in my pockets and head toward it. I just want to get back to my hotel and spend the rest of the day doing nothing, but as I climb onto the streetcar, I decide against that.

I can't keep wallowing in misery. Canning and I are over. And in a few days, I'll be immersed in training, which won't leave me much time to explore my new home.

I grab a late lunch at a small café overlooking the lake, then wander around for a bit, slightly amazed by my surroundings. The streets are so clean, and the people are so damn polite. I can't even count how many times I hear the words "excuse me" and "sorry" and "thanks so much" in the two hours I spend exploring.

Eventually I go back to the hotel, where I take a quick shower before tackling the next item on the day's to-do list. Email agent —check. Find apartment—check.

Next up is a phone call to my father. Gee. Can't wait.

I dial my home number, then sit at the edge of the bed, already dreading hearing the sound of his voice. But my mom is the one who picks up the phone.

"Ryan, how nice to hear from you," she says in her crisp, emotionless tone.

Yeah, I'm sure she's thrilled. "Hi, Mom. How's everything in Boston?"

"It's lovely. I just walked through the door, actually. I was meeting with the historical society tonight. We're talking with the city about restoring the old library on Washington."

"Sounds fun." As if. "Is Dad around?"

"Yes. Let me ring him on the intercom for you."

Yup, our house in Beacon Hill has intercoms in every room, because that's how rich people roll. Who has time to walk into another room and hand someone a phone when they're so busy counting their piles of money?

My father comes on the line a moment later, greeting me coolly. "What is it, Ryan?"

Hello to you too, Dad. "Hey. I just wanted to talk to you about the *Sports Illustrated* interview."

He immediately goes on guard. "What about it?"

"I'm not going to do it." I pause. When he doesn't respond, I hurry on. "Rookie seasons are too unpredictable, Dad."

"I see." His tone is clipped. "And this has nothing to do with you wanting to hide your...activities...from the magazine?"

"It's not about that," I insist. "I can't have a reporter following me around for a whole year, especially if that year ends up being a bust." I clench my teeth. "As for my *activities*, you don't have to worry about that. As of this moment, it's a non-issue."

"I see," he says again. "Then it *was* a phase. " He sounds smug.

Yes, Dad. My sexuality is a phase. Who I am, to my very core, is a phase.

Bitterness clogs my throat, threatening to choke me alive. I can't deal with him right now. Or ever. But especially right now.

"Anyway, I appreciate the opportunity, but the interview won't be happening. Please thank your friend for me."

I hang up without saying goodbye, then bolt to my feet, resisting the urge to hit something. Am I a bad person for hating my parents? No, for *loathing* them? Sometimes I feel like I'm going straight to hell for the thoughts I harbor.

Biting the inside of my cheek, I glance around the suite. I guess I can watch some TV. Order room service. Do *something* to distract myself from thinking about Jamie or my parents or my fucked-up life.

But it feels like the walls are closing in on me. I need to get out of this room. I need to get out of my *head*.

I grab my wallet and keycard, tuck them in my pocket, and

hightail it out of the hotel. Once I'm on the sidewalk, I falter, because I honestly don't know where the hell I'm going. I consider ducking into the bar across the street for a drink, but I'm scared I won't stop at one. My first night in Toronto, I got blackout drunk, alternating between kneeling over the toilet puking my guts out, and curling up on my bed missing Jamie. I refuse to make that a habit.

I start walking. It's eight o'clock on a weekday, so stores are still open and the sidewalks are crowded. Nothing or no one catches my interest, though. So I keep walking. And then I walk some more, until the neon sign of a storefront in the distance snags my attention.

The tattoo parlor beckons me like a light at the end of a tunnel. I find myself walking toward it without really thinking about it, and suddenly I'm in front of the door.

I've been considering getting this done for a while now, but it felt too cheesy. Now, it feels bittersweet. And fitting.

I hesitate for a beat, then study the store hours posted next to the door. The shop's closing at nine. It's eight-twenty now. Chances are, it won't be enough time for the artist to see me, but I'm nothing if not impulsive.

A bell rings over the door as I stride inside and approach the longhaired guy behind the counter. He's in a black wife-beater, leaning back in a swivel chair with a magazine in his lap. His neck, arms and shoulders are covered in ink.

"Hey," he says easily. "How can I help you?"

"Do you take walk-ins?" I ask.

"Yep, but it depends on what you're getting done. Bigger pieces require multiple sittings." He gazes at the tats peeking out of my sleeves. "But you probably already knew that."

I look around, examining the photos plastered all over the walls. There are some incredible pieces up there. "Did you do all these?"

"Damn right I did." He grins. "Are you looking for a custom piece?"

"No, just something simple." I hold up my right wrist. "One line of text here."

"I can do that for you no problem." He rises from his chair and sets the magazine aside, then talks prices with me.

It's affordable, and I feel an instant trust toward the guy, so when he says, "Why don't you come on back?" I follow him without any further questions.

He leads me through a dark curtain into a workspace that's clean and uncluttered. That's a good sign.

"I'm Vin," he says.

I arch a brow. "Is your last name Diesel?"

He snickers. "Nope. It's Romano. Vin's short for Vincenzo. My family's Italian."

"I'm Wes."

We shake hands, and then he gestures to the chair. "Have a seat." After I sit down, he rolls up his sleeves and asks, "So what text do you want inked?"

I reach into my pocket for my phone, tapping on the screen to pull up the note I'd left in my notepad app. I find it, then hand him the phone. "Those numbers exactly."

He studies the screen. "You want it as numerals or spelled out?"

"Numerals."

"How big?"

"Half an inch maybe?"

Nodding, Vin grabs a sketchpad and scribbles down the numbers before handing the phone back. His pencil flies across the pad as he sketches something. A moment later, he holds up the page. "Something like this, maybe?"

I nod. "Perfect."

"You're easy to please." With a grin, he quickly bustles

around to prepare his station, grabbing supplies from a nearby cupboard while I scrutinize his every move. I'm pleased to see that the medical-grade needle he brings over is packaged, which means this shop is disposing of the needles after every use.

Vin settles in front of me. He snaps on a pair of latex gloves, takes the needle out of its packaging, then reaches for the tattoo gun.

"So where is it?" he asks.

I wrinkle my forehead. "Where's what?"

He swipes disinfectant over the inside of my right wrist. "Those numbers...they're longitude and latitude, right? Coordinates? Where would I wind up on the map if I looked them up?"

"Lake Placid," I say gruffly.

"Huh." He looks intrigued. "Why Lake Placid? And feel free to tell me to mind my own business, if you want."

I swallow. "No, it's fine. The place means a lot to me, that's all. I spent the best summers of my life there."

Vin pours black ink into one of the plastic cups on the tray in front of him. "I hate the summer."

I can't help but grin. You'd think someone who deals with the frigid Canadian winter for half the year would welcome the hot weather. "Why's that?"

"Because it always ends." He lets out a glum sigh. "We get, what, two, three months? And then it's gone and we're back to shivering in our long johns. Summer's a total cocktease." He shrugs, repeating himself. "It always ends."

He's right about that. Summer always ends.

THIRTY-SIX

JAMIE

I am nailing this interview. That's not me being cocky—it's just the truth.

My potential boss, Bill Braddock, is about forty years old, and a good guy, too. I can tell already. We've just spent forty minutes nerding out about the best methods for training forwards to be more responsible defensively. When Bill talks strategy, his eyes light up.

I want this job. I really do.

"Sorry," Bill says. "I got us off track again."

"That's quite all right," I answer. "This is the crux of it, right? Teaching kids to relax so they can defend their zone effectively."

He nods enthusiastically. "How did you learn to be so calm, anyway? I've seen your tape."

"Ah." I chuckle. "I'm the youngest of six kids. I was born into mayhem. It's all I know."

I've got Braddock laughing now. He actually slaps his own knee. "Priceless. Was it ever a drag?"

"Sure. When you have six kids, you're always losing one. And when you're the youngest, it's usually you. I remember standing in the cereal aisle of the grocery store, trying to decide between Cheerios and Chex. I'd look up and everyone would be gone. Once they left me at a rest stop outside Lake Tahoe. At least they only got fifteen miles away before they realized I wasn't in the car."

Bill is red-faced from laughing. "How old were you?"

"Seven? Eight? I don't know. But I knew not to panic."

"Incredible." He chuckles, then reaches a hand across the desk. "Come to work for me, Jamie. I think we'll get along great."

I lean in for the handshake. "I'd like to do that."

"It's a big decision, you can take the weekend…"

Now I shake my head. "I *want* to coach. I don't need the weekend."

He sits back, his expression telling me he's impressed. "Well, all right then. Can I hook you up with a rental agency? Housing is going to be a little tricky. Toronto is expensive. We pay our coaches what we can, but nobody's getting rich…"

"Yeah, I'm going to need to sort that out." For the first time in an hour, I think of Wes. He might be only a few miles away right now, looking for an apartment, too.

I need to speak to him—I've already decided that. But then I'll have to find a way to put him out of my mind. I don't want to always be looking for his face when I walk down the street.

Moving on is going to be hard.

I stand up and offer my hand one more time. Bill shakes it, still smiling as if he's just won the lottery. At least I'll be working for a good man. I'm hoping that means good things about this organization, too.

"Let me know how I can help you get settled in," Bill says, rising from his chair. "I mean it. Shoot me an email if you have any questions about neighborhoods or whatever."

"I'll do that."

Five minutes later, I'm outside again on the streets of Toronto, loosening the tie I'd worn to my interview. I missed lunch today, so I take a seat at an outdoor cafe on Lakeshore and order a wrap sandwich and iced coffee.

Toronto is a nice place. A big city, too. Somehow I have to find Wes today. I tried calling him this morning after I got off the plane, but his number has been disconnected. At first I'd panicked, thinking he'd gone to great lengths to shut me out. But when my phone carrier sent me a text explaining the international charges I was racking up in Canada, I realized Wes had probably switched to a Canadian carrier.

That has to be it, right?

Either way, I need another plan for reaching him quickly. I could go to the rink, but I doubt they'll let me just waltz in. And even if they do, Wes might not appreciate it…

My phone rings, startling me, and for a second my heart leaps. But of course the caller isn't Wes. The phone says HOLLY.

"Hi there," I answer, trying to keep my tone light. We haven't spoken since our awkward evening in Lake Placid, but I'm really hoping she meant what she said about us still being friends. "You'll never guess where I am right now."

She laughs, and the sound is comforting. "Not Detroit, then?"

"Nope. Toronto. I'm taking a coaching job."

"Really? That's great, Jamie. I'm so proud of you. Glad you went with your gut."

My heart swells a little. Everyone likes to hear they've done well. "Thanks. It's going to be an adjustment. Canadian money is funny looking."

Holly giggles. "Why Toronto? Are you going to tell me about your mystery woman?"

"Um…" *Ouch.* "Not sure if that's going to work out. And I'm not too happy about it."

"Oh honey." There's genuine sympathy in her voice. "I'm sorry. Why not?"

The waitress drops off my food, and I take a moment to thank her. "So," I say, glancing over my shoulder. I'm alone and outside, which is why I answered my phone in the first place. "Here's something that will crack you right up." I need to tell someone. And Holly will keep my secret. She's a good friend.

"What?"

"My mystery woman? There isn't one. I was seeing a guy."

There is deep silence for a moment. "Really?" She sounds incredulous.

"Really. Apparently I'm, um…" I've never said it out loud before. "Bisexual." There. That really wasn't so hard.

"I'm… Wow," Holly says. "I didn't see that coming."

"Me neither." I laugh. "It's been a really interesting summer."

"Who is he? Wait—that friend from the hotel! And the rink in Lake Placid! Ryan somebody."

Well, fuck. I forgot that women are so weirdly intuitive. "Holly, you can't tell anyone. It doesn't matter so much to me, but it could really hurt him."

Her sigh is loud in my ear. "I won't tell a soul. But…he *dumped* you? I'll kill him."

Now she has me smiling. "You are the best. Have I ever told you that?"

"Eh," she sighs. "I have my moments. Hey, now I can stop trying to figure out what sort of girl you'd fallen for. Wondering what she had that I don't was really taking up a lot of my free time. Now at least I know the answer—a dick."

I burst out laughing. "Damn, Holly. It's good to talk to you."

"Likewise."

When we hang up, there's still a smile on my face. I eat my lunch thinking of all the crazy things I've done these past six weeks.

And one memory in particular solves the problem of finding Wes.

I flag down the waitress and pull out my phone. I have an app to download.

THIRTY-SEVEN

WES

My first practice is brutal, but that's how I like it. Coach Harvey starts us off with a crossover drill designed to strengthen our ability to accelerate on curves, and it only takes five seconds for me to fully grasp that I'm in the big leagues now. *Nope, you're not in college anymore, Dorothy.*

This is a whole new level of intensity, and I'm sweating my balls off as I weave in and out of traffic, changing directions on Coach's whim. Pushing myself to keep up with players who've trained together for much longer than the five minutes I've been with them.

And it just picks up in intensity from there, but I'm cool with that. This is all I have. This is the choice I've made. Playing the best hockey I can will be the focus of my life for the next several years.

By the time we're done, I'm so sweaty there's steam rising from the inside of my helmet when I finally pull it off. My legs are like jelly as I walk down the chute into the locker room.

"Good hustle out there, man. You're gonna make a good addition," my teammate Tomkins says. He's three seasons in and doing well, so I'm pleased to hear him say it.

"Thanks. I'm happy to be here."

And I am. Mostly.

After a shower, I get dressed and leave the rink. I'm tired, and I don't need to be social anyway, because there's a team dinner starting in two hours.

I check my phone for calls, but there aren't any. The Brandr app has a new notification, though. That's weird, because I haven't messaged a soul since I came to Toronto. I've been a good boy. In fact, I should really just delete the fucking app. Lead me not into temptation, and all that.

But I read the notification anyway, just in case it's from someone I actually know. There's a message from a brand new profile, with a thumbnail picture I don't recognize. My thumb hovers over the delete button when the sender's name sinks in.

The message is from PurpleSkittle. And when I open it, his location is clocked at 3.3 km away.

There's an instant shimmy in my chest. Jamie Canning is in Toronto.

I steel myself as I open the message, because he's got to be so angry at me. But it's for the best.

Wes—I need fifteen minutes of your time. I'm going to take this coaching job, and there's something I want to say. We're going to share a city. It's a big one, but still. Tell me where we can meet. I don't care where—Starbucks or whatever the Canadian equivalent is.

Do me this favor.

J.

I am responding before I even think it through. I tell him yes. Not because it's the right thing to do, but because I'm powerless to say no. A coffee shop isn't the best idea, though. Too public. So I ask him to meet me at the empty apartment I've agreed to rent.

The real estate agent had asked me if I wanted to get in there to take measurements. That's a thing, apparently. I'd told her yes, and she'd left me a key at the front desk.

Now I'm racing there.

The concierge gives me the key and I tell him I'm expecting someone to look at the place with me. He promises to send him right up.

I ride the elevator with a hammering heart, and when I open the door to the apartment, I look at it with new eyes. It's too much space for one guy. I should have looked for a one-bedroom. Jamie is going to look at this place and think I walked away from him so that I could have a big NHL lifestyle. As if I give a fuck about the perks.

But the granite countertop and the cherry wood floors laugh at me. *This is what you wanted.*

I'm supposed to be here taking measurements, but I haven't even brought a measuring tape. And it's not the apartment I need to measure—it's the size of my balls. Jamie is on his way here to tell me I'm a fearful asshole, and I really can't argue the point.

When the knock comes, I'm not ready.

But I man up and open the door, and he walks through in a fucking suit and tie, looking hot enough to scorch me. I back up instinctively, because I cannot touch him. I've never had any willpower where Jamie Canning is concerned. And I'm done sending him mixed signals. I can't do that to him anymore.

"Hi," he says cautiously. "Nice place."

I shrug because my mouth is too dry to speak. His big brown eyes take in the room, which gives me a minute to admire this man I love, maybe for the last time. His face is tan, and his hair has been trimmed. I know exactly how soft it feels sifting through my fingers. And I know it's really a million different colors up close.

My ass hits the kitchen counter, and I almost stumble.

"You okay there?" he asks.

I nod, helpless. This is so hard. But I brought it on myself. I rest a hand on the granite countertop, and its cool temperature steadies me.

"Well, there's something I came here to say, even though I know you don't want to hear it."

Jamie's eyes search me, but I don't know for what. I'm done being a jerk to him, and I can't show him how I really feel. That leaves me mute. That's the best I can do.

"I don't know what you think happened this summer," he continues, fitting his hands into his trouser pockets. If this coaching thing doesn't work out, he should try becoming the CEO of a company somewhere. Because he really rocks the look. "In fact, I'm sure you've invented a lot of bullshit in that stubborn head of yours. You think you've corrupted me, or manipulated me, or some shit."

My face is hot now. Because I do think that.

"You think that I was just playing around. Taking a walk on the wild side. You think I'm just going to—" He brushes his hands together as if dusting them off. "—go back to girls. Chalk this up as an experiment."

Yeah, I think that, too.

"That's *not* what happened, Ryan. Not for me. What happened is that I got my best friend back for a little while, and I also fell for him." His voice thickens. "I'm not just saying that. I fucking *love* you, and I know that's inconvenient. But I didn't get a chance to tell you in Lake Placid, so I'm telling you right now. Just in case we can ever get more than a summer. I love you, and I wish things were different."

There's pressure in my ears, and the world goes a little blurry.

I find myself sinking down toward the floor, my back sliding along the expensive wood cabinet, my ass hitting polished cherry. My eyes are wet, so I look out the window. I see blue. That fucking view. It's beautiful, and I just don't care.

Because nothing is as beautiful as the man who just told me he loves my fucked-up self.

"Wes." The voice is soft, and it's coming closer. I hear the rustle of a suit jacket being removed. A few seconds later, Jamie seats himself on the floor beside me.

In my peripheral vision I see muscular forearms jutting from rolled-up shirtsleeves. He links his hands around his knees and sighs. "I didn't mean to upset you," he says quietly. "But it needed to be said."

He's *right there*. The clean scent of his shampoo and the warmth of his elbow against mine are overwhelming. I've missed him. So fucking much I've been walking around with a hollow chasm in my chest where my heart used to be.

But that gaping hole is full again. My heart is back, because Jamie is here.

And he fucking *loves* me.

My next breath escapes as a shudder. "I can't choose," I grind out.

"You've already chosen, and I understand why…"

I give my head a violent shake. "No. I mean it—I *can't* choose. I *won't* choose between you and hockey. I want both. Even if it's a disaster." I look at Jamie again, finally, just in time to see him wince.

"I do *not* want to be the reason your NHL career doesn't work out," he says vehemently. "I *get* it, Wes. I really do."

There's a tear running down my face and I don't even care. I scoop Jamie's hand off his knee and kiss it. He feels so fucking good.

"Sorry," I choke out. "We're going to have to work something out. I *love* you, goddamn it."

His breath hitches. "Yeah?"

"Fuck yeah. And I'm not letting you walk out of here."

"Ever?" he teases, squeezing my hand. "That's one way to prevent gossip."

I sigh. "We need a strategy. I have to stay out of the newspapers as long as I can."

"But, see, that's why—"

"Quiet, baby," I murmur. "Let me think for a second."

We can't lie forever to save my career—that isn't fair to Jamie. Maybe he hasn't thought it through, but I've been gay a long time and I know how much the closet sucks.

"I need to be sneaky until next June," I finally decide. "But that's it. And that's only if Toronto gets pretty far in the playoffs. Just one season."

"And then what?"

I shrug. "Then you can be my date at the next team barbecue or what-the-fuck-ever."

Jamie chuckles, but I'm dead serious. It only took one look at him today to realize I can't keep the parts of myself in separate drawers. It was never going to work.

"What if something happens before June? I mean…" He sighs again. "I can't lie to my family. I can ask them to be discreet, and they'll try. But I'm not kidding when I say that I don't want to be your downfall. Think hard about how much risk you're willing to take."

"You're worth it," I whisper. Fuck, *I'm* worth it. My change of heart isn't pure generosity. If Jamie is brave enough to walk in here and tell me he loves me, I've got to take some chances, too. "I'm going to have a talk with the PR department. I'm going to warn them."

His hand tightens on mine. "You can't be serious."

I turn my head against the little wooden wall where we're sitting. "I'm dead serious. It's my *life*, and yours. I've loved you for years, babe. If the NHL can't deal with it, then that's just the way it is."

Jamie's expression softens. "That will be a really bad day, though."

"No. A bad day is you giving up on me." I rake one hand through my hair, and he suddenly captures my wrist, his brown eyes narrowing.

"When did you get this done?"

He's looking at my new tat, and I feel sheepish as I answer, "Couple days after I left camp."

Rough fingertips skim the line of black ink. "What are these coordinates for?" I'm not surprised he's figured it out. My man is smart.

"Lake Placid," I tell him.

His eyes lock with mine. "I see." He clears his throat, but when he speaks again, his voice is still lined with gravel. "You really do love me, huh?"

"Always have." I swallow hard. "Always will."

It's not clear who moves first. But a second later our lips brush, then press together. I moan even before Jamie's tongue parts my lips. I kiss him hard, and he gives as good as he gets.

Time slips. Once we start kissing we don't stop. My lips are swollen and I'm so hard it's painful. But this isn't about sex. Each kiss is a promise of more to come. I know we need to stop. There are plans to make, and there's a dinner I have to get to, but each time I tell myself that *this* is the last kiss, I go back for one more. And then one more.

I pull back eventually. "You have to live here," I blurt out.

"Wha?" Jamie says, looking dazed. His cheeks are flushed and I've tousled his hair.

"A twenty-two-year-old rookie might have a roommate, especially an old hockey friend. It would actually be weirder if you were coming and going all the time."

He smiles, and I think he's going to make a joke about *coming* and going. "Did you just ask me to move in with you?"

"Well...yeah. Would you?"

Jamie's eyes sweep the room. "I can't afford this place."

I'm already shaking my head. "That is not going to be an issue. You can pay the utilities or some shit."

"I can't..."

"Yeah, you can. Consider it a gift for putting up with ten months of hiding."

"I can't pay *nothing*."

"Fine. Contribute what you would otherwise budget for rent money." I stand, offering him a hand. "Come on, let's have a tour." I don't want to talk about money. Fuck that.

Jamie takes my hand and follows me to the little hallway off the kitchen.

"We'll put a bed in this room, but it's not going to be our room. You can have a desk in here, though, if you need one for your job. It will give you a place to work."

This all seems so easy now. Toronto just became a place I really want to be. "And this is our bedroom." I walk him into the big room, which is slotted into a corner of the building. "See how private? When we fuck, nobody can hear us." I risk a look at Jamie, and his eyes are molten.

Fucking hell. Shouldn't have said that. I'm hard, and there's no time to do anything about it. "Wait. What time is it, anyway?"

He checks his watch. "Six."

Shit! "I have to be at this restaurant in a half hour. And my hotel is on the other side of town..." I look down at what I'm wearing. Track pants and flip-flops. Great. I'm going to be late for my first team event. *Goddamn it*. I chuckle, because it's either that or cry. And I've already done the latter today.

"Babe, do you want to wear this?" Jamie indicates his suit.

"Really?"

He shrugs. "You don't have to, but…"

"Let's try it." I laugh, because this is crazy. But that's what happens when he and I are together. Crazy happens.

And we *are* just about the same size. Jamie's waist might be a little wider than mine, but he's wearing a belt.

He's looking down at himself, doing the same math. "What size are your feet?"

"Ten and a half."

"I'm eleven," he says. "Close enough."

We're grinning like idiots as we strip off our clothes in the big empty bedroom. Jamie is down to only his dress socks, and I groan at the view. "I hope this dinner doesn't last too long. Will you stay with me tonight at the hotel?"

He licks his lips. "Sure. But you'll have to tell me where that is." He passes me his shirt and I put it on. It smells like him. I'm going to be horny all evening. The best kind of torture.

We make the switch and I don't look half bad. The jacket shoulders are a little wider than I'd wear them, but fuck, who cares. "I forgot something."

"What?"

I work on tying Jamie's tie, but there's no mirror, so it's slow going. "That night we were making the list of benefits of being gay? Borrowing your boyfriend's clothes."

Clucking his tongue, he pushes my hands out of the way and straightens the knot. "You look hot in my suit."

"You look hot in anything."

He reaches down and squeezes my dick through the wool trousers. "You get a blowjob later, just for saying that."

I groan. Then I have a thought so evil I almost can't say it with a straight face. "Tonight, I want you in nothing but my Toronto jersey."

Jamie sputters with laughter and gives my cheek a fake slap. "You ass. I'm not your puck bunny."

"Please? I've never fucked a puck bunny. This is my only chance."

He wraps his arms around my body and squeezes my ass. I receive a single, bruising kiss before he steps back. "Now give me your hotel key and go to your dinner already. No more lip."

When I step out onto the sidewalk a few minutes later, I'm a little dazed and walking carefully in shoes that are slightly too big.

And I've never felt better in my life.

THIRTY-EIGHT

AUGUST

Wes

At the end of my first week of training camp, Coach Harvey shifts the lines around and puts me in the second line with Eriksson and Forsberg. The latter led Chicago to a Stanley Cup win three seasons ago before being traded to Toronto. The former was tied for highest-scoring offensive player last season. And then there's me—Ryan Wesley, wet-behind-the-ears rookie, skating with two goddamn legends.

It's a promising sign, because that means they're seriously considering me for the roster this season, instead of sending me down to the farm team for more development.

Our shift lasts two minutes, and just before Coach shouts for a line change, I slap a one-timer past the goalie (another former Stanley Cup champ) and accept a vigorous back clap from Eriksson, who's grinning behind his facemask.

"Shi-it, kid, that was a beauty!"

The praise warms me up inside. And I'm even giddier when I notice Coach nodding in approval from the bench. "You've got solid instincts," he tells me when I heave myself over the boards a moment later. "No hesitation. I like that."

Is hearing that good for my ego? Damn right it is. These past two weeks, I've learned that praise from our head coach comes about as often as a solar eclipse. But even though he pushes us hard and is tough as nails, he's a nice guy when we're not on the ice, and the man sure knows his hockey.

Forsberg sidles up to me as I head down the chute, ruffling my hair like I'm a five-year-old. "You're fast, Wesley. Keep showing off that speed in practice, okay? I want you on my line."

My heart does a crazy somersault. Jesus Christ. How is this my life?

But my good mood doesn't stick. I'm scheduled to meet with one of the team publicists in thirty minutes, and depending on how that goes, practice might not be the only thing that's over today. My career might end, too.

Before it even begins.

I haven't changed my mind, though, no matter how many times Jamie has urged me to reconsider. I'm not giving him up. This next year might be tough for us, especially if my publicist goes all fire and brimstone on my ass to keep the relationship under wraps. But I know we can weather through it.

I love Jamie. I've *always* loved Jamie. And now that I know he feels the same way, I can't wait to see him again. To live with him again.

After accepting the coaching job and informing Detroit of his decision, Jamie went back to Lake Placid for two weeks. He told me this plan when we were lying in my hotel room after sex. And even in that blissed-out state, I'd thought it was a terrible idea. "Don't go," I'd argued. "I just got you back."

Smiling, he'd kissed me. "We can't get into the apartment yet, anyway. And Pat needs the help. Plus, this means you can focus all your energy on impressing your coach."

I miss the hell out of him, but I've done what he suggested. All I do is practice and talk to him on the phone at night. My lease on the condo began three days ago. I went shopping for the essentials—a king-sized mattress and a giant flat-screen TV. But that's all I'm buying until Jamie comes back next week to help me pick everything out.

Actually, I found an armchair on the curb yesterday and hauled it upstairs. But when I set it in front of the living room windows I noticed that it wobbled.

I snapped a pic of the chair and texted it to Jamie with a note about finding it outside. His response was fast and furious: *It has to go! People throw shit out for a reason! I bet you someone died on that chair!*

Tonight's agenda: getting rid of the death chair and going grocery shopping.

Look at me being all domestic. I'm kinda digging it.

After I've showered in the locker room and changed into my street clothes, I walk toward the elevator bank at the far end of the training arena. The PR guy agreed to meet me in the upstairs offices, saving me from having to trek to the team's head offices on the other end of the city during rush hour.

He waits for me in the corridor when I step off the elevator. I've already met him once before. It was after I signed my contract, when he'd given me an info packet about the promotional events I'll be expected to attend this season.

"Ryan," he says warmly, extending his hand. "Good to see you again."

"Frank," I greet him as we shake hands. "Thanks for coming down to meet with me."

"Anything for our new rookie superstar." He grins and gestures for me to follow him.

A moment later, we're seated in a small office with a view of the parking lot. Frank dons a wry look. "Not exactly the lap of luxury here. I can't even offer you anything to drink."

"That's fine. I just chugged two bottles of water in the locker room."

"I caught the end of practice. It looks like you're meshing well with the other guys."

"I think so," I admit. "Hopefully Coach agrees."

Frank smiles. "Trust me, kid, Hal loves you. I heard that when the coaches were going over the draft prospects, he refused to look at any other centers. You were his first and only choice."

Pleasure shoots through me. Then guilt. Because the thought of disappointing my new coach makes me sick to my stomach.

But the thought of not having Jamie in my life makes me even sicker.

"So, listen. I had something important to discuss with you," I start awkwardly.

Frank's expression goes serious. "Is everything okay? Someone giving you trouble?"

I shake my head. "No, nothing like that." A rueful sigh slips out. "If anything, I'm the one who's about to give *you* trouble."

He actually laughs. "Gotta tell you, lots of conversations start this way. By now, I'm unshockable, Ryan. Just hit me."

I clasp my hands in my lap to stop from fidgeting. "Frank... the roommate I listed as my emergency contact on my health forms? He's actually my boyfriend. But, uh, nobody else knows."

He doesn't even blink. "Right."

Right? Confusion fills my gut as I attempt to make sense of his response. It hadn't sounded sarcastic, like *riiiiight, sure he is*. It hadn't sounded hostile. It hadn't sounded like anything.

"I'm only telling you this, uh, because it could leak out. I'd never try to bring negative publicity to the team," I hurry on. "My sexual orientation has nothing to do with my skills as a hockey player. I plan on playing my ass off for this club, and I truly hope that who I date in my spare time won't affect my teammates' opinions of me as a player. But I also know the media will jump on this story if it gets out."

Frank is nodding now.

"I…" I take a breath. "I mean, I'm living with someone. It's serious. The only, um, scandal is that he's a he."

His lips twitch.

Fucking hell. Is he *laughing* at me?

I clench my teeth and force myself to continue. "We're willing to be as discreet as the team needs us to be, but we can't hide our relationship forever. We shouldn't have to." My breath comes out in a rush. "So I figured I'd disclose this information and let you and the team decide what happens next."

Frank leans forward, resting his arms on the desktop. "Ryan." He chuckles. "I appreciate you coming forward, but…we already knew about your sexual orientation."

I cough in surprise. "You did?"

"Son, we have a thorough vetting process for all our draft prospects. The last thing a club needs is to draft a kid in the first round, only to find out later that he's got a criminal record a mile-long or he's addicted to pills or has some other skeleton in his closet that might negatively impact the league."

Jesus. So they knew I was gay *before* they drafted me? How?

I voice the troubled thought. "How did you know?"

He chuckles again. "Were you trying to keep it a secret? Because from what we gleaned, your college teammates—and coaches—were well aware of it."

I'm…dumbfounded. "My coach *told* you?"

He shrugs like this is nothing surprising. "The coach didn't want you to hitch your wagon to a team that wouldn't treat you right. He did you a favor. And like I said, Hal was impressed with you, and not just with the level of talent you bring to the team. You're smart, discreet, you've got a good head on your shoulders. That's all that matters to him. To *us*."

"So…" I try to find my voice. "You guys don't care that I'm involved with another man?"

"Not at all." He folds his hands together. "In fact, I've already written the press release for whenever this eventually leaks. The organization has agreed on all the supportive language. We're ready."

I just sit there, my mind reeling. There's something tickling the back of my brain about this discussion. It almost sounds as if they're hoping to issue that press release. "What's in it for you?" I blurt.

He grins. "Faith in our fellow man?"

"Bullshit. What does this get you?"

Frank opens his hands in a gesture of humility. "Last year we traded Kim to Anaheim, and Owens to Miami. Because we had—"

"—too many right-handed D-men," I finish.

Frank nods. "Only Kim is Korean-American and Owens was…" He stares at the ceiling trying to remember. "I forget. But some dipshit sports reporter made a big stir about how we didn't want to be a diverse team. Someone jumped on that and started a petition that somehow gathered twenty-five thousand signatures."

I can't believe what I'm hearing. "So you drafted the faggot."

Frank rolls his eyes. "I'll have to ask you not to use that word, son. It's not nice."

My groan echoes off the walls of the office. "Please tell me you're not going to leak my sexual orientation the next time some asshole writes that Toronto isn't a PC organization. I don't want to be your pawn."

He grins. "We're not interested in turning you into a poster boy for gay athletes. We don't need to invite the circus to town—it always shows up eventually. But we won't be sending you out to face the media waving a rainbow flag, or ask you to give interviews touting yourself as the 'first openly gay player in the NHL.'"

He air-quotes the headline, chuckling again, and I realize they've put a lot of thought into this. And meanwhile, I've spent every waking moment since I got drafted worrying about how I would keep it under wraps.

"I gotta say, though. If you're telling me you're in a committed relationship, I'm doing a happy dance. When the press finally catches on to you, it won't be some photo of you in a skeezy bathhouse on Jarvis Street. I prefer the visual of you and your boyfriend having a candlelit dinner."

I open my mouth to argue with this bit of cynicism, and then discover I don't care enough to fight this fight. Toronto is keeping me, even if Jamie and I are outed. *That's all that matters*, I tell myself. And the man in front of me is paid to think like a jackass, just like I'm paid to think like a killer.

"Is there anything else you wanted to discuss, Ryan?"

I blink. "Um...no. That was it."

Frank scrapes his chair back and stands up. "Then I hope you don't mind if we cut this chat short. I need to speak to Hal before I head home to the wife and kids."

My legs are wobbly as I follow him to the door, where he stops to clap me on the shoulder. "You should come to dinner at our place sometime. Your boyfriend's welcome, too."

I blink again. What fucking *planet* am I on right now?

He grins at my confusion. "I know you're new to the city and probably haven't met a lot of folks yet. And my wife loves to host members of the team. She'll be thrilled if you came by."

"Oh. Um, sure, then. I appreciate the invite."

We go our separate ways once we reach the lobby. I'm not feeling too steady on my feet as I head outside and walk toward the subway stop. It's like a huge weight has been lifted off my shoulders, and I'm not sure how to handle the sensation it leaves behind. Lightness, giddiness. Relief.

I can't wait to tell Jamie.

THIRTY-NINE

JAMIE

It's been a long day of coaching.

Pat runs a two-week intensive at the end of camp, and we really fill the place up. Since the dorm is jam-packed, the kids who show up stay in condos with their parents. We max out our ice time, and we max out our waking hours.

It's tough, but I love it.

I'm on pins and needles all day, though, because Wes has his meeting with the PR guy. So after the last session of the day, I run back to the dorm. This morning I intentionally left my phone in the room so I wouldn't spend the day checking it.

There's something in front of my door. It's a FedEx package. When I pick it up, it's weightless.

I unlock the door and push inside my mostly empty room. Pat is still a coach short, which means it's a good thing I came back to help him.

Checking the phone is the first thing I do. There aren't any voicemails, and the only email is a solicitation for discount sunglasses. So I turn my attention to the package, tearing off the strip at the edge and opening the envelope.

A gift box falls out—the same one I recently filled with purple

Skittles. I yank open the top and find a piece of paper inside, grinning when I see a single purple Skittle taped to the page.

It's the result of recent medical tests on Mr. Ryan E. Wesley, Jr. Every STD known to man is listed there, and the word "negative" appears after each one.

He's scribbled something at the bottom: *I was going to fill this box with purple condoms, but then I had a better idea.*

Annnnd now I'm horny as well as impatient.

So I commence pacing the room.

When the email program on my phone pings a few minutes later, I yank it out of my pocket to read the message.

But it's not from Wes.

Dear Coach Canning,

I can't believe that I didn't get to finish the session with you. I'm still not speaking to my father, either. Working with you has been the best summer of my life, and I'm pissed that it ended on a bitter note.

My team for this year is the Storm Sharks U18. Here's the link, just in case you were ever curious about my stats. I think they're about to improve, and it's all because of you.

Sincerely,

Mark Killfeather, Jr.

I read the email twice. And then I read it one more time. It doesn't say a thing about Wes and me, and there aren't any slurs. Just a kid who wants to play hockey, and knows enough to say thank you to the people who've tried to help him.

Damn, I'm proud of this email. And I feel just a little more optimistic about life than I did five minutes ago.

I tap out a quick response, because I sure don't want to forget.

Killfeather—you are an amazing goalie and it was my pleasure to work with you this summer. Of course I'll check out your stats as the winter progresses. You're going to rock this season.

    Sincerely, Jamie Canning

Then I go back to pacing and worrying about Wes. What if they show him the door, and I'm not even there for him?

And where in Lake Placid can I get a blood test, like, tomorrow?

When my phone rings, I jump about a foot, then hurriedly swipe to answer. "Hey babe! You okay? What happened?"

"Yeah, I'm okay." His husky voice slides into my ear and wraps around my heart. I can hear that he's out on the street somewhere, and I wonder what he'll be able to tell me. "Damn, I wish you were here right now," he says.

I brace myself.

"I'd take you out to this Italian restaurant on Queen Street that the guys love. I'm starving and I want to tell you every word of the trippy conversation I just had."

I'm practically dizzy with stress right now. "What kind of conversation?"

"The good kind," he assures me.

My heart rate drops one notch, but I'm still afraid to be hopeful. Because it seems impossible to believe a high-profile NHL team would shrug off Wes's confession. None of this computes.

"But... wouldn't we *avoid* the places where your team likes to eat?" I ask slowly. "You know that means people will see us, right?"

"Yeah, but some day soon that's not going to matter."

"Really?" I want a guarantee. I want a notarized document.

I want a Valium. Or a blowjob. Or both.

"I'm having a really good day," Wes whispers.

My blood pressure drops again. "I'm glad," I whisper back.

"I love you," he adds.

"I know."

Wes laughs in my ear, and the happy sound of it is what convinces me we might be okay.

FORTY

JAMIE

On a Friday in mid-August I move in to our apartment. Though "moving in" requires air quotes, because we don't own much of anything.

Earlier in the week Wes ordered a couch—a macho leather thing, if I've understood the description correctly. It seems his taste runs to "early man cave," and I can't say I mind. He also picked up three bar stools for the kitchen island, which means we can put off worrying about an actual table.

Last night, after round one of our I-missed-you-so-much sexual marathon, Wes made a show of going to the grocery store, but he only came back with chips, dip and beer, which means I need to go back again and buy actual food. I may not have mentioned to him yet that I'm a pretty good cook. Wes seems prepared to survive on take-out, and in Toronto that's easily done. I'm going to have to acquire some pots and pans and blow his mind one of these days. That sounds like a whole lot of fun, actually.

Meanwhile, we blew each other's minds (and other parts) in our new bedroom last night. Then we passed out and slept for nine hours in our brand new king-sized bed.

Now it's Saturday, and there's still plenty to do. This morning, after breakfast at a diner, I drag Wes around Toronto for a few more necessary items. By the time we finally get home, Wes is in a state of agitation. I'm pretty sure I'm going to have to calm him down with a blowjob.

"That's three hours of my life I'm never getting back," he fusses as we walk in. His words echo, because our apartment is still awfully bare.

The reason for Wes's bad mood is the fact that shopping took three hours, because we're just a couple of jocks who don't know one store from another. We went into four stores before we found one that didn't look like the Queen of England was planning a visit. That's where we picked out a rug and coffee table, which we bought. But the place didn't stock coffee makers, so we had to keep shopping.

"Good coffee is non-negotiable," I told him while he grumbled. But after I chose a dual drip/espresso machine with an integrated grinder, I started checking out the towels. That's when Wes lost it a little bit, and I gave up and brought him home.

"Oh, the irony," he moans, kicking off his shoes. "My boyfriend dragged me to a fucking *mall*."

"You're right," I say drolly. "That trip was entirely gratuitous. Who needs towels? We can just air dry."

Grumpy Wes stomps into the bedroom and I follow him, because it's one of two functional rooms in our place.

I set down the coffee maker and watch while he throws off his shirt and climbs onto our giant bed. "Would you please get over here?" he whines. "It's an emergency."

"It's a good thing you're so attractive," I mutter as I ditch my shoes. "I had no idea that stepping into a store turned you into cryin' Ryan." I walk over to the bed where a shirtless, ripped man lies waiting for me, his expression burning up with lust.

"It doesn't usually," he mumbles. "But we have a situation."
He grabs my hand and tugs.

I climb onto his body, leaning down to tongue his nipple, and
he moans. "What kind of situation?" I ask between licks.

He lets out a shaky breath. "I thought it would be fun to wear
a plug out to breakfast today. That way you could fuck me when
we got home…"

My eyes snap up to his. "Seriously?"

He nods, his expression miserable. "But then you said, 'Let's
just look at a couple of rugs.' And that was, like, *hours* ago. Every
time I walk across another store, this thing massages my prostate.
If you don't fuck me in the next five minutes I'm going to
explode."

I'm speechless. But my dick has plenty to say. I'm already
hard at the idea of Wes being prepped and ready for me. I drop
my mouth onto his and he moans again. My tongue glides across
his piercing and we're off to the horny dog races.

We kiss as if there's a meteor heading straight for the Toronto
metropolitan area. Wes's eager hands roam my ass while I suck
on his tongue. His eagerness is like a drug, and I want hit after hit.
I can feel how hard he is, even through all of our clothes. He
wants me to fuck him, and he's all primed and ready?

"Mmm," I moan into his mouth. Sexiest fucking thing I ever
heard.

That's when the doorbell rings.

"Hold that thought," I say, pushing up on one arm.

"Nooooo!" Wes lifts both his legs to trap me in them. "No."
Kiss. "No." *Kiss.* "Don't even think about it."

Pinning his hands to the quilt is easy, because he's horny to
the point of distraction. "Stop it, baby. It's the couch delivery.
We're paying seventy-five bucks for them to show up on a
Saturday."

"I hate you," he says, but he releases me.

"I can tell," I argue, squeezing his hard dick as I climb off him. He moans one more time, cursing me, the sofa and also the universe.

I close the bedroom door for Wes's privacy and for my own sanity. I use the intercom to buzz down to the front desk, and I ask the doorman to send the sofa up on the freight elevator. Then I adjust myself and try to think about boring stuff to deflate the tent I'm pitching in my shorts.

But there *is* no boring stuff. I start my job next week, and I can't freaking wait. Meanwhile, I get to explore this gorgeous city where I'm living with the man whose company I've craved since I was thirteen. And moving in together isn't even scary. If you tally up all the weeks we'd spent at camp over the years, we've actually lived together for more than a year already.

There's a whole lot of sex involved now, of course. Everything is different, and yet it's exactly the same. And it's a whole lot of fun.

When I let the delivery guys in, there are three of them. "Where do you want it?" they ask.

"Anywhere over here," I indicate the living room. "We're going to have to move it when our rug comes, so it doesn't matter where."

"Nice place," the man in charge remarks, cracking his gum. His guys set the sofa in the middle of the space. It's wrapped in a lot of plastic, so I hope it's the one Wes ordered.

"Thanks." I sign for the sofa.

After they troop out, I close and lock the door, then walk over to the sofa and run a hand along the length of it. "Hey, Wesley!" I call loud enough for him to hear me behind the bedroom door. "Getcha ass out here!"

"No!" he counters.

I tug my shirt off. Then I drop my shorts. "I'm naked!"

That does it. He throws open the bedroom door and speed-walks down the hallway, nude, carrying a bottle of lube. By the time he reaches me, I'm sitting spread-eagled on the back of the sofa like a porn star, stroking myself.

Wes spares the couch a single glance. "Dude, my couch is wearing a condom."

I grab his hips and pull him close to me. "I noticed that," I say, kissing his jaw. "That's because it knows I'm about to bend you over it."

Wes groans. "Promises, promises." He slips a hand between our bodies and cups it over my hand. We stroke each other while our kisses grow deeper and hotter.

I reach around his body and cup his ass. When my hand finds the toy lodged there, I groan into his mouth.

"Do it," he pants.

Everything begins to happen very fast. With a firm grasp, I remove the toy, while Wes slicks up my dick. He yanks me off the sofa's back and braces himself against it. "Go," he orders.

I come up behind him and grip his hips, the head of my cock sliding between his taut ass cheeks. Just like the other night, I'm floored by the sensation of being skin to skin. There's no barrier between my throbbing dick and his tight ass, and when I drive deep on the first stroke, we both groan with abandon.

"*Fuck* me," he demands when I go still.

But I'm too busy savoring the incredible feeling of being inside him without a condom. I roll my hips and he growls like a grumpy bear.

"I swear to God, Canning, if you don't move, I'm gonna—"

I pull out, then slam right back in. He makes a choked sound, his entire body trembling.

"You're gonna what?" I ask mockingly.

Rather than answer, he just moans again. Low, agonized. Shit, he's desperate for it. I guess I would be too if I'd walked around all day with a plug rubbing on my prostate.

I smooth my hand down his strong back, then lean in and plant a kiss between his shoulder blades as I withdraw again. "I like you like this," I murmur. "That sexy ass in the air. Having you at my mercy. Hearing you beg."

He blows out a breath. "You're a sadist."

Laughing, I quicken the pace. Three, four frantic thrusts before I slow down again, which draws a strangled groan from his lips.

"You need to learn some patience," I tell him. But shit, I'm teasing myself as much as I'm teasing him. My balls are so tight they hurt, already tingling with the telltale signs of impending release.

"Screw patience," he grumbles. "Wanna come."

"Sulking ain't helping your cause, dude."

"No? How about this then?" He pushes his ass back against me and starts fucking my cock, fast and greedy.

Holy hell. There's no way I can hold back now. It's too good. I'm too horny.

My fingers dig into his hips as I slam into him, each deep thrust sending me closer and closer to the edge. Our breathing grows labored as our bodies slap together, but I need more. I need… I plant my hands on his chest and tug him up so his back is plastered to me. The new angle makes him cry out in pleasure, and then he twists his head toward me and our lips meet in a scorching kiss that fogs my brain.

We're joined in every way possible. My cock inside him, our tongues fused together, his powerful body straining against mine.

I reach around him and grip his erection, slowing the movement of my hips. I jerk him in long, lazy strokes that match the languid thrusts of my cock.

"I don't come until you do," I whisper. Then I slip my tongue in his mouth and suck on his tongue ring, and that's all it takes for him to shoot all over my hand.

Wes gasps for air. His ass ripples around my cock, squeezing me so hard it triggers an orgasm I feel in the tips of my fingers and the soles of my feet. I give in to it, my arms wrapped around my boyfriend's strong chest as I come inside him.

We're both unsteady on our feet, so I pull out and tug him onto the couch. He collapses beside me, his dark hair tickling my chin as we lie there recovering from yet another round of spectacular sex. I don't think I'll ever get used to how good the sex is.

Wes suddenly laughs. "Thank God for the couch condom."

"Wha…" I grin when I realize what he means. "The bareback thing is kinda messy, huh?"

"Messy's fun." His breath heats my shoulder. "But once the plastic comes off, we should probably lay down a towel or something if we're going to fuck on this couch."

"If?" The way we go at it, there won't be a single surface in this apartment we haven't fucked on.

He chuckles again, then releases a contented sigh and nestles even closer.

As it happens, snuggling on a plastic-wrapped couch is not that comfortable.

So we have a quick shower together, then lie down on the bed. We're wet, of course, and our hair is dripping.

"I'm beginning to see your point about towels," Wes says as I kiss a drop of water off his shoulder.

"Now he gets it," I sigh, and then hunt for more drops on his taut skin. I lick the barbell in his eyebrow, and the slightly metallic taste makes me shiver. I love having my own personal bad boy in bed with me.

Wes strokes a lazy hand up and down my back, and it's

divine. "We need towels, and a plug for you. So you can walk a mile in my horny shoes."

"That was so hot, though," I concede. "Damn."

He runs a hand through my wet hair. "Glad you liked it. I wanted to make it easier for you."

"What?" There's something serious in his tone, so I stop kissing him everywhere to look him in the eye. "Easier?"

But he looks away. "You know. Easier. When you were with women, it didn't take them half a fucking hour to prepare for sex."

A chuckle rises in my throat, but I choke it back because his expression is so serious. "How many women have you fucked, Wes?"

Sheepish, he holds up one finger.

I'm startled for a second, until I remember the summer we were sixteen, when Wes had shown up at camp and admitted to losing his virginity. Getting the dirty details out of him, however, had been like pulling teeth. Now I know why.

"Right, *one*. And you were both too inexperienced to know what you were doing." I shrug. "*Plenty* of women need a lot of warm-up time. So I have to call a technical foul here just on rules alone. But also—that's just not the point. We have a lot of quick and dirty times. That's what blowjobs are for."

He gives me a weak grin. "Sure. But…"

"But *what*?"

"Well, I'll never be able give you everything you like."

Ah. "Dude, stop. I'm not pining for pussy." That sounded *much* funnier coming out of my mouth than I'd expected it to, so we both laugh. "I'm serious, though. I enjoyed women, but I was never in love with one." Every time I say it, it seems more obvious. And every time I say it, Wes's face goes soft. "Can you promise me you won't worry about this? Because there's no way I can prove it to you, except by having lots of sex with you."

"That works." His cocky smile is back, and I'm happy to see it.

"Good." I roll over and fit myself against him. "In a little while I have to check my Facebook page."

"Why?"

My stomach tightens just thinking about it. "Tomorrow is Sunday dinner, right? So I outed myself to them today."

"On Facebook?" he yelps.

I reach back and give his ass a pinch. "Give me a little credit? My family has a private group. It's just the kids, their spouses and my parents. I didn't even tell them your last name."

He goes very quiet behind me, but his hand traces lazy circles on my back. "Are you worried?" he finally asks.

That's a fair question. "Not really. They won't freak about the fact that you're a dude. But they might be like, 'Why didn't you tell us? Is this why you quit the NHL? And why did you leave the country?' I don't like to be grilled."

"When did you post it?"

"This morning before we went out for breakfast. So, like, five hours ago. It's one o'clock in Cali right now. They've probably seen it."

"Go get your phone," he whispers.

FORTY-ONE

WES

I wait on the bed by myself saying an unlikely prayer for Jamie. He is quite possibly the most laidback person I've ever met. I love that about him. But it makes him vulnerable. People can be assholes about smaller stuff than their brother having a gay relationship. If anyone has said something ugly to Jamie on that Facebook page, I'll probably punch something.

He doesn't come back, though. And then I hear a groan from the living room.

That gets me on my feet and running through the apartment. I find Jamie perched on the edge of the condom couch, his face in his hands.

My stomach lurches. I don't want this for Jamie. It's taken me four years to get over my parents' reaction to my coming out. Hell, I'm probably still not over it.

He holds out his phone to me, and I take it with a shaking hand.

His Facebook post is pure Jamie:

Hi all. I feel like a heel doing this over Facebook, but I can't reach everyone by tomorrow. You're all going to discuss me on Sunday, anyway. And in case you think my account was hacked, it wasn't. As proof I'll confess that I'm the one who broke Mom's Christmas tree angel when I was seven. It was death by baseball, but I swear she didn't suffer.

Anyway, I have to catch you up on a few developments. I've taken the coaching job in Toronto, and I've declined my spot in Detroit. This feels like the right career move, but there's something else. I'm living with my boyfriend (that was not a typo.) His name is Wes, and we met at Lake Placid about nine years ago.

In case you were lacking something to talk about over dinner, I've fixed that problem. Love you all.

Jamie

Beneath the post there's a selfie that we took yesterday. We're in our new kitchen, and the groceries I'd just bought are strewn around. Jamie was teasing me about my shopping habits, and I was giving him shit about something. I don't even remember what. But we'd leaned our heads together, and I'm making the sign of the devil. And we just look so fucking happy, I practically don't even recognize myself.

I scroll down to the comments, and my stomach rolls over in dread.

<u>Joe</u>: *OMG. Jamester, really? You did not just confess to dating a Patriots fan. That is a sin, little brother. I fear for your everlasting soul.*

I squint at the picture and sure enough I'm wearing my Super Bowl 2015 Victory shirt. Whoops.

<u>Tammy</u>: *Joe, you asshole! Don't listen to him, Jamie. Your boyfriend is hot. And Jess owes me twenty bucks.*

<u>Brady</u>: *I'm going to have to side with Joe on this one. What if football comes up at Thanksgiving? If your boyfriend wants to talk about balls, it's going to be awkward!*

<u>Joe</u>: **High fives Brady**

<u>Jess</u>: *I do not owe you twenty bucks! You said he was moping about a GIRL.*

<u>Tammy</u>: *I said "a relationship."*

<u>Jess</u>: **cough* *bullshit**

<u>Mrs. Canning</u>: *Jess, language! Jamie honey, when are you bringing your boyfriend home for Sunday dinner? And are those Doritos in the background? Is there Whole Foods in Canada? I'm going to look on their website and send you the address.*

<u>Mrs. Canning</u>: *And thank you for telling me about the angel. I knew it was you, though, sweetie. You've never been good at deception.*

<u>Scotty</u>: *Jamie, Dad can't remember his Facebook password. But he says to tell you he loves you no matter what and blah blah blah.*

That's when I snort, and Jamie looks up. "They're pretty ridiculous, right?"

"I think they're…" I have to swallow hard, because I'm so happy for him. "I think they're great."

He shrugs. "I spent my whole life trying to stand out from the crowd. I swear to God, I could announce I wanted to live my life as a transsexual vampire yeti, and they'd still say 'Oh, Jamie. You're so cute.'"

It's a challenge for me to swallow again, but this time because of the massive lump obstructing my throat.

As always, Jamie senses my distress. This man knows me, inside and out. He always has. "What's wrong?"

"Nothing's wrong. It's just…" I speak past the lump. "You're really lucky, Canning. Your family loves you. I mean, they really, truly love you, and not just because you're related by blood and they *have* to love you."

His brown eyes soften. I know he's thinking about *my* family, but I don't give him the chance to make excuses for my folks.

"My mother is a trophy wife," I say roughly. "And I'm a

trophy son. Neither one of my parents ever saw me as anything more than that, and they never will. It...sucks."

Jamie tugs me toward him. "Yeah, it sucks," he agrees. "But here's the thing about family, Ryan...blood doesn't mean shit. You just need to surround yourself with people who do love you, and *they* become your family."

I sink down on the couch beside him, the plastic crinkling beneath my boxers. He slings one muscular arm around me, then brushes his lips over my temple. "I'm your family, babe." He takes the phone from my hand and taps the screen. "And these crazy maniacs? They'll be your family too if you let them. I mean, they'll fucking drive you bananas sometimes, but trust me when I say it's totally worth it."

I believe him. "I can't wait to meet them," I say softly.

His mouth travels along the edge of my jaw before hovering over my lips. "They're going to love you." He kisses me, slow and sweet. "*I* love you."

I rub the pad of my thumb over his bottom lip. "Loved you every summer since I was thirteen years old. Love you even more now."

Our lips are millimeters from meeting again when he says, "I need to know something, and you have to promise to be honest."

"I'm always honest with you," I protest.

"Good. I'm holding you to that." Those gorgeous brown eyes gleam. "Did you throw the shootout?"

I know exactly which shootout he's referring to. My lips quiver, so I press them together to keep from grinning.

"Well?"

I shrug.

"Wesley..." There's a warning note in his voice now. "Tell me what happened during that shootout."

"Well." I hesitate. "I really don't know. I was terrified to win, because I knew I'd have to let you off the hook. And I was terrified of losing, because I wanted to touch you so bad, and I was afraid you'd figure that out."

His face is full of sympathy, but I don't need it anymore. It's water under the bridge now. I lean closer and kiss him on the nose. "So, those last two shots? I hardly remember what happened. I was all—*Jesus, take the wheel!*"

Jamie laughs at me. And then he kisses me. I lock my hands at the nape of his neck and tug him closer. Warm skin slides against mine, and I know I'm home.

Because home is with *him*.

EPILOGUE

Wes

Thanksgiving

"Ryan Theodore Wesley! Put that knife down this instant!"

I freeze like an ice sculpture as Jamie's mother barrels toward me, one hand planted on her hip, the other pointing to the chef's knife in my hand.

"Who taught you how to chop onions?" she demands.

I glance down at the cutting board in front of me. As far as I can tell, I haven't committed any major onion-related crimes.

"Um…" I meet Cindy Canning's eyes. "Well, that's kind of a trick question. Nobody *taught* me, per se. My parents have a cook that comes in four times a week to prepare meals and—wait, I'm sorry, did you call me Ryan *Theodore*?"

She waves her hand as if the question is inconsequential. "I don't know your middle name so I had to make one up. Because, sweetie, you really needed to be middle-named for mangling those poor onions."

I can't stop the laugh that flies out of my mouth. Jamie's mother is so fucking awesome. I'm far more relaxed in her kitchen than I expected to be.

Jamie and I arrived in California two days ago, but since I had a game the first night, Jamie went to his folks' place while I stayed at the hotel with my teammates. After the team crushed San Jose, I did the usual post-game press, and then yesterday morning I drove up to San Rafael to join Jamie and his family.

The big holiday meal today will be the real test of their acceptance. I've already met Jamie's mom and dad and one brother. So far, so good.

"These need to be chopped into smaller pieces," Cindy tells me. She smacks my butt to move me aside, then takes my place. "Have a seat at the counter. You can watch while I chop. Take notes if you need to."

I grin at her. "So I guess Jamie didn't tell you how much I suck at cooking, huh?"

"He most certainly did not." She fixes me with a stern look. "But you'll have to learn, because I can't spend all my time worrying that my baby boy isn't being fed over there in Siberia."

"Toronto," I correct with a snort. "And I'm sure you can guess he's the one who's been feeding me."

Now that the hockey season is underway, life is hectic as fuck. Practice is brutal, and our schedule is exhausting. Jamie's my rock, though. He comes to all my home games, and when I drag my tired self home from the airport after an away game, he's waiting there to rub my shoulders, or shove food down my throat, or screw me until I can't see straight.

Our apartment is my safe place, my haven. I can't even believe I considered trying to make it through my rookie season without him.

It's easy to figure out where he got that nurturing gene from, because his mom has been fussing over me all day.

Another snort sounds from the doorway, and then Jamie's father strides into the kitchen. "Toronto," he echoes. "What kind of city doesn't have a football team? Explain that to me, Wes."

"They do have one," I point out. "The Argonauts."

Richard narrows his eyes. "Is it an NFL team?"

"Well, no, it's CFL, but—"

"Then they don't have a team," he says firmly.

I stifle a laugh. Jamie warned me that his family was football fanatics, but I genuinely thought he was exaggerating.

"Where's Jamie?" Richard glances around the kitchen as if he expects Jamie to pop out of a cupboard.

"He went to pick up Jess," Cindy tells her husband. "She wants to have a few drinks tonight so she's leaving her car at home."

Richard nods in approval. "Good girl," he says, as if Jess can somehow hear him all the way across town.

I have to admit I was terrified to meet Jamie's family. I mean, I already know they're good people. But a father and three older brothers? I had this nagging fear they'd hate me just on principle. You know, for being the guy who's fucking their baby boy.

But Jamie's dad has been great, and I've already met Scott, who's staying here at the house. The three of us went out for beers at a sports bar last night, and when the highlights from the previous night's games played on the TV screens, Scott had clapped his hands against the table and shouted, "That's my brother!" every time I skated into view. And when the goal I scored late in the second flashed on the screen? Jamie and Scott went nuts.

Yup, my first ever NHL goal. I'm still fucking ecstatic about it. This past month, I've been seeing more and more playing time, and last night was a record for me—twelve minutes of ice time, and a goal for my efforts. Life is good.

So good, in fact, I'm feeling more generous than usual, which is why I slide off my stool and say, "Will you excuse me for a moment? I need to call my folks to wish them a happy Thanksgiving."

Jamie's mother beams at me. "Aw, that's so sweet of you. Go ahead."

I duck out and fish my phone out of my pocket. Fuck, I'm even smiling as I dial my parents' number in Boston. The smile fades fast, however. It always does when I hear my father's voice.

"Hey, Dad," I say gruffly. "Is this a good time?"

"Actually, it isn't. Your mother and I are on our way out. We have reservations at six."

Of course they do. The only time my family held a Thanksgiving dinner at home was the year the president of my dad's brokerage firm was going through a divorce. The guy had nowhere to go, so he invited himself over to our place, and my mother hired a gourmet caterer to cook a fucking banquet for us.

"What did you want, Ryan?" he asks briskly.

"I…just wanted to say Happy Thanksgiving," I mumble.

"Oh. Well, thank you. Same to you, son."

He disconnects the call. Without even putting my mother on the line. Then again, he speaks for both of them.

I stare at the phone long after he hangs up, wondering what I did in another life to lose so royally in the parent lottery. But the depressing thought doesn't have time to take root, because the front door suddenly flies open and I'm assaulted with *noise*.

Footsteps. Voices. Loud laughter and happy squeals. It sounds like an entire platoon has marched into the house. Which is pretty much the case, because holy shit, Jamie's family is huge.

I feel an unfamiliar surge of nerves in my chest.

Within seconds, I'm surrounded, being yanked in all directions and hugged by people I've never met in my life. Introductions fly around, but I can barely keep up with the names. I'm too busy answering all the questions being hurled my way like slapshots.

"Did Jamester give you a tour of the house?" *Yes*.

"Has Mom shown you the pictures from the Halloween when Jamie dressed up as an eggplant?" *No, but that should be corrected immediately*.

"Do you get a monetary bonus every time you score a goal?" *Um...*

"Are you in love with my brother?"

"*Tammy*!" Jamie sputters as his older sister voices that last question.

I look up and find him in the mob, and it's like the sun just came out. It's only been an hour since I saw him last, but he has the same damn effect on me every time.

I used to fight my reaction to him, but I don't have to anymore. And that's more shocking than the way his family seems ready to embrace the complete stranger who's shacking up with their brother. Unless they're just really good actors.

Jamie slips between his siblings and slings his arm around my shoulder. "Leave the poor guy alone, will ya? He just got here yesterday."

His brother Joe snorts. "You think we're gonna go easy on him because he's only been here a day? Have you met us?"

Jess wiggles her way between me and Jamie and links her arm through mine. "Come on, Wes, let's get you a drink. I find it's easier to tolerate these dum-dums when you're drunk."

I snicker as she drags me toward the dining room, but Jamie's mom calls out from the kitchen just as we pass by. "Jessica, I need Wes! Jamie, too. You can raid the liquor cabinet later."

"I wasn't going to raid the—" Jess stops abruptly and turns to me, heaving a defeated sigh. "I swear that woman is a mind reader."

I find myself being ushered into the kitchen again, except this time Jamie is by my side. As his mom gestures for us to wait, he brings his mouth close to my ear and says, "Are we having fun yet?"

"Yes," I say truthfully. Because fuck, the Canning clan has been great. Maybe I can stop worrying so much. Maybe there's one corner of the world where I don't have to prove myself all the time. Okay—two corners. Because life in a certain Toronto condo is going really well, too.

"Okay, boys, here's your housewarming present."

I look up to see Jamie's mom setting two gift boxes on the counter. One says "Jamie" on the tag and the other "Ryan."

"Aw," Jamie says. "You didn't have to do that."

"My last bird has flown out of the nest." Cindy sighs. "If I can't see your apartment, at least I can give you a little something for it."

"You can see it," I hear myself volunteer. "Come visit."

Jamie and I lock eyes then, and there's humor in his. Maybe he's thinking the same thing I am—if his mom visits, we'll have to hide all the sex toys in the bathroom cabinet.

"I'll do that!" she says cheerily. "Now open them!"

The siblings crowd us as Jamie and I each open a box. I lift the lid and push some tissue paper aside. Then I pull out a gorgeous hand-thrown coffee mug. It says "HIS" on the side. I hear laughter and look over at Jamie's gift.

Another mug reading "HIS."

"Mom!" Jess hollers. "The point of labeled mugs is so that they can tell them apart! You should have done their initials."

"But that wouldn't *amuse* me," his mother explains, grinning.

"Thanks," I chuckle while my boyfriend laughs.

I turn the mug over in my hands, imagining Cindy making this for me in her pottery studio. The glaze is glossy and bright, the cup broad and solid in my hands. It's beautiful, and receiving it from her feels like the membership card to a club I really want to join.

Grasping the handle, I turn the mug upside down to see if she's signed it. Sure enough, there's something etched into the unglazed bottom. I have to squint to read the tiny letters.

Dear Ryan. Thank you for making Jamie so happy. He loves you and so do we. Welcome to the Canning clan.

Oh boy. There's a burn at the back of my throat, and I concentrate hard on settling the mug back into the box. I spend more time than necessary tucking the tissue paper around it with the care of someone performing neurosurgery. When I'm finally ready to look up again, Jamie's mom is waiting for me. The warm look in her eye makes the sting in my throat even worse.

I try to give her a casual smile, but I can't quite pull it off. Nobody's ever said anything so sweet to me. Nobody except Jamie.

As if I've summoned him, a warm hand slides onto my lower back. I adjust my stance just a fractional degree, leaning in to that hand.

Cindy is still watching us. She gives a quick wink I know is just for me. Then, just as quickly, her face is all business. She claps her hands once. "Okay, troops! The turkey is in the oven, but there's still some heavy lifting to be done! I need someone to sauté the vegetables for stuffing. I need someone to start the grill. I need two people to whip the cream! And the rest of you get the heck out of my kitchen."

Without ceasing their chatter, the Cannings move around the

kitchen, opening and shutting cabinets and passing around bottles of beer. Jamie doesn't leave my side, though. He and I are the calm eye of a friendly, familial hurricane.

And I hope the storm will never pass.

THE END

ALSO BY SARINA BOWEN & ELLE KENNEDY

Need more from Wes and Jamie?

US (Him #2)

EPIC (Him #2.5)

GOOD BOY (for Jess and Blake)

STAY (Hailey and Matt)

And don't miss our other gay romance:

TOP SECRET by Sarina Bowen & Elle Kennedy

9 781954 500495

AN INTRODUCTION TO BUDDHIST ETHICS

This systematic introduction to Buddhist ethics is aimed at anyone interested in Buddhism, including students, scholars and general readers. Peter Harvey is the author of the acclaimed *Introduction to Buddhism* (Cambridge, 1990), and his new book is written in a clear style, assuming no prior knowledge. At the same time it develops a careful, probing analysis of the nature and practical dynamics of Buddhist ethics both in its unifying themes and in the particularities of different Buddhist traditions. The book applies Buddhist ethics to a range of issues of contemporary concern: humanity's relationship with the rest of nature; economics; war and peace; euthanasia; abortion; sexual equality; and homosexuality. Professor Harvey draws on texts of the main Buddhist traditions, and on historical and contemporary accounts of the behaviour of Buddhists, to describe existing Buddhist ethics, to assess different views within it, and to extend its application into new areas.

PETER HARVEY is Professor of Buddhist Studies at the University of Sunderland. Co-founder of the UK Association for Buddhist Studies, he was the first Professor specifically of 'Buddhist Studies' in the UK. He also serves on the editorial board of the very successful Internet *Journal of Buddhist Ethics* and that of *Contemporary Studies in Buddhism*.

AN INTRODUCTION TO BUDDHIST ETHICS

Foundations, Values and Issues

PETER HARVEY

University of Sunderland

CAMBRIDGE
UNIVERSITY PRESS

PUBLISHED BY THE PRESS SYNDICATE OF THE UNIVERSITY OF CAMBRIDGE
The Pitt Building, Trumpington Street, Cambridge, United Kingdom

CAMBRIDGE UNIVERSITY PRESS
The Edinburgh Building, Cambridge CB2 2RU, UK   www.cup.cam.ac.uk
40 West 20th Street, New York, NY 10011-4211, USA   www.cup.org
10 Stamford Road, Oakleigh, Melbourne 3166, Australia
Ruiz de Alarcón 13, 28014 Madrid, Spain

© Cambridge University Press, 2000

First published 2000

Printed in the United Kingdom at the University Press, Cambridge

Typeface Monotype Baskerville 11/12½ pt.   *System* QuarkXPress™ [SE]

A catalogue record for this book is available from the British Library

Library of Congress cataloguing in publication data

Harvey, Peter (Brian Peter)
An introduction to Buddhist ethics: foundations, values and
issues / Peter Harvey.
p. cm.
Includes bibliographical references and index.
ISBN 0 521 55394 6 (hb)
1. Buddhist ethics. I. Title.
BJ1289.H37 2000
294.3′5–dc21   99–27718   CIP

ISBN 0 521 55394 6 hardback
ISBN 0 521 55640 6 paperback

Not to do any evil,
to cultivate what is wholesome,
to purify one's mind:
this is the teaching of the Buddhas

(Dhammapada, verse 183)

Contents

Plates

Acknowledgements

My thanks to Damien Keown, of Goldsmith's College, London, and co-editor of the Internet *Journal of Buddhist Ethics* for comments on aspects of chapters 7 and 8, and to my research student Liz Williams for checking and offering comments on a draft of this work, especially on chapter 9, and for help with the indexes. Over many years, while teaching a University of Sunderland final-year undergraduate module, Ethics in Buddhism, Christianity and Islam, both my colleagues Dr James Francis and Phil André and our students have also helped me to reflect further on Buddhist ethics.

Abbreviations

Note that below:
Th. = a text of the Pali Canon or later Theravān literature
My. = a Mahāyāna text in Sanskrit, Chinese or Tibetan

A.   *Aṅguttara Nikāya* (Th.); (tr. F. L. Woodward and E. M. Hare), *The Book of Gradual Sayings*, 5 vols., London, PTS, 1932–6.

A. A.   Commentary on *A.*; untranslated.

AKB.   *Abhidharma-kośa-bhāṣyam* [of Vasubandhu; a Sarvāstivāda work]; (tr. from Louis de La Vallée Poussin's French translation by Leo M. Pruden, *Abhidharmakośabhāṣyam*), Berkeley, Calif., Asian Humanities Press, 1988–90. References are to chapter and section numbers in original text.

Asl.   *Aṭṭhasālinī* [Buddhaghosa's commentary on *Dhs.*] (Th.); (tr. Pe Maung Tin), *The Expositor*, 2 vols., London, PTS, 1920 and 1921.

ASP.   *Ārya-satyaka-parivarta* (My.); (tr. L. Jamspal), *The Range of the Bodhisattva: A Study of an Early Mahāyānasūtra, 'Āryasatyakaparivarta', Discourse of the Truth Teller*, Columbia University Ph.D. thesis, reproduced on microfiche, Ann Arbor, UMI, 1991 (Tibetan text and translation, with introduction, pp. 1–73). References are to page numbers of the translation.

Asta.   *Aṣṭasāhasrikā Prajñā-pāramitā Sūtra* (My.); (tr. E. Conze), *The Perfection of Wisdom in Eight Thousand Lines, and its Verse Summary*, Bolinas, Four Seasons Foundation, 1973.

Bca.   *Bodhi-caryāvatāra* [of Śāntideva] (My.); translations as in: Shantideva, *A Guide to the Bodhisattva's Way of Life (Bodhisattvacharyavatara)*, tr. from Tibetan by S. Batchelor, Dharamsala, India, Library of Tibetan Works and Archives, 1979. References to chapter and verse. Other translations are:

Crosby, K. and Skilton, A., *Śāntideva: The Bodhicaryāvatāra*, World's Classics, Oxford and New York, Oxford University Press, 1996.

Matics, M. L., *Entering the Path of Enlightenment: The Bodhicaryāvatāra of the Buddhist Poet Śāntideva* (from Sanskrit), London, George Allen & Unwin, 1971.

BCE   Before the Christian era.

BPS   Buddhist Publication Society

Bv.   *Buddhavaṃsa* (Th.); (tr. I. B. Horner), in *Minor Anthologies*, vol. III, London, PTS, 1975. Also includes translation of *Cp.*

c.   *circa.*

CE   Christian Era.

Cp.   *Cariyāpiṭaka* (Th.); (tr. I. B. Horner), in *Minor Anthologies*, vol. III, London, PTS, 1975. Also includes translation of *Bv.*

D.   *Dīgha Nikāya* (Th.); (tr. T. W. and C. A. F. Rhys Davids), *Dialogues of the Buddha*, 3 vols., London, PTS, 1899–1921. Also translated by M. Walshe, *Thus Have I Heard: The Long Discourses of the Buddha*, London, Wisdom Publications, 1987, in one volume.

D. A.   Commentary on *D.*; untranslated.

Dhp.   *Dhammapada* (Th.); (tr. Nārada Thera), *The Dhammapada*, London, John Murray, 1954 (the same translation, accompanied by the Pali text, is also published by the Buddhist Missionary Society, Kuala Lumpur, 1978 – available from Wisdom Publications, London); (tr. Acharya Buddharakkhita), *The Dhammapada: The Buddha's Path of Wisdom*, Kandy, Sri Lanka, BPS, 1985. In verse.

Dhp. A.   *Dhammapada Commentary* (Th.); (tr. E. W. Burlingame), *Buddhist Legends*, 3 vols., Harvard Oriental Series, Cambridge, Mass., Harvard University Press, 1921; repr. London, PTS, 1979.

Dhs.   *Dhamma-saṅgaṇī* (Th.); (tr. C. A. F. Rhys Davids), *Buddhist Psychological Ethics*, London, PTS, 1900, 3rd edn, 1974.

It.   *Itivuttaka* (Th.); (tr. F. L. Woodward), *As it was Said*, in *Minor Anthologies, Part II*, London, PTS, 1935; also tr. J. D. Ireland, *The Itivuttaka: The Buddha's Sayings*, Kandy, Sri Lanka, BPS, 1991.

J.   *Jātaka with Commentary* (Th.); (tr. by various hands under E. B. Cowell), *The Jātaka or Stories of the Buddha's Former Births*, 6 vols., London, PTS, 1895–1907.

Khp.   *Khuddaka-pāṭha* (Th.); (tr. with its commentary, Bhikkhu Ñāṇamoli), *Minor Readings and Illustrator*, London, PTS, 1960.

Khp. A.   Buddhaghosa's commentary on *Khp.*

Kvu. *Kathāvatthu* (Th.); (tr. S. Z. Aung and C. A. F. Rhys Davids), *Points of Controversy*, London, PTS, 1915.

M. *Majjhima Nikāya* (Th.); (tr. I. B. Horner), *Middle Length Sayings*, 3 vols., London, PTS, 1954–9. Also tr. Bhikkhu Ñāṇamoli and Bhikkhu Bodhi, *The Middle Length Discourses of the Buddha*, Boston, Mass., Wisdom, 1995, in one volume.

M. A. Commentary on *M.*; untranslated.

Miln. *Milindapañha* (Th.); (tr. I. B. Horner), *Milinda's Questions*, 2 vols., London, PTS, 1963 and 1964.

Miln. Ṭ. Commentary on *Miln.*, untranslated.

Mvs. *Mahāvastu* [of the Lokottaravāda school]; (tr. J. J. Jones), *The Mahāvastu, Translated from the Buddhist Sanskrit*, 3 vols., London, PTS, 1949–56.

Nd. II. *Cullaniddesa* (Th.); untranslated.

Ps. *Paṭisambhidā-magga* (Th.); (tr. Bhikkhu Ñāṇamoli), *The Path of Discrimination*, London, PTS, 1982.

PTS Pali Text Society.

Pug. *Puggala-paññatti* (Th.); (tr. B. C. Law), *Designation of Human Types*, London, PTS, 1969.

Pv. *Petavatthu* (Th.); (tr. H. S. Gehman), *The Minor Anthologies of the Pali Canon, Part IV* (also includes a translation of *Vv.* by I. B. Horner), London, PTS, 1974. References to chapter and story number.

RPR. *Rāja-parikathā-ratnamālā* [of Nāgārjuna] (My.); (tr. J. Hopkins and Lati Rinpoche), Nagarjuna and the Seventh Dalai Lama, *The Precious Garland and the Song of the Four Mindfulnesses*, London, George Allen & Unwin, 1975 (also includes translation of a short text by the Seventh Dalai Lama). Reference is to verse number.

S. *Saṃyutta Nikāya* (Th.); (tr. C. A. F. Rhys Davids and F. L. Woodward), *The Book of Kindred Sayings*, 5 vols., London, PTS, 1917–30.

S. A. Commentary on *S.*; untranslated.

Skt Sanskrit.

Sn. *Sutta-nipāta* (Th.); (tr. K. R. Norman), *The Group of Discourses (Sutta-Nipāta) Volume I* (in paperback, *The Rhinoceros Horn and Other Early Buddhist Poems*), London, PTS, 1984; revised translation by Norman, with detailed notes, *The Group of Discourses (Sutta-Nipāta) Volume II*, Oxford, PTS, 1992. Also tr. H. Saddhatissa, *The Sutta-Nipāta*, London, Curzon Press, 1985. In verse.

Ss.   *Śikṣā-samuccaya* (My.); (tr. C. Bendall and W. H. D. Rouse, *Śikṣā Samuccaya: A Compendium of Buddhist Doctrine, Compiled by Śāntideva Chiefly from the Early Mahāyāna Sūtras*, Delhi, Motilal Banarsidass, 1971 (1st edn, 1922). References are to translation pagination.

Svb. *Suvarṇa-bhāsottama Sūtra* (My.); (tr. R. E. Emmerick), *The Sūtra of Golden Light*, London, Luzac & Co., 1970. Reference to Sanskrit pagination, as indicated in Emmerick's translation.

Taishō *Taishō Daizōkyō*: Japanese edition of the Chinese Buddhist Canon, published 1924–9.

Thag. *Thera-gāthā* (Th.); (tr. K. R. Norman), *Elders' Verses*, vol. I, London, PTS, 1969. In verse.

Thig. *Therī-gāthā* (Th.); (tr. K. R. Norman), *Elders' Verses*, vol. II, London, PTS, 1971. This translation is also found, with C. A. F. Rhys Davids' 1937 translation of the texts and extracts from the commentary, *Psalms of the Sisters*, in C. A. F. Rhys Davids and K. R. Norman, *Poems of Early Buddhist Nuns*, Oxford, PTS, 1989. In verse.

Thig. A. Commentary on *Thig.*; (tr. W. Pruitt), *The Commentary on the Verses of the Therīs*, Oxford, PTS, 1998.

Ud.   *Udāna* (Th.); (tr. F. L. Woodward), *Verses of Uplift*, in *Minor Anthologies Part II*, London, PTS, 1935. Also tr. P. Masefield, *The Udāna*, Oxford, PTS, 1994, and J. D. Ireland, *The Udāna: Inspired Utterances of the Buddha*, Kandy, Sri Lanka, BPS, 1990.

Ud. A. Commentary on *Ud.* (tr. P. Masefield), *The Udāna Commentary*, vol. I, Oxford, PTS, 1994.

Uss. *Upāsaka-śīla Sūtra* (My.); (tr. Heng-ching Shih), *The Sutra on Upāsaka Precepts*, Berkeley, Numata Center for Buddhist Translation and Research, Bukkyō Dendō Kyōkai, 1994 (translation from Chinese of Taishō, vol. 241034a–1075b, no. 1488). References are to translation pagination.

Vc.   *Vajracchedikā Prajñā-pāramitā Sūtra* (My.); (tr. and explained by E. Conze), in *Buddhist Wisdom Books: The Diamond Sutra and the Heart Sutra*, London, George Allen & Unwin, 1958.

Vibh. *Vibhaṅga* (Th.); (tr. U. Thittila), *The Book of Analysis*, London, PTS, 1969.

Vin. *Vinaya Piṭaka* (Th.); (tr. I. B. Horner), *The Book of the Discipline*, 6 vols., London, PTS, 1938–66. *Vin.* III and IV are translated as *Book of the Discipline*, vols. I, II and III, and *Vin.* I and II are translated as *Book of the Discipline*, vols. IV and V. Note, also, that in

Horner's translations, the page number of the original Pali text, which appears in bold in the midst of the English, means 'Page *x ends* here.' In all other translations by the PTS, it means 'Page *x starts* here.'

Vin. A.   Commentary on *Vin.*; untranslated directly into English, but translated from the Chinese translation: Bapat and Hirakawa, 1970.

Vism.   *Visuddhimagga* [of Buddhaghosa] (Th.); (tr. Bhikkhu Ñāṇamoli), *The Path of Purification*, 3rd edn, Kandy, Sri Lanka, BPS, 1975, and 2 vols., Berkeley, Calif., Shambhala, 1976.

Vv.   *Vimānavatthu* (Th.); (tr. I. B. Horner), *The Minor Anthologies of the Pali Canon, Part IV* (also includes a translation of *Pv.* by H. S. Gehman), London, PTS, 1974. References to story number.

Vv. A.   Commentary on *Vv.*; untranslated.

WFBR   *World Fellowship of Buddhists Review.*

Most of these works are still in print; reprints have only been mentioned where the publisher differs from the original one. Translations given in this book are not necessarily the same as the cited translations, particularly in the case of translations from Pali. For Theravāda texts, the references are to the volume and page number of the edition of the text by the PTS, or to the verse number for texts in verse. The page numbers of the relevant edition of an original text are generally given in brackets in its translation, or at the top of the page. The volume number of the translation generally corresponds to the volume of the PTS edition of the texts, except for the *Vinaya* (see above).

A note on language and pronunciation

Most of the foreign words in this work are from Pali and Sanskrit, which are closely related languages of ancient India. Pali is the scriptural, liturgical and scholarly language of Southern Buddhism, one of the three main cultural traditions of Buddhism. Sanskrit, or rather 'Buddhist Hybrid Sanskrit', is the language in which many of the scriptures and scholarly treatises of Mahāyāna Buddhism came to be written in India. Northern and Eastern Buddhism, where the Mahāyāna form of Buddhism predominates, generally use the Tibetan or Chinese translations of these texts. Many works on Buddhism give only Sanskrit versions of words, but this is artificial as Sanskrit is no longer used by Buddhists (except in Nepal), but Pali is still much in use.

This work therefore uses Pali versions of terms for most of early Buddhism, for Southern/Theravāda Buddhism, and when discussing Buddhism in general. Sanskrit versions are used when particularly discussing Mahāyāna forms of Buddhism, for some early schools which also came to use Sanskrit, and when discussing Hinduism. Sanskrit is also used for certain key terms that have come to be known in English: *Nirvāṇa* (Pali *Nibbāna*), *karma* (Pali *kamma*), *Bodhisattva* (Pali *Bodhisatta*) and *Stūpa* (Pali *Thūpa*). In many cases, Pali and Sanskrit terms are spelt the same. Where they are spelt differently, the Pali spelling is the simpler.

Both Pali and Sanskrit have more than twenty-six letters, which means that when they are written in the roman alphabet, the extra letters need to be represented by the use of diacritical marks. Once the specific sounds of the letters are known, Pali and Sanskrit words are then pronounced as they are written, unlike English ones. It is therefore worth taking account of the diacritical marks, as they give a clear guide to pronunciation. The letters are pronounced as follows:

(i)   *a* is short and flat, like the *u* in 'hut' or 'utter'

     i is short, like *i* in 'bit'

     u is like *u* in 'put', or *oo* in 'foot'

       e is like *e* in 'bed', only pronounced long

       o is long, like *o* in 'note' (or, before more than one consonant, more like *o* in 'not' or 'odd').

(ii)   A bar over a vowel makes it long:

       ā is like *a* in 'barn'

       ī is like *ee* in 'beet'

       ū is like *u* in 'brute'.

(iii)   When there is a dot under a letter (*ṭ, ḍ, ṇ, ṣ, ṛ, ḷ*), this means that it is a 'cerebral' letter. Imagine a dot on the roof of one's mouth that one must touch with one's tongue when saying these letters. This produces a characteristically 'Indian' sound. It also makes *ṣ* into a *sh* sound, and *ṛ* into *ri*.

(iv)   *ś* is like a normal *sh* sound.

(v)   Aspirated consonants (*kh, gh, ch, jh, th, dh, th, dh, ph, bh*) are accompanied by a strong breath-pulse from the chest, as when uttering English consonants very emphatically. For example:

       ch is like *ch-h* in 'church-hall'

       th is like *t-h* in 'hot-house'

       ph is like *p-h* in 'cup-handle'.

       When aspirated consonants occur as part of a consonant cluster, the aspiration comes at the end of the cluster.

(vi)   *c* is like *ch* in 'choose'.

(vii) *ñ* is like *ny* in 'canyon'; *ññ* is like *nnyy*.

(viii) *ṃ* is a pure nasal sound, made when the mouth is closed but air escapes through the nose, with the vocal chords vibrating; it approximates to *ng*.

(ix)   *ṅ* is an *ng*, nasal sound said from the mouth, rather than the nose.

(x)   *ḥ* is like a normal *h* sound, but followed by a faint echo of the preceding vowel.

(xi)   *v* may be somewhat similar to English *v* when at the start of a word, or between vowels, but like *w* when combined with another consonant.

(xii) Double consonants are always pronounced long: for example *nn* is as in 'unnecessary'.

All other letters are pronounced as in English.

ō is used to denote a long *o* in Japanese (as in 'note', rather than 'not'). For Tibetan words, this book gives a form which indicates the pronunciation, followed by the Wylie form of writing Tibetan in roman script, which includes unpronounced letters.

Introduction

Buddhist ethics as a field of academic study in the West is not new, but in recent years has experienced a considerable expansion, as seen, for example, in the very successful Internet *Journal of Buddhist Ethics.* The schools of Buddhism have rich traditions of thought on ethics, though this is often scattered through a variety of works which also deal with other topics. This book aims to be an integrative over-view of ethics in the different Buddhist traditions, showing the strong continuities as well as divergencies between them. It seeks to do this in a way that addresses issues which are currently of concern in Western thought on ethics and society, so as to clarify the Buddhist perspective(s) on these and make Buddhist ethics more easily available to Western thinkers on these issues. In exploring Buddhist ethics, this work aims to look at what the scriptures and key thinkers have said as well as at how things work out in practice among Buddhists, whose adherence may be at various levels, and who naturally operate in a world in which their religion is only one of the factors that affect their behaviour. Even when Buddhists fall short of their ethical ideals, the way that they tend to do so itself tells one something about the way the religion functions as a living system.

Chapters 1–3 prepare the way for looking at ethical issues by exploring the framework of Buddhist ethics in terms of the foundations of ethics in Buddhism's world-view(s), and the key values which arise from this. While the ethical guidelines of different religions and philosophies have much in common, each is based on a certain view of the world and of human beings' place in it. Such a world-view gives particular emphases to the related ethical system, gives it a particular kind of rationale, and provides particular forms of motivation for acting in accord with it. A religion is more than beliefs and ethics, though, so its ethics also need to be understood in the context of its full range of practices.

1

The term 'ethics' is used in this work to cover:

(1) thought on the bases and justification of moral guidelines (normative ethics), and on the meaning of moral terms (meta-ethics);

(2) specific moral guidelines (applied ethics);

(3) how people actually behave (descriptive ethics).

David Little and Sumner Twiss, in their work on comparative religious ethics, have defined a 'moral' statement as one which addresses problems of co-operation among humans. It gives an 'action-guide' for individuals and groups so as to initiate, preserve or extend some form of co-operation, by guiding actions, character, emotions, attitudes etc. that impinge on this. Morality is 'other-regarding': focused on the effect of our actions etc. on others (1978: 28–9). While this is a reasonable view, it is an incomplete one for Buddhist morality, as this is also concerned with the quality of our interactions with non-human sentient beings too.

Moral 'action-guides' demand attention, though they sometimes conflict with each other – should one protect someone by lying to someone else? – and may conflict with religious action-guides, such as in the story of Abraham and the burning bush, where he is prepared to kill his son through faith in God. Actions done for purely prudential reasons – I do not want to go to jail, or to hell – are not really done from *ethical* considerations, though they may help form behavioural traits that are supportive of moral development. Religions sometimes use prudential considerations, for example karmic results, to help *motivate* actions benefiting others, without *justifying/validating* such actions on prudential, non-moral grounds. Broadly, religious-based ethical systems support ethics by motivating and justifying positive other-regarding actions and discouraging actions harmful to others, and strengthening the character-traits which foster moral action.

Little and Twiss regard a 'religious' statement as one that expresses acceptance of a set of beliefs, attitudes and practices based on a notion of a sacred source of values and guidance, that functions to resolve the 'ontological problems of interpretability' (1978: 56). That is, religion is focused on making sense of life, including suffering, death and evil, so as to help people understand, and resolve, the human predicament. Morality and ethics can exist apart from religion, for example in humanism or utilitarianism, or ethics can be integrated into a religious system. The same prescription, for example 'do not kill', may be justified by a purely ethical reason, for example this has a bad effect on the welfare of others, or a purely religious one, for example it is forbidden by God, or a mixture, for example it is forbidden by God because it harms others.

In a Buddhist context, the effect of actions on the welfare of others is itself a key consideration, as is the effect of an action on spiritual progress, and what the Buddha is seen as having said on it. Religions often move imperceptibly from ethical concerns, relating to material welfare of others, to more 'spiritual' ones such as self-discipline and renunciation, though these may, in turn, have ethical spin-offs.

The history of Buddhism spans almost 2,500 years from its origin in India with Siddhattha Gotama (Pali; Siddhārtha Gautama in Sanskrit; c. 480–400 BCE), through its spread to most parts of Asia and, in the twentieth century, to the West. While its fortunes have waxed and waned over the ages, over half of the present world population live in areas where Buddhism is, or has been, a dominant cultural force.

The English term 'Buddhism' correctly indicates that the religion is characterized by a devotion to 'the Buddha', 'Buddhas' or 'Buddhahood'. 'Buddha' is not, in fact, a proper name, but a descriptive title meaning 'Awakened One' or 'Enlightened One'. This implies that most people are seen, in a spiritual sense, as being asleep – unaware of how things really are. In addition to 'the Buddha' – i.e. the historical Buddha, Gotama, from its earliest times the Buddhist tradition has postulated other Buddhas who have lived on earth in distant past ages, or who will do so in the future. The Mahāyāna tradition also postulated the existence of many Buddhas currently existing in other parts of the universe. All such Buddhas, known as *sammā-sambuddha*s (Pali; Skt *samyak-sambuddha*s), or 'perfect fully Awakened Ones', are nevertheless seen as occurring only rarely within the vast and ancient cosmos. More common are those who are 'buddhas' in a lesser sense, who have awakened to the truth by practising in accordance with the guidance of a perfect Buddha such as Gotama.

In its long history, Buddhism has used a variety of teachings and means to help people first develop a calmer, more integrated and compassionate personality, and then 'wake up' from restricting delusions: delusions which cause attachment and thus suffering for an individual and those he or she interacts with. The guide for this process of transformation has been the *Dhamma* (Pali; Skt *Dharma*). This means the eternal truths and cosmic law-orderliness discovered by the Buddha(s), Buddhist teachings, the Buddhist path of practice, and the goal of Buddhism, the timeless *Nirvāṇa* (Skt; Pali *Nibbāna*). Buddhism thus essentially consists of understanding, practising and realizing *Dhamma*.

The most important bearers of the Buddhist tradition have been the monks and nuns who make up the Buddhist *Saṅgha* (Pali; Skt *Saṃgha*):

'Community' or 'Order'. From approximately a hundred years after the death of Gotama, certain differences arose in the *Saṅgha*, which gradually led to the development of a number of monastic fraternities, each following a slightly different monastic code (*Vinaya*), and to different schools of thought. All branches of the *Saṅgha* trace their ordination-line back to one or other of the early fraternities; but of the early schools of thought, only that which became known as the Theravāda has continued to this day. Its name indicates that it purports to follow the 'teaching' which is 'ancient' or 'primordial' (*thera*): that is, the Buddha's teaching. While it has not remained static, it has kept close to what we know of the early teachings of Buddhism, and preserved their emphasis on attaining liberation by one's own efforts, using the *Dhamma* as guide.

Around the beginning of the Christian era, a movement began which led to a new style of Buddhism known as the Mahāyāna, or 'Great Vehicle'. This has been more overtly innovative, so that for many centuries, Indian Mahāyānists continued to compose new scriptures. The Mahāyāna is characterized, on the one hand, by devotion to a number of holy saviour beings, and on the other by several sophisticated philosophies, developed by extending the implications of the earlier teachings. The saviour beings are both heavenly Buddhas and heavenly *Bodhisattva*s (Skt; Pali *Bodhisatta*), 'beings for enlightenment' who are near the end of the long *Bodhisattva* path – much elaborated and emphasized by the Mahāyāna – that leads to Buddhahood. In the course of time, in India and beyond, the Mahāyāna produced many schools of its own, such as Zen.

Our knowledge of the teachings of the Buddha is based on several canons of scripture, which derive from the early *Saṅgha*'s oral transmission of bodies of teachings agreed on at several councils. These canons gradually diverged as different floating oral traditions were drawn on, and systematizing texts peculiar to each school were added. The Theravādin 'Pali Canon', preserved in the Pali language, is the most complete extant early canon, and contains some of the earliest material. Most of its teachings are in fact the common property of all Buddhist schools, being simply the teachings which the Theravādins preserved from the early common stock. The Mahāyāna, though, added much to this stock. While parts of the Pali Canon clearly originated after the time of the Buddha, much must derive from his teachings. There is an overall harmony to the Canon, suggesting 'authorship' of its system of thought by one mind.

The early canons contain a section on *Vinaya*, or monastic discipline, and one on *Suttas* (Pali; Skt *Sūtras*), or 'discourses' of the Buddha, and some contain one on *Abhidhamma* (Pali; Skt *Abhidharma*), or 'further teachings', which systematizes the *Sutta*-teachings in the form of detailed analyses of human experience. The main teachings of Buddhism are contained in the *Suttas*, which in the Pali Canon are divided into five *Nikāyas* or 'Collections', the first four (D., M., S., A.; sixteen volumes) generally being the older. The Pali Canon was one of the earliest to be written down, in Sri Lanka in around 80 BCE, after which little, if any, new material was added to it. The extensive non-canonical Pali literature includes additional *Abhidhamma* works, historical chronicles, and many volumes of commentaries. An extremely clear introduction to many points of Buddhist doctrine is the *Milindapañha* (*Miln.*), a first-century CE text which purports to record conversations between a Buddhist monk and Milinda (Menander; *c.* 155–130 BCE), a king of Greek ancestry.

Mahāyāna texts were composed from around the first century BCE, originating as written works in a hybrid form of the Indian prestige language, Sanskrit, rather than as oral compositions. While many are *Sūtras* attributed to the Buddha, their form and content clearly show that they were later restatements and extensions of the Buddha's message. The main sources for our understanding of Mahāyāna teachings are the very extensive Chinese and Tibetan Buddhist Canons. While most of the Pali Canon has been translated into English, only selected texts from these have been translated into Western languages, though much progress is being made.

Of the above sources, *Vinaya* (*Vin.*) texts often include material relevant to ethics, both in the form of specific rules for monks and nuns and in the reasons given for these and mitigating factors for offences against them. Ethical material is scattered throughout the Theravāda *Suttas* and Mahāyāna *Sūtras*, with some particularly focusing on ethical matters. The *Abhidhamma* literature contains material on the psychology of ethics, and the commentaries of all traditions contain useful explications of moral points in the scriptures as well as stories with a moral message. One sees this particularly in the commentary to the *Jātakas*, which expands on canonical verses about past lives of the Buddha to develop morality tales.

All traditions also have treatises by named authors which include ethical material. Of these, the following are particularly of note. In the Theravāda tradition, Buddhaghosa (fifth century CE) wrote the

Visuddhimagga (*Vism.*), whose ninth chapter contains some excellent material on lovingkindness and compassion. He also compiled many commentaries, which are often treatises in their own right. In the Sarvāstivāda tradition, an early school which has died out, is the compendious *Abhidharma-kośa-bhāṣyam* (*AKB.*) of Vasubandhu (fourth century CE), which influenced the Mahāyāna tradition. In the Mahāyāna tradition, the poet Śāntideva (seventh century CE) produced both the *Bodhi-caryāvatāra* (*Bca.*), an outline of the *Bodhisattva*-path with some inspiring material on compassion and patience, and the *Śikṣā-samuccaya* (*Ss.*), a compendium of quotations from Mahāyāna *Sūtras*, often on ethical themes. Nāgārjuna (*c.* 150–250 CE) wrote the *Rāja-parikathā-ratnamālā* (*RPR.*) as advice to a king on how to rule compassionately, and Asaṅga (fourth or fifth century CE), in his *Bodhisattva-bhūmi*, gives material on the ethics of the *Bodhisattva* (Tatz, 1986). Of course, contemporary Buddhists in Asia are also involved in ethical thought, action and innovation, as will be seen in the course of this book, and Buddhists in the West, whose numbers have grown steadily since the 1960s, are also participating in this process.

In reading Buddhist texts, stylistic features peculiar to them become apparent. The *Suttas* contain chunks of material which are repeated several times in a story or analysis, as they originated as oral literature which found this mode of composition congenial. They also contain many numbered lists, such as the Four Noble Truths, the five hindrances, and the seven factors of awakening. These aided the memorizing of oral material as well as reflecting what seems to have been the Buddha's very analytical turn of mind, breaking things down into their components. While he sometimes explicitly showed how these factors then related to each other and to the purpose for which the list was made, this is sometimes only implicit, and has to be teased out.

While Buddhism is now only a minority religion within the borders of modern India, its spread beyond India means that it is currently found in three main cultural areas. These are those of: 'Southern Buddhism', where the Theravāda school is found, along with some elements incorporated from the Mahāyāna; 'Eastern Buddhism', where the Chinese transmission of Mahāyāna Buddhism is found, and the area of Tibetan culture, 'Northern Buddhism', which is the heir of late Indian Buddhism where the tantric or Mantrayāna version of the Mahāyāna is the dominant form. In recent years, it has become possible to start talking about 'Western' Buddhism, too, but this as yet has no overall cultural cohesion, as it is drawing on all the Asian Buddhist traditions, as well as innovating in certain ways.

The main countries of Southern Buddhism are Sri Lanka, Burma and Thailand, along with Cambodia and Laos, where religion has suffered because of wars and Communism in recent decades. Northern Buddhism is found mainly in Tibet, now absorbed into the People's Republic of China, among Tibetan and Mongol people in the rest of north-west China, in Mongolia – recently free of Communism – in the small kingdom of Bhutan, alongside Hinduism in Nepal, and among Tibetan exiles living in India. Eastern Buddhism is mainly found in Taiwan, South Korea, Japan and Singapore, as well as in Communist China, Vietnam and North Korea. The world's Buddhist population (excluding Western and Asian Buddhists in the West) is roughly 495 million: 105 million Buddhists of the Southern tradition, 25 million of the Northern tradition, and perhaps 365 of the Eastern tradition, though it is difficult to give a figure for the number of 'Buddhists' of this tradition, particularly China, on account of traditional multi-religion allegiance and the current dominance of Communism in the People's Republic of China.

Buddhism's concentration on the essentials of spiritual development has meant that it has been able to co-exist with both other major religions and popular folk traditions which catered for people's desire for a variety of rituals. There has hardly ever been a 'wholly' Buddhist society, if this means a kind of religious one-party state. In the lands of Eastern Buddhism, Buddhism has co-existed with Confucianism, a semi-religious system of social philosophy which has had a strong influence on people's ethics in this area. Buddhism has been very good at adapting to different cultures while guarding its own somewhat fluid borders by a critical tolerance of other traditions. Its style has been to offer invitations to a number of levels of spiritual practice for those who have been ready to commit themselves.

CHAPTER I

The shared foundations of Buddhist ethics

Life is dear to all. Comparing others with oneself, one should neither kill nor cause to kill. Whoever, seeking his own happiness, harms . . . beings, he gets no happiness hereafter.   *Dhammapada* 130–1

Fundamental features of Buddhism's world-view relevant to ethics are the framework of karma and rebirth, accepted by all schools of Buddhism, with varying degrees of emphasis, and the Four Noble Truths, the highest teachings of early Buddhism and of the Theravāda school. In the Mahāyāna tradition, an increasing emphasis on compassion modified the earlier shared perspective in certain ways, as will be explored in chapter 3.

SOURCES OF GUIDANCE TO BUDDHISTS

In ethics as in other matters, Buddhists have three key sources of inspiration and guidance: the 'three treasures' or 'three refuges': the Buddha, *Dhamma* and *Saṅgha*. The Buddha is revered as (1) the 'rediscoverer' and teacher of liberating truths and (2) the embodiment of liberating qualities to be developed by others. In addition, in the Mahāyāna, heavenly Buddhas are looked to as contemporary sources of teaching and help. The *Dhamma* is the teachings of the Buddhas, the path to the Buddhist goal, and the various levels of realizations of this goal. The *Saṅgha* is the 'Community' of Noble Ones (Pali *ariyas*; Skt *āryas*): advanced practitioners who have experienced something of this goal, being symbolized, on a more day-to-day level, by the Buddhist monastic *Saṅgha* (Harvey, 1990a: 176–9).

The *Dhamma*, in the sense of teachings attributed to the Buddha(s), is contained in voluminous texts preserved and studied by the monastic *Saṅgha*. The advice and guidance that monks and nuns offer to the laity are based on these texts, on their own experience of practising the Buddhist path, and on the oral and written tradition from earlier generations of monastics and, sometimes, lay practitioners. Lay people are under no strict *obligation* to do what monks or nuns advise, but rather *respect* for their qualities and way of life is the factor that will influence

8

them, depending on the degree of the lay person's own devotion to the Buddhist way.

A common source of material for popular sermons is the *Jātaka* collection, containing stories which purport to be of the previous lives of Gotama when he was a *Bodhisattva* (see Jones, 1979). They occur in the canonical collections of all the early schools, became popular subjects for Buddhist art by the third century BCE, and were also taken up in the Mahāyāna. The stories often function as morality tales, being full of heroes, heroines and villains. The form of a *Jātaka* is a prologue purporting to be about events in the Buddha's day, the story itself, about a past time, and then a brief epilogue which identifies the Buddha with the hero of the story, and certain disciples or relatives with others in it. In the stories of the past, Gotama is mostly human, but sometimes a god and sometimes a (talking) animal. In the case of the Theravādin *Jātaka* collection of 547 stories (see *J.*), the form in which we now have them consists of some verses, seen as canonical, set in a lengthy prose frame, which was compiled by a later commentator, probably in Sri Lanka. Many stories are also found in the commentary on the *Dhammapada* (*Dhp. A.*), dating from fifth-century CE Sri Lanka, which gives around fifty *Jātaka*s, plus other stories set at the time of the Buddha.

As regards the order of priority among sources relevant to resolving points of monastic discipline – and by extension, one could say matters relevant to lay ethical discipline – the fifth-century Theravādin commentator Buddhaghosa gives:

(1) scripture in the form of *Vinaya*, but it could be seen more widely for non-monastic matters;

(2) that which is 'in conformity with scripture';

(3) the commentarial tradition (*ācariyavāda*);

(4) personal opinion (*attanomati*), based on logic, intuition and inference independent of (1)–(3), but whose conclusions should be checked against them (*Vin. A.* 230).

Here Damien Keown comments that conscience is not irrelevant, but scripture is 'a check that one's own moral conscience is calibrated correctly', and that 'it is not the text itself that is important, but the fact that it is "in conformity with the nature of things"' (1995a: 16). Nevertheless, less scholastic monks than Buddhaghosa might put more emphasis on the living oral tradition and meditation-based insights. Mahāyānists would also take 'scripture' to include Mahāyāna texts not acceptable as authoritative to Buddhaghosa.

The teachings attributed to the Buddha(s) are seen as an authoritative guide to the nature of reality and the best way to live, based on the vast, meditation-based knowledge of such spiritually 'awakened' beings. Such teachings are not to be simply *accepted*, though, but used, investigated and, as far as is possible for a particular individual, *confirmed* in experience. This emphasis on testing out the teachings is seen in the well-known *Kālāma* Sutta (*A.* 1.188–93). Here, the Buddha advises the Kālāma people not to accept teachings simply through tradition, speculative reasoning, personal preferences, what one thinks *should* be true, or respect for a particular teacher. Rather:

When you, O Kālāmas, know for yourselves: 'these states are unwholesome and blameworthy, they are condemned by the wise; these states, when accomplished and undertaken, conduce to harm and suffering', then indeed you should reject them. (p. 189)

Accordingly, the Buddha then gets them to agree that greed, hatred and delusion (*lobha, dosa* (Pali; Skt *dveṣa*), *moha*) are each states which are harmful to a person when they arise. Being overcome by any of them, he or she kills, steals, commits adultery, lies, and leads others to do likewise, so that he or she suffers for a long time (on account of the karmic results of his or her actions, in this life or beyond). The Kālāmas are then led to agree that the arising of non-greed, non-hatred and non-delusion is beneficial, without such bad consequent actions and results. Accordingly, these states can be seen to be wholesome, unblameworthy, praised by the wise and conducive to happiness, so that the Kālāmas should 'undertake and abide in them'.

Here, personal experience, checked out by reference to the guidance of wise people, is taken as the crucial test of what mental states, and consequent behaviour, to avoid or indulge in. Using this criterion is seen to put a high value on states of mind which are the opposite of greed, hatred and deluded unclarity or misorientation, for they can be seen to conduce to happiness rather than suffering. Moreover, it is suggested that people are trustworthy guides to the extent that they are free of greed etc., as seen in a passage on how there can be a reliable 'awakening to truth' (*M.* II.171–6). A lay person first assesses a monk for the presence of states of greed, hatred or delusion, which might lead to lying or bad spiritual advice. If he sees that the monk's mind is purified of these, he reposes trustful confidence (*saddhā*) in him. A series of activities then follows, each being 'of service' to the next: 'approaching', 'drawing close', 'lending ear', 'hearing *Dhamma*', 'remembering *Dhamma*', 'testing the meaning', 'reflection on and approval of *Dhamma*', 'desire-to-do', 'making an effort', 'weighing up', 'striving'; and finally, 'he realizes, with his person, the highest truth itself; and penetrating it by wisdom, he sees'. Thus there is a progression from trust in one who has overcome greed, hatred and delusion to the development of insight which itself destroys these in the practitioner.

Ethical behaviour is seen as greatly aided by formally undertaking to follow specific ethical precepts, done by reciting or chanting them, whether by oneself or after a monk, who is then seen as 'administering' these precepts to one (see chapter 2). Such acts are seen to set up beneficial tendencies in the mind, and to support the sense of letting oneself and others down if one then breaks a precept one has undertaken to follow. Accordingly, the great Mahāyāna writer Asaṅga said that the essence of ethics is 'To correctly receive it from someone, to have a quite purified intention, to make correction after failure, and to avoid failure by generating respect and remaining mindful after that' (Tatz, 1986: 47).

The role of 'conscience', in Buddhism, is performed by a small group of qualities, starting with *hiri* (Pali – or *hirī*, which is also the Skt form) and *ottappa* (Pali; Skt *apatrapya*), seen as the immediate cause of virtue and as two 'bright states which guard the world' (*A.* 1.51). *Hiri* is 'self-respect', which causes one to seek to avoid any action which one feels is not worthy of oneself and lowers one's moral integrity. *Ottappa* is 'regard for consequences', being stimulated by concern over reproach and blame for an action (whether from oneself or others), embarrassment before others (especially those one respects), legal punishment or the karmic results of an action (*Asl.* 124–7). Heedfulness (Pali *appamāda*; Skt *apramādya*), a combination of energy (Pali *viriya*; Skt *vīrya*) and mindfulness (Pali *sati*; Skt *smṛti*) (Rājavaramuni, 1990: 51), is also said to be the basis of all virtues (*S.* v.44). Mindfulness is alert presence of mind, cultivated strongly in meditation practice, which enables one to be more aware of one's mental states, including intentions and motives. It is complemented by 'clear comprehension' (Pali *sampajañña*; Skt *sampajānya*), which acts to guide one's actual behaviour to be in harmony with one's ideals and goals.

REBIRTH AND KARMA

In Buddhism, 'right view' (Pali *sammā-diṭṭhi*; Skt *samyak-dṛṣṭi*) is seen as the foundation of moral and spiritual development. While this begins in the form of correct belief, it can go on to become direct personal knowledge. As outlined at *M.* III.72, preliminary 'right view' is the belief that:

(1) 'there is gift, there is offering, there is (self-) sacrifice': these are worth-while;

(2) 'there is fruit and ripening of deeds well done or ill done': what one does *matters* and has an effect on one's future;

(3) 'there is this world, there is a world beyond': this world is not unreal, and one goes on to another world after death;

(4) 'there is mother and father': it is good to respect parents, who establish one in this world;

(5) 'there are spontaneously arising beings': some of the worlds one can be reborn in (for example some heavens) are populated by beings that come into existence without parents;

(6) 'there are in this world renunciants and brahmins[1] who are faring rightly, practising rightly, and who proclaim this world and the world beyond having realized them by their own super-knowledge': spiritual development is a real possibility, actualized by some people, and it can lead, in the profound calm of deep meditation, to memory of past rebirths in a variety of worlds, and awareness of how others are reborn in such worlds.

The realms of rebirth

In Buddhism, one's present life is seen as one of a countless number of lives stretching back into the past, with no discernible beginning to the series. Such lives take various forms. They may be relatively pleasant, as in the case of rebirth as a human or in one of the many heaven worlds (for example Law, 1973). They may be unpleasant, though, as in the case of rebirth as some kind of animal, as a 'departed one' (Pali *peta*; Skt *preta*; *Khp.* 6) in the form of a frustrated ghostly being, or in one of a number of hells, where life is like an extended nightmare of intense suffering (*M.* III.165–7, 183–7) with feelings that are 'exclusively painful, sharp, severe' (*M.* 1.74–6).[2] The Mahāyāna poet Śāntideva, for example, cites the *Saddharma-smṛtyupasthāna Sūtra* as describing murderers being eaten alive by birds in hell, 'But each time he is devoured, so each time he is reborn more sensitive than before' (*Ss.* 75–6).

None of these realms lasts for ever, though, for all end in death and

---

[1] 'Renunciants' refers to Buddhist or Jain monks and nuns, or other ascetics, 'brahmins' to the most-respected people in the pre-Buddhist Brahmanical religion, an early form of Hinduism.

[2] Some passages also refer to *asuras* or jealous gods. The Sarvāstivādins saw them as a sixth, and lowest rebirth (McDermott, 1984: 5). The Theravādins, though, saw them as belonging to either the ghost-realm or heaven-realms, depending on their type (*Kvu.* 360).

Plate 1. The Tibetan 'Wheel of Life'. At its hub, a cock, snake and pig symbolize greed, hatred and delusion, which keep beings within the round of rebirths. Around the hub is a disk showing beings rising to better rebirths and falling to worse ones. The main sections show the realms of rebirth: going clockwise, those of humans, ghosts, hell-beings, animals and gods. Around the rim, the twelve links of Conditioned Arising (see p. 33) are shown. The wheel is held by a being who symbolises death, indicating that all rebirths end in death. The Buddha points beyond the wheel of rebirths to *Nirvāṇa*.

then (for the unenlightened), another rebirth (Harvey, 1990a: 32–7). Thus even life in the hells, though long lasting, is not eternal. This means that there is hope even for Adolf Hitler: at some time in the far far distant future, he might even become enlightened! – *if* he were to strive to develop moral and spiritual perfection. At the other end of the scale, the life-span in the many heaven worlds varies from 9 million human years (but only 500 'divine years'!) up to 84,000 aeons, an aeon being a huge time-span (*Vibh.* 422–7). And yet even the gods die, to be reborn and die again.

The Buddhist perspective on the cycle of rebirths is that it is not a pleasant affair, but that all unenlightened people are reborn whether they like it or not, and whether they believe in rebirth or not. The process of life and rebirth is not seen to have any inherent purpose; for it was not designed and created by any being. Thus it is known as *saṃsāra*, or 'wandering on' from life to life. Thus the only sensible aim, for one who understands *saṃsāra* to some extent, is to strive, firstly, to avoid its more unpleasant realms, and ultimately to transcend it altogether, by attaining *Nirvāṇa* (Skt; Pali *Nibbāna*), and to help others to do so. Most Buddhists therefore aim to attain a heavenly or a human rebirth, with *Nirvāṇa* as the long-term goal. Buddhist heavens, then, are *this* side of salvation; for *Nirvāṇa* is beyond the limitations of both earthly and heavenly existence.

Within the round of rebirths, worlds belong to one of three broad categories. The 'realm of sense-desire' comprises the worlds of hells, ghosts, animals, humans and the six lowest heavens. In all these, beings' likes and dislikes dominate and distort their perception of the world. The 'realm of (elemental) form' comprises sixteen heavens, paralleling deep states of meditative calm, which are progressively more subtle and refined, and where various sorts of *brahmā* deities live. Their perception is not distorted by sense-desire, but they have faults such as pride. The 'formless realm' consists of four extremely subtle realms which, being devoid of *anything* visible, tangible etc., are purely mental.

Karma and its effects

The movement of beings between rebirths is not seen as a haphazard process, but as ordered and governed by the law of karma. Karma (Pali *kamma*) literally means 'action', and the principle of the 'law of karma' is that beings are reborn according to the nature and quality of their actions. Past actions are said to 'welcome' one in a future life like a person being welcomed by kinsmen (*Dhp.* 219–20), so that:

Deeds are one's own . . . beings are heir to deeds, deeds are matrix, deeds are kin, deeds are arbiters. Deeds divide beings, that is to say by lowness and excellence. (*M.* III.203)

This is explained as referring to the karmic effect of various actions. A person's actions mould their consciousness, making them into a certain kind of person, so that when they die their outer form tends to correspond to the type of nature that has been developed. What begins as a trace in the psyche later crystallizes out as an aspect of a person and their world.

Prior to the time of the Buddha, the basic idea of karma and rebirth had been expressed in the Brahmanical (early Hindu) compositions known as *Upaniṣad*s. Here, though, there was as much emphasis on karmas/actions being *ritually* right as on their being *ethically* right. In Buddhism, though, the emphasis is strongly on the ethical aspect of action as the relevant factor in causing karmic results.

It is said that acts of hatred and violence tend to lead to rebirth in a hell, acts bound up with delusion and confusion tend to lead to rebirth as an animal, and acts of greed tend to lead to rebirth as a ghost. It is also said that 'By constantly committing evil deeds we are reborn in hell, by doing many we become spirits [i.e. ghosts], and when we do only a few we are reborn as an animal' (Guenther, 1959: 79). Rebirth in a hell is also seen as particularly due to both doing evil actions and encouraging others to do them, by approving of and praising such actions. Abstaining from evil actions and encouraging others to do so leads to a heavenly rebirth (*A.* v.306–8). In Mahāyāna Buddhism, it is also held that obstructing a *Bodhisattva* – a heroic, compassionate being – in a good deed has terrible karmic consequences, for it hinders the welfare of many beings (*Bca.* IV.9).

Actions can also lead to karmic fruits in a human life. This might be the present life, or a future human life, be this one's next life, or one that comes after one or more other types of rebirth. In textual descriptions of such fruits, one sees that they reflect back on a person something which is particularly appropriate to the nature of the relevant action. In the present life, killing or harming living beings conduces to being short-lived; stealing to loss of wealth; sensual misconduct to rivalry and hatred from others; lying to having to eat one's false words; backbiting to the break-up of friendships; harsh words to having to listen to unpleasant sounds; frivolous chatter to unacceptable, ineffective speech; intoxication to madness (*A.* IV.247–8). As regards the fruits of actions in a future human life: mercilessly killing and injuring living beings leads to being short-lived; striking living beings lead to being often ill; being easily angered leads to being ugly; being jealous and spiteful leads to being of no account; being stingy leads to being poor; being haughty and disrespectful leads to being of a lowly family; and not asking about what is morally wholesome and unwholesome leads to being weak in wisdom. The opposite good actions lead to a heavenly rebirth or the opposite kinds of human life.[3] Poor, ill or ugly people are not to be presently blamed for their condition, however, for the actions of a past life are behind them, and the important thing is how they behave in the present and how others act towards them.

Living an ethical life is variously said to lead to: wealth, through diligence; a good reputation; joyful recollection of moral purity; self-confidence in all types of company, without fear of reproach or punishment; easier progress in meditation; dying without anxiety, and rebirth in a heaven world.[4] It is said that to develop generosity and moral virtue to a small degree leads to rebirth as a human of ill fortune; to develop them to a medium degree leads to being a human of good fortune; to develop them to a high degree leads to rebirth in one of the six sense-desire realm heavens. To reach the heavens of the (elemental) form realm requires meditation, which leads to the attainment of one or other *jhāna*, lucid trances which 'tune' the mind to this level of existence (*A.* IV.241–3). The different affiliations of unwholesome and wholesome impulses is nicely expressed by Śāntideva thus:

'If I give this, what shall I (have left to) enjoy?' – such selfish thinking is the way of ghosts; 'If I enjoy this, what shall I (have left to) give?' – such selfless thinking is the quality of the gods. (*Bca.* VIII.125)

The status and working of the law of karma

The law of karma is seen as a natural law inherent in the nature of things, like a law of physics. It is not operated by a God, and indeed the gods are themselves under its sway. Good and bad rebirths are not, therefore, seen as 'rewards' and 'punishments', but as simply the natural results of certain kinds of action. Karma is often likened to a seed, and

---

[3] *M.* III.203–6; cf. *Miln.* 65, *Uss.* 74–6 and *ASP.* 169–72.   [4] *D.* II.86; *M.* III.170–1; *M.* I.33.

the two words for a karmic result, *vipāka* and *phala*, respectively mean 'ripening' and 'fruit'. An action is thus like a seed which will sooner or later, as part of a natural maturation process, result in certain fruits arising to the doer of the action.

What determines the nature of a karmic 'seed' is the will behind an act: 'It is will (*cetanā*), O monks, that I call karma; having willed, one acts through body, speech or mind' (*A.* III.415). *Cetanā* encompasses the motive for which an action is done, its immediate intention (directed at a specific objective, as part of fulfilling a motive), and the immediate mental impulse which sets it going and sustains it (Keown, 1992: 213–18). 'Karma' is the overall psychological impulse behind an action, that which sets going a chain of causes culminating in a karmic fruit. Actions, then, must be intentional if they are to generate karmic fruits: accidentally treading on an insect does not have such an effect, as the Jains believed.

Nevertheless, thinking of doing some bad action is a bad mental action (karma), especially when one gives energy to such a thought, for example by jealousy or anger, rather than just letting it pass. Deliberately putting such a thought down is a good mental karma. The mind is thus seen as constantly generating good and bad karma – whether mild or heavy – by the way it attends to and responds to objects of the senses, memory or imagination (Payutto, 1993: 6–8).

An important point to note, here, is that an action's being good does not consist in its having pleasant karmic results. Rather, it is seen as having pleasant results because it is itself good or wholesome (see Keown, 1992: 178). It is thus said that good actions are those which are *themselves* 'bright' as well as being 'with bright result' (*M.* I.390). Why is the moral tone of an action seen to cause certain results? It is said that wrong view leads on to wrong thought, and this to wrong speech and thus wrong action, while right view has the opposite effect (*A.* v.211–12). As wrong actions thus come from the misperception of reality, they can be seen to be 'out of tune' with the real nature of things. As they thus 'go against the grain' of reality, they naturally lead to unpleasant results. Thus it is said to be impossible that wrong conduct of body, speech or mind could result in a 'fruit that was agreeable, pleasant, liked', or for right conduct to lead to a 'fruit that was disagreeable, unpleasant, not liked' (*M.* III.66).

The 'karmic fruitfulness' of actions

Good actions are said to be 'lovely' (*kalyāṇa*) and to be, or have the quality of, *puñña* (Pali; Skt *punya*), a term which can be used as an adjective or a noun. As an adjective, Cousins sees it as the 'fortune-bringing or auspicious quality of an action' (1996: 153), while as a noun 'it is applied either to an act which brings good fortune or to the happy result in the future of such an act' (1996: 155). Thus we see:

Monks, do not be afraid of *puññas*; this, monks, is a designation for happiness, for what is pleasant, charming, dear and delightful, that is to say, *puññas*. I myself know that the ripening of *puññas* done for a long time are experienced for a long time as pleasant, charming, dear and delightful. After developing a heart of lovingkindness for seven years, for seven aeons of evolution and devolution, I did not come back to this world . . . [being reborn in a delightful heaven for that time]. (*It.* 14–15; cf. *A.* iv.88–9)

Puñña is usually, rather limply, translated as 'meritorious' (adjective) or 'merit' (noun). However, 'meritorious' implies deservingness, but what is referred to is something with a natural power of its own to produce happy results (cf. Cousins, 1996: 155); it does not depend on anyone to give out what is due to the 'deserving'. A *puñña* action is 'auspicious', 'fortunate' or 'fruitful', as it purifies the mind and thus leads to future good fortune (McDermott, 1984: 31–58). Indeed, through other Indo-European languages it may be related to the English words 'boon' and 'bounty' (the Thai word for *puñña* is *bun*). As the noun *puñña* refers to the auspicious, uplifting, purifying power of good actions to produce future happy results, one might translate it as 'goodness-power', but this offers no convenient related adjective. A better translation would be '(an act of) karmic fruitfulness', with 'karmically fruitful' as the adjective. This makes a connection with the fact that actions (karmas) are often likened to 'seeds' and their results are known as 'fruits' (*phalas*) or 'ripenings'. While such *phalas* can be the results of either good *or* bad actions, and *puñña* relates only to good actions, the English word 'fruit' can also mean only edible, pleasant fruit such as apples, without referring to inedible, unpleasant ones. The link to 'fruitfulness' is also seen in the fact that the *Saṅgha* is described as the best 'field of *puñña*', i.e. the best group of people to 'plant' a gift 'in' in terms of karmically beneficial results of the gift (see pp. 21–2).

The opposite of *puñña* is *apuñña*, which one can accordingly see as meaning '(an act of) karmic unfruitfulness' or 'karmically unfruitful', i.e. producing no pleasant fruits, but only bitter ones. A synonym for *apuñña* is *pāpa*, which, while often translated as 'evil', really means that which is 'infertile', 'barren', 'harmful' (Cousins, 1996: 156) or 'ill-fortuned' (Cousins, 1996: 148). A good way of rendering these meanings would be to see *pāpa* as an adjective as meaning '(karmically) deadening', and as a noun as '(karmic) deadness', meaning that what is so described has a deadening effect on the psyche, making it more constricted and lifeless, rather than having an uplifting, fruitful effect.

Buddhists are keen to perform 'karmically fruitful' actions; for *puñña* is an unlosable 'treasure', unlike physical goods (*Khp.* 7). The early texts refer to three 'bases for effecting karmic fruitfulness' (*puñña-kiriya-vatthu*s): giving (*dāna*), moral virtue (*sīla*) and meditation, and later texts add to this list (see p. 61). Nevertheless, an act of giving is not such a basis if it is done 'through fear, or with hope of reciprocity, or through attachment, etc.', rather than 'Through desire to render homage or service' (*AKB.* IV.113a).

Karmic fruitfulness and motive

It is said that 'the mental aspiration of a moral person is effective through its purity' (*D.* III.259–60). That is, when such a person gives a gift to a monk or brahmin with the hope of being reborn in a certain way, this will occur, whether the heart is set on rebirth as a rich human, or in any of the six heavens of the desire-realm, or even in the world of the *brahmās*. Yet if such an aspiration is really going to work, it must not be itself the sole motive of the giving, for this is seen to affect the nature of the beneficial karmic result. If a person gives something to a monk 'with longing, with the heart bound (to the gift), intent on a store (of karmic fruitfulness), thinking "I'll enjoy this after death" ', it is said that he will be reborn for a while in the lowest of all the heavens. A series of what seem to be meant as progressively higher motives is then outlined: giving because one feels 'it is auspicious (*sāhu*) to give'; wishing to continue a family tradition of giving; wishing to support those who do not cook for themselves; because great sages of the past were supported by alms; because giving leads to mental calm, joy and gladness; or because giving enriches the heart and equips it for meditation (*A.* IV.60–3). Giving from the last of these motives is then said to lead to rebirth in the first heaven of the realm of (elemental) form, where the *brahmās* dwell. Thus doing a good action simply because it is seen to have pleasant results is not the highest of motives – it is better to value goodness in itself, and the peace and wisdom that it facilitates (Payutto, 1993: 54–6). Accordingly, the Theravādin commentator Buddhaghosa says, on moral virtue:

That undertaken just out of desire for fame is inferior; that undertaken just out of desire for the fruits of karmically fruitful actions is medium; that undertaken for the sake of the Noble state thus, 'This is to be done', is superior. (*Vism.* 13)

A generous supporter of the Buddha and his monks and nuns was Anāthapiṇḍika ('Feeder of the Poor'), who never showed any interest in the results of his generosity, though the Buddha often spoke of these to him. 'He just gives, joyful in the chance to do so' and 'would be less than a perfect giver if he gave for the sake of the rewards that, according to his Master, are derived from the gift' (Falk, 1990: 129). Nevertheless, acting so as to generate karmic fruitfulness is an effective motive for getting people to begin to act in a more generous and moral way.

While Buddhists often see a large gift as generating more karmic fruitfulness than a small one, a small gift from a poor person is said to be worth as much as a large one from a rich person (*S.* 1.20–2). Here, purity of mind makes up for the smallness of a gift, for 'where there is a joyful heart, no gift is small' (*J.* II.85; *Vv.* I). Thus, 'If you have a little, give little; if you have a middling amount, give a middling amount; if you have much, give much. It is not fitting not to give at all' (*J.* v.382). Thus it is emphasized that even the poor have the means to give, be this as little as leftover noodles as food for ants (*Uss.* 113).

The karmic fruitfulness of a gift is not seen to depend on its usefulness to the recipient (which may be variable and unpredictable), but on the donor's state of mind when giving.[5] Indeed, a person with nothing to give can do an act of karmic fruitfulness by helping someone else to give (*Uss.* 113) or by simply rejoicing at another person's giving, which is a good mental act in itself. This even applies to the joyful contemplation of one's own past wholesome deeds (*Miln.* 297). Indeed, two types of beneficial meditation are said to be the recollection of one's own unbroken virtue and of one's liberal generosity (*Vism.* 223–34), though the karmic fruitfulness of actions is said to dwindle if one brags about the relevant good act (*Ss.* 147). It is said that an act of karmic fruitfulness is greater than its opposite, as regretting a bad action can stop one repeating it, but one has no need to regret a karmically fruitful action, and it leads on to further spiritual progress – joy, calm, concentration and insight – which generates more karmic fruitfulness (*Miln.* 84).

The state of mind in which an act is done is partly a matter of motive, but also of the manner in which it is done. This is also seen as having an effect on the karmic result. It is said that to give 'disrespectfully, without due consideration, not with one's own hand, of something unwanted (by oneself), not with a view to the future (i.e., not recognizing the giving as having a karmic fruit)' leads to a karmic fruit where the mind does not

---

[5] At least, this is the Theravādin view (*Kvu.* 343–7) – a few other early schools disagreed.

incline to the enjoyment of the best of sense-pleasures (i.e. being miserly with what one has (*S.* 1.91–2)), and to one's family and workpeople not being considerate towards one (*A.* IV.392–3). This is how a bad man gives, a good man giving in the opposite way (*M.* III.22–4). More specifically, it is said: (1) giving with faith (*saddhā*) leads to the giver having wealth and being handsome; (2) giving respectfully or carefully leads to the giver's wife, family and workpeople listening carefully to him and helping him in an understanding way; (3) giving at the appropriate time leads to wealth coming at the appropriate time; (4) giving with no reluctance in the heart leads to the mind inclining to enjoyment of the best of sense-pleasures; (5) giving without harm to self or other leads to future wealth being free from harm from fire, water, kings, thieves or unfriendly heirs (*A.* III.172–3). The Mahāyāna tradition agrees with such passages from Theravāda texts; for Śāntideva cites the *Akṣayamati Sūtra* as saying that a 'gift' is no real gift if it harms someone, or is less than has been promised, or is accompanied by contempt, boasting or hostility, or causes distress, or is of what would otherwise have been thrown away, or is not given with one's own hand, or is improper, or given at the wrong time (*Ss.* 248).

The Saṅgha as the best 'field of karmic fruitfulness'

The karmic fruitfulness of an act of giving is said to be great not only if the state of mind of the donor is pure, but also if the recipient is very virtuous or holy. Thus 'even so little as a handful of rice-beans . . . bestowed with devout heart upon a person who is worthy of receiving a gift of devotion will be of great fruit, of great splendour' (*Vv.* 1). A gift is said to be 'purified' by the donor, the recipient, both or neither, according to whether they are virtuous and of good character or not. To be 'purified' by a donor, a gift must be 'rightfully acquired, the mind well pleased, firmly believing in the rich fruit of karma' (*M.* III.257). Even if a gift is given by an evil person, in the opposite way, it may be 'purified' by the virtue of the recipient. While a gift to an animal yields a hundred-fold, and to an unvirtuous human a thousandfold, one to an ordinary virtuous person yields a hundred thousandfold, and one to a spiritually Noble person has an immeasurable fruit. A gift of the virtuous to the virtuous has the greatest fruit, though (*M.* III.255–7; cf. *A.* 1.161–2).

A gift given to renunciants and brahmins who are not endowed with the qualities of the path to *Nirvāṇa* is of little fruit, like a seed sown on poor, ill-watered soil. The opposite applies for a gift to those endowed with the factors of the Eightfold Path (see p. 37), which leads to much good karma and conduces to spiritual accomplishment (*A.* IV.237–8). The well-trained Noble *Saṅgha* (which includes some lay people) is said, in a well-known chant, to be 'worthy of respect, worthy of hospitality, worthy of gifts, worthy of salutation, an unsurpassed field of karmic fruitfulness for the world' (*D.* III.5; *M.* III.80). For this description to apply to a monk, he should be such that objects of any of the senses do not engender attachment, elation or depression so as to disturb his calm concentration (*A.* III.157–61, 279). He controls his senses, uses his robe and alms-food without greed, patiently endures unpleasant sensations or abuse, avoids situations in which he might be suspected of misconduct, abandons lustful or cruel thoughts, and develops the seven factors of awakening, beginning with mindfulness (*A.* III.387–90). He is endowed with straightforwardness, speed of understanding, gentleness, patience and restraint (*A.* III.248; cf. *A.* I.244–6). One can summarize this by saying that the saintly members of the Noble *Saṅgha* (see pp. 39–40), being of exemplary, inspiring character, engender much joy in those who give to them, such that the giving generates a powerful purifying effect in the givers' minds, leading to abundant karmic fruitfulness.

As Noble persons are relatively few in number, the best 'field of karmic fruitfulness' normally available is the monastic *Saṅgha*, which symbolizes the Noble *Saṅgha* and is also likely to contain some members of it. According to the Theravādin *Milindapañha*, even a monk of poorly developed virtue 'purifies gifts of faith' through the good effects of participating in the life of the *Saṅgha*, and associating with those more strongly intent on spiritual development. In any case, the gift of a virtuous person to a monk will always be purified by the giver (*Miln.* 257–8). When giving to the *Saṅgha*, it is best to give without discrimination or favouritism, even if one knows that some monks are more spiritually advanced than others (*A.* IV.215), and irrespective of whether a monk is a relative or friend (Bunnag, 1973: 59–60). It is also better to give to the *Saṅgha* of monks or nuns as a whole, or to a group specified by them, than to an individual monk or nun (*M.* III.255–6). As the alms-giver bestows long life, a good appearance, happiness and strength on the recipient of alms, then such qualities, in a human or heavenly rebirth, are said to be the karmic results of alms-giving (*A.* IV.57). This means that the monks' virtuous way of life can be of powerful benefit to others. Accordingly, it is said that the Buddha was not uncompassionate when he went with his monks on alms-round in an area where there was famine, for giving is the source of good fortune (*S.* IV.322–5).

Nevertheless, the 'field' of giving can also be excellent when one gives to the sick or a parent or other benefactor (*AKB*. iv.117a–b and 118).

Karma and fatalism

While belief in the law of karma can sometimes degenerate into a form of fatalism, the Buddha emphasized that deterministic fate (*niyati*) and karma are very different. The idea of karma emphasizes the importance of human action and its effects: people make their own 'destiny' by their actions. Karma and fatalism differ on two scores. Firstly, humans have freedom of choice; their present actions are not the karmic results of previous actions, though karmic results may influence the type of action that a person tends to think of doing, because of the character he or she has developed. Secondly, not everything that happens to a person is seen as due to karma. Any unpleasant feelings or illnesses that one has can arise from a variety of causes: 'originating from bile, phlegm, or wind, from union (of bodily humours), born from seasonal changes, born from disruptive circumstances, arriving suddenly [due to the action of another person], or born of the fruition of karma' (*S.* iv.230–1; *A.* v.10).

The aspects of life which are seen as the result of past karma include one's form of rebirth, social class at birth, general character, crucial good and bad things which happen to one, and even the way one experiences the world. Out of the mass of sense-data, one only ever gets 'edited high-lights' of what lies around one. Some people tend to notice pleasant things, while others tend to notice unpleasant things; these differences are said to be due to karma (cf. *S.* 1.91–2).

As a person never knows what aspect of any situation may have been determined by karma, difficult situations are not to be passively accepted, but a person should do his or her best to improve them. Only when things happen in spite of efforts to avert them might they be put down to past karma (Ingersoll, 1966: 210–15). If the situation can be averted or changed, fine, but then any anxiety or suffering it led to may be still seen as due to past karma. As an aid to planning courses of action in a karma-influenced world, many traditionalist Buddhists use divination methods such as astrology at certain points in their lives, so as to try to gauge what their karma has in store for them (Ingersoll, 1966: 207–9). The idea of the influence of karma, while not fatalistic, does encourage a person to live patiently with a situation. Rather than making new bad karma by getting angry with society, family, or other people, blaming them for his or her lot, he or she can view the situation as the result of his or her own past actions. This attitude arises from a person's taking responsibility for the shape of his or her life. Thus the Buddha criticized theories which saw all experiences and associated actions as due either to past karma, the diktat of a God, or pure chance (*A.* 1.173; *M.* 11.214). Like people of other religions, however, Buddhists sometimes have an idea of fate, in parallel with their idea of karma, or they may even use past karma as an excuse for continuing with present bad karma.

Flexibility in the working of karma

It is mostly at the human level that good and bad actions are performed. The gods are generally seen to have little scope for doing either good or evil, and most simply enjoy the results of the previous good actions which led to their existence. Animals, ghosts and hell-beings have little freedom for intentional good or bad actions, though Vasubandhu claims that hell-beings can do *some* good and bad actions, but any good actions will only bring fruits in a later life (*AKB.* IV.51d). Moreover, the higher animals can sometimes act virtuously, if not in a self-consciously moral way. Beings in the lower rebirths generally just reap the results of previous bad actions. When these results come to an end, the results of some previous good actions will come to fruition and buoy up the being to some better form of life, until sooner or later the being reaches the human level again.

The law of karma is not regarded as rigid and mechanical, but as the flexible, fluid and dynamic outworking of the fruits of the volition associated with actions. Thus the full details of its working out, in specific instances, are said to be 'unthinkable' (*acinteyya*) to all but a Buddha (*A.* IV.77).

Delayed results of karma

Karma does not just bring results in the next life: an action can have effects later in the present life, the next life, and also in some subsequent ones. Only very evil or good actions are certain to bring their result in the immediately following rebirth. When King Ajātasattu became his disciple, the Buddha said (not to his face) that he was done for, with his fate sealed, as he had earlier killed his own father (*D.* 1.85). One who has deliberately killed his or her mother or father, or an *Arahat*, or has shed the blood of a Buddha, or caused a schism in the monastic *Saṅgha*, is said to have done an action with immediate karmic effect (*Vibh.* 378), leading to rebirth in a hell for the remainder of an aeon (*M.A.* IV.109–10).[6] No good actions can avert such a rebirth in the next life (*Asl.* 358). Such people cannot be monks or nuns (*Vin.* 1.88–90), and cannot understand *Dhamma* even if they try (*Miln.* 310). On the other hand, those who are 'Noble persons', through some degree of experience of *Nirvāṇa*, will as a result certainly be free of all sub-human rebirths (*Pug.* 13), so that their insight has an invariable effect on their next rebirth.

All other actions are indeterminate as to when they will bring their results. It is thus said that the next life of one who lives a moral life and is of right view might be in a heaven *or* a hell (*M.* III.209–15). The latter will be the case if he or she did a strong evil deed in a previous life that had not yet produced its result, if he or she took to evil deeds late in life, or if he or she firmly took up a wrong view at the time of dying. That might be the case if an habitually generous person were to come to regret his generosity as worthless, and resent those who had not repaid his kindness. In that case, he would die in a bad state of mind and make a bad transition to the next life. This accords with *It.* 13–14, which says that one who dies at a time when his mind is corrupted is reborn in a hell, while one who dies while his mind is clear and calm is reborn in a heaven. In a similar way, a generally immoral person, with wrong view, might be reborn in a heaven if there were some previously unexpended strong good karma from the past, if he took to good ways late in life (cf. *S.* IV.321–2), or firmly took up a right view at the time of dying. Nevertheless, the results of the good or bad actions would catch up with the person sooner or later, perhaps in an attenuated form, just as a smouldering fire will burst into flames at some time in the future (*Dhp.* 71).

The effect of character

The karmic result of an action is not necessarily of precisely the same nature and magnitude as the action itself. Killing a goat does not necessarily lead to being reborn as a goat and being killed – though it may do (*J.* 1.167). The Buddha says that if 'just as a man does an action, so does he experience (its fruit)' were the case, there would be no opportunity for spiritual improvement, no way of growing beyond previous unvirtuous ways. He goes on (*A.* 1.249–53) to say that, for a person whose virtue, mind and wisdom are undeveloped, a small evil deed may lead to rebirth

---

[6] The terrible results of killing a parent do not occur if the act was unintentional (*Kvu.* 593), if the intended victim was another person (*AKB.* IV.103d), or if the parent is not known to be a parent (*Uss.* 179), though *Vin. A.* 445 differs on the last two points (Harvey, 1990: 275).

in a hell, just as a pinch of salt in a cup of water makes it undrinkable. For a person with developed virtue, mind and wisdom, though, the same action will produce its karmic results in the present life, with little, if any, in a future life, just as a pinch of salt does not make the river Ganges undrinkable. This seems to imply that, in a spiritually developed person, a small moral slip will have less effect, as it will be 'diluted' by his or her generally moral nature. For a spiritually undeveloped person, described here as having a 'small self', the same act has a greater impact. It, so to speak, 'flavours' a person's character more, setting up greater reverberations within it, in tune with other such reverberations. The good person suffers less from his or her bad action, though as most of the karmic results come in *this* life for him or her, this may not be immediately apparent. The Mahāyāna *Upāsaka-śīla Sūtra* also holds that one with self-discipline and spiritual effort may change some karmic effects from being serious ones in a future life into lighter ones in the present life (*Uss.* 180–1).

Remorse and the acknowledgement of fault

An important way in which the karmic result of a bad action can be lessened is by a person's regretting it, thinking that 'that evil deed cannot be undone by me' and resolving not to do it again (*S.* IV.320). This can be seen to lessen the psychological impact of the act, so as to reduce its karmic fruit. In the Sarvāstivādin view, an action is not 'accumulated' (*upacita*), with a full karmic result, if it is not repeated (the number of times is dependent on the nature of the action), so as to be 'complete', or is regretted.[7] The notion of regret, or acknowledgement of fault, as lessening the karmic fruit of an action is also affirmed in the Mahāyāna (*Ss.* 147, 59). It is said that a *Bodhisattva* who quarrels with another *Bodhisattva*, but who confesses this fault and promises future restraint, escapes from the consequences of that action (Conze, 1968: 52). In a recent Tibetan account, based on canonical sources, it is said that to confess, with regret, even to the actions of killing one's father and an *Arahat*, will lessen – to some extent – the terrible bad karma of such actions (Tharchin, 1984: 47).

The importance of regretting a bad action is seen in the refrain, 'It is a mark of progress in the discipline of the Noble Ones, if anyone recognises the nature of his transgression and makes amends as is right, restraining himself for the future.'[8] Among monks and nuns, the

---

[7] *AKB.* IV.120; cf. McDermott, 1984: 141–2.
[8] *D.* III.55; *S.* II.127–8, 205; *Vin.* II.192; *Vin.* IV.18–19.

acknowledgement, to another monk or nun, that one has broken a monastic rule is a vital part of monastic discipline. Likewise, in the Mahāyāna, *Bodhisattva*s, whether monastic or lay, should conceal their good points as well as acknowledge their faults (*Ss.* 100–1).

Regret has an impact on karmic results even in the case of good actions. Thus it is said that a man who, in a past life, had given alms to an enlightened ascetic, but then regretted doing so, was born as a rich man – because of his giving – but as a miser unable to enjoy his wealth, because of his regret (*S.* 1.91–2).

The Mahāyāna makes much of the power of acknowledgement of past evil, particularly when done to heavenly Buddhas or *Bodhisattva*s (*Bca.* 11). In this tradition, such actions, if sincere and devout, are seen as able to remove past bad karma. Chapter 8 of Śāntideva's *Śikṣā-samuccaya* describes how to purify oneself from evil deeds. It cites the *Catur-dharmaka Sūtra* as saying that, to overcome the accumulation of evil, the *Bodhisattva* should: (1) practise self-reproach, by immediately regretting any bad action; (2) follow any bad action by counteractive good ones; (3) resolve to abstain from such bad actions and (4) express faith in the three refuges, and not neglect the compassionate aspiration to Buddhahood (the *bodhicitta*) (*Ss.* 159). On (1), *Ss.* 160 cites the *Suvarṇa-prabhāsottama Sūtra*'s chapter on acknowledging faults, which says that one should call on all Buddhas to look on with compassion, acknowledge all the evil deeds one has done, and say:

On account of the evil done by me previously even in hundreds of aeons, I have a troubled mind oppressed with wretchedness, trouble and fear. With an unhappy mind I continually fear evil acts. Wherever I go there is no enjoyment for me anywhere. All the Buddhas are compassionate. They remove the fear of all beings. May they forgive my sin[9] and may they deliver me from fear. May the Tathāgatas [Buddhas] take away for me the defilement of impurities (and) acts. And may the Buddhas bath me with surging waters of compassion. (*Svb.* 31)

Counteractive good actions are seen as the development of deep insight, or clearly understanding the difference between evil and good action, with the latter stopping the effect of bad karma. It is also said that reciting a certain hundred-syllable *mantra* 8,000 times, while meditating on Buddhas and *Bodhisattva*s, makes one's evil pass away (*Ss.* 168–9). In one

---

[9] 'Sin' is a word loaded with Christian theological connotations. It alludes to an evil action as not only morally wrong, but as against the will of God, and setting up a gap between the perpetrator and God. While it is inappropriate as a translation in Theravāda Buddhism, it does not seem too inappropriate here, where an action is seen, in effect, as against the will of the Buddhas.

Tibetan account, it is said that, while the death of the *Arahat* Udrayana was due to his having killed an enlightened ascetic in a past life, his being able to become an *Arahat* was due to his immediate regret at this deed, followed by building a shrine to the ascetic and making offerings there, with continual confession of his evil deed (Tharchin, 1984: 77). In line with the above, Eastern Buddhism contains a rite in which a person repeatedly bows before an image in a spirit of repentance for any past evil deeds that have been committed.

In the Theravāda tradition, while the Buddha is generally seen as no longer contactable by humans, there is a chant from Sri Lanka in which a person, expressing reverence to the Buddha, *Dhamma* and *Saṅgha*, asks each to 'forgive' or 'be patient' (*khamatu*) if they have been wronged in any way (Saddhatissa and Webb, 1976: 10–13). Likewise, a chant from Thailand asks the Buddha, *Dhamma* and *Saṅgha* to 'accept' (*paṭigganhātu*) any wrong actions done towards them, using the same sort of wording as used by monks when acknowledging, to another monk, monastic transgressions (Mahāmakuṭ, 1990: 72–5).

However much Buddhism may value genuine remorse, it does not – certainly in its Theravāda form – encourage feelings of guilt; for such a heavy feeling, with its attendant anguish and self-dislike, is not seen as a good state of mind to develop, being unconducive to calm and clarity of mind. Indeed, it can be seen as an aspect of the fourth spiritual hindrance, of agitated 'restlessness and worry'. Such a feeling might arise as part of the natural karmic result of an action, but is not to be actively indulged in. In the Mahāyāna, Śāntideva says that a *Bodhisattva* should not be *excessively* regretful for wrong actions, citing the *Upāli-paripṛcchā* as saying that a *Bodhisattva* retains his great virtue if he returns to the aspiration for Buddhahood not more than a few hours after doing an evil deed (*Ss.* 173).

Rebirth, karma and motivation

Belief in rebirth and karma clearly has an impact on the way people view their actions: good and bad actions *matter*; they are of consequence, not things with no impact on life. Good actions are thus encouraged because, through their goodness, they lead to pleasant, uplifting effects for the doer. Bad actions are discouraged as their badness leads to unpleasant karmic results. Thus Melford Spiro found that, in Burma, the two most common reasons given for keeping the precepts are fear of hell and the fact that the precepts were ordained by the Buddha (1971: 449).

The idea of the cycle of rebirth also provides a perspective on life which is supportive of sympathy and respect for other beings. Within the round of rebirths, all beings are part of the same cycle of lives. Each human being has been an animal, ghost, hell-being and god in the past, and is likely to be so again at some time in the future. Any form of suffering one witnesses in another human or other being has been undergone by oneself at some time (*S.* ii.186): thus one should not cling to rebirths and should have compassion for other sentient beings. In one's innumerable past lives, the law of averages dictates that most beings one comes across, however one may dislike them now, have at some time been close relatives or friends (*S.* ii.189–90), so that loving-kindness towards them is appropriate. Thus in *Jātaka* story no. 68 (*J.* 1.308–9), a man and his wife address the Buddha as their son, and say that it is the duty of children to comfort their parents in old age. As the man and woman are not the Buddha's recognized parents, they explain that, in past lives, the man had been his father, uncle and grandfather 500 times each; likewise the woman had been his mother, aunt and grandmother 500 times each.

Such teachings, of course, urge a kindness and non-violence towards all forms of life. Humans are part of the same cycle of lives as other beings, and are not separated from them by a huge gulf. Nevertheless, the more complex and developed a being is, the worse it is to harm or kill it; so it is worse to kill a human than an animal (see p. 52).

Working with a rebirth perspective also helps sustain a long-term motivation for moral and spiritual practice. While death means that one loses all physical possessions, and is parted from one's loved ones and one's life's 'attainments', the purification of character that is developed by ethical and meditative practice is seen as something that death does not destroy (*Khp.* 7). It becomes part of one's mental continuum that will 'spill over' into another life. In that life, the spiritual development of this life may be neglected or further built on: but at the very least, it can act as a positive residue of this life, to be used as a foundation for further development. The opposite applies in the case of bad character-traits.

In the Tibetan tradition, there is a series of reflections, drawing on central Buddhist principles, to help motivate spiritual practice. The first reflection concerns the rarity of human life. Given the other forms of rebirth, and the fact that there are many more animals (including birds, fish, insects etc.) than humans, being born as a human is a rare and precious opportunity for spiritual improvement. To gain a human or divine rebirth, or have two in a row, is said to be rare (*S.* v.475–6; cf. *Dhp.* 182).

As against the number of beings born in other realms, those reborn as humans are like a pinch of sand compared to the size of the earth (*S.* II.263), or the number of India's pleasant groves compared to its rough terrain (*A.* 1.35). The chance for a being in a hell to be reborn as a human is less than that of a blind turtle, surfacing once a century, to happen to put its head through a ring moved by the winds across the surface of the sea. Even if a human rebirth is attained, the person will be poor, ugly and ill, and will tend to do evil actions which will send him or her back to hell (*M.* III.169; *Bca.* IV.20).

The Tibetan Buddhists talk of having attained a 'precious human rebirth' (Guenther, 1959: 14–21): a marvellous opportunity for spiritual growth that should be used wisely and respected in others. As it may be cut short at any time by death, it should not be frittered away: 'So if, when having found leisure such as this, I do not attune myself to what is wholesome, there could be no greater deception, and there could be no greater folly' (*Bca.* IV.23). In the lower realms, there is much suffering and little freedom of action. In the heavenly realms, life is blissful in comparison with human life, but this tends to make the gods complacent, particularly those in the highest heavens, so that they may also think that they are eternal, without need of liberation. The human realm is a middle realm, in which there is enough suffering to motivate humans to seek to transcend it by spiritual development, and enough freedom to be able to act on this aspiration. It is thus the most favourable realm for spiritual development.

Not *any* human rebirth has this precious quality, though. The early texts say that one cannot lead the holy life of the monk at a time when Buddhism has died out, or in a region devoid of Buddhist monastics and lay followers, or if one has a wrong view which denies the efficacy of karma and the possibility of spiritual development, or is stupid or deaf and dumb (*D.* III.264–5). Śāntideva cites the *Gaṇḍavyūha Sūtra* on the hard-to-attain favourable circumstances which make liberation possible: (1) rebirth as a human, (2) at a time when there has been a Buddha, (3) the perfection of one's bodily senses, (4) hearing the *Dharma*, (5) the company of good men, (6) a true 'good friend' (teacher), (7) the means for 'instruction in the true rule of life' and (8) the holy life (*Ss.* 2). Reflecting on this, he says 'If the arising of a Tathagata, faith, the attainment of a human body, and my being fit to cultivate virtue are scarce, when will they be won again?' (*Bca.* IV.15).

The second of the Tibetan reflections is on the uncertainty as to when one's life will end: no-one knows how much longer they have before they die – it might not be long. In line with this, the early texts say that human life, however long it lasts, is comparable to a line drawn on water (*A.* IV.138). Those entering a hellish rebirth, moreover, are told that they have ignored the significance of the suffering of birth, ageing, sickness and death, not being motivated to do karmically fruitful deeds by the realization that they were themselves still liable to such states (*M.* III.179–83). It is emphasized that death and old age come to all people, whatever their social class: 'As though huge mountains made of rock, so vast they reach up to the sky, were to advance from every side, grinding beneath them all that lives, so age and death roll over all' (*S.* 1.2). Once the Buddha advised a good king distracted by the affairs of state that if he, King Pasenadi, were told that such mountains were advancing on him, he would of course be full of fear at such a destruction of human life, given that a human rebirth is so hard to obtain. When asked what he could do in such circumstances, Pasenadi says he could only 'live in accord with *Dhamma*, live rightly, do what is wholesome and do karmically fruitful actions'.

The third reflection is that, after death, one will be reborn according to one's karma – and the backlog of one's karma from this and previous lives might not be such as to lead to a human rebirth next time. The fourth reflection is that, in whatever form one is reborn, suffering will be part of that life, whether as hellish agony, human pain and worry, or the more subtle unsatisfactoriness of a heaven realm. The fifth reflection is that such suffering can only be transcended by attaining *Nirvāṇa*, and the sixth is that to attain *Nirvāṇa*, one needs to practise under the guidance of a spiritual preceptor. Accordingly, one should apply oneself to spiritual practice *now*, for the benefit that this will bring both to oneself and others: 'As from a heap of flowers many a garland is made, even so many good deeds should be done by one born mortal' (*Dhp.* 53).

THE FOUR NOBLE TRUTHS

In early Buddhism and in the Theravāda tradition, the most central teaching is that on the Four Noble Truths (Harvey, 1990a: 47–72). These express spiritually ennobling insights which basically assert that:

(1) the processes of body and mind and the experience of life are *dukkha* (Pali; Skt *duḥkha*): unsatisfactory, frustrating and productive of suffering, whether in a gross or subtle form;

(2) this situation is caused by 'craving' (Pali *taṇhā*; Skt *tṛṣṇa*), demanding desires which lay one open to frustration and disappointment, and

keep one within the round of rebirths, with its attendant ageing, sickness and death;

(3) this situation can be transcended by destroying craving, and associated causes such as attachment, hatred and delusion, in the experience of *Nirvāṇa*. Once this is attained during life, a person will no longer be reborn, but will pass into final *Nirvāṇa* at death, beyond space, time and *dukkha*;

(4) the way to attain this goal is the 'middle way' consisting of the Noble Eightfold Path.

The first of these 'Truths' is elaborated through an analysis of personality through five kinds of unsatisfactory processes:

(1) material form (*rūpa*), consisting of various physical processes;

(2) feeling (*vedanā*), consisting of the 'taste' of any experience as pleasant, unpleasant or neutral;

(3) identification (Pali *saññā*; Skt *saṃjñā*), consisting of the interpretative function of mind, acting so as to label sense-objects, either correctly recognizing them or misperceiving them;

(4) constructing activities (Pali *saṅkhāras*; Skt *saṃskāras*), consisting of will (*cetanā*), and various other active mental processes such as moods and emotions;

(5) discernment or discriminative consciousness (Pali *viññāṇa*; Skt *vijñāna*), the basic awareness of there being an object of the senses or mind, and the discernment of it as having various parts or aspects, which are then labelled by identification.

These comprise the five 'groups' (Pali *khandhas*; Skt *skandhas*), or 'personality factors'. All of them are seen as mutually conditioning each other, as well as being affected by sense-objects. They are seen as in a state of constant change, whether of a subtle or more obvious kind. Consequently, they are seen as impermanent (Pali *anicca*; Skt *anitya*), so as to be unstable and not fully satisfactory (Pali *dukkha*; Skt *duḥkha*), and to be all 'not-Self' (Pali *anatta*; Skt *anātma*): not a permanent, self-secure I or Self. It is emphasized, though, that normally we erroneously look on ourselves and the world as made up of permanent, desirable, substantial things. We are thus attached to aspects of ourselves and the world, and so suffer when they change or disappear.

Nevertheless, in this collection of impersonal, ever-changing and conditioned events or processes, there are relatively stable, repeated patterns of arising that account for the persistence of what one might call a person's 'character'. Moreover, the dynamic pattern which is a person, though devoid of a permanent Self or essence, flows on from life to life, driven by the forces of craving and karma. This process is explained by Conditioned Arising (Pali *paṭicca-samuppāda*; Skt *pratītya-samutpāda*; Harvey, 1990a: 54–60), which at an abstract level is the principle that mental and physical phenomena only arise or exist when their appropriate conditioning factors arise or exist. In its usual concrete application, Conditioned Arising spells out a specific sequence of twelve conditioned and conditioning states that explains the ongoing flow of personality and rebirths: (1) spiritual ignorance or misperception underlays the (2) intentions and concerns of unenlightened people – karma – so that these direct (3) consciousness into noticing certain things and into being reborn in a certain way. Thus (4) the sentient body is sustained in life or develops in the womb at the start of a new life. This supports the (5) senses, the basis of (6) sensory stimulation and thus (7) feeling. Thus (8) craving for and against pleasant and unpleasant feelings arises, hence (9) grasping and (10) further involvement in the stream of existence. This leads on to (11) rebirth in either a new situation or a new life, which leads on to (12) ageing and then death of these: *dukkha*.

Suffering

The emphasis that all the conditioned processes that compose a person, and all worlds of rebirth, are impermanent, *dukkha* and not-Self forms an important part of the philosophical basis of ethics in Buddhism. The aim of overcoming *dukkha*, both in oneself and others, is the central preoccupation of Buddhism, and one towards which ethical action contributes. As Buddhists come to appreciate the extent of *dukkha* in their own lives, and to see that they so often contribute to it by their deluded response to life's happenings, the natural human feeling of sympathy (*anukampā*) for others – solidarity with them in the shared situation of *dukkha* – is elicited and deepened.[10] Accordingly, the importance of 'comparing oneself with others' is stressed, for both self and other 'yearn for happiness and recoil from pain' (*M.* 1.341). When explaining the five basic ethical precepts (see pp. 67–8 below), the Buddha once gave the following reflection as a reason for keeping them:

For a state that is not pleasant or delightful to me must be so to him also; and a state that is not pleasing or delightful to me, how could I inflict that upon another?[11]

---

[10] Aronson, 1980: 1–23; Keown, 1992: 73–7.   [11] *S.* v.353–4; cf. *M.* 1.97 and Tatz, 1986: 87, 255.

In a more general context, the Buddha is also reported to have said: 'Having traversed the whole world with my thought, I never yet met with anything that was dearer to anyone than his own self. Since the self of others is dear to each one, let him who loves himself not harm another' (*Ud.* 47, *S.* 1.75). Thus, on finding some boys tormenting a snake and poking it with sticks, the Buddha said:

> All tremble at punishment,
> Life is dear to all.
> Comparing others with oneself,
> One should neither kill nor cause to kill. (*Dhp.* 130)

Likewise:

Comparing oneself to others in such terms as 'Just as I am, so are they, just as they are, so am I', one should neither kill nor cause others to kill. (*Sn.* 705)

These passages emphasize that other beings are just like oneself in desiring pleasure and disliking pain, so that there is no good reason to add to the common lot of suffering by inflicting it on others. Doing so, moreover, harms oneself as well as others, for:

> Whoever, seeking his own happiness,
> Harms with sticks
> Pleasure-loving beings,
> He gets no happiness hereafter. (*Dhp.* 131).

The benefit of self and other are intertwined, because of the law of karma, so that concern to lessen one's own suffering goes hand-in-hand with lessening that of others. Helping others helps oneself (in terms of karmic results and good qualities of mind that are developed), and helping oneself (by purifying one's character) enables one to help others better.

Impermanence

While impermanence often leads to suffering, it also means that people, having no fixed Self, are always capable of change for the better,[12] and should be respected accordingly, rather than dismissed as unworthy by saying, for example, 'Oh, *he's* a thief.' A famous example of such change is reported in Buddhist texts, which tell of a time when the Buddha deliberately visited the haunt of the murderous ascetic-bandit

---

[12] Though if they have committed one of the heinous acts with immediate karmic result (see pp. 24–5), they will not be able to attain enlightenment in the present lifetime.

Aṅgulimāla, as he saw that he needed only a little exhortation to change his ways, become a monk, and soon attain *Nirvāṇa* (*M.* ii.97–105).

Whatever a person is like on the surface, it is held that the depths of their mind are 'brightly shining' and pure (*A.* 1.10). This depth purity, referred to as the 'embryo of the Truth-attained One' (*Tathāgata-garbha*) – or 'Buddha-nature' – in the Mahāyāna, represents the potential for ultimate change: the attainment of enlightenment, and as such is a basis for respecting all beings.

The changes involved in the round of rebirths are also relevant to ethics, for they enable one to consider beings aside from their present roles, character and nature. No matter how 'bad' beings may be, they will have been different in previous lives, and at some point in their incalculable number of lives, they must have crossed paths with one and been good to one: 'It is not easy, monks, to find a being who has not in the past been one's mother, or one's father, brother, sister, son or daughter' (*S.* ii.189–90). Viewing them in such a light enables one to have a positive regard for them. Not only past, but also future changes are relevant. In advising that one should always attend to the good points of people, so as to overcome ill-will towards them, the Theravādin commentator Buddhaghosa advises that if a person is so evil as to have no apparent good points, then compassion should be had towards him or her on account of the great suffering that he or she will undergo as a karmic result of such evil (*Vism.* 340).

Labelling someone as having a certain fixed nature often has a bad effect on him or her, whereas respecting him or her helps elicit change for the better. This cannot be forced, however: it is up to him or her. Nor should one passively accept negative traits in oneself as unchangeable. They need acknowledgement, but as they, like all else, are conditioned phenomena, they can be changed if their causes are understood and undermined. The same applies to wholesome states of mind: they can decay if not sustained by appropriate practice, so they are not grounds for being complacent or conceitedly looking down on others. Indeed, to do so or to treat others badly is just the way to undermine one's existing wholesome states.

From the Buddhist point of view, there are three forms of 'conceit' (*māna*), all based on the delusion of having a fixed 'I' as one's nature. Looking at others and comparing oneself to them, one then either sees oneself as 'superior', 'inferior' or (in a competitive or complacent way) 'equal' (*S.* iv.88), rather than simply calmly assessing what qualities one presently has, and how these might be strengthened or weakened.

Not-Self and respecting others

The teaching that no permanent Self or I exists within a person is also a support for ethics. While it does not itself support a positive regard for persons as unique entities, as the Christian emphasis on the value of individual persons does, it works in other ways. Primarily, it undermines the attachment to self – that '*I*' am a positive, self-identical entity that should be gratified, and should be able to brush aside others if they get in '*my*' way – which is the basis of lack of respect for others. It undercuts selfishness by undercutting the very notion of a substantial self. Anger, for example, feeds off the notion that 'I' have been offended.

The idea of not-Self does not deny that each person has an individual history and character, but it emphasizes that these are compounds of universal factors. In particular, it means that 'your' suffering and 'my' suffering are not inherently different. They are just suffering and so the barrier which generally keeps us within our own 'self-interest' should be dissolved, or widened in its scope till it includes all beings. The aspect of the not-Self teaching which emphasizes that we are not as in control of our own minds as we would like to think also adds a leavening of humility and a sense of humour to our attitude to the weaknesses of ourselves and others, for it is said that all those who have not yet had any glimpse of *Nirvāṇa* are 'deranged' (*Vibh.* A. 186).

'Respect for persons' is in many ways a key basis of Western ethics. It may be summed up as comprising four main elements (Smart, 1972):
(1) the right to 'individuation': to be treated not just as *a* human being, but as a particular one, with all one's personal difference;
(2) the right to 'acceptance': to be taken as one is, good or bad;
(3) the right to 'self-direction': to autonomy and the making of one's own choices;
(4) the right to impartial treatment.
Buddhism has not traditionally expressed its ethics in terms of 'rights' (see pp. 119–20), but more in terms of the appropriateness and benefit of treating others well. This is partly because no unchanging 'owner' of inalienable 'rights' is accepted, and because 'demanding rights' can lead to anger and greed if one is not careful. Nevertheless, the Buddhist perspective on how one should treat others provides analogues to the above four 'rights' (Harvey, 1987):
1 *Individuation*: while there is no permanent Self, each person is seen as a particular, individual combination of changing mental and physical processes, with a particular karmic history. This means that specific spir-

itual advice must be adapted to a person's character, to help them evolve in a better direction. The goal may largely go beyond individual differences, but the path must take account of them.

2 *Acceptance*: good and bad qualities are not fixed parts of an unchanging 'Self', so one should never tie a person down to what he or she has done or been in the past. Persons should always be addressed with regard to their present state, and openness to possible future changes. The faults that others have or have had are also something that we have or have had at some time.

3 *Self-direction*: any worthwhile change must come from within, by understanding and personal development.[13] It cannot be forced from without. People can be offered opportunities to change, but it is up to them if they take them.

4 *Impartial treatment*: all have the potential for *Nirvāṇa*, in this or a future life, and all bring themselves into their situations, good or bad, by their own karma. Thus all should be viewed with equanimity and impartiality.

The Noble Eightfold Path

The Noble Eightfold Path is the Middle Way of practice that leads to the cessation of *dukkha*. The Path has eight factors, each described as right or\perfect (Pali *sammā*; Skt *samyak*): (1) right view or understanding, (2) right resolve, (3) right speech, (4) right action, (5) right livelihood, (6) right effort, (7) right mindfulness and (8) right concentration or unification. These factors are also grouped into three sections (*M.* 1.301). Factors 3–5 pertain to *sīla* (Pali; Skt *śīla*), moral virtue; factors 6–8 pertain to *samādhi*, meditative cultivation of the heart/mind (*citta*); factors 1–2 pertain to *paññā* (Pali; Skt *prajñā*), or wisdom.

The eight factors exist at two basic levels, the ordinary (Pali *lokiya*; Skt *laukika*), which leads to good rebirths, and the transcendent (Pali *lokuttara*; Skt *lokottara*) or Noble (Pali *ariya*; Skt *ārya*), which builds on this preliminary development to go beyond rebirths, to *Nirvāṇa*. There is thus both an ordinary and a Noble Eightfold Path (*M.* III.71–8). Most Buddhists seek to practise the ordinary Path, which is perfected only in those who are approaching the lead up to 'stream-entry'. At stream-entry, a person gains a first glimpse of *Nirvāṇa* and the 'stream' which leads there, and

---

[13] This statement would not, though, be accepted, by some forms of Pure Land Buddhism, one form of the Mahāyāna in China, Korea and Japan (see pp. 142–3), for it sees salvation as coming from the heavenly Buddha Amitābha.

enters this, the *Noble* Eightfold Path. Each Path-factor conditions whole-some states, and progressively wears away its opposite 'wrong' factor, until all unwholesome states are destroyed.

Ordinary 'right view' (Pali *sammā-diṭṭhi*; Skt *samyak-dṛṣṭi*) relates mainly to such matters as karma and rebirth (as described on pp. 11–12 above), making a person take full responsibility for his or her actions. It also covers intellectual, and partial experiential, understanding of the Four Noble Truths. Noble right view is true wisdom, knowledge which pene-trates into the nature of reality in flashes of profound insight, direct seeing of the world as a stream of changing, unsatisfactory, conditioned processes (*S.* ii.16–17). Right resolve concerns the emotions, with thought rightly channelled towards peaceful freedom from sensuality, and away from ill-will and cruelty to lovingkindness and compassion. At the transcendent level, it is the focused applied thought of one practising the Noble Path. Right speech, at the ordinary level, is the well-established abstaining from lying, divisive or harsh speech, and empty gossip. At the transcendent level, each of the three factors relating to 'virtue' is a person's spontaneous restraint from wrong speech, action or livelihood, or immediate acknowledgement to another person when such acts are done. Right action is abstaining from wrong bodily behaviour: onslaught on living beings, taking what is not given, and wrong conduct with regard to sense-pleasures. Right livelihood is avoiding ways of making a living which cause suffering to others: those based on trickery and greed (*M.* iii.75), or on trade in weapons, living beings, meat, alcoholic drink or poison (*A.* iii.208).

The three last factors of the Path are of the Noble level when they are accompanied by other factors at this level (*M.* iii.71). Right effort is directed at developing the mind in a wholesome way. The first effort is to avoid the arising of unwholesome states of mind which express attachment, hatred or delusion. The second seeks to overcome or under-mine unwholesome states which nevertheless arise. The third is directed at the meditative development of wholesome states of mind, while the fourth is the effort to maintain and stabilize wholesome qualities of mind which have been generated. Right mindfulness (Pali *sati*; Skt *smṛti*) is a crucial aspect of any Buddhist meditation, and is a state of keen aware-ness of mental and physical phenomena as they arise within and around one, and carefully bearing in mind the relationship between things. Right concentration or unification (*samādhi*) refers to various levels of deep calm known as *jhāna*s (Pali; Skt *dhyāna*s): states of inner collected-ness arising from attention closely focused on a meditation object.

The order of the eight Path-factors is seen as that of a natural progression, with one factor following on from the one before it. Right view comes first because it knows the right and wrong form of each of the eight factors; it also counteracts spiritual ignorance, the first factor in the chain of Conditioned Arising, leading to *dukkha* (see p. 33). From the cold knowing of right understanding blossoms a right way of thinking, which has a balancing warmth. From this, a person's speech becomes improved, and thus his or her action. Once he or she is working on right action, it becomes natural to incline towards a virtuous livelihood. With this as basis, there can be progress in right effort. This facilitates the development of right mindfulness, whose clarity then allows the development of the calm of meditative concentration. Neither the ordinary nor the Noble Path is to be understood as a single progression from the first to eighth factor, however. Right effort and mindfulness work with right understanding to support the development of all the Path-factors: the Path-factors mutually support each other to allow a gradual deepening of the way in which the Path is trodden.

Noble persons

Any person not yet on the Noble Path is known as a *puthujjana* (Pali; Skt *prthagjana*), an 'ordinary person' who lacks the mental balance of those on the Noble Path, the eight kinds of spiritually 'Noble' (*ariya*) persons. These comprise the Noble *Saṅgha*, which with the Buddha and *Dhamma* are the 'three refuges' of a Buddhist (see p. 8). The Noble persons are those who have been permanently changed, to some degree, by insight into *Dhamma*: the Stream-enterer, Once-returner, Non-returner and *Arahat* (Pali; Skt *Arhat*), and those established on the specific paths which lead up to each of these states. The Stream-enterer is one who gains a first glimpse of *Nirvāṇa*, and so will be free from rebirth at anything less than a human level (*S.* v.357), and be bound to become an *Arahat* within seven lives at most (*A.* 1.235). The Once-returner is one whose remaining lives will include only one in the 'sense-desire-realm' (see p. 14), as a human or god in a lower heaven. The Non-returner will not be reborn again in the desire-realm, but will be reborn in one or more of the 'pure abodes', a small group of heavens in the '(elemental) form-realm'. Here, the Non-returner will go on to become an *Arahat*. The *Arahat* is one who fully experiences *Nirvāṇa* during life, and who destroys the causes of *any* more rebirths. At death, he or she passes into final *Nirvāṇa*, beyond all time, space, conditions and *dukkha*.

The progression through these grades of sanctity is measured by the number of the ten spiritual 'fetters' which have been destroyed. The Stream-enterer destroys the first three:

(1) 'views on the existing group', which takes a permanent Self as exist-ing in some relation to one or all of the five personality groups;

(2) vacillation in commitment to the three refuges and the worth of morality;

(3) grasping at moral precepts and vows.

The Stream-enterer has unblemished morality (*S.* II.69–70), not in the sense that no unwholesome action is ever done, but in the sense that, if it is, he or she always freely acknowledges having done such a deed (*Sn.* 232). There is no grasping at moral precepts because, though they are carefully followed, there is no belief that these alone will lead to becom-ing an *Arahat*: meditation and wisdom are also needed. Moreover, a person keeps the precepts without thinking what he or she will gain by doing so.[14] The Once-returner destroys the gross forms of the next two fetters:

(4) sensual desire;

(5) ill-will.

The Non-returner destroys even subtle remnants of them, so as to have great equanimity. The *Arahat* destroys the remaining five fetters:

(6) attachment to the (elemental) form heavenly world;

(7) attachment to the formless heavenly worlds;

(8) the 'I am' conceit, perhaps now in the form of lingering spiritual pride;

(9) restlessness;

(10) spiritual ignorance.

In order for such negative traits to be eradicated from the mind, other positive ones must also be developed: the factors of the Noble Eightfold Path, and other associated ones such as the 'seven factors of awakening': mindfulness, *Dhamma*-investigation, vigour, joy, tranquillity, mental unification and equanimity.

The place of ethics on the Path

From the perspective of the Four Noble Truths, ethics is not for its own sake, but is an essential ingredient on the path to the final goal. This is

[14] *D. A.* III.784, though *Vibh.* 365 sees this fetter as believing that non-Buddhist precepts and vows lead to spiritual purification.

well expressed in a passage which explains that 'purity of virtue' leads onward to 'purity of mind', this to 'purity of view', and this, through various stages of increasing spiritual insight, to 'utter *Nirvāṇa* without attachment', 'unshakeable freedom of mind' (*M.* 1.149–50). It is emphasized that while each stage supports the next, the 'holy life' is not lived for any of them except the final one. This is because at any lower stage of spiritual progress, there is still attachment and a person may become complacent, conceited or arrogant about his or her attainments, thus hindering further progress. The foundational importance of ethics for the rest of the Path is, however, crucial:

So you see, Ānanda, wholesome virtues have freedom from remorse as object and profit; freedom from remorse has gladness; gladness has joy; joy has tranquillity; tranquillity has happiness; happiness has concentration; concentration has seeing things as they really are; seeing things as they really are has turning away and non-attachment; turning away and non-attachment have release by knowing and seeing as their object and profit. So you see, Ānanda, wholesome virtues lead gradually up to the summit. (*A.* v.2)

In this process of development, the cultivation of one stage leads naturally on to the cultivation of the next, so that the components of the Path support one another and interact to form a harmonious whole. The basis for them all, however, like the earth for plants or a foundation for a building, is moral virtue (*Miln.* 33–4).

In terms of the division of the Path into virtue, meditation and wisdom (always given in this order), the Path can be seen to develop as follows. Influenced and inspired by good examples, a person's first commitment will be to develop virtue, a generous and self-controlled way of life for the benefit of self and others. To motivate this, he or she will have some degree of preliminary wisdom, in the form of some acquaintance with the Buddhist outlook and an aspiration to apply it, expressed as *saddhā*, trustful confidence or faith. With virtue as the indispensable basis for further progress, some meditation may be attempted. With appropriate application, this will lead to the mind becoming calmer, stronger and clearer. This will allow experiential understanding of the *Dhamma* to develop, so that deeper wisdom arises. From this, virtue is strengthened, becoming a basis for further progress in meditation and wisdom. Accordingly, it is said that wisdom and virtue support each other like two hands washing each other (*D.* 1.124). With each more refined development of the virtue–meditation–wisdom sequence, the Path spirals up to a higher level, until the crucial transition of stream-entry is reached. The *Noble* Path then spirals up to Arahatship.

Defilements such as greed, hatred and delusion exist in the form of unwholesome activities of body and speech, unwholesome thoughts, and the latent tendencies in the mind which are the root of all these. Moral virtue restrains the external expression of the defilements, meditation undermines active defilements in the mind, and liberating insight destroys defilements in the form of latent tendencies. These three levels of development can perhaps be seen in the popular verse:

> Not to do any evil,
> To cultivate what is wholesome,
> To purify one's mind:
> This is the teaching of the Buddhas. (*Dhp.* 183)

Wise, skilful, wholesome actions

In the Pali Canon, the term *puñña* (see pp. 17–18) occurs mainly in the context of giving and other aspects of lay practice, as a pan-Indian term for good, beneficial actions. However, a more frequently occurring term for good actions, with more particularly Buddhist connotations, is *kusala* (Pali; Skt *kuśala*) (Cousins, 1996: 154–5). A *kusala* action is a blameless one (*A.* 1.263), which is 'wise' or 'skilful' in producing an uplifting mental state and spiritual progress in the doer (unless he or she has already attained the goal), or 'wholesome', in that it involves a healthy state of mind – stable, pure, unencumbered, ready-to-act, calm and contented (Payutto, 1993: 19). The opposite term, for a bad action, is *akusala*: 'unwholesome' or 'unskilful'. L. S. Cousins traces the meaning of *kusala/kuśala* in pre-Buddhist and Buddhist sources and summarizes thus:

1. An original meaning of 'intelligent' 'wise';[15]
2. Expert in magical and sacrificial ritual (in the [pre-Buddhist] *Brāhmaṇas*); for brahmins, of course, this would precisely constitute wisdom.
3. A) Skilled in meditational/mystic (/ascetic?) practices (in the early Pali sources and, no doubt, in other contemporary traditions), including skilled in the kind of behaviour which supported meditation, etc., i.e. *śīla* [keeping moral precepts], etc.
   B) Skilled in performing *dāna* [giving] and *yañña* [sacrifice], now interpreted in terms of central Buddhist ethical concerns; and associated with keeping the precepts and so on.

[15] Though in an unpublished paper commenting on Cousins' account, '*Kusala*: Good or Skilful or What? Reconsidering the Meaning of *kusala/kuśala* in Buddhist Texts' (UK Association for Buddhist Studies conference, 6 July 1988), Lambert Schmithausen has argued that such a usage was originally only applied to *persons* and not actions or states.

4. *Kusala* in later Buddhist and Jain sources becomes generalized to refer to something like wholesome or good states.
So there is no reason to doubt that by a later period (i.e. in the commentaries and perhaps later canonical sources) *kusala* in non-technical contexts means something which could be translated as 'good'. (1996: 156)

Under 3.A), Cousins sees the meaning as states 'produced by wisdom' that contribute to the development of various qualities leading to awakening (1996: 137). While this meaning often occurs in the *Suttas*, and is emphasized in the Canonical *Abhidhamma*, the *Suttas* also often see *kusala* as meaning 'blameless' (Cousins, 1996: 139–40).

The criteria for determining whether an action is *kusala* or *akusala* will be discussed below. Before that, the somewhat ambiguous relationship between karmically fruitful actions and *Nirvāṇa* will be discussed.

The Arahat as 'beyond fruitful and deadening actions'

At the culmination of the Noble Eightfold Path stands the *Arahat*, who is actually said to have 'passed beyond' *puñña* and *pāpa* (*Sn.* 636) and to have 'abandoned' them (*Sn.* 520): 'Not clinging to karmically fruitful or deadening actions, he abandons what has been taken up, and does not fashion (anything more) here' (*Sn.* 790). He or she constructs no karmically fruitful or unfruitful action (*S.* II.82). What could this mean? It certainly does not mean that an *Arahat* abandons moral behaviour: an *Arahat* is said to be fully endowed with moral virtue and insight (*Dhp.* 217), one with the highest wholesomeness (*M.* II.25), incapable of killing (*D.* III.235). The Buddha, himself an *Arahat*, is foremost in moral virtue (*D.* I.174), even though this is only part of his perfection (*D.* I.3). The *Nirvāṇa* experienced by the *Arahat* during life is said to be the destruction of attachment, hatred and delusion (*S.* IV.251). As the *Arahat* is one in whom attachment/greed, hatred and delusion, the roots of unwholesome action, have been destroyed (*S.* IV.252), he or she is no longer capable of morally unwholesome action, though he or she may inadvertently break a monastic rule, such as not eating after noon, through ignorance of worldly matter (*Miln.* 266–7). His or her actions are morally wholesome, but arise spontaneously, without resistance from unwholesome traits (*D.* III.217). This is one sense in which the *Arahat* has 'abandoned karmic fruitfulness': he or she no longer has to deliberate about doing the 'right thing'.

A second way in which he or she is beyond karmic fruitfulness is that his or her actions no longer have either good or bad karmic fruits. It is said that karma is conditioned by craving (*S.* v.86–7; *Miln.* 51) – destroyed by the *Arahat* – and that only when there is greed, hatred and delusion can fruit-bearing karma originate (*A.* 1.134–5). While non-greed, non-hatred and non-delusion are causes of action, like their opposites, the wholesome actions springing from them are said to conduce to the future cessation of (good or bad) karma, while the unwholesome actions springing from their opposites are said to conduce to the continued arising of karma in the future (*A.* 1.263). In one who still has remnants of greed, hatred and delusion, acts rooted in non-greed etc. still bring good karmic results. In one in whom they are destroyed, actions are wholesome, but do not generate future fruits. Thus the Buddha once spoke of four kinds of action (*M.* 1.389–91):

(1) that which is dark, and with dark result: harmful actions that lead to rebirths with harmful experiences in them;

(2) that which is bright and with bright result: non-harming actions that lead to rebirth with non-harmful experiences in them;

(3) that which is both dark and bright and with dark and bright result: a mixture of the first two;[16]

(4) that which is 'neither dark nor bright, neither dark nor bright in result, the action that conduces to the destruction of actions': the will to get rid of the first three types of action.

Elsewhere, *Nirvāṇa* is said to be 'neither black nor white' (*A.* iii.384–6), and the fourth type of action is said to be the Noble Eightfold Path.[17] This path is also said to be 'the way leading to the stopping of karma', with the stopping of karma being 'that stopping of bodily action, verbal action and mental action by which one touches freedom'.[18] That is, the Noble Eightfold Path leads up to a profoundly still experience, *Nirvāṇa*, in which the capacity of actions to bring future karmic fruits comes to an end.

The *Arahat* is one for whom both unwholesome and wholesome moral conduct (*sīla*) are said to have have 'stopped' completely (*M.* ii.26–7). Unwholesome conduct is stopped by replacing wrong conduct with right conduct. Wholesome conduct is stopped by being 'virtuous (*sīla-vā*), but not *sīla-maya*'. Now, '*maya*' means something like 'made of' or 'consisting in'. At *It.* 51, there is reference to the 'basis of effecting an act of

---

[16] That is, an action in which good and bad motives are juxtaposed. As the *Abhidhamma* texts deny that wholesome and unwholesome mental states can be literally simultaneous (*Kvu.* 344), this means that there is a flicking between good and bad motives in certain actions: for example, in an act of giving, genuine generosity may alternate with a desire to show someone up as less generous than oneself.   [17] *A.* ii.236; see Payutto, 1993: 73–81.   [18] *S.* iv.132–3; cf. *A.* iii.415.

karmic fruitfulness' 'consisting in moral virtue (*sīla-maya*)'. The commentary (*M.A.* II.270) explains the term at *M.* II.26–7 as meaning that the *Arahat* has nothing further to add to his or her already developed moral virtue, and accordingly I. B. Horner translates 'and has no addition to make to moral habit'.[19] K. N. Jayatilleke translates the term as meaning 'not virtuous through conditioning' (1972: 26), and *Bhikkhus* Ñāṇamoli and Bodhi translate 'but he does not identify with his virtue', meaning that he or she is not attached to it, seeing it as not-Self, like everything else.[20] The upshot of these different readings is the same, though: the *Arahat*, standing at the culmination of the Noble Eightfold Path, has perfected all its factors, including those relating to moral virtue. He or she has nothing further to add to this moral and spiritual perfection, but his or her virtue is not constrained by ideas of what he or she *ought* to do: he or she just naturally acts in a virtuous way, without being attached to virtue. Thus an *Arahat* says that he is non-violent because of his destruction of attachment, hatred and delusion, not because of grasping at precepts and vows (*Vin.* I.184).

As the Noble Eightfold Path leads to rendering karmic fruitfulness ineffective, karmic fruitfulness is clearly seen to have some limitations. Thus it is sometimes said that a monk may think of returning to the lay life because he can then enjoy life's pleasures and still perform karmically fruitful acts (see, for example, *Vin.* I.182). Also relevant is a distinction between 'ordinary' and Noble right view (see p. 38 above). The first, concerning belief in karma and rebirth (see pp. 11–12 above), is said to have 'cankers [mental limitations holding the mind back from *Nirvāṇa*], it is on the side of karmic fruitfulness, it ripens in cleaving (to another rebirth)'. The second, wisdom or direct insight, is said to be 'Noble, cankerless, transcendent, a factor of the path [the Noble Eightfold Path to *Nirvāṇa*]' (*M.* III.72). The point here seems to be that 'karmically fruitful' actions, while they have the beneficial result of leading to good rebirths, have limitations in that they cannot, unaided, lead to *Nirvāṇa*, which transcends all rebirths – and their unsatisfactory nature – whether bad or good. To attain *Nirvāṇa*, wisdom or insight is also needed. While 'karmically fruitful' actions strengthen character-traits which facilitate the development of wisdom, the latter is an extra step. Moral virtue is said to be the 'gateway to the city of *Nirvāṇa*' (*Vism.* 9), though not to go all the way. Karmic fruitfulness is necessary for movement towards

---

[19] *Middle Length Sayings*, vol. II (London: PTS, 1957), p. 226.
[20] *The Middle Length Discourses of the Buddha* (Boston, Mass.: Wisdom, 1995), p. 651.

Nirvāṇa – thus some texts even say the latter is attainable by karmic fruit-fulness (*Khp.* 7) – but not itself sufficient. Nevertheless, it is incorrect to see actions orientated to karmic fruitfulness and actions of the Noble Path as radically different, as King (1964) and Spiro (1971) have in their analyses of Burmese Theravāda Buddhism. They see the former kind of actions as the sphere of the laity and the latter as the sphere of the monks. That this is a false dichotomy has been well argued by Keown (1992: 83–105), Aronson (1980: 78–96) and Katz (1982: 175–80). Both monks and laity can and do practise both types of action, and the first type is the very foundation – and continued sustainer – of the second. It is not the case that moral virtue (a prime source of karmic fruitfulness) is a mere instrumental means towards a goal consisting only of insight (see Keown, 1992: 8–14). One standing at the goal of Buddhism has *both* moral virtue *and* deep insight, for he or she has perfected all factors of the Noble Eightfold Path, covering moral virtue and meditation as well as wisdom.

PHILOSOPHY OF ACTION

Criteria for differentiating good and bad actions

The criteria for deciding what action is 'wholesome' (*kusala*) and what is 'unwholesome' (*akusala*) (see pp. 42–3) are of three kinds:
(1) the motivation of the action;
(2) the direct effects of the action in terms of causing suffering or happiness;
(3) the action's contribution to spiritual development, culminating in *Nirvāṇa*.

The three possible motivating 'roots' of 'unwholesome' action (*M.* 1.47) are:
(1) greed (*lobha*), which covers a range of states from mild longing up to full-blown lust, avarice, fame-seeking and dogmatic clinging to ideas;
(2) hatred (Pali *dosa*; Skt *dveṣa*), which covers mild irritation through to burning resentment and wrath;
(3) delusion or spiritual misorientation (*moha*), the veiling of truth from oneself, as in dull, foggy states of mind through to specious doubt on moral and spiritual matters, distorting the truth or turning away from it, and misconceptions, such as that it is acceptable to kill animals as a religious sacrifice or to eat, or to kill criminals (*AKB.* IV.68d).

The opposites of these are the three 'roots' of wholesome action:

(1) non-greed, covering states from small generous impulses through to a strong urge for renunciation of worldly pleasures;
(2) non-hatred, covering friendliness through to forbearance in the face of great provocation, and deep lovingkindness for all beings;
(3) non-delusion, covering clarity of mind through to the deepest insight into reality.

While phrased negatively, these three are nevertheless seen as positive states. The importance of seeing the harmfulness of the unwholesome roots and the benefit of the wholesome ones is emphasized in the *Kālāma Sutta* (p. 10 above). The three roots of the unwholesome are intertwined. Greed and hatred are grounded in delusion, and greed may lead to hatred. It is said that greed is a lesser fault, but fades slowly, hatred is a great fault, but fades quickly, and delusion is a great fault and fades slowly (*A.* 1.200). This gives a clear indication of Buddhist values, especially the need to develop wisdom, so as to overcome delusion. It is also said that common motives for evil deeds are partiality, enmity, stupidity and fear (*D.* III.181–2), and that greed, hatred and delusion can each lead a person to abuse others with the thought 'I am powerful' (*A.* 1.201–2).

An action is also assessed in terms of its direct effect in terms of causing suffering or happiness. This is shown by a passage where the Buddha advises that one should reflect before, during and after any action of body, speech or mind, to consider whether it might conduce to the harm of oneself, others or both, so that it is unwholesome and results in *dukkha*. If one sees that it will, one should desist from the action. If one sees that the action conduces to the harm of neither oneself nor others, nor both, it can be seen to be wholesome, with a happy result (*M.* 1.415–16). The 'harm' to oneself which is relevant here is spiritual harm, or material harm if this arises from self-hatred (for example by harsh asceticism, *M.* 1.342–9): an act which benefits others at the expense of material harm to oneself is not unwholesome. Harm to oneself is also seen to arise as an immediate result of unwholesome action: 'One who is thus caught up, whose mind is thus infected, in the karmically deadening, unwholesome states born of greed . . . of hatred . . . of delusion, experiences suffering, stress, agitation and anxiety in this present life' (*A.* 1.202).

An action is also assessed in terms of its contribution to spiritual development, culminating in *Nirvāṇa*, which criterion is seen to lead on from the one just described above. Thus it is said that unwholesome conduct is that which causes injury, that is, having *dukkha* as fruit, because it leads to the torment of oneself, others or both, *and* conduces to the arising of further unwholesome states and the diminution of wholesome ones: that is, having unhealthy effects on the psyche. Wholesome actions are of the opposite kind (*M.* II.114–15). Moreover, 'wrong resolve', for example, is said not only to conduce to the harm of self and other but to be 'destructive of intuitive wisdom, associated with distress, not conducive to *Nirvāṇa*', while 'right resolve' has the opposite effect (*M.* I.115–16).

Overall, one can say that an 'unwholesome' action is one that arises from greed, hatred or delusion, leads to immediate suffering in others and/or oneself – and thus to further karmic suffering for oneself in the future – and contributes to more unwholesome states arising and liberating wisdom being weakened. 'Wholesome' actions have the opposite characteristics. They arise from a virtuous motive, are free of all direct harm to self and other, contribute to the improvement of the character of the person who performs them, and thus assist in moving a person along the Path to *Nirvāṇa*.

While saying that an action is 'karmically fruitful' refers to its potency to produce happiness as a karmic result, saying that it is 'wholesome' has a different emphasis. Any karmically fruitful action is also wholesome, but there is a range of mental states which are referred to as wholesome, but are not specifically said to be karmically fruitful.[21]

Using the above criteria, one list of what is unwholesome is: (1) onslaught on living beings, (2) taking what is not given, (3) sensual misconduct, (4) lying speech, (5) divisive speech, (6) harsh speech, (7) gossip, (8) covetousness, (9) ill-will and (10) wrong view. That is, it is wrong action of body ((1)–(3)), speech ((4)–(7)) and mind ((8)–(10)). What is wholesome is restraint from each of these (*M.* 1.47). Such actions are said to be 'of unwholesome will (*akusala-sañcetanikā*), yielding *dukkha*, ripening in *dukkha*' (*A.* v.292). Of these actions, only those relating to body and speech would normally be seen as coming under the purview of the English words 'morality' or 'ethics'; indeed, the Pali word *sīla*, or 'moral virtue', has a similar range. That which is 'wholesome' or 'unwholesome', then, goes beyond the purely moral/immoral to include states of mind, which may have no direct effect on other

---

[21] For example, constructing activities (*saṅkhāras*) involved in actions are said to be of three types: karmically fruitful, karmically unfruitful, and imperturbable (*āneñja*) (*D.* III.217). The third of these is seen by the commentary (*D. A.* 998) as wholesome (*kusala*) acts of will that lead to rebirth in the formless realms, an idea supported by *A.* II.184. As such rebirths contain only neutral feelings, but not pleasant or unpleasant ones (*Vibh.* 267), actions leading to them are not said to be karmically fruitful or unfruitful, though they are wholesome as they can contribute to spiritual development.

people. All the factors of the Eightfold Path, for example, are seen as 'wholesome'.

Comparisons with Western ethical systems

Various scholars have reflected on the question of what is the nearest analogy to Buddhist ethics in Western ethical theory. One theory it is commonly likened to is Utilitarianism,[22] which holds that a specific act (Act Utilitarianism), or a general type of action (Rule Utilitarianism) is right if, and only if, it results in a greater amount of happiness, or a reduction in unhappiness, for anyone affected by it. That is, the right-ness of an action consists in the nature of its effects. However, in Buddhism, while good actions are seen as leading to future happiness as a karmic fruit, they do so because they are right; they are not right *because* they happen to lead to happy karmic fruits (see p. 17 above).[23] That good actions are seen as having happy karmic fruits for the agent will be *one* factor relevant to his or her motivation for doing such acts:

Buddhism says that, if one wants to attain prosperity, amicable social relation-ships or a good reputation, self-confidence or calm and joy, a good rebirth or progress towards *Nibbāna*, then act in such and such a way: for this is how such things are fostered. If one behaves otherwise, then one will suffer in this and subsequent lives, as a natural (karmic) result of unwholesome actions. (Harvey, 1990a: 196)

Nevertheless, happy fruits are not what make good actions good. Motive and intention are crucial, though when simple joy is observed to arise from an action, it is often a sign that it is a good action, and the imme-diate effect of an action on the happiness of others is *one* factor in assess-ing it.

A danger in Utilitarianism (particularly Act Utilitarianism) is that it tends to a perspective of 'the end justifies the means', so a means which one might want to say is evil might be 'justified' by the goal it is seen to lead to. In Buddhism, certainly in its Theravāda form (though see chapter 3 on the Mahāyāna idea of 'skilful means'), this is not possible: only wholesome means have the ability to conduce to truly wholesome ends. Admittedly, the goal of Buddhism, *Nirvāṇa*, is equivalent to the end of *dukkha*, the end of suffering, a goal which a Utilitarian would share. But *Nirvāṇa* is also the destruction of attachment, hatred and

[22] See, e.g., Dharmasiri, 1989: 24–7; Kalupahana, 1976: 61. [23] Keown, 1992: 8–23, 165–91.

delusion (*It*. 38–9), and the Path to this is good or wholesome because it is intrinsically related to this goal, not contingently so: it is not the Path which *just happens* to conduce to it. As it consists of actions rooted in non-greed, non-hatred and non-delusion, the Path has natural affinities to *Nirvāṇa*, the destruction of the opposites of these. Moreover, it is not that *Nirvāṇa*, the absence of greed, hatred and delusion, is (arbitrarily) chosen as the ultimate goal, and then actions seen as 'good' if they happen to conduce to this (cf. Dharmasiri, 1989: 24). Actions rooted in non-greed etc. can be recognized as good or wholesome whether or not one is a Buddhist with *Nirvāṇa* as one's ultimate goal (see p. 47).

This shows that a better broad Western analogue to Buddhist ethics is Aristotelian ethics, as argued by Keown (1992, especially pp. 193–227), supported by Tatz (1986: 1) and Shaner (1989: 175) for Mahāyāna ethics and Mahāyāna-shaped Japanese ethics respectively. For Aristotle, ethics is about developing one's *ethos* or 'character' by the cultivation of virtues – wholesome dispositions and inclinations – which conduce to the goal of *eudaimonia*. This goal involves true happiness and a human flourishing in which the psyche is marked by excellencies of both reason and character (Keown, 1992: 193, 203, 209–10). Both Aristotle and Buddhism aim at human perfection by developing a person's knowledge and character, his or her 'head' and 'heart' (Keown, 1992: 72, 209). In Buddhist terminology, this is done by eliminating both spiritual ignorance and craving, which feed off each other, by cultivating intellectual, emotional and moral virtues sharing something of the qualities of the goal towards which they move (Keown, 1992: 194). In both Aristotelian and Buddhist ethics, an action is right because it embodies a virtue which conduces to and 'participates' in the goal of human perfection. Both are 'teleological' in that they advocate action which moves towards a *telos* or goal/end with which they have an intrinsic relationship (Keown, 1992: 184, 194). This is as opposed to being simply 'consequentialist', like Utilitarianism: judging an act by the effects it happens to have (Keown, 1992: 23, 202) – though some Utilitarians would dispute this distinction.

Another possible Western analogue for Buddhist ethics is Kantian ethics, which sees what is good as residing in a good will, which respects other people as ends in themselves rather than as means to one's own ends. While there are clearly some similarities with Buddhist ethics, Buddhism does not ignore the actual results of action on others as opposed to the will or motive behind it. More importantly, Kantian ethics is deontological, or based on duty. For Buddhism, though, moral constraints are not imposed on people without regard to their own good (Keown, 1992: 202[24]), and the Buddha said that he gladly taught others out of compassion and sympathy, not because he felt that this was a burdensome duty (*S.* 1.206). A moral life is not seen as a bald 'ought', but as an uplifting source of happiness, in which the sacrifice of lesser pleasures facilitates the experiencing of those which are more enriching and satisfying, for both oneself and others. Nevertheless, duty is not a concept foreign to Buddhism; it is simply that what one *should* do is also seen as what is enriching and rewarding.

Overall, the rich field of Buddhist ethics would be narrowed by wholly collapsing it into any single one of the Kantian, Aristotelian or Utilitarian models, though Buddhism agrees with each in respectively acknowledging the importance of (1) a good motivating will, (2) cultivation of character, and (3) the reduction of suffering in others and oneself. This is because the first two of these are seen as crucial causes of the third of them, while aiming at the third, in a way which does not ignore aspects of the full karmic situation, is a key feature of the first two.

A key aspect of Western ethical systems is that moral prescriptions should be universally applicable to all people who can understand them. Buddhism, though, is generally gradualist in approach, so while it has ethical norms which all should follow from a sense of sympathy with fellow beings (such as not killing living beings), others only apply to those who are ready for them, as their commitment to moral and spiritual training deepens. This most obviously applies to the monastic level of commitment as compared with that of an ordinary lay person. A monk or nun vows to follow over 200 precepts or training rules, as compared with the usual five of a lay person. Many of these relate to behaviour which does not directly harm other beings – and thus do not come under the scope of ethics, as such – but are simply part of a training system to help a person overcome his or her greed, hatred and delusion: the roots of any behaviour which *does* harm others.

The level of morality and general conduct of a monk or nun is expected to be of a higher level than that of a lay person, because he or she has made the commitment to be ordained. Actions which would be totally unacceptable for a monk or nun, such as sexual intercourse, are acceptable (within certain limits) for a lay person.

---

[24] Keown's treatment, here, is better than that of Dharmasiri, 1989: 27–8.

Intention, knowledge and degrees of unwholesomeness in actions

The degree of unwholesomeness of an action is seen to vary according to the degree and nature of the volition/intention behind the action, and the degree of knowledge (of various kinds) relating to it. A bad action becomes more unwholesome as the force of the volition behind it increases, for this leaves a greater karmic 'trace' on the mind. The Theravādin commentator Buddhaghosa discusses the unwholesome act of 'onslaught on breathing (i.e. living) beings' as follows:

'Onslaught on breathing beings' is, as regards a breathing being that one perceives as living, the will to kill it, expressed through body or speech, occasioning an attack which cuts off its life-faculty. That action, in regard to those without good qualities (*guṇa-*) – animals etc. – is of lesser fault when they are small, greater fault when they have a large physical frame. Why? Because of the greater effort involved. Where the effort is the same, (it is greater) because of the object (*vatthu-*) (of the act) being greater. In regard to those with good qualities – humans etc. – the action is of lesser fault when they are of few good qualities, greater fault when they are of many good qualities. But when size or good qualities are equal, the fault of the action is lesser due to the (relative) mildness of the mental defilements and of the attack, and greater due to their intensity. Five factors are involved: a living being, the actual perceiving of a living being, a thought of killing, the attack, and death as a result of it. There are six methods: with one's own hand, by instigation, by missiles, by contrivance (trap or poison), by sorcery, by psychic power.[25]

Here, one can see that an act is made worse by a stronger or more perverse volition motivating and accompanying it. To kill a virtuous human, or one deserving respect such as a parent (cf. p. 24; *D.* 1.85; *Vibh.* 378), is particularly perverse, just as giving to a virtuous person is particularly good (see p. 21; *A.* IV.237–78). That killing in a state of intense defilement is worse would mean that premeditated killing, from a mix of greed, resentment and also delusion, would be very bad. Other aspects of the above quotation will be discussed in later chapters, as appropriate. One can see similar principles at work, though, in the Mahāyāna *Upāsaka-śīla Sūtra*, which holds that the object of the act of killing can be heavy (such as a parent) or light (an animal), and the thought behind it heavy or light dependent upon the degree of viciousness in it. In such an act, there is the motivating root, the means, and sometimes the thoughts and actions which come after it as its completion, such as eating an animal one has

---

[25] *M. A.* 1.198; cf. translation of Conze, 1959: 70–1; cf. almost identical passages at *Khp. A.* 28–9 and *Asl.* 97, and cf. also *AKB.* IV.73a–b.

killed (*Uss.* 165). Of these, just the means, just the completion, the root and means, or the means and completion may be heavy. 'If the object is the same, it is the thought that makes the difference of heavy or light retribution' (*Uss.* 180).

One can also outline a five-fold gradation of types of bad action according to the degree of both intention and knowledge involved:

(1) *An action performed without intending to do that particular action, for example accidentally treading on an insect, without any thought of harming.*

Such an action is not blameworthy and generates no bad karmic results. There is no offence for a monk if he kills a living being unintentionally, not realizing that his actions would harm a living being (*Vin.* iv.125). Likewise, in regard to the case of the monastic offence – entailing defeat in the monastic life – of deliberately killing a human, there is no actual offence entailing defeat 'if it was unintentional, if he did not know, if he were not meaning death, if he was out of his mind, the first offender (who caused the rule to be made)'.[26] It is also said that to crush worms accidentally while crushing sugar-cane for its juice is not blameable (*Miln.* 166), nor was the Buddha blameable when, after a certain sermon of his, monks of wrong view vomited blood (*Miln.* 165–7). Again, *Ud.* 28–9 says that a certain monk was not to be blamed for addressing other monks as if they were outcastes, for it was merely a habit arising from his last 500 lives, in which he had been a member of the brahmin class, who were accustomed to speak in such a harsh manner. The text explains that the monk had no hatred in his heart when saying this, and its commentary (*Ud. A.* 193), which actually sees him as an *Arahat*, says that his harsh speech was not something that he himself desired. In the *Jātakas* is another story on non-intentional action. A captured partridge is hit by a hunter so that its cry attracts other birds to their deaths. As it has no bad intention, and only plays a passive part in the hunter's actions, it is not blameworthy (*J.* iii.64–6). What, though, of an act which is not *intended* to harm any being, but is such that one knows, or has strong reasons to expect, that a being or beings will be harmed? For example, crushing the sugar-cane when one knows, or strongly suspects, that it contains worms? Or driving a car on a hot day when it is very likely that many insects will be killed? Are these cases of (a) culpable carelessness, or (b) simply a lack of extra-mile altruism? In the V*inaya*, certain forms of careless behaviour, such as throwing a stone off a cliff, are small offences (*Vin.* iii.82).

---

[26] *Vin.* iii.78; cf. *Vin.* ii.91. Of course, it would still be a *moral* offence for the first offender to act in this way. Likewise, lesser acts which are normally monastic offences are excused if committed by a first offender (see, e.g., *Vin.* iii.155).

Nevertheless, the *Kurudhamma Jātaka* (*J.* III.366–81), of which Andrew Huxley gives a good analysis (1995c), emphasizes the idea that unintended harm to others should not be counted against one, and that it is not wise to agonize over such matters (see also Harvey, 1999).

(2) *If one knows that a certain kind of action is evil, but does it when one is not in full control of oneself, for example when impassioned.*

This is a lesser evil than doing it with full knowledge of what one was doing, and with full intention. The *Milindapañha* discusses the case of a *Jātaka* story (*J.* III.514–19) in which the *Bodhisattva*, as an ascetic, sacrifices (or almost does?) many animals when a king says that he can marry his beautiful daughter if he does so (*Miln.* 219–21). The *Miln.* says that this was an action done when he was 'out of his mind (*visaññinā*) with passion, not when he was thinking of what he was doing (*sañcetanena*)'. The action was not in accordance with his nature, for he was 'unhinged, impassioned. It was when he was out of his mind, thoroughly confused and agitated, with thoughts confused, in a turmoil and disturbed', like a madman. Thus it is said that 'Evil done by one who is unhinged . . . is not of great blame here and now, nor is it so in respect of its ripening in a future state.' Indeed, if an actual madman kills, his action is pardonable. Likewise, a monk who breaks a monastic rule when mad does not commit an offence (*Vin.* IV.125). Here, one can say that the actions of a madman are blameless (as at (1) above), while actions done when impassioned are of little blame – though getting into such a state can be held to be blameworthy. Actions done when drunk can perhaps be assessed in a similar way.

(3) *If one does an evil action when one is unclear or mistaken about the object affected by the action.*

This is moderately blameable. Thus, while it is an offence requiring expiation for a monk to kill a non-human living being intentionally, it is a lesser offence, of 'wrong-doing', if (a) he is in doubt whether it is a living being, or (b) if he tries to damage a non-living thing that he thinks is, or might be, living, for example by shooting an arrow at it. There is no offence, though, if he fires an arrow at a living being not knowing that it is a living being (*Vin.* IV.125). An attempt to use such reasoning to lessen the evil of an action can be seen in the actions of the Buddhists of Zanskar, a Kashmiri valley bordering Tibet, who feel that they have to kill predatory wolves. The killing is done as indirectly as possible: after the wolves have been lured into high-walled stone traps, large stones are thrown over the wall by a group of people – consequently nobody knows for sure whether their stones are among those that kill a wolf. In this way, the people seek to put a distance between themselves and what they see as a practically necessary evil. This is comparable to the way in which, in the West, only *some* of the rifles used in a firing squad are loaded with live bullets, so that nobody knows whether they have fired one of the fatal shots.

(4) *An evil action done where one intends to do the act, fully knows what one is doing, and knows that the action is evil.*

This is the most obvious kind of wrong action, with bad karmic results, particularly if it is premeditated. Thus Buddhaghosa states, at the start of this section, that in the case of killing a living being, the precept against this is only broken if five factors are present: 'a living being, the perception of a living being, a thought of killing, the action of carrying it out, and death as a result of it'. If any of these factors is absent, as when death results from a person striking something that he does not realize is living, the precept is not broken.

(5) *An evil action done where one intends to do the act, fully knows what one is doing (as in (4)), but do not recognize that one is doing wrong.*

This is seen as the worst kind of action. Such an action is discussed at *Miln.* 84, which says that if an evil action is done 'unknowingly (*ajānato*)', it has a worse karmic effect than if it is done 'knowingly'. This is illustrated by saying that a person taking hold of a red-hot iron ball is more severely burnt if he does so unknowingly. This suggests that an evil action – such as an onslaught on a living being (*Miln.* 158) – is worse if it is done without hesitation, restraint or compunction. This will be the case if an action is not seen to be wrong,[27] as there will be no holding back on the volitional force put into the action. On the face of it, this may seem unjust; but perhaps not on further reflection. In an English court of law, the 'ringleader' of a crime is often punished more harshly than those who had been led on, half-reluctantly. The leader may well be held to see no wrong in the action, but the others have some compunction. Relevant to this is the case of doing a so-called 'necessary evil', for example killing an enemy to prevent one's country being invaded. Here, a recognition that such an act is still evil is preferable to a glorying in the act. Indeed, some of the worst crimes of the twentieth century

---

[27] *Miln. Ṭ.* 29, on *Miln.* 158, talks of the 'non-knowing of evil (*pāpa-ajānana-*)'. Note that in the monastic discipline, the only viewpoint that a monk can be disciplined for is the persistent claim, even when admonished, that what the Buddha calls 'stumbling-blocks' – namely sense-pleasures – are not stumbling-blocks in the monastic life (*Vin.* IV.133–6). Elsewhere, this 'evil' view is said to be very karmically unfruitful (*apuñña*) (*M.* I.132). That is, it is seen as very bad to have a view which denies the genuine spiritual unskilfulness of something.

have been carried out under the banner of an ideology which saw them as 'right' actions: Hitler's Holocaust, Stalin's purges and the Khmer Rouge's murder of many Cambodians. If one has the wrong view, for example that one belongs to the 'master race' and that Jews are 'vermin' who should be killed, one is not likely to hold back in one's evil actions. Here, wrong physical action is both accompanied by and strengthened by wrong view (cf. Payutto, 1993: 62–5).

In all the above, intention, knowledge and ignorance are crucial factors, though there are different kinds of 'ignorance', only some of which excuse an action. If one knows that sentient beings should not be harmed, but not that one's action is actually harming one, this 'ignorance' of a matter of ordinary fact excuses one. The spiritual ignorance which leads one to deny that harming living beings is wrong is no excuse, however, but compounds a wrong action. Of course, lesser degrees of spiritual ignorance – lack of spiritual insight – are seen to affect all beings until they are enlightened. This forms a background to all unenlightened actions, good or bad, though it specifically feeds into wrong actions when they are 'rooted' in, that is, motivated by, delusion (and associated greed and hatred): 'whatever unwholesome states there are, all are rooted in spiritual ignorance . . . are fixed together in spiritual ignorance', like rafters in a roof-top (*S.* II.263). Among other things, spiritual ignorance feeds the 'I am conceit': the conviction that one has a permanent Self to protect and bolster up: the root of selfishness.

It is no coincidence that the Buddha's criticism of people is not couched in terms of their being evil or sinful, but usually in terms of their being 'fools'; thus, when dismissing a person, he always did so without anger (*Miln.* 186–8). It is said that a person is known as a 'fool' by immoral conduct of body, speech and mind, just as a wise person is known by moral conduct. Moreover, a fool neither recognizes a transgression for what it is (*A.* 1.102–3) nor accepts another person's acknowledgement of having committed a transgression (*A.* 1.59). That is, it is good to see one's own faults and pardon those of others. Indeed, 'a fool who knows he is a fool is to that extent a wise person; the fool who thinks he is wise is called a fool indeed' (*Dhp.* 63). Given this, it is clear that one is, for example, doing a slaughterer a favour if one tries to get him to see that what he is doing is wrong (though to do so in an aggressive manner is unwholesome as it is an expression of ill-will). Even if he carries on in his trade, he is better off if he is at least uneasy about what he is doing, and starting to have some compunction about his actions. The unease might unsettle whatever calm he had, but the Buddha, at least, was willing to tell people things that they found unpleasant if it would be of spiritual benefit to them (*M.* 1.395).

Of course, this assumes that there is such a thing as objectively wrong action. Only then does it make sense to say that one could be *mistaken* in holding something not to be wrong. Given Buddhism's clear criteria of what is unwholesome action, it is quite happy to agree to this, with an action's 'wrongness' subsisting in a combination of the action itself and the state of mind in which it is done. It is not a matter of what a person happens to like or dislike (emotivism), or of what his or her society happens to approve or disapprove of (cultural relativism) (Keown, 1992: 64, 231–2).

Parallel things to the above could mostly be said for good actions: (1) an unintentionally beneficial action is not to one's credit; (2) a beneficial action done when one was in a disturbed state is only of little credit; (3) an action done when one is unsure that there is someone to benefit from it is moderately good; (4) an intentional good action is straightforwardly good. The straightforward parallel breaks down at (5), though: if one thinks that a right action is a wrong one but still does it, one will do it with compunction, so that it is a less good action than it would otherwise be. This perhaps shows the wholesome potency of 'right view'. Indeed, it is said that the thing which is the greatest cause of the arising or increase of unwholesome states, and the non-arising or decrease of wholesome states, is wrong view. It is likewise the greatest cause of rebirth in hell. For one of wrong, evil view, whatever deeds of body, speech or mind 'undertaken in complete accord with (that) view, whatever volitions, aspirations, resolves, activities, all those states conduce to . . . suffering' (*A.* 1.31–2; cf. *M.* III.178–9). The opposite is said of right view. As a wholesome mental action, right view is defined as holding that good and bad actions do have results beyond this life, and that spiritually developed people have knowledge of such things, wrong view being to deny this (see pp. 11–12). On the other hand, one who holds the false view that there are no good or bad actions, and no karmic results of these, have their 'roots of wholesomeness' (*kuśala-mūlas*) cut off (*AKB.* IV.79a–c), though they return if they start to doubt this view or come to see that it is wrong (*AKB.* IV.80c).

A partial 'good' parallel to (5) would be doing a truly good action even though *others* say that it is a bad one. Here, great determination is needed, so the action can be seen as a very good one. Another partial parallel is the case of a young child doing a good action even though he or she has not been told that it is 'good', as at *Asl.* 103, where a young boy is told to catch a hare to provide healing food for his sick mother; he cannot do so, though, for he intuitively recognises that it is wrong to kill; here natural right view enhances the action.

If the child *did* kill the hare, or he or an adult stole to feed a starving parent, this would be seen as an act which is a mixture of bad and good (cf. p. 44), in which the good aspect counterbalances the bad to an extent, especially if the act is done with recognition of its wrongness. Indeed, Buddhism acknowledges that poverty in a society makes theft more likely (*D.* 1.76–7). It is thus less blameable in such circumstances, though still not unblameworthy.

CONCLUSION

The above perspective thus views morality as part of a spiritual path which largely consists of cultivating a more wholesome character by undermining moral/spiritual defilements and cultivating counteractive virtues. This process of – generally gradual – transformation is seen to culminate in a state of liberation from all traces of greed/attachment, hatred and delusion, and their consequent suffering, through the experience of *Nirvāṇa*. Such a vision assumes that people have no fixed, unchanging Self, but are capable of radical transformation, brought about by attention to the nature of the mind and actions.

Attention is given to actions out of a concern for:
(a) their motivating root;
(b) the happiness/unhappiness that actions directly bring to the agent and others;
(c) moral praise and blame, or sanctions within a monastic community;
(d) contribution to spiritual development, or its opposite;
(e) the natural karmic effects that are seen to arise, in the future, for the agent.
All of this entails that what one does, and how and why one does it, is of great import: for one's actions both express and shape one's character, and contribute to one's destiny. Much emphasis is put on the state of mind, and intention, lying behind any action; yet some actions are identified as always unwholesome to some degree, dependent on precise motivation. Consequently, it is good not only to seek to avoid such actions, but to vow formally to avoid them.

Criteria are spelt out to identify, in as objective a way as possible, which action-intentions should be recognized as morally unwholesome or wholesome. In this, ignorance of ordinary matters of fact is seen as excusing what might otherwise be seen as an unwholesome action, but moral/spiritual ignorance is seen as compounding an action's unwholesomeness. That is, to perform an unwholesome action while regarding it as acceptable or wholesome is seen to be particularly perverse. In other words, it is held that some action-intentions – primarily those that deliberately cause harm to a sentient being – are wrong, and that it is wrong to deny this and to act on this denial, or from moral blindness.

Such moral objectivism is derived from:

(a) the notion that we all have a natural sympathy for the plight of others, however much we try to ignore or bury it;

(b) acting in accord with, and strengthening, this sympathy naturally leads to more happiness and less suffering for oneself and those one interacts with;

(c) no substantial, permanent Self or I exists, and actions selfishly rooted in the I-view or -attitude are out of accord with reality, so as to be both morally unwholesome and naturally productive of unpleasant karmic result.

Of course, for Buddhism, an act is seen to have unpleasant karmic results because it is *wrong*; it is not seen as 'wrong' *because* it happens to produce bad karmic results. Reference to karmic fruits acts simply as a way to help motivate good actions, and to emphasize that they are in harmony with and registered by the basic structure of reality.

A final point is that it is better to do a wrong action with compunction than without it (though subsequent guilt-trips are not encouraged, as they lead to an agitated, beclouded mind-state). Moreover, a key aid to moral development is the formal avowal of moral precepts, which are seen to strengthen one's moral vision and help to increase the momentum of moral development. In other words, it helps to have some moral 'aims and objectives' that one agrees with and can happily affirm, even if one is not always so good at achieving them!

CHAPTER 2

Key Buddhist values

Conquer anger by non-anger; conquer evil by good; conquer the stingy by giving;
conquer the liar by truth   *Dhammapada* 223

Supported by and in part arising from the world-view(s) and ideals of
Buddhism, what are the central values that have been and are espoused?
While greed, hatred and delusion are seen as the roots of unwholesome
actions, with their complete destruction being equivalent to *Nirvāṇa* (*S.*
iv.251), non-greed, non-hate and non-delusion are regarded as the roots
of wholesome action, and can thus be seen as the central values of
Buddhism. While expressed negatively, they are equivalent to: generosity and non-attachment; lovingkindness and compassion; and wisdom,
in the sense of clear seeing of the nature of life and the absence of delusion or misorientation.

A fuller list of wholesome qualities is found in the *Abhidhamma* literature. In its Theravādin form, this lists twenty-five wholesome or 'beautiful' mental qualities (Bodhi, 1993: 85–91, 96–7). The first seven are:

faith (trust in one's sense of what is right),
mindfulness (i.e. careful awareness),
self-respect and regard for consequences,
non-greed and non-hate, and
equipoise (a balanced over-seeing of activities and events).

The next twelve consist of six pairs of qualities which each relate both
to consciousness itself and to the 'body' of mental states which accompany it:

tranquillity, a light sense of ease,
open receptivity, readiness to act,
competence, and straightforwardness.

All the above are seen as simultaneously present (though perhaps to
varying degrees) in any wholesome mental state, as a basis for being fully
human, and as a protecting, uplifting refuge. The remaining factors,
when present, strengthen, deepen and channel wholesome mental energies: right speech, right action, right livelihood, compassion, empathetic
joy, and wisdom.

These wholesome qualities counteract a variety of unwholesome ones. A brief list often found in the *Sutta*s is that of the 'five hindrances': desire for sense-pleasures, ill-will, dullness and drowsiness, restlessness and unease, and vacillation, which can be seen as aspects of greed (1), hatred (2) and delusion (3–5). In the Theravādin *Abhidhamma*, the unwholesome qualities common to all unwholesome states of mind are: delusion, lack of self-respect, disregard for consequences, and restlessness. Of those only present in some unwholesome states: (1) some are related to greed, namely greed itself, fixed views, and conceit or self-importance; (2) some are related to hate, i.e. hate itself, jealousy, miserliness and unease; (3) some are related to delusion, i.e. dullness, drowsiness and vacillation (Bodhi, 1993: 83–5, 95).

The above analysis draws on psycho-spiritual teachings primarily aimed at meditators and those seeking the highest goal of Buddhism, but the values described are of more general relevance in Buddhism. As L. S. Cousins says:

Buddhist ethics can be looked at in several different ways. There is the situation of the man in the street who is concerned with life in the world of the senses. On a superior level arises the aim of experiencing the joy and peace of a higher consciousness [through meditation]. Higher still is the desire to achieve the ultimate goal with a direct realization of the supramundane . . . Superficially the last two of these aims are only the concern of a small minority, but in practice such a clear distinction cannot be drawn. The ethic designed for the ordinary man is intended both to be beneficial in its own right and to lead in the direction of the levels above. Normally a given individual will derive his standards from elements of all three, although the 'mix' may vary. (1974: 100)

GIVING

The primary ethical activity which a Buddhist learns to develop is giving or generosity, *dāna*, which forms a basis for further moral and spiritual development. In Southern Buddhism, it is the first of the ten 'bases for effecting karmically fruitful actions' (*puñña-kiriya-vatthus*): giving, keeping the moral precepts, meditative development, showing respect, helpful activity, sharing karmic fruitfulness, rejoicing at the karmic fruitfulness of others, teaching *Dhamma*, listening to *Dhamma*, and straightening out one's views.[1]

---

[1] *D. A.* III.999; cf. Gombrich, 1971a: 73–4. In the *Sutta*s, just the first three are given (*D.* III.218; *A.* IV.214; *It.* 51).

The key focus of giving is the monastic *Saṅgha*, or Community, whose 'homeless' way of life depends for its material support on the laity, to encourage their humility and to ensure that they do not become isolated from the laity. This supportive relationship is not a one-sided one, however, for while the laity provide the *Saṅgha* with such items as alms-food, robes, medicine, and monasteries to live in, the monks and nuns, by their teaching and example, return a greater one, for 'The gift of *Dhamma* excels all gifts' (*Dhp.* 354). Such acts of mutual giving thus form a key feature of the lay–monastic relationship:

Thus, monks, this holy life is lived in mutual dependence, for ferrying across the flood [of the cycle of rebirths], for the utter ending of *dukkha*. (*It.* 111)

Generosity is not only practised towards the *Saṅgha*, but, as a pervading value of Buddhist societies, is also practised towards family, friends, workpeople, guests (*A.* ii.67–8), the poor and homeless, and animals. Fielding Hall, a British official in nineteenth-century Burma, tells of an occasion when, on asking for a bill at what he took to be a village restaurant, he found that he had been fed as a guest in a private house.

In many countries, Buddhists demonstrate a great concern for doing karmically fruitful actions by deeds of giving, such as contributing to ceremonies on occasions like an ordination, a funeral, a sickness, or a festival. Karmic fruitfulness is generated not only by an individual's own giving, but also by rejoicing at the gifts of others. In Southern Buddhism, the touching of donated goods, or uttering the refrain *sādhu*! (roughly, 'well done!', 'amen!') is seen as involving a person in the donations of another person. Thus communities are bound together in communal acts generating karmic fruitfulness, and social obligations are carried out by contributing to a ceremony sponsored by someone who has helped one by contributions in the past. In the case of expensive ceremonies such as an ordination, a rich person may help sponsor the ordination of a poorer person's son. In this way the sponsor, the son and the parents all do a karmically fruitful act, with the mother being seen as benefiting particularly through 'giving' her son to the *Saṅgha*.

While giving may initially be performed for the sake of the material advantages that karmic fruitfulness brings, a motive which is then likely to take over arises from the joy and contentment that giving brings. Indeed, 'a gift should be given in faith so that as a consequence the mind becomes calm and clear' (Cousins, 1974: 100). The constant practice of giving also provides a foundation for moral development by fostering the breaking down of possessiveness and the growth of an open-hearted and

Plate 2. Lay people giving alms-food to monks at a festival at Ratanagiri monastery, north-east England.

sensitive attitude towards others. One expression of the ideal of gene-rosity is expressed thus:

> The Noble disciple lives at home with a heart free from the taint of stinginess, he is open handed, pure-handed, delighting in self-surrender, one to ask a favour of, one who delights in dispensing charitable gifts. (*A.* II.66)

Giving fosters not only moral development, but also spiritual progress, because of its aspect of renunciation and non-attachment. It is the first of the ten *Bodhisattva* 'perfections' in both the Mahāyāna and Theravāda traditions.

The popular *Vessantara Jātaka*[2] expresses the pinnacle of the perfec-tion of generosity. It tells of the *Bodhisattva* in a past life as Prince Vessantara, who so rejoices at generosity that he gives whenever he is

---

[2] *J.* VI.479–593; see Cone and Gombrich, 1977; a short version is found at *Cp.* story I.9.

asked for anything. One day, he gives away his city's auspicious white elephant, which causes him to be banished. Wandering in the forest with his wife Maddī and their two children, he meets an old brahmin who asks him for his children, to serve his young wife. Vessantara at first asks that his wife return from gathering food before the gift is made, but the brahmin refuses, as he fears that she will not agree to it (p. 543). With tears in his eyes, Vessantara then agrees to part with his children, though they do not want to go (p. 551); later his wife returns and is anguished at their absence. When Vessantara explains to her that he has given them away, and this for the sake of attaining Buddhahood, she accepts his action as right and even rejoices in it (p. 568). Later, the god Sakka tests Vessantara further, by appearing to him in the guise of another brahmin who asks for his wife. Vessantara gives, yet again (pp. 569–70), though Sakka then reveals himself and eventually the family is reunited, the children being watched over by the gods.

In discussing the issues raised by this story, the *Milindapañha* explains that the gift of the children was not excessive, for it was the supreme gift, one which showed great heroism, restraint and renunciation, going against deeply ingrained attachments (*Miln.* 274–84). Vessantara's wife and children were the dearest things in the world to him (cf. pp. 98, 100), yet he was willing to give even them, for the sake of future perfect Awakening, which would lead to the benefit of countless people. Vessantara is said not to have been callous, but to have suffered great anguish after giving his children; he knew, though, that an aspiring Buddha's generosity and non-attachment must be unstinting, and knew that his father would redeem the children anyway. It is also said that the children would not have lamented had they understood the nature of their father's action (*Miln.* 275). Such a story, of course, acts as an archetypal support for the idea of renunciation: of 'giving up' the pleasures and attachments of family life for the 'homeless' life of a monk or nun, who aims to grow towards the perfect non-attachment which leads to *Nirvāṇa*. In Southern Buddhism, Gotama's past life as Vessantara is seen as his last human one before he was born in the Tusita heaven, and then as the person who became the historical Buddha.

The Mahāyāna also emphasizes that a *Bodhisattva* should be joyful and unstinting in giving. He should eat only after offering food to his servants, or those about to travel or who have arrived from afar (*Uss.* 67–8). He should be willing even to give away his body-parts or life in aiding others. Highest of all, he should be able to give away his wife and children, though not his parents (Dayal, 1932: 175–6).

Sharing karmic fruitfulness

If generosity is seen as generating karmic fruitfulness, it is also seen as good to share this with others. In the Theravādin tradition, an act of karmic fruitfulness may be performed not only by empathizing (*anumodanā*) with someone else's good deed,[3] but also by the sharing of its karmic fruitfulness – or, more exactly, 'what has been gained' (*patti*) – with another being. This practice may have originated as a Buddhist adaptation of the Brahmanical *śrāddha* ceremony, in which gifts were seen as transferred to deceased relatives by giving them to brahmins at memorial rites (Gombrich, 1971a: 226–40). In an early text, a brahmin asks the Buddha if *śrāddha* rites bring benefit to the dead, and the Buddha replies that the dead will benefit only if reborn as *peta*s (Pali; Skt *preta*s), for these ghostly beings live either on the putrid food of their realm or on what is provided by gifts from relatives and friends (*A.* v.269–72). The *Petavatthu* (*Pv.*), from the later part of the Theravāda Canon, accordingly describes a number of instances where a gift is given in the name of a suffering *peta*, so that the *peta* attains rebirth as a god because of the karmic fruitfulness of the giving. *Miln.* 294 qualifies this by saying that only one of the four types of *peta* can benefit in this way. Theravāda rites for the dead therefore include the feeding of monks and the sharing of the karmic fruitfulness of the deed with the deceased, or whatever other ancestors may be *peta*s, in the hope that this will ease their plight as *peta*s or help them to a better rebirth. This is done especially seven days after a death, but also in yearly memorial services. The feeding of hungry ghosts, in a yearly festival, is also an important part of Chinese Mahāyāna Buddhism.

Another early text also has the Buddha say that it is wise to support monks and to dedicate the gift to the local gods, so that they will look with favour on the donor (*D.* ii.88). Accordingly, Theravādin donations to monks often conclude with a verse sharing the karmic fruitfulness of the gift to gods. These are seen as having less opportunity to do auspicious deeds themselves, but can benefit from shared karmic fruitfulness, which helps maintain them in their divine rebirth; in return, it is hoped that they will use whatever powers they have to aid and protect Buddhism, and the person making the donation. A boy being ordained as a novice or full monk will also share the karmic fruitfulness of this act

---

[3] As also in Mahāyāna Buddhism (Conze, 1968: 45–9). On the practice within a Theravāda context, see: Gombrich, 1971a: 226–40, 251–2; Gombrich, 1971b; Malalasekera, 1967; Keyes, 1983.

with his mother, though she also generates this herself by 'giving up' her son to the monkhood.

Given the Buddhist stress on the idea that a person can only generate karmic fruitfulness by his or her own deeds, the idea of 'sharing' it is potentially anomalous (see *Kvu.* 347). To avoid such an anomaly, the Theravādin commentaries, dating from the fifth century CE or earlier, developed an orthodox interpretation (*Dhp. A.* 1.103–4). This was that the food etc. donated to monks was dedicated to an ancestor or god, so that the donation was done on his or her behalf, with his or her property. This interpretation is in tune with an early text which says that the duties of a child to his or her parents include that 'I will give alms on their behalf when they are dead' (*D.* III.189). The commentaries hold that provided they assent to this donation by rejoicing at it (*Vv. A.* 188), they will themselves generate karmic fruitfulness, both from the donation-by-proxy and from the mental act of rejoicing (*anumodanā*). In sharing karmic fruitfulness, a person does not lose any himself or herself, for his or her sharing is itself karmically fruitful. The sharing of karmic fruitfulness is simply a way of spreading the karmic benefits of good deeds to others, as a gesture of good will. This is expressed in the traditional metaphor to explain such sharing: lighting many lamps from one.

In the Mahāyāna tradition, karmic fruitfulness is often transferred to 'all sentient beings'; though such an aspiration is found not only in Northern and Eastern, but also in Southern Buddhism, perhaps through Mahāyāna influence.

KEEPING THE LAY PRECEPTS

On a basis of developing *dāna*, the Buddhist goes on to develop his or her ethical virtue, or *sīla* (Pali; Skt *śīla*), by observing the self-discipline of keeping certain precepts. Indeed, keeping any of these precepts is itself seen as a form of giving – the best kind (*Uss.* 151): 'great gifts' to others of lack of fear and ill-will, as they feel unthreatened by a precept-keeper (*A.* IV.246). It is said that sub-human rebirths can be avoided by the practice of *dāna* and *sīla*, (*A.* IV.241–3). Moral restraint and self-control are much emphasized as means of protecting others and purifying one's own character:

> Irrigators lead waters,
> Fletchers bend the shafts,
> Carpenters bend the wood,
> The wise control themselves. (*Dhp.* 80)

> Though he should conquer
> A thousand thousand men in battle,
> Yet he is the noblest victor
> Who should conquer himself. (*Dhp.* 103)

Through abstinence from unwholesome actions, the defilements which lead to them are restrained, and their opposites are strengthened, so that the natural purity in the depths of the mind has more opportunity to manifest itself. The Buddha's last words are said to have been 'all conditioned things are subject to decay: strive on with diligence!' (*D.* 11.156). He emphasized that while he pointed the way to liberation, one must oneself make the effort to tread the path he showed. One should thus be one's own person: have *Dhamma* and oneself as one's refuge, by the practice of careful mindfulness, or moment-to-moment awareness (*D.* 11.100). The fact that the second Noble Truth says that craving leads to suffering clearly underlines the importance of self-control. Desire, greed and attachment are seen as leading to quarrels and wars (*D.* 11.58–9), to worry over guarding one's possessions (*M.* 1.85–6), and disappointment when what seems desirable is lost, dies or fades (*M.* 1.87–90).

The most commonly observed set of precepts followed by lay people are the 'five precepts' (properly, the 'five virtues': *pañca-sīlāni*). In Southern Buddhism, these are chanted in their Pali form, though their overall meaning, if not precise translation, is generally known (Terweil, 1979: 188; Gombrich, 1971a: 254):

1. I undertake the training-precept (*sikkhā-padaṃ*) to abstain from onslaught on breathing beings.
2. I undertake the training-precept to abstain from taking what is not given.
3. I undertake the training-precept to abstain from misconduct concerning sense-pleasures.
4. I undertake the training-precept to abstain from false speech.
5. I undertake the training-precept to abstain from alcoholic drink or drugs that are an opportunity for heedlessness.

In the Mūla-Sarvāstivādin tradition used in Tibet, the precepts are given in a formula which affirms that a person will follow the precepts for all his or her life, as this accords with the practice of *Arahat*s (Hirakawa, 1995: 11). Acting in accord with precepts is said to lead to confidence and a lack of fear (*A.* 111.203), well-earned wealth, a good reputation, a peaceful death, and rebirth in a heaven (*D.* 11.86). On the other hand, one who kills etc. 'digs up his own root in this very world' (*Dhp.* 247), and suffers a bad rebirth (see pp. 15–16).

Each precept is a 'training-precept', the same term as that for an item of the monastic code, though while the monastic code goes into great detail on rules for monks and nuns, the lay precepts are left, in the *Suttas*, fairly general and non-specific. It has been left to later commentators, and the advice of the *Saṅgha* in various cultures, to make them more specific.[4]

Emphasis is sometimes laid on the need for a 'middle way' in keeping the precepts, avoiding the extremes of laxity and rigid adherence. In any case, Buddhism does not encourage the developing of strong guilt feelings if a precept is broken (see p. 28). Regretting misdeeds is wholesome, but Buddhism emphasizes a future-directed morality in which one always seeks to do better in the future, taking the precepts as ideals that one is seeking to live up to in an increasingly complete way.

While each precept is expressed in negative wording, as an abstention, one who keeps them increasingly comes to express positive virtues as the roots of unwholesome action are weakened. Each precept thus has a positive counterpart. The counterpart of the first is kindness and compassion, so as to be 'trembling for the welfare of others' (*D.* 1.4). That of the second is generosity and renunciation: in Buddhist cultures, greed is strongly disapproved of, and generosity much praised. The counterpart of the third is 'joyous satisfaction with one's own wife' (*A.* v.138; cf. *Sn.* 108), contentment and fewness-of-wishes. Contentment is seen as the 'greatest of wealths' (*Dhp.* 204), and the height of this virtue is shown by a remark of the eleventh-century Tibetan saint Milarepa, who, living in threadbare cotton robes in a freezing Himalayan cave, said that, for him, 'everything is comfortable'! (Evans-Wentz, 1951: 201). The counterpart of the fourth precept is being honest, trustworthy and dependable, a 'bondsman to truth' (*A.* IV.249; *M.* 1.345): searching it out, recognizing falsity, and attaining precision of thought. The counterpart of the fifth precept is mindfulness and awareness.

Closely related to keeping the precepts is the concept of 'right livelihood', a factor of the Eightfold Path (see p. 38). This refers to making one's living in a way that does not involve one in habitually breaking the precepts by bringing harm to other beings, but that is, it is hoped, helpful to others and an aid to the development of one's faculties and abilities (see pp. 187–9).

---

[4] As regards textual discussions, for the Theravāda, see: *M. A.* 1.198–202, translated by Conze, 1959: 70–3, and related passages at *Asl.* 97–101. In the discussion at *Khp. A.* 22–34, the third precept is the third in a set of ten, and entails complete abstinence from sexual intercourse, while the third of the five precepts does not. For the Mahāyāna, see Lamotte, 1949: 782–819. For the Tibetan tradition, see Guenther, 1959: 75–7 and Patrul, 1994: 102–10. For the Chinese tradition, see *Uss.* 165–74. For reflections on the precepts in a Western context, giving a 'socially engaged' formulation, see Nhat Hanh et al., 1993.

The first precept: non-injury

The first precept corresponds to the Hindu and Jain concept of *ahiṃsā*, 'non-injury', and is generally regarded as the most important one: 'Non-injury is the distinguishing mark of *Dhamma*' (*Miln.* 185). Thus in Burma, while most lay people, when asked which is the most important precept, specify the one on sexual misconduct, they nevertheless agree that killing leads to the worst karmic results and that physical and verbal abuse is the most blameable behaviour (Spiro, 1971: 101–3).

Taking the first precept rules out the *intentional* killing of any living being, human or otherwise. The spirit of this precept is expressed thus:

Laying aside violence in respect of all beings, both those which are still and those which move . . . he should not kill a living creature, nor cause to kill, nor approve of others killing. (*Sn.* 394)

Abandoning onslaught on breathing beings, he abstains from this; without stick or sword, scrupulous, compassionate, trembling for the welfare of all living beings. (*M.* 1.345; cf. *D.* 1.4)

Injuring but not killing a being is clearly against the spirit of the precept, but does not fully break it – though a verse form of the precept at *A.* III.213 expresses it simply in terms of non-injury – and likewise death accidentally resulting from an attack does not break it (*Uss.* 171).

The object of this precept is not limited to humans, as all sentient beings share in the same cycle of rebirths and in the experience of various types of suffering. It is, however, worse to kill or injure a human than an animal, or a larger or more highly developed animal than a lesser one (see p. 52). The first precept is broken even if a being is killed by someone else being ordered to do this, when both the orderer and the agent break the precept, unless the agent mistakenly kills a being other than the intended one, when only he or she is responsible (*Khp. A.* 29–30). The first precept has many potential implications for behaviour, and these will be traced through the chapters of this book on nature, war, suicide and euthanasia, and abortion. Likewise, the chapter on economic ethics is relevant to the second and fourth precepts and those on sexual equality and homosexuality are relevant to the third.

The second precept: avoiding theft and cheating

The second precept is seen as ruling out any act of theft. In the equivalent rule for monks, a monk is completely defeated in the monastic life if he steals an amount that makes him liable to prosecution (*Vin.* III.45). Something is seen as the 'property' of someone else, and thus not to be taken, if that person can do what he or she wants with it without punishment or blame (*Asl.* 98; *Khp. A.* 26). Theft is seen as worse according to the value of what is stolen, but also according to the virtue of the person stolen from (*Asl.* 98).

The second precept also covers fraud, cheating, forgery (*Asl.* 98) and falsely denying that one is in debt to someone (*Sn.* 119–21). The *Upāsaka-śīla Sūtra* sees it as broken by claiming more compensation for a theft than is appropriate (cf. fiddling an insurance claim), accepting the gift of two robes when one only needs one, and giving to one monk what one has promised to another (*Uss.* 172–3). In Thailand, it is seen as broken by borrowing without permission and breaking a promise, as this takes a liberty which has not been given (Terweil, 1979: 188–9). The Burmese meditation teacher Mahāsi Sayadaw gives a good summary:

taking surreptitiously what belongs to another person without his knowledge . . . To cheat a buyer using false weights and measures, to fob off a worthless article on a buyer, to sell counterfeit gold and silver, not to pay due wages or conveyance charges or customs or taxes etc., to refuse to repay loans of money or property, or what is entrusted to one's care and to refuse to compensate for any damage or loss for which one is responsible . . . using force to obtain other people's property . . . intimidation and extortion of money or property, excessive and coercive taxation, unlawful confiscation of property for the settlement of debt, court litigation for illegal ownership through false witnesses and false statements. (1981: 65)

Gambling is generally included under the rubric of this precept in Thailand (Terweil, 1979: 188), and is otherwise criticized thus:

Gambling causes avarice,
Unpleasantness, hatred, deception, cheating,
Wildness, lying, senseless and harsh speech,
Therefore never gamble.   (*RPR.* 147)

The *Sigālovāda Sutta* says:

There are these six dangers attached to gambling: the winner makes enemies, the loser bewails his loss, one wastes one's present wealth, one's word is not trusted in the assembly, one is despised by one's friends and companions, one is not in demand for marriage, because a gambler cannot afford to maintain a wife. (*D.* III.183)

This is not to say, though, that Buddhists never gamble. Charles Bell reports that gambling on dominoes and dice has been popular in Tibet

(1928: 265–7). In Sri Lanka, however, on the advice of the 1956 Buddhist Committee of Enquiry, the government banned horse racing as associated gambling led to greater gain of wealth by the rich and further degradation of the poverty-stricken (Bond, 1988: 87, 96). Sri Lankans now bet on British horse races!

In Zen Buddhism, the spirit of this precept is seen to entail such things as not stealing time from oneself by daydreaming during time for meditation (Aitken, 1984: 28), not greedily exploiting workers (p. 30), and carelessness with precious things, for example meditation cushions (p. 34).

The third precept: avoiding sexual misconduct

The monastic ideal of Buddhism involves celibacy, but it is acknowledged that not everyone feels able or willing to follow this ideal:

The wise man should avoid the uncelibate life (*abrahmacariyaṃ*) like a pit of burning coals. But if he is incapable of living a celibate life, he should not transgress against another's wife. (*Sn.* 396)

The third precept relates primarily to the avoidance of causing suffering by one's sexual behaviour. Adultery – 'going with the wife of another' (*A.* 1.189) – is the most straightforward breach of this precept. The wrongness of this is seen as partly in terms of its being an expression of greed, and partly in terms of its harm to others. The first of these is seen in the following verse:

Not to be contented with one's own wife but to be seen with prostitutes or the wives of others – this is a cause of one's downfall. (*Sn.* 108)

The second can be seen in the rationale for the precept: you would not like someone to commit adultery with your wife, so do not commit adultery with someone else's wife (*S.* v.354). Thus one should not go 'with others' women, who are as dear to them as life' (*D.* III.184), and Nāgārjuna says: 'the pleasure of husband and wife is to be two bodies but one flesh; to take away one who another loves and destroy this deep sentiment is a crime' (Lamotte, 1949: 801). What counts as 'adultery' varies according to the marriage patterns of different societies, though, and Buddhism has been flexible in adapting to these (see below, pp. 101–2). Adultery with a woman without her husband's knowledge, or with his compliance, still breaks the precepts on account of the malicious nature of the act (Lamotte, 1949: 801). Moreover, the precept is extended to intercourse with any woman who is, in modern parlance, 'in a relationship' with another man (*Asl.* 98).

The third precept does not relate only to not having sex with someone else's wife or partner. It is said that a man breaks the precept if he has intercourse with women who are engaged, or who are still protected by any relative (*M.* 1.286; cf. *Vin.* III.139), or young girls not protected by a relative, this being seen as offending against the wishes of the king (*AKB.* IV.74a–b). Clearly, rape and incest are breaches of the precept, and Nāgārjuna includes intercourse with a courtesan or prostitute (Lamotte, 1949: 800). A breach is worse according to the virtue of the woman, as shown by the way in which she keeps the precepts (*Asl.* 98). In Thailand, flirting with a married woman may also be seen as a breach (Terweil, 1979: 188). In Sri Lanka, some see premarital sex as breaking the precept, but few stick to this view if the parties subsequently marry (Gombrich, 1971a: 255). In rural Thailand, young men are allowed to roam around freely, but young women are always kept under a careful watch. A young woman's parents prefer courting to be at her home, for example on the verandah (H. E. Smith, 1979: 27): sexual contact is to be avoided as it is seen as offending the spirits of the ancestors, who are seen as strict regarding morals, jealous, and loth to leave their former property in the hands of descendants. Nhat Hanh sees this precept as involving 'sexual responsibility' (1993: 29) and as entailing 'not to engage in sexual relations without love and long-term commitment' and 'to protect children from sexual abuse and prevent couples and families being broken by sexual misconduct' (pp. 3–4).

Buddhist discussion of the third precept mainly focuses on various circumstances in which men can be seen as breaking it. On women, the discussion is shorter and more direct. Thus Theravādin Bhikkhu Bodhi says that a married woman should have intercourse only with her husband (cf. Mahasi, 1981: 78), and no woman should have intercourse with men such as a close relative or those under a vow of celibacy (1984: 63). Of course, this does not see sexual activity by non-married adult women as a breach of the precept.

In addition to the above, socially taboo forms of sexuality have been seen as breaches of the third precept, doubtless because of the guilt feelings that they entail.[5] Obsessive sexual activities also come within the precept, as do other obsessive forms of sensuality, for example gorging oneself with food. The fourth century CE *Abhidharma-kośa-bhāṣya* (IV.74a–b) holds that a man breaks the third precept by:

---

[5] Cousins, 1974: 101. For a useful review of evidence on sexual practices in ancient India, as reflected in Buddhist texts, see Perera, 1993, though this sometimes adds in inappropriate opinions.

1. Intercourse with a forbidden woman, that is, the wife of another, one's mother, one's daughter, or one's paternal or maternal relations;
2. Intercourse with one's own wife through a forbidden orifice;
3. in an unsuitable place: an uncovered spot, a shrine or forest;
4. at an unsuitable time: when the wife is pregnant, when she is nursing, or when she has taken a vow. Some say: when she has taken a vow only with the consent of her husband.

On item 2, Nāgārjuna says that it is 'repugnant to the spirit of a woman', so that 'to be coerced into this unseemliness' breaks the precept (Lamotte, 1949: 801). The *Jewel Ornament of Liberation* of sGam po pa (1079–1153), founder of the Kagyu (bKa'brgyud) school of Tibetan Buddhism, concurs with and expands on the above. One should not have intercourse:

i) in an improper part of the body, i.e. 'by way of the mouth or the anus';
ii) in an improper place, i.e. 'near the retinue of a Guru, a monastery, a funeral monument (*stūpa*), or where many people have gathered';
iii) at an improper time, i.e. 'with a woman who has taken a vow, is pregnant or nursing a child, or in daylight';
iv) too often, i.e. 'more than five successive times';
v) in a generally improper way, i.e. by coercion, or with a man. (Guenther, 1959: 76)

The *Upāsaka-śīla Sūtra*, popular in China, includes i) and ii) in its list (*Uss.* 173). Holmes Welch also reports that Chinese Buddhists include visiting brothels, or intercourse in an improper place or time, such as in the living room in the afternoon, or with the use of instruments. Some see the precept as also requiring the putting away of concubines, others as simply not taking any more. Some see sexual intercourse not aimed at begetting children as to be avoided (Welch, 1967: 365).

While none of the above mention masturbation, it is included as a breach of the third precept in the *Kunzang Lama'i Shelung*, a very popular Tibetan work by Patrul Rinpoche, a nineteenth-century Lama of both the Nyingma (rNying-ma) school and an ecumenical movement (Patrul Rinpoche, 1994: 107). In the monastic discipline, a monk's intentional emission of semen is an offence entailing a formal meeting of the *Saṅgha*, i.e. its level of seriousness is just short of that requiring expulsion for a monk, with the Buddha explaining that the act is related to the very attachment, fetters and grasping that the *Dhamma* aims to transcend.[6] Given that sexual intercourse entails expulsion for a monk or nun, it is

---

[6] *Vin.* III.111–12. For a nun, rubbing her genitals is a lesser offence, one requiring expiation (*Vin.* IV.260–1).

not surprising that masturbation is an offence, too, if not quite so serious. As even sexual intercourse is, within certain bounds, acceptable for a lay person, the grounds for counting masturbation as a breach of the third lay precept are weak, though the act clearly goes against the Buddhist emphasis on overcoming attachment to sense-pleasures. Alan James, a contemporary Theravāda meditation teacher, says that masturbation breaks the precept because of fantasy-building and the wish to avoid the involvements that normally arise from sexual relationships (James and James, 1987: 42). Moreover, the Western Zen teacher Aitken Roshi, in interpreting the precept as meaning 'no boorish sex', sees this as any sexual activity, or even celibacy, 'thinking just of one's self' (Aitken, 1984: 37–8). Nevertheless, in the *Upāsaka-sīla Sūtra*, masturbation is mentioned in relation to the third precept only if it is done in a public place or close to a religious building (*Uss.* 173).

The fourth precept: avoiding lying and other forms of wrong speech

The first three precepts relate to physical actions and keeping them is equivalent to the 'right action'-factor of the Eightfold Path (see p. 38). Keeping the fourth precept is equivalent to the Path-factor of 'right speech', for while the precept specifically refers only to avoiding false speech, it is generally seen to entail avoiding other forms of 'wrong speech' (Mahasi, 1981: 207–8), which cause mental turmoil or other forms of suffering in oneself or others. This reading is reasonable in the light of the list of 'ten unwholesome actions', which refer to the three forms of 'wrong action', the four forms of 'wrong speech', and finally three forms of unwholesome mental action: covetousness, malevolence and wrong views (*M.* III.45–53) (see p. 48).

The fourth precept is generally seen as the second most important one (after the first precept): it is said that a person who has no shame at intentional lying is capable of any evil action (*M.* 1.415). Moreover, in the Theravādin *Jātakas*, it is said (in the commentarial prose) that a developing *Bodhisattva* may at times break all the precepts but one: 'he may not tell a lie, attended by deception that violates the reality of things' (*J.* III.499). The Theravādins also count truthfulness as one of the *Bodhisattva* 'perfections'. Likewise, in the Mahāyāna tradition, Śāntideva cites the *Ratnakūṭa Sūtra* as saying that a *Bodhisattva* 'never knowingly speaks an untruth, not to save his life' (*Ss.* 53). The gravest way to break any precept would be lying so as to cause a schism in the *Saṅgha* (*AKB.* IV.105a–b). On the other hand, there is the idea that an 'asseveration of truth' (Pali *sacca-kiriyā*; cf. *sacca-vacana*; Skt *satya-vacana*), in the form of the solemn affirmation of a moral or spiritual truth, or the truthful admission of a failing, has a power to save the utterer, or someone else, from danger (Harvey, 1993: 67–75).

Any form of lying, deception or exaggeration, either for one's own benefit or that of another (*M*. III.48), is seen as a breach of the fourth precept, even non-verbal deception by gesture or other indication (*AKB*. IV.75; *Asl*. 99; *Khp. A*. 26), or misleading statements (*Uss*. 174). Thich Nhat Hanh sees the fourth precept as entailing 'not to spread news that I do not know to be certain and not to criticize or condemn things of which I am not sure' (1993: 4). It is said to be a deluded wrong view to deny that the precept is broken by 'playful lying, lying to women, in marriage, or in danger of death' (*AKB*. IV.68d). Nevertheless, a small 'white lie' is much less serious than lying in a court of law: intentional lying is 'serious or light according to its subject-matter' (*Miln*. 193). It is 'more or less an offence according to whether the welfare destroyed is greater or smaller' (*Asl*. 99): for a lay person, this might vary from denying that one has something that one does not want to give to lying in a court so as to harm someone; for a monk, it might vary from an ironical joke to saying he has seen something which he has not.

Lying is to be avoided not only because it often harms others, but because it goes against the Buddhist value of seeking the truth, seeing things 'as they really are'. The more people deceive others, the more they are likely to deceive themselves; thus their delusion and spiritual ignorance increase. Moreover, one lie often leads to the 'need' for another to cover it up, leading to a tangle in which the liar always has to 'watch his back', increasingly falsifying what he is trying to protect, so as to become increasingly 'unreal'.

Of course, even truth can be harmful if spoken at the wrong time, so it should be withheld if to give it would lead to wholesome states of mind declining and unwholesome ones increasing in those one speaks to (*A*. II.173). Accordingly, well-spoken, unblameworthy speech is said to be 'spoken at the right time, in accordance with truth, gently, purposefully, and with a friendly heart' (*A*. III.243–4). This does not mean, though, that one should never say anything that would be disagreeable to the hearer. It is said that the Buddha only spoke, at the appropriate time, what was true and spiritually beneficial, whether or not it was disagreeable to others (*M*. I.395; cf. *M*. III.234). While, in Japan, right speech is seen to entail that it is not compassionate to tell a sick person the hard truth that he or she is terminally ill (Aitken, 1984: 51), one might question this if the person could better prepare himself or herself for death if he or she knew of this. Nevertheless, the practice follows the advice of the *Upāsaka-śīla Sūtra*, which says that one should not tell an ill person that he or she is dying but should instead encourage him or her to take refuge in the Buddha *Dhamma* and *Saṅgha*, and to express remorse for the past actions that are leading to the illness, showing patience if the person reacts to this with anger (*Uss.* 133).

The other forms of 'right speech' seek to extend a person's moderation of speech, so as to decrease unwholesome mental states and increase wholesome ones. Such speech is free not only of falsehood, but also of divisive speech, harsh, abusive, angry words, and even idle chatter:

Abandoning divisive speech, he is restrained from divisive speech. Having heard something at one place, he is not one to repeat it elsewhere for causing variance among those people; or having heard something elsewhere, he is not one to repeat it among these people for causing variance among them. In this way he is a reconciler of those who are at variance and one who combines those who are friends. Concord is his pleasure, his delight, his joy, the motive of his speech. Abandoning harsh speech, he is restrained from harsh speech. Whatever speech is gentle, pleasing to the ear, affectionate, going to the heart, urbane, pleasant to the manyfolk, agreeable to the manyfolk: such speech does he utter. Abandoning frivolous chatter, he is restrained from frivolous chatter. He is one that speaks at the right time, in accordance with fact, about the goal, about *Dhamma*, about moral discipline. He utters speech which is worth treasuring, with opportune similes, purposeful, connected with the goal. (*M.* iii.49)

This description clearly shows a very comprehensive concern with verbal behaviour. One who slanders and uses harsh speech is said to have a tongue which is like an axe: by its use, he causes himself much future suffering (*Sn.* 657). Speech which is not harsh should be unhurried, otherwise 'the body tires and the thought suffers and the sound suffers and the throat is affected; the speech of one in a hurry is not clear or comprehensible' (*M.* iii.234). In the *Bodhisattva-bhūmi*, the *Bodhisattva* is said to avoid demeaning talk and thought, or to withdraw mindfully from it if it occurs: 'By familiarity with withdrawal from it, his former enjoyment of such behaviour becomes enjoyment of not behaving so and the behaviour becomes repugnant' (Tatz, 1986: 51). The avoidance of frivolous chatter is sometimes explained in the texts in terms of not boring other people (*S.* v.355), and is seen as worse according to how often it is indulged in (*Asl.* 100). While it is most often emphasized in a meditative setting, in general it stresses the need to use one's words wisely, to inform, aid or express kindness to others, not just for the sake of opening one's mouth. Thus in Thailand, the fourth precept is seen as broken not just by straightforward lying, but also by by 'exaggeration, insinuation, abuse, gossip, unrestrained laughter, deceitful speech, joking and banter' (Terweil, 1979: 189).

The fifth precept: sobriety

This precept is not listed under the Path-factors of either 'right action' or 'right speech', but can be seen to act as an aid to 'right mindfulness': when one is intoxicated, there is an attempt to mask, rather than face, the sufferings of life, there is no mental clarity or calm, and one is more likely to break all the other precepts. Thus a well-known story in Thailand is that of an exemplary man who was challenged to break just one precept for once. The only precept he could bring himself to break was the fifth, but on getting drunk, he went on to break the rest too![7] Buddhaghosa holds that while breach of the first four precepts varies in blameability according to the nature of the person or animal harmed (see p. 52), breach of the fifth precept is always 'greatly blameable' as it obstructs the practice of *Dhamma* and can even lead to madness (*Khp. A.* 29). Indeed, in Burma, about half the monks see the fifth precept, rather than the first (or fourth), as the most important, because of the consequences that can follow from breaking it (Spiro, 1971: 99–100). Drunkenness is described as 'the delight of fools' (*Sn.* 399), and in the *Sigālovāda Sutta*, the Buddha says that breaking the fifth precept leads to six dangers:

present waste of money, increased quarrelling, liability to sickness, loss of good name, indecent exposure of one's person, and weakening of one's wisdom. (*D.* III.182–3)

Moreover:

Drinking intoxicating liquors adversely affects one's ability to remember. It also becomes an obstacle to the good path, decreasing as well all great virtues, mundane and supramundane. (*ASP.* 229–30)

> Intoxicants lead to worldly scorn,
> Affairs are ruined, wealth is wasted,
> The unsuitable is done from delusion,
> Therefore never take intoxicants. (*RPR.* 146)

---

[7] Terweil, 1979: 189–90. A similar tale, concerning a monk, is found in Tibet (Yuthok, 1995: 51).

Nāgārjuna lists thirty-five perils of drink (Lamotte, 1949: 817–18). Elsewhere, drink is said to destroy one's self-respect and fear of bad rebirths (*Uss.* 152), to lead to being deluded in this and future lives and insane in one's next life (*ASP.* 229–30; cf. *A.* IV.247–8), or to rebirth in a hell, as a frustrated ghost, a mad dog, and then an insane, ugly, deluded and cruel human (Reynolds and Reynolds, 1982: 150).

In a monastic rule whose wording is very close to the fifth lay precept, there is an offence if even the amount of alcoholic drink that a blade of grass can hold is taken (*Vin.* IV.110), though a small amount of alcohol is permissible as an ingredient in a medicine (*Vin.* I.205; *Vin.* IV.110). Nevertheless, in following the fifth lay precept, while some people seek to avoid any intoxicating or mind-altering substances, except for genuine medicinal purposes, others regard intoxication, and not the taking of a little drink, as a breach of the precept; or regard any drinking as breaking the precept, but take a drink nevertheless.[8] Tibetans, for example, drink much barley beer (Bell, 1928: 214), though this is only slightly alcoholic (Tucci, 1980: 266), and may even be included in offerings at shrines (Tucci, 1980: 116). At dinner parties, hosts do their best to get their guests drunk (Bell, 1928: 158). In Thailand, drunkenness is not rare, alcohol is sometimes drunk at large community religious ceremonies, even within the precincts of monasteries, and it would be bad form for a guest to refuse proffered alcohol unless on medical grounds (Terweil, 1979: 191).

While breaking any of the first four precepts is seen as reprehensible by its very nature (*AKB.* IV.29a–c), there are different opinions as to whether breaking the fifth one is. The *Abhidharma-kośa-bhāṣya* (*AKB.* IV.34d) records that monks specializing in monastic discipline held – like the Theravādin Buddhaghosa (*Khp. A.* 24) – that it *was* reprehensible by nature, explaining that, in the *Upāli Sūtra*, the Buddha said that, even if sick, 'Those who recognize me as their master should not drink any strong liquor, even a drop on the point of a blade of grass.' However, those specializing in *Abhidharma*, or spiritual psychology, denied that it was always reprehensible by nature. It was so only when alcohol was taken by a person whose mind was defiled, as when an amount is drunk which the person knows will be inebriating, but not if a small amount is taken as a remedy, in a quantity that one knows will not be inebriating. Thus the *Upāli Sūtra* forbids alcohol to ill monks only inasmuch as the inebriating effect of a given amount of drink may vary. Thus breaking the fifth precept is only reprehensible by precept, but not by nature. The

---

[8] Terweil, 1979: 189; Gombrich, 1971a: 255.

author of the *Abhidharma-kośa-bhāṣya* agrees with this position, seeing the precept as a support for heedful vigilance (*AKB*. IV.29.a–c; cf. *Uss*. 152). Similarly, the Mahāyāna commentator Jinaputra held that drinking alcohol:

is naturally reprehensible when done with a defiled thought; but when it can be done with an undefiled thought it is what the Lord has prescribed in order to guard against other offences – that is to say, it is reprehensible by precept. (Tatz, 1986: 321)

Its many dangers are a cause for further carelessness. Inasmuch as one cannot know the proper measure to drink, it is absolutely forbidden. On the other hand, it is done by those, among others, who lack desire-attachment, so it is not unvirtuous for them; drinking alcohol without desire-attachment is not reprehensible by nature. (Tatz, 1986: 322)

This seems to say that carefully drinking a small amount of alcohol, with no desire for intoxication, is not reprehensible in itself, but is best avoided for what it may lead on to. This accounts for why drinking is mentioned in the five precepts, but not, for example, as part of 'wrong action' or the ten 'paths of unwholesomeness'.

While making a living by the sale of alcohol is seen as 'wrong livelihood', Buddhists are not generally puritanical about drinking. It would be seen as bad form for a Buddhist who is avoiding alcohol to look down on others who are drinking it in his or her company; rather, it would be appropriate to tune in to their happy frame of mind without having to resort to alcohol. Unlike some Muslim countries, no Buddhist country bans the sale or consumption of alcohol, though in Sri Lanka, where temperance is a widely accepted Buddhist ideal, 1956 saw an unsuccessful attempt to get the government to ban it, as part of a Buddhist revival (Bond, 1988: 62, 87, 96). In T'ang China (618–907), also, there were temperance tracts and advocation of the drinking of tea rather than alcohol.

Smoking is not included in the fifth precept. In Thailand, for example, it is not uncommon to see monks smoking. While it would be seen as impolite to let smoke drift into the face of someone who disliked it, it would equally be seen as inappropriate for a non-smoker to be censorious about those who do smoke. Nevertheless, in pre-Communist Tibet, there were strict laws against smoking in the street of the capital (Bell, 1924: 235), and the import of tobacco was banned. The authorities saw it as annoying the spirits with its smell, so that they then caused illness in people. Monks were completely forbidden to smoke (Bell, 1928: 242–4).

The nature of the precepts and precept-taking

It can be seen that, when the implications of the precepts are spelt out, they become high ideals that are difficult to keep fully; in practice, people may say that they cannot do this, given their circumstances and nature (Spiro, 1971: 449–50). The precepts nevertheless remain respected ideals that are to be striven for.[9] Each is in the form of a personal undertaking, a promise or vow to oneself, rather than a 'commandment' from without, though their difference from these, in practice, can be exaggerated (Gombrich, 1971a: 254–5).

It is usual, when 'taking the precepts', to chant them after 'taking the refuges' (Harvey, 1990a: 176–9). Translated from their Pali form, as used in Southern Buddhism, the latter are:

> I go to the Buddha as refuge.
> I go to the *Dhamma* as refuge.
> I go to the *Saṅgha* as refuge.
> For the second time I go to the Buddha as refuge . . .
> For the third time I go to the Buddha as refuge . . .

While chanting the precepts can be done by a lay person at any time, they are frequently 'taken' by chanting them after a monk, who then takes on the role of 'administering' them. In such a context, the resolve to keep the precepts takes on an added psychological impact.

In Southern Buddhist lands, where Buddhism is the dominant religion, the five precepts are norms which people are expected to seek to live up to. In Sri Lanka, for example, rural people often say that they are the core of Buddhism (Southwold, 1983: 192). The refuges and precepts are usually chanted on a daily basis at home, and at any ceremony at a monastery. At major religious festivals, the precepts may be taken at the start of each of a number of ceremonies (Terweil, 1979: 183), as a kind of 'ritual cleansing, a purification which enables the laymen to receive the benefits of the ceremony in a proper manner' (Terweil, 1979: 188). People try to live up to the precepts as best they can, according to the level of their commitment and circumstances (Terweil, 1979: 190–3). Greater adherence to the precepts is also shown on the four sabbath-like 'observance' (Pali *uposatha*; Skt *upoadha*) days per lunar month, and on festival days.

In Eastern Buddhism, Chinese commentaries see the precepts as definitely more than promises to oneself.[10] Whether for the laity or

---

[9] For a discussion of whether this makes the precepts 'absolutes' or not, see King, 1964, 70–9.
[10] Charles Jones, 'Keeping Precepts' posting to 'Buddha-L' Internet discussion forum, 25 July, 1995.

monastics, to be received in a valid manner, precepts need to be properly 'transmitted' from a monk or nun in a ritual, as asserted in the
Upāsaka-śīla Sūtra (*Uss.* 177). The *Brahmajāla Sūtra*, also influential in
China, holds that precepts should be taken from monastics except in
very exceptional circumstances, and then only after meditating for seven
days until a vision of the Buddha appears and approves of such a form
of precept-transmission. The *Upāsaka-śīla Sūtra* holds that if precepts are
taken without first taking the three refuges, they 'are called worldly precepts, which are not firm; they are like color that is not fixed with glue'.
Unlike the Buddhist precepts, taken with the refuges, they cannot
destroy previous unwholesome karma, and do not purify a person (*Uss.*
150). In the Chinese precept-transmitting ritual, the 'substance of the
precepts' (Skt *saṃvara*, literally 'discipline') is regarded as 'a power issued
by all Buddhas and *Bodhisattva*s coming upon the recipient through the
crown of the head like a cloud and circulating throughout the body',[11]
and has a force to help a person keep the precepts. As expressed by
Hirakawa, 'If one attempts to take the life of sentient beings, this power
becomes manifest in one's mind and stops one from taking life . . . When
one vows to accept and keep the precepts, this power takes root and
grows in one's mind' (1995: 10).

In Eastern Buddhism, Buddhism is only one ingredient in the religious situation, and the precepts are only taken by those with a fairly
strong commitment to Buddhism, as may well have originally been the
case in early Indian Buddhism. In China, they are first taken, usually
during a period staying at a monastery, at a solemn 'lay ordination' ceremony, as an adjunct to the ordination of monks.[12] The lay ordination
ceremony, at which *Bodhisattva* vows may also be taken, means that a
person is formally recognized as a Buddhist, so that he or she is then an
upāsaka (layman) or *upāsikā* (laywoman), and is given a religious name
(Welch, 1967: 358–9). According to the *Upāsaka-śīla Sūtra*, to take the
upāsaka precepts, a man must have the permission of his parents, wife,
servants, and the king, and, in a similar way to monastic ordinations,
must be free of certain impediments such as illness, not being a normal
male, having wronged a monastic or having abandoned his parents (*Uss.*
73).

In the Japanese Sōtō Zen school, devout lay people take the precepts
at *Jūkai*, a week-long set of ceremonies held every spring, while staying

---

[11] Ibid.
[12] Welch, 1967: 361–4. For a modern version of the precept-transmitting ceremony, see Nhat Hanh
et al., 1993: 257–78.

at a temple. A person's first attendance at *Jūkai* also involves a 'lay ordination' ceremony. The precepts taken differ from the usual five, but consist of the 'three pure precepts' and the 'ten great precepts'. The former are 'Cease from evil, do only good, do good for others', and the latter are: not killing, not stealing, not misusing sex, not saying that which is untrue, not taking or selling drugs or alcohol, not speaking against others, not praising yourself and abusing others, not being mean in giving either *Dharma* or wealth, not being angry, not defaming the three treasures.[13] In addition to taking the precepts, a person makes a general confession of past misdeeds and a piece of paper on which a Chinese character representing these is written is ceremonially burnt.

Partial precept-taking and the issue of precept-breaking

Given the importance of living by the five precepts, Buddhists have been concerned about various issues relating to their breaking, one being: if one of the five precepts is broken, is the undertaking to observe all five broken? In Southern Buddhism, the commentator Buddhaghosa held that a lay person can take a set of precepts either as a group or individually. If they are taken individually, a breach of one does not breach the set, and the whole set becomes effective again as soon as the broken one is retaken. If a set of precepts is taken as a group by a lay person, Buddhaghosa holds that the same situation pertains, though he cites some as holding that the breach of one precept breaks the undertaking to hold to the set (*Khp. A.* 28). Barend Terweil reports that in central Thailand, lay people usually ask for the five precepts using a Pali formula that says that they will be observed 'one by one, separately' (*visuṃ visuṃ*), so that if one is broken, the rest are not. Only on particularly solemn occasions do they ask for the five precepts in a way which means that a breach of one breaches the entire set (1979: 184–6). In Sri Lanka, too, very pious lay people sometimes take the five as a group, by saying the Pali for 'I undertake' at the end of the group, rather than at the end of each precept (Bartholomeusz, 1994: 73).

A related concern of Buddhists is whether it is worse to do a bad action covered by a precept if one has formally taken the relevant precept against it, or if one has not so committed oneself. This leads on to the question of whether it is acceptable to take only those of the five precepts that one feels able to keep. Taking only some of the five pre-

---

[13] Kennett, 1972: 213–14; Aitken, 1984: 4–104.

cepts seems not to be a current practice in Southern, Theravāda Buddhism.

Etienne Lamotte (1988: 69) holds that in ancient Indian Buddhism, *upāsaka*s could choose how many of the five precepts to follow, with one who followed only one, for example, being called an *eka-deśa-kārin* (Skt), 'holding to one rule'.[14] Yet in the pre-Mahāyāna schools, there were different views on taking fewer than five precepts. The Sautrāntikas and the Mahā-saṃghikas accepted it, but the Dharmaguptakas, Mahīśāsakas and most Sarvāstivādins did not (Hirakawa, 1995: 19–21; *AKB*. IV.31a–c, 36c–d). Sarvāstivāda arguments included that taking the refuges also committed one to all five precepts, and that all five precepts should be taken to be an *upāsaka*, just as one had to undertake all the monastic precepts to become a monk; or that the refuges and just *some* precepts were sufficient to be an *upāsaka* (Hirakawa, 1995: 19–20). While the Pali *Sutta*s of the Theravāda tradition say that one is an *upāsaka* simply by taking the three refuges, even before one takes the five precepts (*A*. IV.220), they do not refer to *upāsaka*s who keep only some of the precepts. Mahāyāna texts are also divided on the issue, as seen in two texts which are both often attributed to Nāgārjuna: the *Mahā-prajñā-pāramitā-upadeśa* accepts the practice, whereas the *Daśa-bhūmika-vibhāṣā* does not.[15]

In contemporary Tibetan practice, all the precepts are recited in a precept-giving ceremony, but lay people privately commit themselves only to those that they feel capable of following, with those committed to only some of the five precepts still being known as *upāsaka*s or *upāsikā*s.[16]

In the Chinese precept-taking ceremony, the precepts are regarded as quite weighty vows, as implied by the above discussion. Thus a person may not take a particular precept if he or she thinks that he or she cannot live up to it in practice, though the first precept is never omitted (Welch, 1967: 361). In the ceremony, those who wish to take only some are simply silent when it comes to the response for the precepts they wish to avoid taking.[17] Chinese Buddhists also sometimes 'suspend' the fifth precept if a doctor prescribes wine for an illness (Welch, 1967: 366) and in Taiwan, some, including monks, hold that one can formally abandon

---

[14] Citing *Mahā-nāma Sūtra*, quoted in *Kośa-vyākyā*, p. 377.
[15] Respectively Taishō 1509, 25.158c and Taishō 1521, 26.56.b–c, as cited by Hirakawa, 1995: 22.
[16] John Dunne, 'Precept-keeping' and 'Precept Keeping' postings to 'Buddha-L' Internet discussion forum, respectively 2 December and 21 July 1995.
[17] Charles B. Jones, 'Precept Keeping' posting to 'Buddha-L' Internet discussion forum, 4 December 1995.

a precept, before a Buddha image, if one comes to see that it will be too hard to keep it, for example if one will have to drink with business clients. Others, though, disapprove of the idea of abandoning precepts at will.[18] This is a reflection of the fact that Taiwanese Buddhists have different views on whether partial precept-taking is acceptable. Those who allow it are more strict about those precepts that they do take, while those who do not accept partial taking are more permissive in allowing that a precept can be later abandoned if it proves unkeepable:

> The former argue that the bad karma accrued from taking a precept and then breaking it is worse than if one had not taken it in the first place . . . [as] it accrues the bad karma of the act itself and the bad karma of precept-breaking.
> The latter argue that it is better to take a precept even if one cannot keep it, because the act of making a vow has a wholesome effect on the consciousness. They also make it very easy to abandon a precept. One simply says, 'I herewith abandon the precept against . . .'.[19]

The latter view is to some extent supported by the *Abhidharma-kośa-bhāṣya* (iv.41a–b), which says that one who resolves to give up killing does not thereby overcome his moral indiscipline unless he also takes the first precept, for 'Illness does not improve without medicine, even though one may avoid the cause of illness.' Mark Tatz, drawing on Asaṅga's *Bodhisattva-bhūmi*, also says that 'To act morally in accordance with a vow is considered more beneficial than to act morally without one, because the moral conduct is associated with progress toward a higher goal' (1986: 13), and the respected Burmese meditation teacher Mahāsi Sayadaw holds that 'the mere intention to observe the moral precepts' is very beneficial (Mahasi, 1981: 30). One might add that to the extent that taking a precept helps one generally avoid the relevant action, a lapse or two from the precept is better than not taking it in the first place. Another consideration is that it is seen as worse to do a bad action when one does not recognize it as a bad action (see pp. 155–6). To take a precept against doing an action is a way of clearly acknowledging it as wrong, even if one subsequently does it. This need not imply, though, that someone who does not formally take a precept does not acknowledge the relevant action as wrong: he or she may simply feel that he or she is unable to live up to it, given his or her circumstances and nature. Of course, breaking a precept one has promised to follow also involves breaking a promise, but one can argue that unless this is a premeditated

---

[18] Charles Jones, 'Keeping Precepts' posting to 'Buddha-L' Internet discussion forum, 21 July 1995.
[19] Charles B. Jones, 'Precept Keeping' posting to 'Buddha-L' Internet discussion forum, 6 December 1995.

lie, it does not outweigh the goodness of the original promise/resolution.

What, though, of the many monastic rules undertaken by a monk or nun, but not by a lay person? The most obvious one of these is the avoidance of all sexual activity. Sexual activity is acceptable for a lay person, provided it is within certain moral bounds. A monk undertakes to avoid it, as a crucial part of his training to overcome all greed/attachment, hatred and delusion. Any act of sexual intercourse will then lead to 'defeat' in the monastic life, and expulsion from it. In this case, it is seen as better not to take the relevant precept, by remaining a lay person, or disrobing, than to take it and then break it. This is partly because of the solemnity of the monastic vows, and the obligation a monk has to make himself worthy of the alms of the lay-people who support him, and so not betray their faith. Moreover, sexual activity is not itself immoral, so it only becomes blameworthy if indulged in after vowing not to do so (or if done in a way involving suffering to others). Like most of the monastic precepts, it is generally not 'reprehensible by nature' but only by precept, as breaking it brings no direct harm to others (Tatz, 1986: 10; but see Harvey, 1999: 283).

Damien Keown, though, argues that a bad action is worse if one has taken a precept against it, on the principle that law-breakers 'who should have known better', such as policemen or lawyers, are treated more severely in courts as they 'a) knew exactly what they were doing, b) had vowed to uphold the principles they had betrayed and c) brought their office or profession into disrepute'.[20] This form of argument, though, is better suited to monks and their precepts than lay people. D. Gould's argument focuses more directly on the heart of the issue: 'The grave effect of breaking a solemn promise one has made to oneself is that one has created a tendency to ignore one's own wholesome decisions and has opened the door to a much less controllable mind.'[21] The *Abhidharma-kośa-bhāṣya* says that to break a precept one has taken is commiting an act against moral virtue (*śīla*) (*AKB*. IV.122.c), even though it seems to oppose partial precept-taking. While it does not actually say that breaking a precept is worse than doing the act without breaking a precept, this seems to be implied.

The *Upāsaka-śīla Sūtra*, which is influential in China, holds strongly to the view that it is worse to do a bad action that one has taken a precept against:

---

[20] 'Keeping Precepts' posting to 'Buddha-L' Internet discussion forum, 24 July 1995.
[21] 'Keeping Precepts' posting to 'Buddha-L' Internet discussion forum, 25 July 1995.

If two people commit an offense together and one has taken the precepts and the other has not, the former's offense is heavier and the latter's offense is lighter. And why is this? It is because he transgresses the Buddha's teaching. (*Uss.* 150)

Moreover, to break the worldly form of the first precept – that is, without first taking the three refuges – is less bad than breaking one of the precepts which are not transgressions by nature, if this has been taken in a Buddhist way (p. 150). The *Sūtra* agrees that sincerely keeping the precepts has immeasurable benefits (p. 73), with great blessings coming from even taking them for a short time (p. 159), yet it also holds that breaking them leads to countless bad rebirths (p. 73; cf. pp. 176–7). Thus it holds that:

(1) to avoid killing after having taken the Buddhist precept against it is better than to avoid it without the precept;
(2) to kill after having taken a Buddhist precept against it is worse than to kill without having taken this precept.

Indeed, for one who has not taken the first precept, the evil of killing is restricted to the actual time of killing, whereas for one who has taken the precept, the evil of any killing occurs not just at this time (p. 176). Thus taking a Buddhist precept is risky: it offers great rewards if kept, but great dangers if broken. Nevertheless, while the *Sūtra* sees breaking a precept one has taken as making one a 'stinking . . . outcast . . . defiled *upāsaka*' (p. 79), 'staining' the relevant precept, it can be subsequently purified by various reflections and good actions (pp. 157–8). Indeed, 'Even if one commits many great offences, the precepts are not lost. And why is this? It is because the power of the precepts is strong' (p. 150).

Is it possible to decide between these two views on precept-taking? Are we to say that it is 'just a matter of opinion', and that neither is objectively right or wrong? We can say that both views can be objectively right, without actually contradicting each other! Those who prefer not to take a precept that they think they might break, as they regard precept-breaking as a weighty act, will take any precept in a particularly solemn way. In doing so, they get the advantage of generating a strong, wholesome, positive impulse in the mind, but breaking such a *solemnly made* precept *will thereby* be a weighty act. Those who hold that it is better to take a precept even if it might be subsequently broken will regard a precept in a less solemn way, and *thereby*, if it is broken, it will be less serious than the breaking of a precept by the first type of person. Of course, taking a precept in a less solemn way will have a less positive impact on the mind, which is part of the reason why the second type of person holds that it is always good to take a precept. His or her (unconscious) strategy is a 'lower-risk' one of lower potential gain, but lower potential risk. Thus we see that the Buddhist principle of the primacy of the nature of the act of will behind an act, and the dynamic interactions taking place in a world in which states of mind constantly condition each other, affects the issue.

Taking extra precepts

As an extension of the usual five precepts, a set of eight precepts may be taken by lay people (Terweil, 1979: 208–10). These go beyond purely moral concerns – related to that which is, or may be, reprehensible by nature – to forms of self-discipline that reduce stimulating sense-inputs that disturb calm and concentration, and develop non-attachment (*AKB.* IV.29a–c; *Khp. A.* 24). The difference between the eight and five precepts is firstly that the third precept is replaced by an undertaking to avoid *abrahmacariya*: 'unchaste conduct' or 'conduct not of the holy life', that is, sexual activity of any kind. Three more precepts are then undertaken after the usual fifth one:[22]

6. I undertake the training-precept to abstain from eating at an unseasonable time.
7. I undertake the training-precept to abstain from seeing dancing, music vocal and instrumental, and shows; from wearing garlands, perfumes and unguents, from finery and adornment.
8. I undertake the training-precept to abstain from high or large beds (or seats).

The sixth precept entails not eating any solid food after noon, following the practice of monks. The seventh precept means avoiding, or keeping one's distance from, entertainments, and avoiding make-up, perfume, jewellery and colourful clothes, so that, in Southern Buddhism, people wear plain white clothes (Gombrich, 1971a: 66). These particular disciplines are also followed by those observing the Zen *Jūkai* festival. The eighth precept is intended to diminish slothfulness or feelings of grandeur, and entails sitting and sleeping on mats. In practice, however, this is how most rural lay people in South-east Asia generally sleep anyway (Terweil, 1979: 210); luxurious beds are only used by the rich or noble.

In the Southern tradition, the eight precepts are generally only taken by more pious people over forty:[23] a few do so permanently, but more do

---

[22] *Sn.* 400–2. For a discussion of these, and the ten precepts, see *Khp. A.* 34–7, with some discussion of the third of the eight or ten precepts included on pp. 22–37.
[23] Terweil, 1979: 195–210; Gombrich, 1971a: 66, 273–4.

so temporarily on some of the observance days (*uposatha*s), while staying at a monastery for a day and a night, a practice which is also found in Chinese Buddhism (*Uss.* 146). There are four such observance days per lunar month, but observance of the eight precepts is more common on those falling in the three months of the rainy season, when monks remain in their monasteries for more intense practice. By taking extra precepts, lay people who are becoming less actively involved in the concerns of lay life undertake a discipline which approximates to that of monks. In Thailand a lay person is therefore known – while under the discipline of eight precepts – by the term for a male or female lay disciple, *upāsaka* or *upāsikā* (Terweil, 1979: 198), which terms are used in Mahāyāna Buddhism for anyone who seeks to observe some or all of the five precepts properly. Those who sometimes take eight precepts in the Theravāda tradition also observe the five precepts more faithfully than other people in daily life, and in Sri Lanka such people are known as *upāsaka*s or *upāsikā*s all the time (Gombrich, 1971a: 65). Unlike the five precepts, in Thailand the eight precepts are usually taken as a set, so that breaking any of them breaks all of them (Terweil, 1979: 208). As regards the third of the eight precepts, in rural Thailand, customary advice to married couples is that they should avoid sexual intercourse on observance days even if they are not formally taking this precept (Terweil, 1979: 208).

An extension beyond the eight precepts is found in the ten precepts. These are the same as the eight except that the seventh is split into its two parts, and there is the addition of an undertaking to 'abstain from accepting gold and silver'. While the difference seems a small one, in practice it is large, for the ten precepts are not taken temporarily, but only on a long-term basis (Terweil, 1979: 212). The extra precept precludes the actual handling of money, as in the case of monks. The ten precepts are those observed by novice monks. A few elderly Theravāda men permanently follow the ten precepts, and wear white, but a greater number of women do so (see pp. 395–8). In Sri Lanka, the ten precepts of the householder are seen as easier to maintain than those of novices as the lay person takes them individually, so that all are not broken if one is, whereas novices take them as a group (Bartholomeusz, 1994: 73).

MONASTIC VALUES

The followers of the Buddha are termed the 'four assemblies' (*parisā*s): male and female members of the monastic *Saṅgha*, and male and female lay disciples: *upāsaka*s and *upāsikā*s (*J.* 1.148). In nearly all schools of Buddhism, the monastic life is acknowledged as on a generally higher level of virtue than lay life. Monastics have been the main bearers and preservers of the Buddhist tradition, and have been teachers, guides and examples to the laity. The Pali terms translated as 'monk' and 'nun' are *bhikkhu* (Skt *bhikṣu*) and *bhikkhunī* (Skt *bhikṣuṇī*), literally 'almsman' and 'almswoman'. The original mendicancy of *bhikkhu*s, still current to varying extents, symbolized renunciation of normal worldly activities and involvements; it was an aid to humility, and also ensured that they did not become isolated from the laity. A *bhikkhu* should be content with whatever food etc. he is offered, but should not exalt himself or disparage others on account of his contentment (*A.* 11.27). The often close lay–monastic relationship makes *bhikkhu*s unlike most Christian 'monks'. They also differ from these in that their undertakings are not in principle taken for life, and in that they take no vow of obedience. The Buddha valued self-reliance, and left the *Saṅgha* as a community of individuals sharing a life under the guidance of *Dhamma* and *Vinaya*. The job of its members is to strive for their own spiritual development, and use their knowledge and experience of *Dhamma* to guide others, when asked: not to act as intermediaries between God and humankind, or officiate at life-cycle rites. Nevertheless, in practice they have come to serve the laity in several priest-like ways.

Celibacy

The most obvious and central difference between a monk or nun and a lay person is the former's commitment to celibacy: the total avoidance of sexual intercourse. The importance of celibacy is that sexual activity expresses quite strong attachment, uses energy which could otherwise be used more fruitfully, and generally leads to family responsibilities which leave less time for spiritual practice (see Wijayaratna, 1990: 89–108). Among the various Buddhist lists of states to be overcome on the spiritual path, desire for sense-pleasures (*kāma*) is prominent: it is the first of the five hindrances to meditative calming, and in lists of the three kinds of craving, the four sorts of grasping, and the four deep-seated 'cankers' on the mind, the first item always has sense-pleasures as its focus.

The three 'roots of unwholesome action', to be gradually weakened before *Nirvāṇa* brings their destruction, are greed, hatred and delusion. The practice of the precepts and lovingkindness enables a lay person to minimize hatred, and the practice of the precepts and generosity may reduce greed, but the monastic life with its fewer attachments has clear advantages here. As a form of greed, attachment to sensual pleasures is a lesser fault than hatred or ill-will, but it is seen as taking a long time to uproot (see p. 47), and monastic life is seen as a powerful means to aid this.

Celibacy has to be practised in the right way, though. Rōshi Kyogen Carlson notes that it is:

an extremely powerful method for developing the will. Celibacy has to be undertaken with a gentle heart and compassion, otherwise it can lead to a certain coldness, and can be misused to develop personal power. (Carlson, 1982: 38)

Alan James, who spent time as a Theravādin monk, comments that a 'wrong' and 'right' form of celibacy can be found in religions. The first is a form of escapism based on a rejection and repression of sexuality, so that a person becomes 'wizened and dried out . . . bitter . . . sexless'. In the second, 'sexuality has been accepted and integrated into the life-style . . . not ignored and rejected', so as to be an 'open . . . full face which is happy and very definitely male or female' (James and James, 1987: 40). Indeed, it is sometimes said that an effect of cultivating the spiritual faculty of 'energy' (Pali *viriya*; Skt *vīrya*) is to glow with either manly or womanly energy,[24] and one woman who had an audience with the Dalai Lama later expressed surprise at how *masculine* he was!

An interesting reflection on the value of celibacy, from a Western Buddhist nun, sees celibacy as avoiding the cycle of 'clinging, unfulfilled expectation, the pain of separation' found in normal relationships, where 'often, the longing for a companion is a wish to complement one's missing or underdeveloped qualities' (Tsomo, 1988: 55):

Celibacy, on the other hand, represents a decision to rely on one's own inner authority. It is an attempt to achieve a balance and wholeness within, independent of the feedback of another person.

In such a state, one is free from both the 'gross complications of relationships' and the tendency to synthesize one's own direct experience of the world with that of another person. Thus one is 'free to experience life directly, participating wholeheartedly with undivided attention'. It is also harder to blame one's problems on other people (p. 57). And, of course, it enables one to go beyond sexual attachment, 'the major force that propels beings from one rebirth to the next' (p. 56).

---

[24] For a discussion of attitudes to sexuality in modern Theravāda and Zen Buddhism, see Clasquin, 1992.

The role of monasticism

The life of monks and nuns is not properly an 'escapist' or 'selfish' one, as is sometimes thought. A lay person can distract himself or herself from the realities of life and personal weaknesses with such things as entertainments, pastimes, drink and sex. The simple monastic life, however, is designed to have few distractions, so that there is less opportunity to ignore greed, hatred and delusion, and thus more opportunity to work at diminishing them and to guide others in doing so. Most monks and nuns seek to do this, though a few do take to monastic life as a lazy way of making a living. As regards being 'selfish', the whole aim of monastic life is to help diminish attachment to self and its consequent desires and aversions.

The Buddha felt that the life of a householder was somewhat spiritually cramping, so that it was difficult for a layperson to perfect the 'holy life':

The household life is cramping; it is a path choked with dust; to leave it is to come out into the open air. It is not easy for a householder to live the holy life in all its fullness, in all its purity, polished like a conch-shell. (*D.* 1.63)

Thus the *Milindapañha* refers to a layman's life as 'crowded with wife and children' (*Miln.* 243). As the monastic life of one 'gone forth from home into homelessness' lacks many of the attachments and limiting involvements found in lay life, it is seen as having fewer obstacles to, and more opportunities for, persistent and consistent spiritual practice, which are needed to destroy delusion, along with greed and hatred.

It is said that if either a lay person or one who is ordained is rightly practising, he or she is 'accomplishing the right path': one cannot automatically say that a monk or nun is on the right path and a lay person not (*M.* 11.197). Nevertheless, a householder leads a busy life, with many responsibilities, and so cannot give as consistent attention to moral and spiritual matters as one who is ordained (*M.* 11.205). Moreover, one who has 'gone forth' (if practising rightly) is:

of few wishes, content, aloof, ungregarious, of stirred up energy, without desire, homeless, he fulfils the moral virtues, he is of submissive habits, and skilled in the practice of shaking off (the defilements),

so that all that he does 'prospers quickly and without delay' (*Miln.* 244).

The early texts do refer to many lay Stream-enterers, more than 1,000 eight-precept (celibate) lay Non-returners (*M.* 1.490–1) and a few lay

Arahats.[25] They describe one lay Non-returner, Ugga, as teaching *Dhamma* to monks if they do not themselves teach him (*A.* iv.211). If a gravely ill lay person can abandon all attachments and aspire to an end to rebirth, there is no difference, as regards release, between him and an *Arahat* monk (*S.* v.408–10). Nevertheless, it is said that there is no householder 'not getting rid of the householder's (mental) fetter(s)' who makes an end of *dukkha*, i.e. becomes an *Arahat* (*M.* 1.483).

While the conditions of lay life pose more obstacles, those who make the effort in spite of them can attain good spiritual progress (*Uss.* 24). Nevertheless, most Buddhist schools see monasticism as a superior way of life, one that all should respect and aspire to join in this or some future life. In Chinese Buddhism, it is said that even giving to bad monks is of great benefit, as any monk passes on the teachings and respects the three refuges (*Uss.* 155). In Southern Buddhism, it is said that a lay Stream-enterer should even bow to a monk of lesser attainment, as a way of showing respect for his way of life (*Miln.* 162–4). Moreover, a lay person who attains Arahatship must ordain that day (if he is not to pass away), as the lofty nature of this state cannot be expressed in a lay context (*Miln.* 264–6).

Within the classical Mahāyāna, while the *Bodhisattva*-path gives an increased scope for lay practice, the monastic life is still highly regarded, and is seen as a necessary commitment at some point on the path. Śāntideva's *Śikṣā-samuccaya* talks of the 'innumerable faults' of lay life, and affirms that the *Bodhisattva* should renounce it in each of his rebirths (*Ss.* 190, 15); though for enlightenment to be attained, the *Bodhisattva* precepts (see pp. 132–4) must be followed in addition to the monastic ones (p. 19).

The monastic code of discipline

Saṅgha life is regulated by the *Vinaya*, meaning 'that by which one is led out (from suffering)'. The main components of this section of scriptures are a code of training-rules (Pali *sikkhāpadas*; Skt *śikṣāpadas*) for *bhikkhus*, one for *bhikkhunīs*, and ordinances for the smooth running of communal life and ceremonies. Each code is known as a *pāṭimokkha* (Pali; Skt

---

[25] *A.* iii.450–1; *Dhp.* 142. The later *Miln.* 348 talks of millions of lay people as having experienced *Nirvāṇa*, by which it mainly means Stream-entry up to becoming a Non-returner (pp. 349–50). It then goes on to outline various spiritual advantages, nevertheless, of being a monk or nun (pp. 351–62), and says that lay attainers had been monks or nuns in past lives (p. 353). On the question of lay *Arahats*, see *Kvu.* 268 and Saddhatissa, 1970: 115–221; Katz, 1982: 180–5.

prātimoṣka), containing: (1) the rules themselves, (2) the supposed situation which led the Buddha to promulgate each rule, often involving lay criticism of the behaviour of some monks, and (3) mitigating circumstances which nullify or reduce the usual consequences of digression from it.

The *pāṭimokkha* gradually evolved during the Buddha's life, and for perhaps a century after, on the basis of the original rules – 150 or so for monks. In the early texts, the Buddha says that he only made a rule when a particular form of harmful conduct was carried out by a monk or nun, which increased as the number of monastics, and the time from the simpler early days, grew (*M.* 1.445). Three versions of the code are still in use. The Theravādin code of 227 rules for monks (311 for nuns) is the one used in Southern Buddhism, the Mūla-Sarvāstivādin code of 258 rules for monks (366 for nuns) is used in Northern Buddhism, while the Dharmaguptaka code of 250 rules for monks (348 for nuns) is used in Eastern Buddhism.

The *pāṭimokkha* code has qualities which make it akin to a legal code, to a code of professional conduct, and to a set of training-rules for a (spiritual) athlete (cf. Huxley, 1995b). It is chanted on the observance days at the full and new moons. Before this, a monk must acknowledge any digression from the code to another monk. The code is then chanted by a senior monk, often now in an abbreviated form, and the silence of the others is taken as a sign that their conduct is pure, with any digressions acknowledged. In this way the ceremony serves as a vital liturgical expression of the communal purity of a particular local *Saṅgha*.

The monastic code covers much besides the primarily moral concerns of the five precepts which lay people follow. It is mainly 'formulated' virtue, abstaining from behaviour which goes against a specially formulated precept, not 'natural' virtue, abstaining from behaviour 'reprehensible by nature' (Harvey, 1999: 282–4; Tatz, 1986: 295, n. 374). Yet it supports natural virtue (see p. 78) as it trains the mind in dealing with the roots of immoral behaviour.

As an elaboration of the ten precepts, the code drastically limits the indulgence of desires, and promotes a very self-controlled, calm way of life, of benefit to the monks and nuns themselves and an example which 'inspires confidence' among the laity (*Vism.* 19). Overall, the rules are said to have been established for: protecting and ensuring the comfort of the *Saṅgha*; warding off ill-meaning people who might wish to join it; helping well-behaved monks and nuns; destroying present defilements and preventing future ones; benefiting non-Buddhists and increasing the number of Buddhists; and establishing discipline by observing the rules of restraint (*Vin.* III.21). The rules are not so much prohibitions, as aids to spiritual training that require those observing them to be ever mindful. By constantly coming up against limiting boundaries, they are made more aware of their 'greed, hatred and delusion', and so are better able to deal with them. The rules are thus best seen as tools to help transform the mind and behaviour.

The rules are arranged in categories according to degrees of gravity.[26] The first relates to *pārājika* actions which 'entail defeat' in monastic life, and permanent dismissal. For monks, these are strong breaches of four of the ten precepts (*Vin.* III.1–109): intentional sexual intercourse of any kind; theft of an object that would lead to being taken to court; murder of a human being; and false claims of having attained deep meditative states or become a Noble person, whether made to the laity (a possible way of attracting more alms) or other monks. As serious karmic consequences are seen to follow from a monk's breaking these rules, it is held to be better to become a lay person, who can at least indulge in sexual intercourse, than live as a monk who is in danger of breaking the rule against this. For nuns, there are four extra *pārājika* offences (*Vin.* IV.211–22): (with sensual intent) touching a man or going to a rendezvous with him; not making known that another nun has broken a *pārājika* rule; and persistently imitating a monk suspended for bad behaviour.

The remaining rules explained here are those of the monks' *pāṭimokkha.* They do not entail expulsion if broken, but such penalties as: being put on probation, during which time a monk is treated as the most junior monk and excluded from official *Saṅgha* affairs; not speaking to a monk; censuring; forfeiting an article; or simply acknowledging the digression. These rules can be conveniently grouped in relation to the ten precepts:

(1) harming living beings by directly killing them, digging the ground or destroying plants or trees;

(2) consuming food or drink (except water) that has not been formally offered; 'corrupting families' by giving small gifts in the hope of receiving abundant alms in return;

(3) actions of a sensual nature other than intercourse; sleeping in the same dwelling as a woman, or sitting in a private place with one;

(4) false accusations of an offence involving 'defeat', and various other forms of wrong speech, unfriendly behaviour towards a fellow

---

[26] For general discussion of monastic discipline, see Prebish, 1980. On the Theravāda monastic rules, see: Wijayaratna, 1990; Thanissaro Bhikkhu, 1994; Khantipalo, 1979; Harvey, 1999; and Von Hinüber, 1995. For other monastic codes, see Prebish, 1975.

monk, and true claims to the laity of having attained higher states. Also, disparaging the lesser rules as vexing, pretended ignorance of a rule, or knowingly concealing a monk's digression from one of the more serious rules;

(5) drinking alcohol;

(6) eating after noon;

(7) unseemly, frivolous behaviour, and going to see an army fighting or on parade;

(8) inappropriate ways of wearing monastic robes: seventy-five rules in the Theravādin code (*Vin.* IV.185–206) seek to ensure that the monks (and novices) are graceful and dignified in the way that they wear their robes, walk, move, and collect and eat alms-food. Such a calm deportment is much valued by the laity;

(9) using a high, luxurious bed, or sleeping in the same place as a layman for more than three nights;

(10) receiving, handling or use in transactions of money (this does not prevent the acceptance and use of money by a monastery's lay stewards).

Entry into the monastic *Saṅgha* is by two stages. From the age of seven or eight, a child can take the lower ordination, or 'going forth' (Pali *pabbajjā*; Skt *pravrajyā*), so as to become a *sāmaṇera* (Pali; Skt *śramaṇera*) or *sāmaṇerī* (Pali; Skt *śrāmaṇerikā*): a male or female 'little renunciant' or novice. These novices undertake the ten precepts (see p. 88). When aged twenty, a person can take higher ordination or 'admission' (*upasampadā*) as a *bhikkhu* or *bhikkhunī*. Once someone is ordained, even as a novice, head hair is shaved off, as a sign of renunciation of vanity.

A new novice or monk generally acts as attendant to a senior monk, his teacher and companion in the monastic life, in a relationship explicitly modelled on that of father and son (*Vin.* I.45). In South-east Asia, short-term noviciates, lasting at least a few days or weeks, are quite common. These are to generate karmic fruitfulness for a parent or dead relative, or, in Burma, as a kind of rite de passage for boys near puberty. Some novices, of course, stay on until they become monks.

The Buddha discouraged monks from disrobing, and originally ordination was taken with the intention that it would be for life. However, the monastic status has never been irrevocable. In most Buddhist lands, a person is expected to be a monk or nun for life, but a system of temporary ordination has evolved in the Theravāda lands of South-east Asia (though not in Sri Lanka). Here, the tradition is that every male Buddhist should join the *Saṅgha* at some time for at least a limited period, usually during the three-month rains period, when the number of monks may double. In practice about 50 per cent join, often several times during life. While the continuity of monastic life is kept up by a core of permanent monks, the system makes for a close lay–monastic relationship and a good level of lay religious knowledge and experience. Temporary monk-hood is often a stage prior to marriage (see p. 102) or a way for old people to generate karmic fruitfulness for their next life.

Harmony, sharing and spiritual companionship

Harmony among members of the monastic *Saṅgha* has always been highly valued. Thus the Buddha said that among the conditions for the flourishing of the *Saṅgha* (in any particular locality) were that it should hold regular meetings at which 'they meet in harmony, break up in harmony, and carry on their business in harmony' (*D.* ii.76–7). Another condition was that senior monks – i.e. those ordained longer – should be respected. This applied even if a junior monk was more learned or spir-itually developed than his senior (*Vin.* ii.161–2). This method provided a clear and unambiguous structure for respectful salutations within the *Saṅgha*.[27]

The contemporary valuing, by the laity, of monastic unity is shown by Jane Bunnag's observations on Thailand (1973: 104):

Many informants placed great value upon concerted action between *bhikkhus*, taking it as evidence of strong community spirit; by contrast they tended to dis-parage the independent behaviour of the monks at *Wat* Yanasena and else-where, as being anti-social and selfish. I was frequently told . . . 'it is better (for monks) to eat together'.

Similarly, in Japanese Zen monasteries, there is an emphasis on monks training *together*, and not 'alone up a mountain' in their own thoughts, while supposedly working with others.

Harmony is fostered by friendly thoughts, words and deeds and shared virtues and outlook, but also by sharing possessions. Thus the Buddha counselled that a monk should enjoy impartially sharing even the contents of an alms-bowl with fellow monks (*M.* i.322; *M.* ii.250–1). In Thailand, food, goods and money given to monks are indeed gener-ally shared amongst them and also used to support boys who live at the monasteries to help the monks, often because they need somewhere to live while studying away from home.

---

[27] On monastic life as representing the ideal society, see Dharmasiri, 1989: 79–97.

On one occasion, the Buddha emphasized that 'good friendship (*kalyāṇa-mittatā*), good association, good intimacy' was the whole, not the half of the holy life (*S.* v.2), for good friendship is the most powerful (external) thing to foster the arising of wholesome states and the decline of unwholesome ones (*A.* 1.14). The *Saṅgha*, in having shared values, ideals and practices, acts as a support for the individual monk or nun's efforts. Such support is given by example, the practice of mutual acknowledgement of digressions from the monastic rules, and by gently pointing out faults of other monks, at which they should not take offence (*M.* 1.95). A new monk's guiding senior is his particular 'good friend'. The best of 'good friends' are those who are gifted meditation teachers.

The monks also act as 'good friends' to the laity, through example, teaching, informal advice, chanting protective chants for them and being worthy 'fields of karmic fruitfulness' for them. In a variety of ways, the ethos of the *Saṅgha* thus radiates out into the lay society that supports it.

THE ETHICS OF INTER-PERSONAL RELATIONSHIPS

While Buddhism emphasizes a personal lay ethic of giving, moral restraint and right livelihood, and a more elaborate monastic code, it by no means neglects the area of lay inter-personal and social relationships. Nevertheless, discourses to the laity are not generally given in the form of disciplinary rules, as:

the wider lay society was so open to changing circumstances of space and time that the monks did not consider it as a subject appropriate for fixed rules. Consequently, only some basic rules and general principles were stipulated

as a basis for people to work out more specific codes in their circumstances (Rājavaramuni, 1990: 35). How this has worked out in practice varies considerably from culture to culture, but some central emphases of Buddhist social ethics can be outlined.

An important text in this area is the *Sigālovāda Sutta* (*D.* III.180–93; cf. *Uss.* 71–2), described by the Emperor Asoka and Buddhaghosa as the *Vinaya*, or code of discipline (usually meaning the monastic code), of lay people (Rājavaramuni, 1990: 35). Here the Buddha comes across Sigāla, worshipping the six directions in pursuance of his father's dying wish. The Buddha counsels him that there is a better way to serve the directions: by proper actions towards six types of persons. Before outlining these appropriate actions, he first teaches Sigāla the proper way for a lay person to conduct himself or herself in general. He or she should: keep the precepts; not act from partiality, enmity, stupidity or fear; and avoid the six channels of dissipating wealth (see pp. 189–90). The Buddha then outlines how the six 'directions' are to be 'protected', so as to produce sound social relationships.

Parents and children

The first relationship dealt with is the child–parent one, with the parent seen as in the direction of the rising sun:

In five ways a child should minister to his parents as the eastern quarter: 'Once supported by them,I will now be their support; I will perform duties incumbent on them; I will keep up the lineage and tradition of my family; I will make myself worthy of my heritage; I will give alms on their behalf when they are dead.' In five ways do the parents, thus ministered to as the eastern quarter by their child, act in sympathy with him: they restrain him from vice, they exhort him to virtue, they train him to a profession, they contract a suitable marriage for him, and in due time they hand over his inheritance. (*D.* III.189)

Respect and support for parents is also emphasized in the *Maṅgala Sutta*:

> Aid for mother and father,
> And support for wife and children,
> Work that is free from upset:
> This is a supreme blessing.   (*Khp.* 3)

The *Sigālovāda Sutta* affirms that parents only win the honour and respect of children by their kindly help to them (cf. *Uss.* 178). While the law of karma ensures that children get the parents they deserve (and parents get the children they deserve), it is said that the only way that a child can repay the debt of gratitude owed to his or her parents for caring for him or her in pregnancy and childhood is by getting them to develop or deepen a commitment to Buddhism and a virtuous life. Mother and father should be seen as like both the god Brahmā and 'teachers of old': they are worthy of offerings and help on account of their compassion- ately bringing up their children and introducing them to the world (*A.* 1.132; cf. *Khp. A.* 137–8). In Sri Lanka, it is held that 'the mother is the Buddha at home' (Dharmasiri, 1989: 71), in the sense that she is owed great respect for what she has done for her children. In rural Thailand, parents give great care and affection to their children, and in return get profound respect and deference (H. E. Smith, 1979: 18).

Deliberately killing one's father or mother is listed among the heinous acts that definitely lead to an immediate hellish rebirth after death (see

p. 24). One is said to be an 'outcaste' not by birth but by actions, such as failing to support one's ageing parents when one has the means to do so, or striking or angering one's parents, brother, sister or mother-in-law (*Sn.* 124–5). In *Jātaka* story 222 (*J.* II.199–202), monkeys give up the leadership of a troop to look after their sick, blind mother, and later give up their lives so that a hunter will spare her. As regards respect for elders, *Jātaka* 37 (*J.* I.217–20) tells of a monkey, partridge and elephant who agree to respect whichever among them is the eldest (see also *Vin.* II.161). In Thailand, respect for elders is important, even respect for a slightly older sibling. Such relationships take on a patron–client form: 'the senior member is expected to provide counsel and moral guidance, as well as material assistance when the need arises; whilst the junior partner should in turn pay heed to his advice, and give more tangible evidence of his deference by acting as general factotum for his superior' (Bunnag, 1973: 13).

In East Asia, the practice of Buddhists was influenced by the Confucian ethic, which sees filial piety as the foundation of ethics, and the family head as in a strong position of authority over its members (Ch'en, 1973: 15–55). It is noticeable that one Chinese translation of the *Sigālovāda Sutta* gives one of the child's duties as 'not to disobey the commandments of the parents' (Ch'en, 1973: 19). In Japan, Confucianism and the traditional political system concentrated authority in the family head, to whom absolute obedience was due. In the post-war era, though, American influence has led to laws liberating family members from this authority (Maykovich, 1978: 390). Nevertheless, the idea of the 'return of benefits' remains strong. As explained by the leader of Risshō-kōseikai, a Japanese new religious movement based on Nichiren Buddhism, we are only able to live because of:

our ancestors, parents, and the food and clothes etc. produced by others. People should see that they are able to live only through favors that come from outside themselves . . . We, as individuals, can exist only by being supported by the whole universe. (Niwano, 1977: 143–4)

Understanding this leads to joy and gratitude and a desire to serve others.

Other relationships

Other social relationships are dealt with in the *Sigālovāda Sutta* as follows (*D.* III.189–91):

In five ways should a pupil minister to his teachers as the southern quarter: by rising [from his seat in salutation], by waiting upon them, by eagerness to learn, by personal service, and by attention when receiving their teaching. And in five ways do teachers, thus ministered to as the southern quarter by their pupil, act in sympathy with their pupil: they train him well, cause him to learn well, thoroughly instruct him in the lore of every art, speak well of him among friends and companions, and provide for his safety in every quarter . . .

In five ways should a wife as western quarter be ministered to by her husband: by respect, by courtesy, by faithfulness, by handing over authority to her [in the home], by providing her with adornment. In these five ways does the wife, thus ministered to by her husband as the western quarter, act in sympathy with him: her duties are well performed, she shows hospitality to kin of both, is faithful, watches over the goods he brings, and shows skill and artistry in discharging all her business.

In five ways should one minister to one's friends and familiars as the northern quarter: by generosity, courtesy and benevolence, by treating them as one treats oneself, and by being as good as one's word. In these five ways thus ministered to as the northern quarter, one's friends and familiars act in sympathy with one: they protect one when one is off one's guard, and on such occasions guard one's property; they become a refuge in danger, they do not forsake one in times of trouble, and they show consideration for one's family . . .

In five ways does a noble master minister to his servants and employees as the nadir: by assigning them work according to their strength, by supplying them with food and wages, by tending them in sickness, by sharing with them unusual delicacies, and by granting them leave at all appropriate times. In these ways ministered to by their master, servants and employees act in sympathy with their master in five ways: they rise before him, lie down to rest after him, are content with what is given to them, do their work well, and they carry about his praise and good name.

In these five ways should the householder minister to renunciants and brahmins as the zenith: by lovingkindness in acts of body, speech and mind, by keeping open house to them, by supplying their temporal needs. Thus ministered to as the zenith, renunciants and brahmins act in sympathy with the householder in six ways: they restrain him from evil, they exhort him to good, they love him with kindly good thoughts, they teach him what he has not heard, they correct and purify what he has heard, they reveal to him the way to a heavenly rebirth.

This text, then, places the lay person at the centre of a web of relationships and gives guidelines for how to ensure that these are mutually enriching. In these relationships, a person has no right to *expect* certain behaviour from others unless they are treated appropriately by him or her (cf. Dharmasiri, 1989: 18).

Marriage

Most of what is said above is self-explanatory, but it is worth considering the marriage relationship more deeply. In the above ideal, both
parties have a balanced range of mutual obligations. Elsewhere, the
Buddha, on asked to advise a man's daughters on how to conduct themselves in marriage, says that a woman should train herself as follows. (1)
Regarding her husband 'she gets up before him, retires after him, willingly does what he asks, is lovely (*mānapa-*) in her ways and gentle in
speech', not being one to anger him; (2) she honours all whom her
husband respects, whether relative, monk or brahmin; (3) she is deft and
nimble in her husband's home-crafts, such as weaving; (4) she watches
over servants and workpeople with care and kindness; and (5) she looks
after the wealth her husband brings home.[28] It is also said that a wife is
a man's 'best friend' (*paramā sakhā*) (*S.* 1.37), and in a *Jātaka* story, the
Bodhisattva, seeing how a king treats his wife in a shabby and selfish way,
advises her, in the king's presence, to leave him unless his behaviour
improves, for 'union without love is painful' (*J.* II.205).

While monogamy is the preferred and predominant marital model,
Buddhism has also tolerated polygamy, and sometimes polyandry. The
early texts refer to a variety of kinds of marriage existing in India at the
time of the origin of Buddhism, whether these were for love or money,
permanent or temporary,[29] and they not infrequently refer to problems
such as jealousy arising between co-wives (for example *Thig.* 216–17).
Until 1910, Thai kings had many wives. The great reformist ex-monk
King Mongkut (1851–68) had twenty-seven official wives as well as
around a hundred concubines or female servants (Thitsa, 1980: 6). In
Burma, at that time, King Mindon had fifty-three recognized wives and
many concubines. Today, in rural Thailand, marriages are almost
entirely monogamous. A few well-to-do farmers might have more than
one wife, and this is more common in urban areas. If a second wife is
taken, the first must give permission, and is senior to the second. Both
are usually provided with their own living quarters to manage indepen-
dently (Hanks and Hanks, 1963: 444). In 1935, an attempt was made to
register marriages formally and get rid of polygamy, but it had little
effect (H. E. Smith, 1979: 24–5). In pre-modern Japan, polygamy was a

---

[28] *A.* III.37–8; cf. *A.* IV.265–6 and *S.* 1.6.
[29] *Vin.* III.139–40; cf. *Asl.* 98. See Horner 1930: ch. 1; Murcott, 1991: 21–4 and ch. 6.

recognized form of marriage. The 1868 Meiji code recognized monogamy as the rule, however (Maykovich, 1979: 386). Polyandry, in the form of one woman marrying several brothers, has existed as one of the marriage forms recognized in areas of Tibetan culture (Norberg-Hodge, 1991: 55–8).

As referred to in early Buddhist texts, marriages were generally, but not always, arranged, and were rarely in conflict with a daughter's own wishes (Horner, 1930: 30). Indeed, the parents are seen as arranging a marriage out of love for their daughter (*A.* iv.265). In Burma and Thailand, marriages are usually arranged by a young woman's parents, taking her wishes into account. If permission is refused, elopements are often recognized (Hanks and Hanks, 1963: 434–5). In Japan, from at least 1600, arranged marriages were traditional. A woman was given to the family of the man she was to marry, so the family line could be continued by an heir. In line with Confucian-inspired values, individual wishes were ignored in the interests of the family.

As Buddhism has a monastic emphasis, marriage is not regarded as 'sacred', but as a secular contract of partnership. Thus in Burma, for example, marriages do not usually take place during the three-month 'rains' period of more intense monastic and lay practice. Nevertheless, in Thailand, a man is considered 'raw' before he has been a monk, but 'cooked' and mature enough to marry after a period as one: i.e. with the rough edges knocked off him (Hanks and Hanks, 1963: 441). Marriage services are not conducted by Buddhist monks, though they may be asked to bless the couple at or after the marriage. A Japanese Buddhist, then, would be traditionally married by Shintō rites, though today 'Christian' white weddings are becoming popular. In Thailand, marriage is a personal agreement backed up by public opinion and social pressure (H. E. Smith, 1979: 28). A clear change of status is entailed, though the woman does not change her name or wear a ring. The simplest marriage ceremony is a household one in which the spirits of ancestors are informed that a couple will be man and wife, so that they should not be offended when they have intercourse. More elaborate ceremonies are in three parts. First comes the official betrothal. Then comes the blessing of monks and relatives. This includes monks chanting and sprinkling sacralized water over the couple, and the couple making offerings to the family ancestors and using a single spoon to offer rice to the monks. In this way they do a shared act of generating karmic fruitfulness, so as to link some of their future moments of happiness. In connection with this, it is said that a husband and wife, if matched in faith, virtue, generosity and wisdom, will be reborn together after death if they wish (*A.* 11.61–2). After the monks depart, a ritual is performed by an elder and parents. The third phase is when a person reputed to be happily married gives a range of advice to the couple as they lie on the marriage bed, such as that the husband should be just and considerate, and the wife should be gentle and understanding (Terweil, 1979: 146–52). After marriage, the most common pattern is for the couple to live with the bride's parents until they can obtain a house of their own (Hanks and Hanks, 1963: 442).

While Buddhism has no objection in principle to divorce, it is not a frequent event, because of social pressures against it (see, for example, H. E. Smith, 1979: 28). Buddhism has traditionally held celibate monasticism in the highest regard, but it has also seen marriage and family life as highly suitable for those who cannot commit themselves to celibacy, and as an arena in which many worthwhile qualities are nurtured.

However, one form of Western Buddhism, the Friends of the Western Buddhist Order, has come to criticize strongly the nuclear family form of married life, seeing it as spiritually restricting and 'neurotic', reflecting a fragmentation in modern society (Subhuti, 1994: 162–64, 177). Couples, whether heterosexual or homosexual, are seen as sometimes bound together in projection and dependency, tending to make each a half-person (Subhuti, 1994: 173–4). The FWBO was founded by the monk Sangharakshita (Dennis Lingwood) in the UK in 1967, and is centred on the 'Western Buddhist Order', perhaps half of whose members live in single-sex communities. Members include both married people and those following a celibate, semi-monastic life. While at one stage of the FWBO's development, some Order members sought to 'keep clear of unhealthy attachment by happily enjoying a number of different sexual relationships' (Subhuti, 1983: 167), it is now emphasized that sexual desire should be gradually transcended (Subhuti, 1994: 171). Celibacy is not required, though, and the FWBO is now seeking to ensure that members living with their families do not feel marginalized.[30]

LOVINGKINDNESS AND COMPASSION

In the ethical development of a Buddhist, importance is attached to the development of heart-felt feelings of lovingkindness and compassion, as

---

[30] Vishvapani, 'Buddhism Distorted' in the *Guardian* newspaper, 11 November 1997.

outgrowths from generosity, as aids to deepening virtue, and as factors undercutting the attachment to 'I' (see Aronson, 1980). Lovingkindness (Pali *mettā*; Skt *maitrī*) and compassion (*karuṇā*) are the first two of a set of four qualities which also include empathetic or appreciative joy (*muditā*) and equanimity (Pali *upekkhā*; Skt *upekṣā*). These are known as the 'immeasurables' or as the 'divine abidings' (*brahma-vihāras*), for when developed to a high degree in meditation, they are said to make the mind 'immeasurable' and like the mind of the loving *brahmā* gods. Lovingkindness is the aspiration for the true happiness of any, and ultimately all, sentient beings, for all these are like oneself in liking happiness and disliking pain. It is the antidote to hatred and fear, and is to be distinguished from sentimentality. Compassion is the aspiration that beings be free from suffering, feeling for them; it is the antidote to cruelty, and is to be distinguished from sadness. Empathetic joy is joy at the joy of others, happiness at their good fortune; it is the antidote to envy and discontent and is to be distinguished from giddy merriment. Equanimity is an even-minded, unruffled serenity in the face of the ups and downs of life – one's own and that of others – and comes from developing the reflection that beings suffer and are happy in accordance with their own karma. It is the antidote to both aversion and approval, but should be distinguished from indifference (*Vism.* 318). It also ensures an impartiality towards all beings, so that lovingkindness etc. is felt towards all equally.

Lovingkindness is stressed in such verses as, 'Conquer anger by lovingkindness; conquer evil by good; conquer the stingy by giving; conquer the liar by truth' (*Dhp.* 223). It is also the theme of the *Karaṇīya-metta Sutta*, a popular Theravādin chant:

He who is skilled in good, and who wishes to attain that State of Peace [*Nirvāṇa*], should act thus: He should be able, upright, perfectly upright, of pleasant speech, gentle and humble. Contented, easy to support [as a monk], unbusy, with senses controlled, discreet, modest, not greedily attached to families [for alms]. He should not commit any slight wrong on account of which other wise men might censure him. [Then he would think:] 'May all beings be happy and secure, may they be happy-minded! Whatever living beings there are – feeble or strong, long, stout or medium, short, small or large, seen or unseen [i.e. ghosts, gods and hell-beings], those dwelling far or near, those who are born or those who await rebirth – may all beings, without exception, be happy-minded! Let none deceive another nor despise any person whatever in any place, in anger or ill-will let them not wish any suffering to each other.' Just as a mother would protect her only child at the risk of her own life, even so, let him cultivate a boundless heart towards all beings. Let his thoughts of boundless lovingkindness pervade the whole world: above, below and across without obstruction, without any hatred, without any enmity. Whether he stands, walks, sits or lies down, as long as he is awake, he should develop this mindfulness. This, they say, is divine abiding here. Not falling into wrong views, virtuous and endowed with insight, he gives up attachment for sense-desires. He will surely not come again to any womb [i.e. rebirth].(*Khp.* 8–9)

Thus is lovingkindness, benevolence or friendliness, ideally to be radiated to all beings, in the same strength as a mother's love for her only child – though without the sentimentality and possessiveness that may be part of mother-love. The height of this ideal is expressed in almost superhuman terms: 'Monks, as low-down thieves might carve one limb from limb with a double-handed saw, yet even then whoever entertained hate in his heart on that account would not be one who carried out my teaching' (*M.* 1.129). In this context, the ideal is that the Buddha's disciples should think, 'kindly and compassionate we will dwell, with a mind of lovingkindness, void of hatred', suffusing that person, and then the whole world, with such an 'immeasurable' mind. Such a mind cannot be ignited into anger, just as one cannot set fire to a river (*M.* 1.128). This ideal is seen in the *Khanti-vādi Jātaka*,[31] which tells of a past life of the Buddha in which he was developing the perfection of patience or forbearance (Pali *khanti*; Skt *kṣānti*), and was known as 'Teacher of Patience'. Here an arrogant king, annoyed to find his concubines listening to the teacher, seeks to test him and find out how deeply patience is established within him. The king therefore has him flogged with scourges of thorns, and when he says his patience is not skin deep but lies deep within his heart, he tests him further by having his hands and feet, and then his nose and ears, cut off. When the ascetic's patience is still unruffled, and he has no anger, but only compassion for the foolish king, the king kicks him over his heart and storms off (soon to die and be reborn in hell). Compassion for such assailants is appropriate, for their actions are such as to bring much suffering onto themselves, as future karmic results. Of course, to be able to live up to this ideal completely is only possible for one who has thoroughly seen through the delusion of the 'I am' conceit.

Such a degree of self-sacrificing forbearance is, for most people, a distant, yet inspiring ideal. Moreover, in many cases, firm, determined non-compliance with an oppressor would also be appropriate, ideally done in a way which is free from all anger and ill-will. While the doctrine of karma can sometimes degenerate into fatalistic acceptance, a more balanced approach is to do whatever one can to improve a situation, and

---

[31] *J.* III.39–43, and in the *Jātaka-mālā*: Khoroche, 1989: 193–204 and Conze, 1959: 26–30. Discussed by Gomez (1992: 32–3) and MacQueen, 1981.

Plate 3. A temple mural in Sri Lanka showing the Buddha in a past life as the 'Teacher of Patience', who could not be roused to anger even when cut to pieces with a sword.

only once something has happened might one patiently accept it as (perhaps) due to one's past karma.

Lovingkindness is seen as a potent force:

> Even three times a day to offer
> Three hundred cooking pots of food
> Does not match a portion of the merit
> Acquired by one instant of love. (*RPR.* 283)

In the *Jātaka* commentary (*J.* 1.199–200) is a story in which lovingkindness is described as a protective agent. The *Bodhisattva* and some companions are falsely accused of a crime and are sentenced to be trampled to death by an elephant. The *Bodhisattva* advises his companions to bear in mind the precepts, and develop lovingkindness equally to the slanderer, the sentencing king, the elephant and their own bodies. Consequently, a number of elephants refuse to go near them and flee. When asked if he has a drug or *mantra* to accomplish this, the *Bodhisattva* says that it has happened because he and his companions keep the precepts, develop lovingkindness, give gifts and perform public works, these being their *mantra* and *paritta*, or protective chant. The story also recalls that of the Buddha radiating lovingkindness to an elephant who has been enraged and sent charging down a road to kill him; the elephant comes to a halt and bows to the Buddha (*Vin.* 11.194–5).

Lovingkindness can be practised in daily life by kindly dealings with other living beings, and avoidance of anger: 'Whoso, as a rolling chariot, checks uprisen anger, him I call a charioteer; other folk merely hold the reins' (*Dhp.* 222). To develop it some way towards the ideal, chanting on lovingkindness will help, but a more powerful way of purifying the heart of hatred is the cultivation of the meditation on lovingkindness.

Theravāda Buddhism puts considerable emphasis on this meditation, and a thorough and inspiring treatment of it and the other 'immeasurables' can be found in Buddhaghosa's *Visuddhimagga*, chapter IX.[32] Before lovingkindness is to be meditatively directed to others, it must first be directed towards oneself (though Tibetans start with their mothers: see p. 127). To use a Christian phrase, if you are to 'love thy neighbour as thyself', but you dislike yourself in a variety of ways, you are not going to be doing your neighbour much of a favour. Self-dislike manifests itself in such forms as harping self-reproach, tension, agitation and holding oneself stiffly. Before spreading lovingkindness to others, a person must first come to feel what it is like to feel it for himself or herself, by coming

---

[32] And see Ñāṇamoli, 1958 and Dharmasiri, 1989: 42–52.

to accept himself or herself fully, 'warts and all'. This has nothing to do with complacency, but rather with a good-humoured but realistic attitude towards oneself. If a person can genuinely like and be friendly towards himself or herself in spite of his or her faults, then he or she can more fully accept other people with *their* faults. Thus, he or she neither complacently stays the same nor enters into hostile battle with his or her faults, but gradually melts these with the help of the warmth of lovingkindness, and becomes more open to others and their needs.

The lovingkindness meditation is generally done after another meditation has been used to put the mind in a calm state. The meditator seeks to generate positive aspirations for himself or herself and to experience feelings of loving, accepting patience towards himself or herself; the aim is to feel these as a warm joyful feeling in the chest. To help stimulate such feelings, certain appropriate words will be mentally said, such as: 'May I be well and happy, may my heart be pure and wholesome, may I be free from difficulties and troubles, mental or physical, may I be in harmony with those around me.' After a while, the meditator's mind may then be turned to aspects of himself or herself that he or she does not like, so as to send lovingkindness towards himself or herself as performer of such actions etc. Once lovingkindness has been experienced towards himself or herself, it is then generated towards certain selected others. These should be of the same sex, so as to prevent the lovingkindness from being tinged by feelings of sexual attraction. Firstly, the meditator visualizes the face of someone whom it is easy to like – a friend, or a respected teacher for whom he feels gratitude – and develops positive aspirations for that person, as already done for himself or herself. As the feeling of lovingkindness becomes more established, it is then focused on a neutral person, for example someone the meditator sees in the street every day but to whom he or she does not speak, and then towards someone for whom he or she feels hostility. In this way, he or she gradually moves from people whom it is easier to like to those it is most difficult, enabling the mind gradually to widen its circle of sympathies. The aim, here, is to break down the barriers which make the mind friendly towards only a limited selection of beings. On reflections used to undermine hatred and aid lovingkindness, see pp. 243–6. After lovingkindness has been experienced towards a hostile person, it is then radiated to all living beings in all directions. 'Radiating' is not just seen as a metaphor, for lovingkindness is seen as a mental force which can directly affect others.

In developing the meditation on compassion, Buddhaghosa outlines the following sequence. Firstly the mind dwells on an unfortunate, then on a friend, then on a neutral and then on a hostile person. Empathetic joy is first developed by reflecting on the happiness of a very dear friend, and then it is focused on a neutral, and then on a hostile person. Equanimity is developed firstly towards a neutral person, then towards a dear person, a great friend, a hostile person, and finally oneself. In each case, the meditator begins with the easiest task and progresses to the most difficult.

In the Theravādin tradition, the Buddha is recorded as having said: 'Whoever, monks, would wait upon me . . . honour me . . . follow my advice, he should wait upon the sick' (*Vin.* 1.302). Practical expressions of compassion – in both Theravāda and Mahāyāna lands – have traditionally included monks looking after orphans in monasteries, and the rich and rulers caring for the poor or setting up hospitals. In his *Rāja-parikathā-ratnamālā*, the great Mahāyāna master *Nāgārjuna* advised:

> Cause the blind, the sick, the lowly,
> The protectorless, the wretched
> And the crippled equally to attain
> Food and drink without interruption. (*RPR.* 320)

In modern times, famine-relief societies have been formed (Taiwan), as well as orphanages and 'banks' for donated eyes for use in transplants (Sri Lanka). Temples sometimes care for boys on probation (Sri Lanka: Southwold, 1983: 80), or help cure heroin addicts (Thailand), and compassionate deeds are also directed towards animals. In Taiwan, the nun Cheng Yen has founded the Tzu Chi Foundation, with around 3 million followers, which runs a large programme of medical services in the country and provides emergency relief overseas (Ching, 1995). Richard Hayes tells a touching story of the monk Giac Duc. When the Americans were at the point of being defeated at the end of the Vietnam War, the monk was among a large group of people whom they sought to airlift to safety. Helicopters had to make repeated journeys to do this, but the monk ensured that he was the last one to be rescued. At one point, Buddhists and Christians were being taken out on different days, and he always claimed to belong to the group that was not being taken out that day![33]

SOCIAL ETHICS

Social cohesion and equality

Buddhism greatly values social harmony and cohesion, as seen in the value placed on the four 'foundations of social unity' (Pali *saṅgaha-vatthus*; Skt *saṃgraha-vastus*), as found in the *Sigālovāda Sutta*:

[33] 'Lousy Dharma Practice' posting to 'Buddhist' Internet discussion forum, 30 August 1995.

giving (*dāna*);

kindly speech (Pali *piya-vācā*; Skt *priyavākya*);

helpful action (Pali *attha-cariyā*; Skt *tathārthacaryā*);

impartial treatment and equal participation (Pali *samānattatā*; Skt *samānārthatā*), or evenmindedness to pleasure and pain (Skt *samāna-sukha-duḥkhatā*).[34]

The good of self and others is seen as inter-twined:

> How, monks, guarding oneself, does one guard others? By practice, by develop-ment, by continuous exercise . . . And how, monks, guarding others, does one guard oneself? By tolerance, by nonviolence, by having a mind full of loving-kindness, by care. (*S.* v.169)

As expressed by a noted Thai scholar monk:

> The most basic point to be made about Buddhist social ethics is that in keeping with the Buddhist doctrine of dependent co-arising [Conditioned Arising], individual betterment and perfection on the one hand and the social good on the other are fundamentally interrelated and interdependent. (Rājavaramuni, 1990: 31)

> Friendship is thus the model for social harmony in the mundane sphere and the model for spiritual encouragement of the laity by the monks in the trans-mundane sphere. We might conclude that in Buddhist ethics everyone is a friend, meaning that everyone should be treated as a friend. (Rājavaramuni, 1990: 36)

A society of self-disciplined, self-reliant people will be peaceful, and in turn support individual growth and development (Rājavaramuni, 1990: 36). In this process, the importance of associating with good people is often stressed (see p. 97), so that good qualities are stimulated, reinforced and spread.[35]

As regards social equality, the Buddha was critical of Brahmanical claims, associated with the system of four supposedly divinely ordained social classes – the *varṇa*s of the so-called 'caste system' – that certain people were superior or inferior by birth.[36] He taught:

> Not by birth does one become an outcaste, not by birth does one become a brahmin. By (one's) action one becomes an outcaste, by (one's) action one becomes a brahmin. (*Sn.* 136)

---

[34] *D.* III.152, 232; *A.* II.32, 248; *A.* IV.218, 363; *Mvs.* II.395; cf. Rājavaramuni, 1990: 36, 40. See Payutto, 1993: 69–71 for Thai Buddhism and Cleary, 1986: 116–20 for Sōtō Zen Buddhism.

[35] See e.g. *S.* v.28; *Sn.* 259; and see Rājavaramuni, 1990: 36.

[36] E.g. at *D.* I.119, 199; *D.* III.81; *M.* II.125–33, 147–57, 178–96. See Krishan, 1986 for further discus-sion.

Thus moral and spiritual development makes one a 'brahmin' – which term is used here in the sense of a truly noble spiritual person, an *Arahat* – while breaking the precepts lowers the respect in which others hold one. On ordination, differences of social background are to be ignored, just as waters entering the sea from different rivers all equally become 'sea-water'. Thus respect should be paid between monks according to length of time in the *Saṅgha*, irrespective of social background. Accordingly, when six ex-princes and their servant Upāli came to be ordained, the ex-princes asked that the Buddha ordain the servant first, so that he would be slightly senior to them, so helping to undermine their previously proud nature (*Vin.* II.183). Moreover, the Buddha often criticized brahmin claims to inherent supremacy (for example *M.* II.83–90). He argued that the human race was one species, not four (*Sn.* 594–656; *M.* II.196–7), that the social classes observable in society were not eternal, but had gradually evolved (*D.* III.93–5), that a person was designated as a farmer, trader, thief, Brahmanical priestly celebrant or king by the kind of work he did (*Sn.* 612–19), and that people of the four classes of Indian society (brahmins, warrior-nobles, farmers/tradespeople, and servants) were equally capable of good and bad action, and would reap karmic results accordingly. He argued that, just as, in battle, a king prefers a nonnoble who is skilled in fighting skills to a 'noble' without such skills, gifts to a virtuous monk are of great fruit, no matter from what class he originally came (*S.* 1.98–9). When a monk points out to a king that a rich member of any of the four classes could have a member of any class as a servant, the king says: 'this being so, these four classes are exactly the same; I do not see any difference between them in this respect' (*M.* II.89).

While the Buddha thus criticized the developing class/caste system, he was no social revolutionary advocating the abolishment of all social divisions. He acknowledged the existence of these, but saw them as changeable and conventional, not divinely ordained, as in Brahmanism: 'what has been designated name and clan in the world . . . has arisen by common consent' (*Sn.* 648). Coming from a noble family himself, he tended to list the nobles as the first of the four classes, rather than the brahmins. He did not deny that the social class people were born into was due to their past karma. Nevertheless, he did not teach that people had an obligation to remain within the limitations of their parents' class (as in Brahmanism/Hinduism), if their talents and energy led elsewhere. For nineteenth-century Burma, Fielding Hall remarks, 'There was, and is, absolutely no aristocracy of any kind at all. The Burmese are a community of equals, in a sense that has probably never been known elsewhere'

(1902: 54). Neighbouring Thailand has had a class of royalty and nobility, but of small proportions, because of a uniquely Thai feature: in each generation, the offspring of nobility are reduced in rank by one grade.

As Buddhism spread beyond India, it tended to live with whatever social class system it met with. In Sri Lanka, on account of the influence of Hindus in nearby India, a sort of mild caste system developed. This mainly concerns those whom a person can eat with or marry, but it also, unfortunately, led to different monastic fraternities recruiting from different castes (Gombrich, 1971a: 294–317). It has also been the case that, in a number of Buddhist societies, such people as slaughterers, and, sometimes, fishermen, have been treated as social outcastes, because of their unwholesome way of life.

Engaged Buddhism

In the modern world, a number of Buddhists have come to advocate what has been called 'Engaged Buddhism', a term coined in 1963 by the Vietnamese Zen monk Thich Nhat Hanh, at a time when war was ravaging his country.[37] This draws on traditional Buddhist ethical and social teachings, but applies them in a more activist way than has sometimes been the case in the past, so as to improve society. Christopher Queen holds that 'the most distinctive shift of thinking in socially engaged Buddhism is from a transmundane ... to a mundane liberation', so as to focus on 'the causes, varieties and remedies of worldly suffering and oppression' through the reform of social and political conditions, as well as of the mind (Queen, 1996: 11). The roots of this change of emphasis lie in the meeting of Buddhism with Western values in the colonial era, especially in Sri Lanka from the late nineteenth century (Queen, 1996: 20–1). Here Buddhists responded to Protestant Christian domination, and criticisms of Buddhist social passivity, by a Buddhist resurgence. This borrowed some of the characteristics of the Christianity it was fighting against, so that it developed features that have led some to call it 'Protestant Buddhism', being both reformist and assigning a greater role to the laity. Social activist Buddhists in Asia often claim that they are simply reviving the best features of Buddhism from the pre-colonial era, before the colonial era cut back the social outreach of monks. While there is an element of truth in this, they are also developing new modes of Buddhism in response to the modern world, and in addition are

---

[37] Queen, 1996: 34. On 'Engaged Buddhism', see Queen and King, 1996 and Eppsteiner, 1988.

influencing, and being influenced by, some Western Buddhists in their emphasis on 'Engaged Buddhism'. This can be seen, for example, in the 'Order of Interbeing' that Nhat Hanh, now resident in France, has formed. Its members follow fourteen precepts formulated by him, some of which are:

Do not avoid contact with suffering or close your eyes before suffering . . .
Do not accumulate wealth while millions are hungry . . . Live simply . . .
Do not kill. Do not let others kill. Find whatever means possible to protect life and prevent war. (Eppsteiner, 1988: 150–2)

Political ideals

A number of texts outline an ideal for a Buddhist ruler to follow so as to ensure a peaceful and harmonious society, free of poverty (cf. Saddhatissa, 1970: 149–64). Nothing is said on the duty of subjects towards their ruler, but Buddhism has generally not encouraged rebellions, on account of its emphasis on non-violence.

The Buddha admired some of the tribal republics of his day. At one time, he said that the Vajjian republic would flourish if the people continued to:

i) 'hold regular and frequent assemblies'.
ii) 'meet in harmony, break up in harmony, and carry out business in harmony'.
iii) 'not authorise what has not been authorised, but proceed according to what has been authorised by their ancient tradition'.
iv) 'honour, respect, revere and salute the elders among them, and consider them worth listening to'.
v) 'not forcibly abduct others' wives and daughters and compel them to live with them'.
vi) 'honour, respect, revere and salute the Vajjian shrines at home and abroad, not withdrawing the proper support made and given before'.
vii) 'make proper provision for the safety of *Arahats*, so that such *Arahats* may come in future to live there, and those already there may dwell in comfort' (*D.* II.74–5).

One can see these as the principles of respecting collective decision-making, concord, tradition, elders, women, religion, and holy men and women. The importance of these social principles was such that he saw them, or adapted versions of them, as ensuring the flourishing of the monastic *Saṅgha*. Nevertheless, the Buddha could see that the days of the tribal republics were numbered, as they were gradually being swallowed up by new, expanding kingdoms. Indeed, he saw the falling away from the above principles as the thing that would allow them to be over-whelmed by these kingdoms.

The Buddha also had views on kingship: the role of a king was to serve his people by ensuring order and prosperity for them. In the *Aggañña Sutta* (*D.* II.80–98), the Buddha describes the origins of human society as part of a process of moral decline from relatively ideal conditions at the start of a cycle of world-evolution (Fenn, 1996: 111–17). Here, the first king is said to have been chosen by his people – as the most handsome, pleasant and capable – to punish wrong-doers, in return for a share of the people's rice (*D.* III.92). This can be seen as an early version of what Western political philosophers call the 'social-contract' theory of king-ship. The sixth century writer Candrakīti argues against the Hindu idea of divine kingship thus:

The first king was created by his own action and the people, not by the Almighty One. A king is the same as a common person in lineage and in nature.[38]

The Buddha's advice on how best to run society was often couched in images of ideal legendary rulers of the past known as *Cakkavatti* (Pali; Skt *Cakravartin*), or 'Wheel-turning' kings, whose righteous, compassionate rule, in accordance with *Dhamma*, is said to have caused a divine wheel to appear in the sky. Though not yet a Buddha, such a type of person is seen as a political equivalent of a Buddha: at birth, his body has the same 'thirty-two characteristics of a great man' as one who will become a Buddha (*D.* III.142–79), and at death, his corpse and that of a Buddha should be treated in the same way (*D.* II.141). In the *Cakkavatti-sīhanāda Sutta* ('The Lion's Roar on the *Cakkavatti*', *D.* III.58–79),[39] the duties of such a ruler are said to be passed on from father to son. They are that he should revere *Dhamma* (here meaning something like moral norms and compassionate justice) and rule only in accordance with it. He should look after all his people, including monks and brahmins, and also animals and birds. He should prevent crime and give to those in need. Finally, he should advise good monks and brahmins if they come to ask his advice on what are wholesome or unwholesome actions (*D.* III.61). Such rulers were seen as successively having become world emperors, not by force of arms, but by other peoples coming to appreciate their ideals, such as following the five precepts (*D.* III.63). Thus Gokhale says

[38] *Ṭīkā on Āryadeva's Bodhisattva-yogācāra-catuḥśataka*, cited by Jamspal in *ASP.* 55.
[39] See Saddhatissa, 1970: 154–7, 159–60. Reynolds and Reynolds, 1982: 135–72 gives a developed Theravāda view on *Cakkavattis*. See *ASP.* 182–3 for the view of a text influential in Tibetan Buddhism.

that the key contribution of Buddhism to Indian political theory was 'the acceptance of a higher morality as the guiding spirit behind the state'.[40]

In the *Jātaka* stories, the *Bodhisattva* teaches the ten duties of a true king (*rāja-dhammas*): generosity, moral virtue, self-sacrifice, honesty and integrity, gentleness, self-control, non-anger, non-injury, forbearance and non-opposition/uprightness.[41] Elsewhere, the god Serī says that in the past he had been a generous king who gave to monks and brahmins, paupers and cripples, wayfarers and beggars, using half his revenue from outlying provinces for this (*S.* 1.57–9). In the *Mahā-vastu* (*Mvs.* 1.274–7), a text of the Lokottaravādin early school, advice to a king includes: do not fall under the power of anger; be impartial in arbitrating disputes; do not be indulgent in sensual pleasures; admit large bodies of immigrants; favour the poor and protect the rich; cultivate ties of friendship with neighbouring kings; act justly; and be circumspect, and diligent in the care of the treasury and granary.

It is said that when kings act unrighteously (*adhammika*), this bad example spreads through the various groups of their people. Hence the sun and moon, and then the stars, 'go wrong in their course'; hence 'days and nights, months and fortnights, seasons and years are out of joint; the winds blow wrong, out of season. Thus the gods are annoyed [commentary: particularly tree-gods, who lose their homes]. This being so, the sky-god does not bestow sufficient rain.' Thus crops are poor and the humans who live on them are weak and short-lived (*A.* II.74–6). That is, a king is seen to have a responsibility to maintain, through his actions and influence, the moral fabric of society and nature (cf. Payutto, 1993: 63–8). Stanley Tambiah refers to this as the 'multiplier-effect' of kingship on the conduct of the rest of society (1976: 50), from which he infers that it is acceptable to unseat an unworthy king. In one *Jātaka* story (*J.* III.502–14), a king who is a thief is overthrown. A bad king has the responsibility to reform himself through reflecting on fear of notoriety and of bad karmic results, and should guard against becoming wicked by periodically consulting wise monks and brahmins as to what is virtuous and unvirtuous, and on the duties of rulers (*ASP.* 196).

In Buddhist history, the Indian emperor Asoka (c. 268–239 BCE) is particularly revered as a great example of a Buddhist ruler who sought to live up to the *Cakkavatti* ideal, though he never actually claimed to be

---

[40] Gokhale, 1966: 22. See Tambiah 1976: 9–53 on early Buddhist ideas on kingship, as contrasted with Hindu ones, with pp. 39–53 on the *Cakkavatti* ideal. On the latter, see also Obeyesekere and Reynolds, 1972, which also deals with ideas of kingship and social order in Sri Lanka.

[41] E.g. *J.* III.274, *J.* v.378, and see Eppsteiner, 1988: 103–9, 107–8.

one himself.[42] The Magadhan empire, which he inherited, was the largest India was to see until its conquest by the British, and included most of modern India except the far south. An important source of knowledge on Asoka is the many edicts which he had published by having them carved on rocks and stone pillars.[43] In the Sixth Rock Edict, he expressed his aspiration thus:

No task is more important to me than promoting the well-being of all the people. Such work as I accomplish contributes to discharging the debt I owe to all living creatures to make them happy in this world and to help them attain heaven in the next. (Nikam and McKeon, 1959: 38)

Asoka inaugurated various public works: wells, rest-houses, and trees for both shade and fruit for travellers; and medical herbs and roots for humans and animals. Such measures were also fostered in Indian regions beyond his actual empire, by what must have been early 'foreign aid' measures (Nikam and McKeon, 1959: 64–5). His concern for justice is seen in his setting up a 'Ministry of *Dhamma*', through which he sought to prevent wrongful imprisonment and punishment, to free prisoners when appropriate, and to aid prisoners' families if they were in need (Nikam and McKeon, 1959: 58–63). He exhorted his people to live by moral norms, particularly non-violence, himself abandoning his forebears' custom of violent expansion of their realm. He also gave up hunting, gradually became vegetarian, and passed various animal welfare laws. Though he was personally a Buddhist, and ruled in accordance with Buddhist morality, he did not make Buddhism the state religion, and urged mutual religious tolerance and respect. He supported not only Buddhist monks and nuns, but also brahmin priests, Jain monks and nuns, and ascetics of other religious sects. His Twelfth Rock Edict says:

King Priyadarśī honors men of all faiths, members of religious orders and laymen alike, with gifts and various marks of esteem. Yet he does not value either gifts or honors as much as growth in the qualities essential to religion in men of all faiths.

This growth may take many forms, but its root is in guarding one's speech to avoid extolling one's own faith and disparaging the faith of others improperly or, when the occasion is appropriate, immoderately.

The faiths of others all deserve to be honored for one reason or another. By honoring them, one exalts one's own faith and at the same time performs a

---

[42] He came to be seen as a *Cakkavatti*, though (Jamspal, in *ASP.* 56, citing *Divyāvadāna*, Vaidya edition, 1959, p. 239). On Asoka, see: Ling, 1973: 151–74; Basham, 1982; Swearer, 1995: 64–6 and Kraft, 1992: 64–6. For the later Theravāda view of Asoka, see: Reynolds and Reynolds, 1982: 172–89.   [43] See Nikam and McKeon, 1959 and Dhammika, 1993.

service to the faith of others. By acting otherwise, one injures one's own faith and also does disservice to that of others. For if a man extols his own faith and disparages another because of devotion to his own and because he wants to glorify it, he seriously injures his own faith.

Therefore concord alone is commendable, for through concord men may learn and respect the conception of Dharma accepted by others.

King Priyadarśī desires men of all faiths to know each other's doctrines and to acquire sound doctrines. (Nikam and McKeon, 1959: 51–2)

To varying extents, many Buddhist rulers have sought to follow Asoka's example, or to imitate and invoke the model of king as *Bodhisattva*, *Cakkavatti* and *Dhamma*-king, charged with revival, protection and promotion of Buddhism. Sometimes, though, they only went in for a 'self-serving proclamation' to this effect (Tambiah, 1976: 226). In Sri Lanka, the king came to be seen, from at least the tenth century, as the lay head of Buddhism, its protector, and as a *Bodhisattva*, with the idea that 'The king is a *bodhisattva* on whom the sangha bestows kingship in order that he may defend the bowl and robe' (Tambiah, 1976: 97). Kings of the Pagan (1084–1167) period in Burma came to see themselves as *Cakkavatti*s and *Bodhisattva*s (Tambiah, 1976: 81). In Thailand too, in Sukhothai and Ayutthaya times (fourteenth to eighteenth centuries), and into the nineteenth century, kings were seen in these terms and sometimes identified themselves with Metteyya, who will be the next Buddha on earth (Tambiah, 1976: 96–7). They have also been expected to follow the above ten duties of a king and the twelve duties of the *Cakkavatti*.[44] Nevertheless, as elsewhere:

The heads of kings rolled frequently because succession rules were vague, rebellions endemic, the overall political scaffolding fragile, and the territorial limits expanding and contracting with the military fortunes of the ruler, his subordinate chiefs, and his rivals. (Tambiah, 1976: 482)

Where Buddhism has been the dominant religion:

Kingship as the crux of order in society provides the conditions and the context for the survival of the *sasana* (religion). They need each other: religion in being supported by an ordered and prosperous society is able to act as a 'field of merit [karmic fruitfulness]' in which merit making can be enacted and its fruits enjoyed, while the king as the foremost merit maker needs the sangha to make and realize his merit and fulfil his kingship. (Tambiah, 1976: 41)

The dominant model of society, especially in lands of Southern Buddhism, has thus been a triangular one with the king supporting and

---

[44] See *D.* III.61 with *D. A.* III.46, and Rājavaramuni, 1990: 38–9.

being advised by the *Saṅgha*, the *Saṅgha* drawing members from and
being supported by the people, and the people acquiescing in the rule of
a king provided he was not too immoral (see Ling, 1973). In modern
times, though, we see Buddhist ideas being drawn on to support socialism in Burma, capitalism in Thailand and Communism in China and
Laos.

Over the ages, Buddhist rulers have periodically taken note of the
advice of leading Buddhist monks. While monks are generally expected
to keep aloof from overt political activity, this is not always the case. In
modern times, in Tibet, monks and nuns have been active in demonstrations against the Chinese Communist colonization of the country. In
Burma, monks have sometimes led the populace in demonstrations
against the present corrupt military regime. In Sri Lanka, monks have
publicly voiced their allegiance to particular political parties – though
the laity often see this as inappropriate for them. In Thailand, monks
have co-operated in government-inspired community development projects in poorer regions, partly as a foil to the appeal of Communism in
such regions, particularly in the 1960s and 1970s. In Japan, the Sōka
Gakkai lay religious movement (see p. 146) developed a political wing in
1964, in line with Nichiren's ideal of the union of politics and religion.
The political wing is known as the Kōmei-tō, or 'Clean Government'
Party, and has become the third or fourth largest in the Japanese
Parliament. While it severed formal links with the movement in 1970, it
remains influenced by it, and attracts a similar membership (Metraux,
1996: 385–8).

'Human rights' and Buddhism

A consideration of politics leads on to reflection on the idea of 'human
rights': inalienable, fundamental rights to be treated in certain ways (cf.
pp. 36–7), usually cited in contexts in which a government or quasi-gov-
ernment is seen as abusing its citizens. What are the limits of a state's
power over its citizens? A good place to start in a Buddhist consideration
of this is with the *Aggañña Sutta*'s simple social-contract model of kingship (see p. 114): this clearly gives a ruler no right to abuse the people he
rules, for the very basis of his legitimacy is that he should benefit them.

To say that someone has a 'right' means that others have a 'duty' to
treat a person in a particular way. If the 'right' is a circumscribed one
based on contract and transactions, such as a right to have a loan repaid
by someone who borrows from one, then the duty falls on the borrower.

Nevertheless, the state then has a duty to make the borrower carry out this duty if he or she fails to do so of his or her own accord, and there can be said to be an abstract 'right' that anyone who lends things should have them returned by the borrower (unless he or she abrogates this right). In such a case, explicit talk of a 'right' does not arise until the normal business of human relationships breaks down. This applies equally to 'human rights', but these rights are not seen as circumscribed but as based on the fact that one is a living human being. One is thus seen as having a 'right' to such things as life, liberty, and not to be tortured. The UN Declaration of Human Rights lists a variety of other rights which spell out the implications of these, and specifies subsidiary rights to such things as education and health care. Such 'universal rights' are, in effect, 'universal duties' incumbent on any person *not* to treat other humans in certain negative ways; and 'positive rights' to things like education are duties incumbent on governments to provide what they can for people, or ensure that others make it available.

It is true that Buddhism does not usually talk in terms of 'rights', which is a term that arose from the Western philosophical tradition. That does not mean, however, that Buddhists cannot agree with the substance of what is expressed in 'human rights' language. Buddhists are sometimes unhappy using the language of 'rights' as they may associate it with people 'demanding their rights' in an aggressive, self-centred way, and may question whether talk of 'inalienable rights' implies some unchanging, essential Self that 'has' these, which is out of accord with Buddhism's teaching on the nature of selfhood. Nevertheless, as rights imply duties, Buddhists are happier talking directly about the duties themselves: about 'universal duties', or, to use a phrase much used by the Dalai Lama, 'universal responsibilities' (see, for example, Piburn, 1990: 111–15), rather than 'universal rights'. Moreover, while aggressively *demanding* rights is not in tune with the spirit of Buddhism, being calmly firm and determined in upholding rights, particularly of other people, is so. On the matter of what 'has' the rights, the raising of the not-Self teaching is actually a red herring: for if a permanent Self were the 'owner' of rights, it would not have any use for them, as a truly permanent Self would be invulnerable and could never be harmed! Thus one can simply say that living, changing, vulnerable beings are, conventionally, the 'owners' of rights, with the locus of their value seen as their ability to suffer, their very vulnerability, and their potential for enlightenment, referred to in Mahāyāna Buddhism as the 'Buddha-nature', and in Theravāda Buddhism as the 'brightly shining mind' (see p. 35).

The five precepts imply a code of behaviour and responsibility for the right treatment of others, whether these be humans or animals. A basic principle of Buddhist ethics is that all beings are alike in disliking pain and in wanting to be happy, so that we should not inflict on another being what we would not like done to ourselves (see p. 33). We have a duty to others to respect their interests, and a duty to ourselves not to coarsen ourselves by abusing others.

Having said the above, one may ask whether, as Buddhists sometimes choose not to 'take' all five precepts (see pp. 82–3), one can still see the primary content of the precepts as universally binding, even on those, Buddhist or otherwise, who do not formally 'take' them. One can perhaps omit the one on drinking alcohol as a special case, as this is sometimes not seen as concerning what is 'reprehensible by nature', i.e. wrong in itself. Those who choose not to 'take' a particular precept do so because they see precepts as weighty vows. This does not mean that they do not regard their substance as morally binding; it is simply that they do not wish it to be the case that, if they act out of accord with a precept, they also break a weighty vow. As for non-Buddhists, one can say that the key emphases of the precepts encode moral teachings that are shared in all societies.

The duties so far referred to are duties owed to any sentient being, though Buddhism would agree that we owe more to other humans because of the great value and potential of those who have attained a 'precious human rebirth' (see p. 30). We also have a range of responsibilities and duties to our parents and children, secular and religious teachers and pupils, spouses, friends, employees and employers (see pp. 98–100). While these can be seen as universal duties, to *whom* they are owed depends on who is in these particular relationships to us. However, Buddhism teaches that it is unlikely that any being we meet has not been a close relative or friend in some past life (see p. 29), so beyond the people in this life to whom we have specific duties, such duties in the end are owed to all humans and animals!

'Human rights' can be 'negative' ones – to freedom *from* something, such as arbitrary arrest – or 'positive' ones, *to* something, such as an adequate education. The first kind of rights are negated by being *abused*, and the second by being *neglected*. One can certainly make a case for the first type of human rights being the primary ones, and Buddhism is strong in this area because of its emphasis on non-harming. When it comes to the rights to positive benefits, Buddhism's emphasis is somewhat less strong, seeing such things less as *entitlements* and more as something that it is good for others to choose to provide. Nevertheless, its political ideals, as outlined above, and in chapter 5, clearly see governments as having key responsibilities to look after their people.

In October 1995, the Internet *Journal of Buddhist Ethics* held a two-week on-line conference on Buddhism and human rights.[45] At the end of this, the following statement, in which I had a hand, was produced:

Declaration of Interdependence
Preamble
Those who have the good fortune to have a 'rare and precious human rebirth', with all its potential for awareness, sensitivity, and freedom, have a duty not to abuse the rights of others to partake of the possibilities of moral and spiritual flourishing offered by human existence. Such flourishing is only possible when certain conditions relating to physical existence and social freedom are maintained. Human beings, furthermore, have an obligation to treat other forms of life with the respect commensurate with their natures.

To repress our basic sympathy by abusing other sentient beings, human or otherwise, cripples our own potential, and increases the amount of suffering in the world for both others and ourselves. The doctrine of Conditioned Arising shows that our lives are intertwined, and abusing others can only be done when we are blind to this fact. As vulnerable beings in a conditioned world, our mutual dependency indicates that whatever can be done to reduce suffering in the world should be done.

The Buddhist teaching that we lack an inherently existing Self (*anatta*) shows that suffering does not really 'belong' to anyone. It arises, in the life-stream of various sentient beings. To try and reduce it in 'my' stream at the expense of increasing it in another life-stream is folly, both because this will in fact bring more suffering back to me (karma), and because it depends on the deluded notion that 'I' am an inviolable entity that is not dependent and can treat others as if only *they* are limited and conditioned.

Whereas in its teachings Buddhism recognizes:
1. The interdependency of all form of life and the reciprocal obligations which arise from it, such as the duty to repay the kindness of those who in previous lives may have been our parents, relatives and friends;
2. The need for universal compassion for sentient beings who are all alike in that they dislike pain and wish for happiness;
3. The inalienable dignity which living creatures possess by virtue of their capacity to achieve enlightenment in this life or in the future,

The Conference affirms:
1. Every human being should be treated *humanely* both by other individuals and governments in keeping with the Buddhist commitment to non-violence (*ahiṃsā*) and respect for life.

---

[45] The papers used as the basis for discussion in this are published as Keown, Prebish and Husted, 1998. See also Keown, 1995b; Inada, 1995; and papers by Unno and Thurman in Rouner, 1988.

2. Every human being must be treated *equally* and without discrimination on grounds of race, nationality, religion, sex, color, age, mental ability, or political views.
3. Human beings have obligations to other sentient beings and to the environment that all depend on for life and flourishing, now and in the future. Accordingly, humans have an obligation to present and future generations to protect the environment they share with other sentient beings, and to avoid causing direct or indirect harm to other forms of sentient life.

CONCLUSION

Buddhist values are rooted in the project of overcoming greed/attachment, hatred and delusion, which are seen as the roots of unwholesome actions and the key causes of suffering. Greed is to be overcome by generosity and sharing, combined with restraint from theft and cheating, with subtler forms of attachment overcome by monastic training and meditative training. Hatred and anger are to be dealt with by restraint from behaviour harming others, cultivation of lovingkindness and compassion, and insight into the distorted vision that makes hatred possible. Delusion is to be overcome by avoiding intoxication, and cultivating the mental clarity that allows one to see things directly 'as they really are'. This project begins with moral virtue, but also entails the other aspects of the Buddhist path: meditative development and the cultivation of insight. It has implications for individual conduct as well as inter-personal relationships and social ethics.

CHAPTER 3

Mahāyāna emphases and adaptations

May the pain of every living creature be completely cleared away
Bodhi-caryāvatāra III.7

THE PATH OF THE *BODHISATTVA*

The Mahāyāna is focused on the *Bodhisattva* (Skt; Pali *Bodhisatta*), or Being-for-Enlightenment: one on the path to perfect Buddhahood, whose task is to help beings compassionately while maturing his or her own wisdom. In early Buddhism and still in the Theravāda school, a *Bodhisattva* was seen as a rare heroic figure who, by a longer, more compassion-orientated route than that leading to Arahatship, sought to become eventually a full and perfect Buddha. Such a Buddha is one who brings benefit to countless beings by immense insight which rediscovers liberating truth when it had been lost after being taught by another Buddha many thousands of years previously. In the Mahāyāna, though, *many* are urged to take the long path of the *Bodhisattva*, which is spelt out in considerable detail. The Noble Eightfold Path of 'disciples' (Skt *śrāvaka*s) of a perfect Buddha, directed at Arahatship, was still respected, but was seen to be in need of supplementing by the *Bodhisattva*-path to perfect Buddhahood, now exalted into the state of a heavenly saviour-being. While wisdom was a key part of the Eightfold Path, and itself encompassed compassion (see pp. 37–8), the Mahāyāna developed a more philosophically sophisticated account of it, and made compassion an equal complementary virtue which was the motivation of the whole path. Mahāyāna texts sometimes criticize *śrāvaka*s as concerned only with their own liberation: rather an unfair caricature of the discipline of the Noble Eightfold Path, which contains many other-regarding virtues. Nevertheless, even the Theravāda acknowledges that aiming at the deliverance of all beings is more perfectly virtuous than working for one's own deliverance (*Vism.* 13). It simply feels, though, that while the Buddha's teachings remain in the world, only a few need to take this path, for the benefit of future generations. The Mahāyāna emphasizes, though, that in the vast universe, there is always a need for more Buddhas.

Compassion and wisdom in the Mahāyāna

The spirit of Mahāyāna compassion (*karuṇā*), the root-motivation of the *Bodhisattva*, is well expressed in Śāntideva's *Bodhi-caryāvatāra*:

> Thus by the virtue collected through all that I have done, may the pain of every living creature be completely cleared away.
> May I be the doctor and the medicine and may I be the nurse for all sick beings in the world until everyone is healed.
> May a rain of food and drink descend to clear away the pain of thirst and hunger, and during the aeon of famine may I myself change into food and drink.
> May I be a protector for those without one, and a guide to all travellers on the way; may I be a bridge, a boat and a ship for all those who wish to cross (the water).   (*Bca.* III.7–9, 18)

Thus the *Bodhisattva* is resolute in his efforts to save all, using his roots of good to save those that have no such roots (*Ss.* 258). Śāntideva also cites the *Ratnamegha* as saying that the *Bodhisattva* should reflect, when he opens a door, 'May I open for all beings the door of the good way to *Nirvāṇa*'; when he sits down, 'May I make all beings sit in the seat of wisdom' (*Ss.* 307), etc.

The *Bodhisattva*'s compassion aids wisdom's undercutting of self-centredness, and his or her developing wisdom (Skt *prajñā*; Pali *paññā*) ensures that compassionate action is appropriate, effective, and not covertly self-seeking. The Mahāyāna view of wisdom builds on the idea of all things as being 'not-Self' or 'empty' of Self (see p. 36). It emphasizes not only that no permanent, substantial Self can be found to exist, but that the changing mental and physical processes – *dharmas* (Skt; Pali *dhammas*) – that make up the world and persons are devoid of any inherent nature or separate essence. Like the early schools, the Mahāyāna says that a *dharma* could only arise because other *dharmas* which conditioned it arise: the principle of Conditioned Arising (see p. 33). It goes on to argue, though, that this means that the nature of any *dharma*, for example consciousness, is not something belonging to it as an essence, but is simply the result of the way certain conditions come together. Nothing exists absolutely, with an absolute nature; 'things' only arise in a mutually conditioning network of processes. A key feature of each process, and the network as a whole, is its 'emptiness' (*śūnyatā*): its lack of inherent, substantial existence. This is also expressed by saying that all the *dharmas* lack any nature of their own except this shared quality of emptiness: the 'sameness' of all *dharmas*. Moreover, the mysterious quality of emptiness is also equated with *Nirvāṇa*, for this is empty of the possibility of being adequately described in words, and empty of anything to do with the delusion of 'I am' (Harvey, 1990a: 95–104; Williams 1989: 37–76). The above means, for example, that a *Bodhisattva* can rub shoulders with wrong-doers, to 'reach' them and draw them towards the good, as he knows that their bad characteristics are not inherent realities.

Śāntideva persuasively draws on such ideas to argue that indifference to the suffering of 'others' is as absurd as indifference to one's 'own' suffering. In his *Śikṣā-samuccaya*, he argues that 'self' and 'other' are relative terms, like 'this bank' and 'the further bank' of a river: neither bank is, of itself, the 'further' bank. If one says that one should not protect another from pain, as it does not hurt oneself, then why does one seek to avert pain, or to bring positive benefit to, 'oneself' later in this life or in future lives? One will not be unchangingly *the same* being then, given that beings gradually change both within and between lives (*Ss.* 315). Body and mind consist of a changing series of states. We each, by habit, call these 'I', but why not use this notion as regards 'other' beings? Thus one should strive to prevent suffering in any being (*Ss.* 316). Why bring suffering on oneself by feeling compassion for others? But compassion does not bring pain; it makes possible joy based on awareness of others' being delivered from suffering. Karmic fruitfulness is rejoiced in, whoever generates it. Thus the *Bodhisattva* should constantly identify with others (*Ss.* 317).

In his *Bodhi-caryāvatāra*, Śāntideva adds the following arguments.[1] Realizing that all are equal in wanting happiness and not wanting pain (see pp. 33–4), one should protect others as one protects oneself, for suffering is just suffering, whoever it 'belongs' to: what is so special about me and 'my' suffering (*Bca.* VIII.90–6)?

Being no (inherent) owner of suffering, there can be no distinction at all between (that of myself and others). Thus I shall dispel it because it hurts; why am I so certain (that I should not eliminate the suffering of others)? (*Bca.* VIII.102)

He thus advocates that one who sees the equality of self and other should heroically practise 'the exchange of self for others' (*parātma-parivartanam*), the 'highest secret' which benefits both self and other.[2] In this practice, one looks on another, lowly, person as 'I' and on oneself as

---

[1] See Mitomo, 1991; Williams, 1998: 104–77 gives a critique.
[2] *Bca.* VII.16, VIII.120. See also Wayman, 1991: 59–61.

one would on someone else. Fully identifying with the other person and his or her outlook, one sees oneself through his or her eyes, perhaps as proud and uncaring. One focuses one's ambitions on that person, and whatever indifference one normally has to others is focused on oneself (*Bca.* VIII.140–54). Moreover:

Although others may do something wrong, I should transform it into a fault
   of my own; but should I do something even slightly wrong, I shall openly
   admit it to many people.
By further describing the renown of others, I shall make it outshine my own
                                                      (*Bca.* VIII.162–3)

However, there should be no self-congratulation if one benefits others by practising the exchange of self for others, just as this is inappropriate when one benefits oneself (*Bca.* VIII.116). In any case, any potential pride at the good a *Bodhisattva* does is tempered by the reflection that his or her karmic fruitfulness is as 'empty' as all else (*Vc.* sec. 8).

The arising of the thought of enlightenment

The *Bodhisattva*-path begins with the arising of the *bodhi-citta* or 'thought of enlightenment': the heart-felt aspiration to strive for Buddhahood, both for its own sake and for the sake of helping suffering beings. For this momentous event to occur, a person requires karmic fruitfulness and insight developed in the present and past lives, devotion, and reflections on the sufferings of beings and the need for Buddhas.

A series of meditations are used to arouse the *bodhi-citta* (Wayman, 1991: 45–57). First of all, the meditator cultivates an impartial attitude of equanimity towards all beings. He or she visualizes a friend, then an enemy, then a neutral person. He or she examines, in turn, the nature of his or her feelings towards these, and reflects that such feelings are not so much based on inherent characteristics of these people as on how he or she has settled into seeing them, because of what they are seen to have done for him or her. He or she then reflects that the uncertainties of life may upset his or her stereotypes, for a friend may turn away from him or her, or hold him or her back in spiritual progress; an enemy may become a friend if treated well; and a neutral could become a friend or an enemy. In this way, the meditator develops an unbiased evenmindedness towards all people, overcoming the partiality that might limit the range of his or her sympathies.

Next, the meditator develops lovingkindness by reflecting on the kindness his or her mother has shown him or her during his or her life, and the sacrifices she has made on his or her behalf. Having thus aroused feelings of love and gratitude in his or her heart, wishing happiness for his or her mother, he or she then reflects that in the long round of rebirths, even neutral strangers and enemies have been his or her mothers in previous lives (see p. 35). He or she then applies such a reflection to beings in every direction, cultivating a heart-felt aspiration for their happiness, and wishing that they be free from delusion and suffering: the 'great lovingkindness' (*mahā-maitrī*). He or she then develops compassion by a similar series of reflections prefaced by visualization of the pitiful lot of a condemned criminal or animal about to be slaughtered, reflecting that his or her present mother and all past mothers have experienced many kinds of such suffering in the realms of rebirth. Thus arises the aspiration to lead all beings from such sufferings, the 'great compassion'. Finally, there is the development of empathetic joy, which rejoices at the present happiness of beings, particularly enemies. Additionally, there may be practice of the 'exchange of self for others'.

Such practices are seen as building an outlook in which it is natural for the *bodhi-citta* to arise. The initial arising of this 'thought of enlightenment', as a resolve, is known as the 'aspiration-thought' (*praṇiddhi-citta*); when it is put into practice, it is known as the 'implementation-thought' (*prasthāna-citta*) (*Bca.* 1.15). Even the resolve alone, without implementation, is seen as generating much karmic fruitfulness and as wearing out much past bad karma. Even one such thought 'bears in itself the accumulation of boundless, countless good' (*Ss.* 11). The *bodhi-citta* is seen as the seed of all the qualities of Buddhahood: 'It is the supreme medicine that quells the world's disease' (*Bca.* III.30).

The *bodhi-citta* is first formally expressed by taking various *Bodhisattva* vows (*praṇidhāna*s) in the presence of others who live by them, or with 'all Buddhas and *Bodhisattvas*' as witnesses. Some are general vows: to overcome innumerable defilements, to attain incomparable Buddhahood, and to save all beings; others may be to help beings in more specific ways. In some formulations, the vow includes the resolution to stay in *saṃsāra* till all are saved (*Ss.* 15). The vow to save all beings is made more credible and less overly ambitious by the notion that beings already have the *Tathāgata-garbha*, or Buddha-potential, within them (see Harvey, 1990a: 113–18), and non-egoistic by the notion that beings are not ultimately different from the *Bodhisattva*. Such vows are not taken lightly, however. They become a powerful autonomous force within the psyche and lead to much bad karma if broken; for they are seen as solemn promises to beings to save them.

Developing the Bodhisattva perfections

The *Bodhisattva*-path is practised by accomplishing ten 'perfections' (*pāramitās*) in ten *Bodhisattva* 'stages' (*bhūmis*) over aeons of time. The stages pertain to the Noble (*Ārya*) *Bodhisattva*, who has had some direct insight into emptiness, though before attaining this level, an ordinary *Bodhisattva* practises the perfections as best he or she can. In the first stage, the Noble *Bodhisattva* concentrates on developing the perfection of generosity (*dāna*) to a high degree. This is done by giving away wealth, teachings, life, limb, and even spouse and family, for the benefit of others. The karmic fruitfulness from such acts is dedicated to the future Buddhahood of himself or herself and others. In Mahāyāna tradition, karmic fruitfulness is often transferred to 'all sentient beings',[3] such 'transference' (*pariṇāmanā*) being possible as karmic fruitfulness is 'empty' and does not inherently 'belong' to any particular 'being'. Humans should transfer it for the benefit of other humans, and beings in unfortunate rebirths. They should also transfer it to Buddhas and *Bodhisattvas* with a view to increasing their perfections and virtues.[4] In turn, though, heavenly *Bodhisattvas* and Buddhas are seen as transferring it to devotees who ask for such help in faith.

The best expression of the Mahāyānist urge to transfer the benefits of good action to others is chapter 10 of Śāntideva's *Bodhi-caryāvatāra* (*Bca.* x). He aspires that, by the karmic fruitfulness generated by writing this work, various benefits should ensue for other beings: those plagued by physical and mental sufferings should be relieved by great joy (verse 2); those in hell should see many *Bodhisattvas* (verse 15), experience 'fragrant lotus pools, beautiful with exquisite calls of wild ducks, geese and swans' (verse 7), and be reborn in the Pure Land of Amitābha Buddha (verse 4); animals should be free from the fear of being eaten by one another, and hungry ghosts be full of happiness (verse 16); moreover:

May the blind see forms, may the deaf hear sounds, and . . . may pregnant
    women give birth without any pain.
May the naked find clothing, the hungry find food . . .
May all beings . . . be endowed with faith, wisdom and kindness.

(verses 18–19, 27)

---

[3] See e.g., Tatz, 1994: 24, equivalent to Chang, 1983: 428.
[4] *Ss.* 205–6, citing the *Vajradhvaja-pariṇāmanā Sūtra*.

He goes on to aspire even that the bad karma of others should ripen in him (verse 56), which goes beyond the sharing of good karma with others. In his *Śikṣā-samuccaya*, Śāntideva also cites the *Vajra-dhvaja Sūtra* as saying that the *Bodhisattva* looks on those who have done bad actions and aspires:

do I take away in each several rebirths in hell ... may all those creatures be born out of those places, all that burden of pain I take upon myself, I assume, I endure ... I have the courage ... to experience every abode of pain ... I resolve to abide in each single state of misfortune through numberless future ages ... And why so? Because it is better indeed that I alone be in pain, than that all those creatures fall into the place of misfortune ... I must be charioteer, I must be guide, I must be torch-bearer, guide to safety. (*Ss.* 256–7)

In eighth-century Tibet, Yeshe Tsogyel (Ye-shes mTsho-rgyal) is said to have practised 'the exchange of my karma for that of others', in which she took on and worked with the bad karma of others, and rescued beings from hell. This was based on the *tong-len* practice of breathing out one's positive qualities to others and breathing in their negative qualities and suffering (Willis, 1989: 18, 137).

In the second stage, the *Bodhisattva* concentrates on the perfection of moral virtue (*śīla*) till his or her conduct becomes spontaneously pure. He or she also urges others to avoid immorality, as it leads to unfortunate rebirths. In the third stage, he or she concentrates on the perfection of patience (*kṣānti*; see p. 105), aided by meditations on lovingkindness and compassion. In the fourth stage, the perfection of vigour or strength (*vīrya*) is developed, because of increasing aspiration and compassion. Mindful alertness is emphasized, and the stage is particularly appropriate for practising the discipline of a monk or nun. In the fifth stage, the focus is on the perfection of meditation (*dhyāna*). Meditative trances are mastered, but the heavenly rebirths that they can lead to are not accepted. The Four Noble Truths are comprehended and the exchange of self for others is practised (see pp. 125–6). Abilities in such fields as mathematics, medicine and poetry are cultivated, as ways to help others and teach the *Dharma* (Pali *Dhamma*).

In the sixth stage, the perfection of wisdom (*prajñā-pāramitā*) is attained. *The Bodhisattva* gains full insight into the conditioned, not-Self, empty nature of everything, and thus reaches a level of development parallel to that of the *Arahat*. At death, he or she *could* leave the round of rebirths and enter *Nirvāṇa*, but his or her Mahāyāna 'great compassion' prevents him or her from doing so. By the perfection of wisdom, the five previously emphasized perfections become transcendent, attaining completeness and full perfection (*Asta.* 172). Their most difficult acts are carried out totally free of self-consciousness or ulterior motive. For example, in giving, he or she does not perceive either 'giver', 'gift', 'recipient' or 'result'; for all dissolve in emptiness (Conze et al., 1954: 136–7). At the seventh stage, the *Bodhisattva* goes beyond being reborn according to karma, and becomes a heavenly saviour being. He or she brings to perfection his or her 'skilful means' (*upāya-kauśalya*), his or her ingenuity in helping beings, and so magically projects himself or herself into many worlds to teach and help beings in appropriate ways. At the eighth stage, he (or she?: see pp. 373–6) reaches a non-relapsing level, so that he is now certain to attain Buddhahood. His vows reach perfection, as they are carried out spontaneously. His knowledge enables him to appear anywhere in the universe at will, teaching beings while appearing just like them. He fully masters the transfer of karmic fruitfulness from his vast store, so that beings who pray to him receive it as a free spiritual uplift of grace. In the ninth stage, the *Bodhisattva* perfects his (or her?) power (*bala*), using his tremendous insight into beings' characters to guide and teach them in the most precisely appropriate ways.

In the tenth stage, the *Bodhisattva* has a resplendent body and is surrounded by a retinue of lesser *Bodhisattvas*, and has the perfection of knowledge (*jñāna*). Buddhas then come to consecrate him (or her?) as ready for perfect Buddhahood, the definitive *Nirvāṇa*, which he attains in the following *Tathāgata*-stage. As a Buddha, he exists as an omniscient being with a hugely long life-span, dwelling in a heavenly 'Pure Land' generated by the power of his perfections: a type of realm which is a paradise and also where the conditions for attaining enlightenment are ideal.

The notion of heavenly *Bodhisattvas* and Buddhas provided the Mahāyāna with many holy saviour beings as focuses of devotion. Among the advanced *Bodhisattvas*, Avalokiteśvara, embodiment of compassion, receives most devotion; Tibetans also greatly revere Tārā, the 'Saviouress'. Among heavenly Buddhas, the most important are Śākyamuni, who is said to have manifested himself on earth as the historical Buddha, and Amitābha, who has generated a particularly marvellous Pure Land in which those with great faith in him can be reborn.

THE ETHICS OF THE *BODHISATTVA*

In the Mahāyāna, the concept of ethics (*śīla*) became broadened so as to be seen no longer as simply one component of the path; in the widest sense it encompassed the whole of it. Ethics came to be seen, by such texts as the *Mahāyāna-saṃgraha* (Keown, 1992: 137–8) and the *Bodhisattva-bhūmi*,[5] as comprising:

(1) the ethics of 'restraint or vow (*saṃvara*)', through both the precepts of lay morality (abstention from harming others) and the monastic code, both termed *prātimokṣa* (Pali *pāṭimokkha*: a term reserved in the Theravāda for monastic precepts);

(2) the ethics of 'collecting wholesome states' (*kuśala-dharma-saṃgraha*), through the practice of the perfections;

(3) the ethics of 'working for the welfare of beings' (*sattvārtha-kriyā*), through active help for them.

The first was seen as the foundation for the other two, but as needing them to supplement it. A *śrāvaka* was seen as only engaged in (1), for he or she supposedly 'excels in being intent upon his own welfare and in disregarding the welfare of others. In undertaking the welfare of others he has meagre aims and few deeds; he dwells in little concern' (Tatz, 1986: 69–70). *Bodhisattvas*, though, were seen as not just engaged in (1), disengaging from evil, but also practising the other two: engaging in good (Tatz, 1986: 87). The ethics of collecting wholesome factors concerns the development of various positive qualities and actions that are, in fact, mostly shared with the Eightfold Path, though the dedication of one's karmic fruitfulness to future Buddhahood goes beyond this (Tatz, 1986: 48–9).

The ethics of benefiting sentient beings is ministering to the needs of others by: nursing those who are ill; advising on how to attain worldly and transcendent goals; gratitude for help received and returning it; protecting from wild animals, kings, robbers and the elements; comforting those stricken by calamities; giving to the destitute; attracting disciples by friendliness and then attracting material support for them; amenability to the (non-harmful) desires of others; applauding and pointing out others' good qualities; compassionately humbling, punishing or banishing others in order to make them give up unwholesome ways and take to wholesome ones; using psychic powers to show the results of unwholesome actions in hells etc., and generally inspiring and teaching others (Tatz, 1986: 50). Practical help should include such things as guiding the blind, teaching sign language to the deaf and giving hospitality to weary travellers (Tatz, 1986: 54–5). In this way, the Mahāyāna brought about a 'shift in the centre of gravity of Buddhist ethics' (Keown, 1992: 142), with

---

[5] Tatz:,1986: 15–17, 480. See also Guenther, 1959: 165–7.

a new emphasis on moral virtue 'as a dynamic other-regarding quality, rather than primarily concerned with personal development and self-control' (Keown, 1992: 131).

The Bodhisattva precepts

In gradually developing a new, compassion-inspired, vision of the Buddhist path, Mahāyāna leaders came to supplement and reassess aspects of the previous Buddhist code of moral precepts. An important statement, here, is the chapter on ethics (*śīla*) of the *Bodhisattva-bhūmi* (see Tatz, 1986) of Asaṅga (third or fourth century CE).[6] This outlines a set of training-precepts for *Bodhisattva*s which avoided: (1) deeds 'analogous to monastic defeats' and (2) 'misdeeds'. The first are seen as most serious as they conflict with the *Bodhisattva* vow, i.e. entail 'defeat' as a *Bodhisattva*, at least temporarily. Misdeeds relate to failure to develop wholesome qualities, and failure to accomplish the welfare of beings (Tatz, 1986: 22). Asaṅga specifies four actions likened to monastic grounds for defeat for a *Bodhisattva*:

i) 'With a longing for gain and respect, to praise himself and deprecate another'.

ii) 'While the goods exist in his possession, to cold-heartedly fail to donate material things,[7] because he has a nature of attachment to them, to those who are suffering and indigent, who have no protector and no recourse, who have approached in a properly suppliant manner; and, out of stinginess in doctrine, not to teach doctrine to those who have approached in a proper manner eager for doctrine'.

iii) 'The bodhisattva develops such involvement in anger that he cannot resolve it with the mere utterance of harsh words, but overwhelmed with anger he strikes, hurts, damages sentient beings with hand, clump of earth or club; while focusing on just that aggravated angry attitude he does not heed, he does not accept even another's apology; he will not let loose that attitude.'

iv) 'To repudiate the bodhisattva collection [of teachings] and, on his own or echoing someone else, to devote himself to counterfeits of the good doctrine, and then to enjoy, to show, and to establish those counterfeits of the good doctrine'. (Tatz, 1986: 64)

The great Tibetan reformer Tsong-kha-pa (1357–1410) cites Samudramegha's view that these four parallel the four grounds for defeat in monastic vows (see p. 94): that i) is parallel to sexual intercourse,

---

[6] For a good discussion of this and other aspects of Mahāyāna ethics, see Keown, 1992: 129–64.
[7] Tsong-kha-pa explains that one should not, however, give if one is asked for unsuitable, harmful things such as weapons or poison (Tatz, 1986: 159).

for in both cases, disgrace is brought on oneself and another, that ii) is parallel to theft, that iii) is parallel to killing a human and that iv) is parallel to boasting of having attained spiritual states that one has not attained (Tatz, 1986: 162). Nevertheless, while an act entailing monastic defeat need only be deliberately committed once for such defeat to ensue (according to non-Mahāyāna schools), defeat as a *Bodhisattva* only comes from doing one of the above repeatedly and without regret – or abandoning the 'thought of enlightenment'. One is then a counterfeit *Bodhisattva*, but can become a real one again by retaking the *Bodhisattva* vows (Tatz, 1986: 65).

Asaṅga lists forty-one 'misdeeds'.[8] Of these, some do not have a particularly Mahāyāna emphasis, such as failing to express devotion to the three refuges each day, or failing to accept a properly offered apology. Others do, such as neglecting the welfare of people who are violent and immoral, not accepting offerings with which others can be helped, not using caustic or severe means if this would benefit someone, and not helping those in need by, for example, being a travelling companion. Some concern the wrong attitudes to non-Mahāyāna Buddhists: it is a fault to hold that a *Bodhisattva* should not learn from their teachings and practices, but also wrong to neglect Mahāyāna texts for theirs.

Asaṅga also outlines factors which moderate the fault in such actions. As summarized by Tatz, these are that:

Misdeeds may be defiled or undefiled, depending upon their motivation; in addition, circumstances may render them innocuous. Mitigating circumstances consist of motivation by laziness, indolence, carelessness, and absent-mindedness (as opposed to defiling enmity, resentment, envy, conceit, lack of faith, and disrespect); exculpatory circumstances are not having taken the vow, distraught thinking, and unanticipated suffering (*Ts.* 39b). There is no fault in any deed done out of desire-attachment, because this is allied with compassion and is therefore the very duty of the bodhisattva (*Ts.* 84a–b). (Tatz, 1986: 22)

The *Bodhisattva-bhūmi* code was the locus classicus for instruction of new *Bodhisattva*s until the eighth century, when it was partly superseded by the system of Śāntideva. He, in his *Śikṣā-samuccaya* (*Ss.* 61–70), outlines eighteen 'root' transgressions (*mūla-patti*), which draw heavily on a list in the *Ākāśa-garbha Sūtra* (for which, see Tatz, 1986: 316–32). These include: putting people off the Mahāyāna by teaching emptiness to them before they can respond to it without fear, telling people that they are incapable of the *Bodhisattva*-path, teaching that this path will prevent

---

[8] Tatz, 1986: 66–83; Keown, 1992: 142–5.

bad karma from ripening and that moral precepts are unnecessary for a *Bodhisattva*, and praising oneself for belonging to the Mahāyāna while depreciating non-Mahāyānists out of envy for respect people pay to them.

SKILFUL MEANS AND OVERRIDING THE PRECEPTS

However much the Mahāyāna added to the precepts outlined in the earlier traditions, it also added a greater flexibility as regards some of these. In this, a key concept emphasized by the Mahāyāna is that of *upāya kauśalya*: means (*upāya*) which are skilful or wholesome (Pali *kusala*). The application of this idea of 'skilful means' (sometimes just referred to as *upāya*) is various (see Pye, 1978). It can refer to the first five of the six *Bodhisattva* perfections, so that the *Bodhisattva*-path consists of *upāya* and wisdom (Keown, 1992: 134). In developing these perfections:

The bodhisattva through skilful means dwells simultaneously in the states of nirvāṇa and saṃsāra . . . in solitude and amongst the bustling crowd . . . in meditation and amidst a circle of women. (*ASP.* 134–5)

In another sense, the Buddha is said to use skilful means in adapting his teachings to the level of his audience's understanding. Thus he is said to teach the Four Noble Truths and the goal of Arahatship to those of 'lower dispositions', *śrāvaka*s belonging to the 'Hīnayāna', or 'Lesser Vehicle', but the *Bodhisattva*-path to perfect Buddhahood to those of 'higher dispositions', who practise the 'Mahāyāna', or 'Great Vehicle'. Heavenly Buddhas and *Bodhisattva*s are also said to use skilful means in the way that they manifest themselves on earth (in the flesh, or in visions) in ways which are ideally adapted to the needs of those who seek their help or teaching. A final application of the concept is in the ethical sphere, referring to the idea that Buddhist ethical precepts may sometimes be broken if this is an unavoidable part of a compassionately motivated act to help someone.[9] Thus the Mahāyāna has a greater tendency than the Theravāda to adapt the precepts flexibly to circumstances, though such an approach is not completely absent in the Theravāda. Thus, in recent years, when the monastery of the Thai meditation master Ajahn Chah was overrun by a swarm of red ants, causing misery to all, he finally allowed the army in to spray insecticides. When the other monks questioned him on the acceptability of this, he simply said

[9] See Keown, 1992: 150–63. Keown compares this approach to that of 'situation ethics' in the West (1992: 185–91).

'I take full responsibility – don't you worry about it!', i.e. he was willing to suffer the karmic results of an act which allowed normal monastic life to resume.[10]

In the Mahāyāna, Śāntideva's *Śikṣā-samuccaya* cites the *Candra-pradīpa Sūtra* to the effect that, where the motive is to help people, there is no fault in an action (*Ss.* 163). The *Akṣayamati Sūtra* is also cited as saying 'At the time for giving one can overlook the practice of morality and so forth. But for all that he must not be lax' (*Ss.* 12). Mahāyāna texts differ on the degree of permissiveness allowed to *Bodhisattva*s. The *Bodhisattva-piṭaka Sūtra*, dating from around the second century CE, allows no scope for breaking the precepts (Pagel, 1995: 180). The *Mahāyāna-saṃgraha* VI.3 allows minor offences to be committed (Keown, 1992: 146) if the act helps others and is irreproachable, which the commentary explains as not arousing attachment, hatred or delusion in oneself or others (Keown, 1992: 147).

Compassionate killing

Some texts justify killing a human being, on the grounds of compassion in dire circumstances. A key text here is the *Upāya-kauśalya Sūtra*.[11] This says that taking life etc. is unreprehensible 'when it develops from a vir-tuous thought' (Tatz, 1986: 323). A key passage in the text tells of the Buddha in a past life as a *Bodhisattva* sea captain named Great Compassion, who was transporting 500 merchants.[12] One night deities inform him in a dream that one of the passengers is a robber intent on killing all the rest and stealing their goods. He realizes that the robber will suffer in hell for aeons from such a deed, as the merchants are all *Bodhisattva*s. He ponders deep and long on how to prevent this, but real-izes that if he informs the merchants of the plot, they will kill the robber – they cannot have been well established on the *Bodhisattva*-path – and themselves go to hell. If he does nothing, many will die. He is thus left with one option, the least of three evils: himself killing the robber. Even though he would himself be reborn in hell for 'a hundred thousand aeons' because of this, he is willing to endure this to prevent others suffering. Accordingly, 'with great compassion and skill in means', he

---

[10] Ajahn Sumedho, 'Facing Death', *Raft – The Journal of the Buddhist Hospice Trust*, no. 2 (1989/90).
[11] Translated from Tibetan (*Upāya-kauśalya-nāma Mahāyāna Sūtra*) by Tatz, 1994, and from Chinese (*Jñānottara-bodhisattva-paripṛcchā*) by Chang, 1983: 427–68 (Taishō 345). Tatz claims that the Indian original dates from the first century BCE (1994: 1).
[12] Tatz, 1994: 73–6; Chang, 1983: 456–8; see Welch, 1972: 284–6; cf. Williams, 1989: 145.

then kills the robber, who is reborn in a heaven. A similar story is also found in the *Mahā-Upāya-kauśalya Sūtra*,[13] where the *Bodhisattva* feels compelled to kill the scout for 500 bandits, even though he is an old friend, to prevent a murderous attack on 500 merchants.

In the first story, while the captain was willing to be reborn in hell for his deed, the text simply says that this actually meant that the round of rebirths was, for him, 'curtailed' by 'a hundred thousand aeons': the time he was willing to spend in hell as a result of the deed. Nevertheless, the text goes on to say that the Buddha's treading on a thorn is 'the residue of the fruition of that deed' (Tatz, 1994: 76; Chang, 1983: 458). While, as a Buddha, he knew of this in advance and could have avoided the thorn, he lets it happen to show to others the effects of karma. The implication seems to be, then, that the act had various bad karmic consequences, though not as bad as if it had not been done with such a compassionate motivation (cf. pp. 19–21, 25–6). If the captain had not acknowledged that the deed could lead to many rebirths in hell, and not been *willing* to suffer accordingly, compassion (and wisdom) would have been lacking, and he *would* have suffered long in hell. That is, hell is only avoided here by willingly risking it in helping others. McFarlane comments, in such a context, that

if the *bodhisattva* were to perform such actions from self-interested motives, or even from disinterested motives, but with an attitude that his actions were justified and would produce much merit, then they would not count as skilful means and would result in woeful consequences. (1995: 4)

Even so, according to John Dunne, most contemporary Tibetans assert that the *Bodhisattva* in the above story 'was reborn in hell because he took a life, but did not remain there long because the attitude behind the act was based on compassion'.[14]

Desperate situations call for those who are heroically compassionate to grasp the nettle of taking the lesser evil, but only if they acknowledge that an evil is being done and they are prepared to take the karmic consequences, because of their compassion. The *Bodhisattva-bhūmi* says that if a *Bodhisattva* sees a robber about to commit many acts of immediate retribution, such as killing – for the sake of a few material goods – many hundreds of *śrāvaka*s and *Bodhisattva*s, he thinks:

---

[13] Chinese: *Ta fang-pien fo-pao-en ching* (Taishō 156, VII, 161b–162a), cited in Demiéville, 1957: 379 and thence in Welch, 1972: 282.

[14] John Dunne, 'Precept Keeping' posting to 'Buddha-L' Internet discussion forum, 26 July 1995, and 'Killing Hitler' posting, 21 March 1996.

'If I take the life of this sentient being, I myself may be reborn as one of the creatures of hell. Better that I be reborn a creature of hell than that this living being, having committed a deed of immediate retribution, should go straight to hell.' With such an attitude, the bodhisattva ascertains that the thought is virtuous or indeterminate[15] and then, feeling constrained,[16] with only a thought of mercy for the consequence, he takes the life of that living being. There is no fault, but a spread of much merit. (Tatz, 1986: 70–1)

Demiéville's translation from the Chinese (1957: 379) and McFarlane's translation from the Sanskrit (1994: 194) add that the act is accompanied by horror.

There are also *Sūtra*s which condone war. The *Ārya-bodhisattva-gocaropāya-viṣaya-vikurvaṇa-nirdeśa Sūtra* offers various forms of advice to a king, including on when war is necessary, and the best strategies and tactics in it (109a ff.). It is emphasized, though, that his motive should be love and compassion in seeking to protect his subjects.[17] Moreover, in Tibet, at the highest level of tantric practice, acts of violence or killing are sometimes permissible to destroy a person or evil spirit that is causing great harm to many or to Buddhism, but *only* under very restricted conditions:

a) there is no peaceful way left which could work,
b) the act is performed by purely spiritual powers,
c) there is no other motivation except the great compassion,
d) the act of violence should have the desired effect,
e) the person should be able to place the person killed onto the path of liberation by the act.[18]

Nevertheless, the Mahāyāna contains less guarded justifications of killing, several of which are contained in the *Mahā-parinirvāṇa Sūtra* (composed around the fourth century CE in India or Central Asia). In one passage, the Buddha says that in a previous life he was a king who found that several brahmins were slandering Mahāyāna teachings. To save them from the bad karma entailed in this (!), and to protect Buddhism, 'I had them put to death on the spot. Men of devout faith, as a result of

---

[15] Tsong-kha-pa sees this as applying to the *Bodhisattva*'s own mind, not that of the victim, as he sees this as senseless (Tatz, 1986: 215). Nevertheless, one Sanskrit manuscript seems to support the latter interpretation (Tatz, 1986: 297, n. 403), as does Demiéville's translation of the Chinese (1957: 379).

[16] Tsong-kha-pa sees this as meaning that there is no alternative to acting in such a way (Tatz, 1986: 215).

[17] Information supplied by John Dunne, 'Buddha-L' Internet forum, posting on 'Just War', 21 March 1996.

[18] Yuthok, 1995: 54. On apparent acceptance of killing etc. in tantric texts, see Broido, 1988.

that action, I never thereafter fell into hell.'[19] In any case, says the *Sūtra*, they were each an *icchāntika* – one incapable of salvation – so there was no evil in killing them to protect the *Dharma*.[20] Such a person is otherwise described as 'perfect in his obstacles to present and future good',[21] being a monastic or lay person who: 'slanders the true *Dharma*' repeatedly and without any signs of remorse; or enacts a monastic offence entailing defeat; or does one of the five deadly actions, such as killing a parent, without contrition. He is a companion to Māra, the embodiment of evil.[22] Thus:

Sentient beings possess the five good roots such as faith, but the *icchāntika* has eternally severed those roots. Thus, while it is a fault to kill an ant, it is not a fault to kill an *icchāntika*.[23]

Fortunately this rather disreputable idea of the *icchāntika* is absent in later versions of the *Sūtra*, which says that *all* beings are capable of attaining Buddhahood: all have the Buddha-nature, and 'are not cut off and do not perish before they attain supreme enlightenment'.[24]

Williams sees the permission to kill those who slander the *Dharma* as the kind of passage which might be used to justify killing those who opposed one's own sect of Buddhism (1989: 158–9), as happened in medieval Japan. McFarlane comments, 'the arguments are hardly convincing in terms of Mahāyāna or more general Buddhist principles' (1986: 101), and such attempts to justify Buddhist involvement in violence have been rare (McFarlane, 1986: 102).

In another passage of the *Mahā-parinirvāṇa Sūtra*, it is said that the true follower of the Mahāyāna should ignore the moral precepts, if the need to protect monks (who uphold them) from attack makes this necessary.[25] Nevertheless, the passage goes on to say that they should never use the weapons that they carry to take life.[26]

[19] Taishō 12, 434c; quoted in Yampolsky, 1990: 32.
[20] Taishō 374, XVI, 459a–460b, as cited in Yampolsky, 1990: 32, Demiéville, 1957: 378 and Welch, 1972: 281.   [21] Taishō 12, 562b. My thanks to my research student Victor He for this.
[22] Taishō 12, 425a–b, 419a and 421c–422a, as cited in Yampolsky, 1990: 31–2, 124. Buddhists see a Māra as a type of deity who has developed a perverse desire to keep beings in the round of rebirths, with all its suffering and repeated death. A Māra is an evil tempter deity, seen to dwell in the highest of the sense-desire-realm heavens (see p. 14), an embodiment of both desire and death.   [23] Taishō 12, 562b. My thanks to my research student Victor He for this.
[24] Taishō 12, 573c. See Williams, 1989: 98; Yampolsky, 1990: 120–1.
[25] Taishō 374, III, 383b–384a, as cited in Demiéville, 1957: 378–9, in turn cited by Welch, 1972: 281 and Williams, 1989: 161.
[26] Taishō 12, 383b–384b, as cited in Yampolsky, 1990: 33–5, and see Niwano, 1977: 27.

Compassionate stealing, non-celibacy, and lying

In regard to the second precept, the *Bodhisattva-bhūmi* says that the *Bodhisattva* overthrows kings or officials who are oppressive, violent and pitiless; he steals back the property of thieves who have stolen from shrines or the *Saṅgha*; he removes from power wasteful or corrupt custodians of *Saṅgha* or shrine property. All of this is faultless taking of what has not been freely given, i.e. going against the moral precept regarding stealing, for the benefit of those who would otherwise have continued to harm others, and those they would have harmed (Tatz, 1986: 71; McFarlane, 1990: 410). McFarlane comments that this suggests that:

when confronted with a systematically unjust and oppressive regime, a *bodhisattva* is justified in taking direct and possibly violent action in overthrowing that regime. If of course the *bodhisattva* had it in his power to overthrow that regime nonviolently, perhaps through the disclosure of damaging confidential information, then that would of course be preferable. (1995: 6–7)

Asaṅga has the following things to say in relation to the third precept. A lay *Bodhisattva* has sexual intercourse with an unmarried woman who strongly desires sex with him, so as to help her avoid enmity (because of his refusal) and come under a wholesome influence (Tatz, 1986: 71). In this there is no fault but much karmic fruitfulness. The commentators Śāntarakṣita and Bodhibhadra say that there is 'virtually' no fault in this, for even if the agent looks on the act in the right way, it is still close to an unwholesome act (Tatz, 1986: 298–9, n. 416). Tsong-kha-pa's commentary says that it is wrong to say that if she is single, it is not a case of sexual misconduct anyway. The *Vimalakīrti-nirdeśa Sūtra* also sees sexuality as a possible means through which a female lay *Bodhisattva* might help divest people of ignorance: 'Of set purpose, they become a courtesan to draw men, and alluring them by the hook of lust, establish them in the Buddha's wisdom' (cited at *Ss.* 291).

Regarding the fourth precept, Asaṅga says that a *Bodhisattva* will lie so as to protect others from death or mutilation, though he will not lie in order to save his *own* life. He will slander an unwholesome adviser of a person, and use harsh, severe words to move someone from unwholesome to wholesome action. He indulges in dance, song, tales and idle chatter to bring others under his influence, and then lead them in a wholesome direction (Tatz, 1986: 72).

The above thus allows a *Bodhisattva* to commit the three unwholesome actions of body and four of speech if this is done with compassionate intent. It does not allow the three unwholesome acts of mind, though: covetousness, ill-will and false view.

Who may perform such acts, and are they obligatory?

Is the 'skilful' breaking of precepts acceptable for *all* types of Bodhisattvas? The *Upāya-kauśalya Sūtra* certainly acknowledges the potential danger of its doctrine of skilful means, as it says that it should be kept secret from non-Mahāyānists (Tatz, 1994: 87; Chang, 1983: 464). Jinaputra holds that only lay *Bodhisattvas* may kill etc., not monastic ones (Tatz, 1986: 327). By contrast, Tsong-kha-pa holds that while a monk may kill, steal and lie on compassionate grounds, without 'defeat' as a monk, he may not have sex on such grounds, as this would lay aside the basis of his training as a monk, with no real benefit to others (Tatz, 1986: 212–13). While the Sanskrit, and old Tibetan translation, of the *Śikṣā-samuccaya* says that murdering etc. out of compassion is only for *Bodhisattvas* who have not yet reached the Noble stages (*Ss.* 165), Tsong-kha-pa seems to favour a newer Tibetan translation in which *only* those in the Noble stages may do such acts. For him, 'this situation is an exclusive province of the capable, and fraught with very imminent peril'. Thus one should not seek to act beyond the level of one's spiritual maturity, or the karmic results will be bad (Tatz, 1986: 213–14). The flexibility that the doctrine of skilful means gave the Mahāyāna, then, is guarded from becoming licence by its association with compassion and warnings about the karmic dangers of abusing it.

If such acts are allowable to an advanced *Bodhisattva*, are they seen as actually being obligatory? The *Bodhisattva-bhūmi* itself, and some of its old commentaries, does not say that it is a misdeed to omit such an act if it is needed, but the new commentary does see it as such (Tatz, 1986: 211–12). This also became the predominant view in Tibet, though Tsong-kha-pa did not list compassionate killing as an obligation (Tatz, 1986: 244). In Chinese tradition, while three translations of the *Bodhisattva-bhūmi* omit the passage allowing such acts, Hsüan Tsang's translation sees it as a misdeed not to do them compassionately when needed (Tatz, 1986: 296, n. 396).

SPECIFIC STRANDS OF MAHĀYĀNA THOUGHT AND PRACTICE

Neither Theravāda nor Mahāyāna is a monolithic tradition, but there is rather more diversity within the latter than the former.

Tantra

In India, from the sixth century CE, texts developed, known as *Tantras*, which sought to accelerate progress on the *Bodhisattva*-path. They thus formed the basis of the Vajrayāna, the 'Diamond' or 'Thunderbolt' spiritual vehicle, also known as the Mantrayāna, or vehicle of *mantras*, or sacred words of power. This approach mainly focuses on the evocation and visualization of holy beings so as to stimulate the growth of corresponding potencies already latent in the practitioner's own mind. In this, an important principle is that unwholesome mental states, such as anger, are seen as distortions of the mind's underlying intrinsic purity. They are thus to be transmuted into positive energies – symbolized by the holy beings – rather than suppressed (Misra, 1984: 153). Such an approach – which is seen to need careful guidance from a *Guru* (Tibetan *bLama*, pronounced Lama) – is seen as able, for the very dedicated practitioner, to lead to Buddhahood in one life.

The adept Saraha (ninth century?), one of the eighty-four Indian tantric *Mahā-siddhas*, or 'Great Accomplished Ones', says in his *Dohā-kośa* (Conze et al., 1954: 224–39) that a man may develop perfect knowledge without being a monk, while married and enjoying sense-pleasures. After he realized that further spiritual progress was not possible for him if he did not find a female partner, he said:

I have taken the sworn vows of a monk and I wander about with a wife: there I do not see any distinction. Some may have doubts and say, 'Here is an impurity!' but they do not know. (Ray, 1980: 235)

He rigorously emphasizes the importance of spiritual practice, under a *Guru*, though.

One strand of Tantrism included taboo- and convention-breaking practices to overcome attachments and aid insight into seeing everything as the *Dharma*-body, or inner nature of all Buddhas. The *Hevajra Tantra* asserts that the world is bound by lust, and may also be released by lust. This refers to the practice of sexual yoga, in which the power of lust is harnessed, and transmuted into a power for liberation, by means of visualizing various processes within the body. At a time when Buddhist influence had led to widespread vegetarianism, and a resurgence in Hinduism had strengthened ideas of purity of caste, such rites might be carried out after eating meat and drinking wine (against Buddhist ethics), in a cemetery at night, the sexual partner being a low-caste woman visualized as a deity (see Ray, 1980: 237). The importance of the body, which the *Tantra*s stress, goes back to the Buddha saying that *Nirvāṇa* is in 'this fathom-length carcase' (*S.* 1.62), while cemeteries were often seen as good places in which to meditate on the nature of the body and death. The bizarre-sounding tantric rites were certainly an innovation, though! It is worth noting, however, that the famous tantric adept Tilopa, while he accepted a woman running a very successful liquor shop as his disciple, made her close it down as a condition of his acceptance (Ray, 1980: 229–30).

While Vajrayāna Buddhism became the dominant form in Northern Buddhism, the above-mentioned tantric approaches are only used to a certain extent. Among Tibet's four main schools of Buddhism, the one most open to practices such as sexual yoga is the Nyingma (rNying-ma), which is the oldest school there. Some of its non-monastic followers – and also monks who disrobe, perhaps temporarily – do sometimes practise sexual yoga with a partner. However, as Barber says:

The use of meat, alcohol, and sexual yoga is highly regulated. A tantric yogi cannot simply drink and engage in sexual intercourse at will; these are permitted only after years of training. Only those who have a proper mental attitude can incorporate these teachings. (1991: 86)

The Gelug (dGe-lugs), the dominant Buddhist school in Tibet, founded by Tsong-kha-pa, holds that tantric practices should only be carried out on a sound basis of monastic practice and Mahāyāna ethics (Tatz, 1986: 97, 111, 30–1), and 'sexual yoga' is only done as a visualization, not physically.[27]

In addition to following Śrāvakayāna precepts and *Bodhisattva* vows, tantric practitioners observe various *samaya*s, or tantric vows. These are seen as indispensable to the success of tantric practices, and powerful enough to lead to Buddhahood within sixteen lifetimes even without the practices. To break the vows leads to a low rebirth. The majority of the vows are identical with or extensions of Śrāvakayāna or *Bodhisattva* vows. Others involve such matters as not revealing secrets, not deriding women, and making offerings to one's *Guru* (Barber, 1991: 85–90).

Pure Land Buddhism

In Eastern Buddhism, one strand of the Mahāyāna, the 'Pure Land' tradition (Chinese Ch'ing-t'u), focused its attention on devotion to Amitābha Buddha (see p. 130) as the main or even only practice (de Bary,

[27] Barber, 1991: 90. For a useful discussion of tantric sexual symbolism and yoga, see Jackson, 1992.

1972: 197–207, 314–44). In Japan, there is the Jōdo, 'Pure Land', school and the Jōdo-shin, the 'True Pure Land' school. These were founded, respectively, by the followers of Hōnen (1133–1212) and his pupil Shinran (1173–1263). Both regarded the traditional Mahāyāna path of gradual spiritual development as too difficult, and so turned to Amitābha (Japanese Amida) to save them.

For Hōnen, devotion was the central religious act, but one should also cultivate one's own virtue. For Shinran, one should have faith in Amida to do all that is necessary for one's salvation, and not pretend that one can contribute to this oneself: one should totally rely on Amida as saving 'other-power', not on 'self-power'. He felt that humans were helpless sinners, full of passion and depravity, ignorant of what is truly good or evil, so attempts to cultivate virtue or wisdom deliberately would lead to pride and lack of faith in Amida. Hōen taught that as even wicked people could be reborn in Sukhāvatī, Amida's Pure Land, good ones certainly could be. Shinran taught that as even good people could be reborn there, 'wicked' ones stood an even better chance: an idea paralleling the Christian concept of the 'salvation of sinners'. Salvation comes from gratefully accepting Amida's saving grace, not by any good works. Even a person's faith comes from grace, for the all-pervading power of Amida can be found within one, prompting the Buddha-nature to overcome arrogance and sin.

Some Jōdo-shin followers came to regard moral conduct as irrelevant to those saved by Amida. Against this view, the school's 'second founder', Rennyo (1415–99), argued that sincere faith implied a pure heart, with a moral life expressing gratitude to Amida for salvation. For Jōdo-shin Buddhists, then, ethics is not part of a path towards liberation, as in most other Buddhist schools, but a consequence of belief that one is *already* saved.

Zen

In a different way, another strand of Eastern Buddhism, Zen (Japanese; Chinese Ch'an) came to modify the classical Buddhist view of ethical action as part of a path of gradual spiritual cultivation. Particularly in the Japanese Sōtō Zen school, founded by Dōgen (1200–53), neither moral virtue nor meditation was seen as a way to *attain* Buddhahood. Rather, they were seen as ways of progressively manifesting one's existing Buddha-nature (Fox, 1971; Ives, 1992: 54). Thus Dōgen held that 'The Buddha-seed grows in accordance with not taking life' (Aitken,

1984: 24). While Zen's approach of 'self-power' contrasts with Pure Land's 'other-power' approach, Dōgen and Shinran share the view that ethical action is a consequence of liberation – whether through one's inner Buddha-nature or Amida Buddha – not part of a way to attain it.

For Dōgen, selfless compassion is what is naturally expressed when one acts in a spontaneous way – from one's underlying Buddha-nature – free from reflection and desire, which come from self-centredness. A disciplined life enables this inner goodness to be expressed in actions (Kasulis, 1981: 97–9), and developing wisdom ensures that good actions become the only natural thing to do (Brear, 1974: 436–7). Thus Dōgen said:

> To study the Buddha-way is to study the self.
> To study the self is to forget the self.
> To forget the self is to be enlightened by the ten thousand dharmas.
>   (Aitken, 1984: 152)

In a more homely way, the American Zen teacher Aitken Roshi says: 'The one who beats his kids and gets drunk has no confidence in his Buddha-nature, we may say' (Aitken, 1984: 102). Aitken quotes Yamada Kōun Roshi as saying 'The purpose of Zen is the perfection of character' (Aitken, 1984: 155), in the sense of bringing out a perfection that normally lies hidden within. In doing this, while Zen has, to varying extents, emphasized traditional Buddhist ethical precepts, as well as Confucian norms on correct social relationships and 'human-heartedness', it has put more stress on 'fundamental ways of being as opposed to principles of good and evil' (Ives, 1992: 3, 37–8).

Zen emphasizes three aspects to the moral precepts, such as that against killing. Firstly, there is the literal aspect, which relates to the Śrāvakayāna cast of mind: simply do not deliberately kill any being. Secondly, there is the compassionate, Mahāyāna aspect: positively nurture beings (cf. pp. 130–2). Thirdly, there is the 'essential' or Buddha-nature aspect: this world of emptiness is no different from *Nirvāṇa*, which contains nothing to do with death; so, ultimately, there is no-one killed and no act of killing. All three aspects must be borne in mind (Aitken, 1984: 16–17). Zen often talks of overcoming all 'dualism', whether of 'like and dislike', 'good and evil' or 'right and wrong'. By this, it seeks to point to a level of awakening in which such distinctions are transcended, and a person spontaneously acts in a way which would otherwise be called 'good' (cf. pp. 43–6). Talk of 'transcending' good and evil is based on the idea that there is no *absolute* or *inherent* good or evil, but that good and evil are relative to each other, and that one must beware of strong attachments or rejections – towards oneself or others – based on these ideas (Ives, 1992: 47–8).

The Zen emphasis on one's Buddha-nature or 'innate awakening' meant that it is sometimes said that 'passions are awakening'. This occasionally led to antinomianism, or at least quietism (Faure, 1991: 56, 59, 67, 129), though this was generally resisted (62–5, 128). On a related point, Zen came to emphasize 'formless repentance', which aims to realize the emptiness of transgressions and delusion, rather than focus on actual 'phenomenal' transgressions. This is found in the 'Platform' *Sūtra*, composed in China, and lent itself, in some quarters, to laxity (Faure, 1991: 237–8). Such laxity was not supported by Dōgen, who encouraged earnest resolve and expression of repentance before the Buddhas for past misdeeds.

Nichiren Buddhism

Another important strand of Japanese Buddhism is the Nichiren group of schools, founded by the fiery reformist Nichiren (1222–82) (de Bary, 1972: 345–54). He emphasized devotion to the saving truth of the Lotus *Sūtra*, a key Mahāyāna text which sees the Buddha as a long-enlightened heavenly figure who manifests himself on earth to teach in compassionately skilful ways. For Nichiren, chanting 'Na-mu myō-hō ren-ge-kyō', 'Honour to the Lotus *Sūtra* of the True *Dharma*', and contemplating a wooden plaque or scroll on which this invocation was written (the *Gohonzon*) was the key practice. It would activate the Buddha-nature and lead to the moral uplift of the individual and society and to the attainment of Buddhahood.

As with the Pure Land schools, Nichiren felt that history had reached the 'period of the Latter-day *Dharma*', when moral and spiritual decline meant that formal moral precepts were too difficult to keep. While the Pure Land schools advocated an 'other-power' way as the one appropriate to this period, Nichiren advocated the 'self-power' one of active devotion to the Lotus *Sūtra*. He saw the words 'Myō-hō ren-ge-kyō' as embodying the actions and virtues of the 'eternal' Buddha Śākyamuni, and as the seed of Buddhahood. Reverencing them was equivalent to keeping the precepts, and aligned one with the will of the Buddha, so as to bring peace and righteousness to oneself and society (Otani, 1991).

In twentieth-century Japan, after the Second World War, a number of so-called 'New Religions' have flourished or arisen. They are lay-led movements with roots in Buddhism, Shintō, or even Christianity. Their followers are mostly urban members of the upper-lower classes, who feel economically and socially frustrated, dislike the anonymity of the sprawling cities, and feel the need for a modernized spiritual tradition to guide them in a confusing secularized world. The 'New Religions' promise that religious practice will lead to health, wealth, personal fulfilment and success. The major Buddhist ones give members both a sense of belonging and a sense of personal importance. They are organized into small discussion groups, where personal and social problems are discussed in the light of religious faith, but the groups are also part of a well-organized and successful movement.

One of the most successful originated as the lay arm of the Nichiren Shōshū school.[28] This is probably because of Nichiren's emphasis on reforming society, which appealed in the post-war period. The Lotus *Sūtra* also holds out the promise of earthly happiness to those who revere it, and gives prominence to the lay *Bodhisattva*. The Sōka Gakkai ('Value-Creating Society') sees the teachings of Nichiren and the Lotus *Sūtra* as representing absolute truth, but regards values as having to be positively created, drawing on faith in the Lotus *Sūtra*. Basic values include respect for the dignity of all life, and karma. Chanting is regarded as a way to overcome obstacles in life, such as poverty, domestic disharmony, and ill health, and as a means to giving up drinking and smoking and to attaining happiness. It is seen as bringing out a person's Buddha-nature, in the form of enhanced compassion, courage, wisdom and vital life force, so as to generate a 'human revolution'. At first, chanting is for personal goals, but it then moves on towards helping solve national or world problems, such as an end to all war (Causton, 1988).

The movement has been very successful in winning converts overseas. For many, one of its attractions is its lack of any formal moral precepts or commandments. Nevertheless, as people practise, behaviour tends to start to align itself with many traditional Buddhist norms (Wilson and Dobbelaere, 1994: 17, 29–30, 57). Another part of its appeal is the claim that practising it can 'expiate all negative karma', for 'the shackles of one's karma are progressively weakened until they are finally severed completely' (Causton, 1988: 231, 182).

MAHĀYĀNA REASSESSMENT OF MONASTICISM

In the Mahāyāna, monasticism is still seen as an important aid to spiritual development, but increasing weight has come to be given to the role of

---

[28] Though formal links with it were severed in 1991 (Wilson and Dobbelaere, 1994: 232–45).

the lay Buddhist. It was emphasized that the specifically monastic precepts were simply a means to the end of purifying the mind, and should not be made into ends in themselves, as some monks were perhaps making them (Tatz, 1986: 13). As the *Bodhisattva* aimed to remain in the round of rebirths for a huge length of time, to aid others, he or she did not need to overcome the defilement of attachment as quickly as a follower of the early schools, a *śrāvaka*, sought to, using monastic practice as an aid. Thus the lay *Bodhisattva* had an important role alongside the monastic one, and the lay–monastic division became blurred to some extent.

In Northern Buddhism, a Lama (Tibetan *bLama*; Skt *Guru*) is generally a monk (*gelong*) or nun of long standing or special charisma, but a lay person accomplished in meditation or advanced rituals may also be such a revered teacher, particularly in the Nyingma (rNying-ma) school. Moreover, many 'monks' only follow the precepts for novices throughout their life, though they also follow a number of *Bodhisattva* precepts (Tatz, 1986: 21).

In China, monks have followed both the full monastic precepts and a supplementary 'Mahāyāna' code consisting of the 'three pure precepts' (see p. 82), and a set of *Bodhisattva*-precepts outlined in the *Brahmajāla Sūtra* (De Groot, 1893; Dharma Realm, 1981). These consist of the 'ten great precepts' (see p. 82) and forty-eight minor ones, which positively require such things as vegetarianism, preaching, caring for the sick and exhorting others to give up immoral behaviour.

In Japan, the lay–monastic distinction gradually diminished in importance. Saichō (767–822), founder of the Tendai school, set aside the traditional monastic code as too difficult to keep in an age of moral and spiritual decline, so long after the Buddha. He retained only the supplementary code, which does not seem formally to require total celibacy. Nevertheless, Dōgen (1200–53), founder of Sōtō Zen, stressed a simple but rigorous life-style. He emphasized the 'three pure' and 'ten great' precepts, but also developed a meticulously detailed code for *unsui*, or trainee monks. This outlines how juniors should behave respectfully in the presence of seniors, how trainees should behave when relaxing or eating, and even how they should clean their teeth. In practice, these rules precluded any sexual activity. Yet Shinran (1173–1263), founder of the intensely devotional Jōdo-shin school, came to see celibacy as part of a futile attempt to save oneself, rather than depending on the saving power of Amida Buddha. Having dreamt that the *Bodhisattva* Avalokiteśvara told him to marry, he regarded monasticism as unnecessary for salvation, and marriage as a realistic admission of human weakness. He thus initiated a kind of married hereditary clergy, and advocated the family as the centre of religious life. This precedent of a married priesthood was one that monks of other schools sometimes followed.

From this period, Japanese Buddhism also came to develop a more this-worldly orientation, which generally saw ultimate reality as pervading everyday activities, to be known by those with true faith (Pure Land and Nichiren schools) or strong awareness (Zen). The role of the monk or nun thus became less central, with less charisma, and Buddhism became more lay-orientated, with devotion mainly focused before a home altar, rather than at a temple.

Japanese Buddhists have much respect for Vimalakīrti, a lay *Bodhisattva* whose teachings are given in the *Vimalakīrti-nirdeśa Sūtra*:

Though he is but a simple layman, yet observing the pure monastic discipline;
Though living at home, yet never desirous of anything;
Though possessing a wife and children, always exercising pure virtues;
Though surrounded by his family, holding aloof from worldly pleasures . . .
Though frequenting the gambling house, yet leading gamblers into the right path . . .
Manifesting to all the error of passions when in the house of debauchery; persuading all to seek higher things when at the shop of the wine dealer . . . [29]

Nevertheless, it is surely true that 'not every layperson can visit prostitutes or indulge in gambling and drinking, as did Vimalakīrti, without becoming attached'! (Barber, 1991: 85).

After the Meiji restoration of 1868, the Japanese government decreed that monks of all schools could marry; since then, so many monks have married that genuine (celibate) monks are now mostly young men in training. The nuns remain celibate. Monastic training is now seen as a preparation for the role of the priest, who performs rituals such as funerals for the laity, and often hands on his temple to a son, though the 'New Religions' have little need for priests or monks.

CONCLUSION

The Mahāyāna has its roots in the values broadly shared by all forms of Buddhism, but its greater emphasis on compassion has meant that it has accepted that this may, in certain circumstances, override the constraints of normal Buddhist morality. Here one sees a rough parallel to the way

[29] Tsunoda, de Bary and Keene, 1964: 99.

in which Christianity puts 'love' as a central value which might override constraints expressed in the precepts of Jewish law, though this covers both ritual and ethical matters, unlike Buddhist precepts. As in certain minority developments in Christianity, one also sees an antinomian attitude occasionally developing, though it never escapes criticism. Even when, as in the Japanese Jōdo-shin and Nichiren schools, the idea of formally undertaking precepts is abrogated, the ideals of behaviour remain broadly in accordance with them. Accordingly, Japanese Buddhists sometimes like to say that Mahāyānists are concerned to act from the 'spirit' rather than by the 'letter' of the precepts. In Tantra, one sometimes has practices whose form seems in tension with aspects of sexual morality, but which are intended as ways to confront and transmute the power of lust. The lay–monastic distinction, whilst still important in Tibet and China, comes to be downgraded in Japan, while in Tibet it is modified by the elevation in status of certain non-celibate practitioners.

CHAPTER 4

Attitude to and treatment of the natural world

May all beings be happy and secure. *Karaṇīya-metta Sutta*, Khp. 8

HUMANITY'S PLACE IN NATURE

Buddhism does not see humans as a special creation by 'God', or as having been given either 'dominion' or 'stewardship' over animals etc. Like all other sentient beings, they wander in the limited, conditioned realm of *saṃsāra*, the round of rebirths. Nevertheless, a human rebirth is seen as a very rare and fortunate one – a 'precious human rebirth' (see p. 30) – as it is the only one where the key work for enlightenment can be accomplished. Accordingly, in the Buddhist account of the types of rebirth – gods, humans, animals, ghosts and hell-beings – humans are listed in one group, while all other animals (i.e. land animals, birds, fish, worms, insects: *M.* III.167–9) are listed in another. That is, while all sentient beings are 'in the same boat' – *saṃsāra* – humans are in a specific compartment of this. This is because they have a greater freedom and capacity for understanding than animals (and a greater motivation for spiritual progress than gods). Most moral and spiritual progress, or its opposite, is made at the human level. This is not to say that animals are all seen as amoral automatons. Buddhist *Jātaka* stories often attribute noble actions to such animals as monkeys and elephants, and there is also a reference to some animals keeping the five precepts (*Vin.* II.162). Nevertheless, animals clearly have much less of a capacity for choice than humans, and if they are virtuous, for example less greedy, or generous, this is more an expression of their existing character, or a response to an encouraging human example, than any deliberate desire for moral development (Story: 1976). Moreover, it is clear that there is a gradation among animals as regards their relative degree of freedom, or capacity for virtue (*AKB.* IV.97b–c). Insects would seem to have little, if any, of either.

The relatively special place of humans in the Buddhist cosmos means that they can be seen as at a 'higher level' of existence than animals. This, however, is not seen as a justification for domineering and exploiting animals. Humans are 'superior' primarily in terms of their capacities for moral action and spiritual development. The natural expression of such 'superiority' is not an exploitative attitude, but one of kindness to lesser beings, an ideal of *noblesse oblige* (Hall, 1902: 229–47). This is backed up by the reflection that one's present fortunate position as a human is only a temporary state of affairs, dependent on past good karma. One cannot isolate oneself from the plight of animals, as one has oneself experienced it (*S.* ii.186), just as animals have had past rebirths as humans. Moreover, in the ancient round of rebirths, every being one comes across, down to an insect, will at *some* time have been a close relative or friend, and have been very good to one (*S.* ii.189–90). Bearing this in mind, one should return the kindness in the present.

The Western concept of 'nature' is one which places humans and their artifices over and against the 'natural' world of animals, plants and the physical environment. In the present century, industrialization etc. has led to many environmental problems, and thus to reflection on how humans should act and live so as to be in a less destructive and self-undermining relationship with 'nature'. As the Vietnamese monk Thich Nhat Hanh says, though:

We classify other animals and living beings as nature, acting as if we ourselves are not part of it. Then we pose the question 'How should we deal with Nature?' We should deal with nature the way we should deal with ourselves! We should not harm ourselves; we should not harm nature . . . Human beings and nature are inseparable. (Eppsteiner, 1988: 41)

Rather than divide the world into the realms of the 'human' and 'nature', the classical Buddhist perspective has seen a more appropriate division as that between sentient beings, of which humans are only one type, and the non-sentient environment, the 'receptacle-world' (*bhājana-loka*), in Sarvāstivādin terminology (*AKB.* iii.45). In this division, plants would generally come on the non-sentient side of the line, but there is some ambiguity here, and differences of view (see pp. 174–7). The key quality, then, is sentience, the ability to experience and to suffer, and the related ability, in this or a future life, to transcend suffering by attaining enlightenment. A good image of this notion of the community of sentient beings is a genre of painting popular in Japan, showing humans, gods, and a variety of animals mourning at the death of the Buddha (Suzuki, 1959: 377–80).

Another Western dichotomy is, indeed, between the 'supernatural' – the realm of God, or gods, and angels etc. – and the natural world, with man partaking of something of both. Within the Buddhist perspective, the gods are themselves sentient beings subject to the natural law of karma. Their actions do not subvert natural laws, though they may go against the *normal* course of things. In the same way, meditation-based psychic powers, such as walking on water, are not seen as supernatural or miraculous, but as law-governed natural manifestations of certain potencies latent in the human mind. Except for *Nirvāṇa*, everything in the universe is subject to Conditioned Arising, the natural process of law-governed arising-according-to-conditions. In this sense, there *is* nothing 'supernatural', except perhaps *Nirvāṇa*. The gods, then, and also humans, are part of the play of natural processes that is *saṃsāra*.

Gods are seen as existing at various levels, with some being seen as (normally) invisible beings sharing the earth with humans. Buddhist texts refer to certain gods living in large trees (*Vin.* IV.34–5) and even in healing herbs (*S.* IV.302; *M.* 1.306): thus one should not anger such a being by damaging or destroying his or her home (Hall, 1902: 248–71). Other gods dwell on the land. Thus a Thai custom, upheld even in the busy modern city of Bangkok, is to build a small 'spirit house' next to a building erected on a previously open plot of land. This is to house any gods displaced from the land: to be considerate to them and thus not rouse their anger. Similarly, in Ladakh, a ceremony at the first planting of the year seeks to pacify the spirits of the earth and water, as well as worms and fish, all of which might be disturbed by agricultural activity (Batchelor and Brown, 1992: 43).

As part of Conditioned Arising, humans are seen as having an effect on their environment not only through the purely physical aspects of their actions, but also through the moral/immoral qualities of these. That is, karmic effects sometimes catch up with people via their environment. It is thus said that, if a king and his people act unrighteously, this has a bad effect on the environment and its gods, leading to little rain, poor crops and weak, short-lived people (*A.* II.74–6; see p. 115). Right actions have the opposite effect. The Buddha is also seen to have had a positive effect on his environment: when he lay down between two *sāl* trees to die and pass into final *Nirvāṇa*, these are said to have burst into a mass of unseasonal blossom, which fell on him in homage (*D.* II.137–8). Likewise, in the Mahāyāna '*Sūtra* of the Buddha Teaching the Seven Daughters', it is said that, after the Buddha taught, 'One-hundred year old trees bore fruit and flowers . . . the blind could see . . . Hundreds of birds and beasts were harmonious in their cries' (Paul, 1979: 24).

The environment is thus held to respond to the state of human morality; it is not a neutral stage on which humans merely strut, or a sterile container unaffected by human actions. This clearly has ecological ramifications: humans cannot ignore the effect of their actions on their environment. This message is also strongly implied by the *Aggañña Sutta*,[1] which gives an account of the initial stages of the development of sentient life on earth. This occurs when previously divine beings fall from their prior state and, through consuming a savoury crust floating on the oceans, develop physical bodies, and later sexual differentiation. At first their environment is bountiful, but it becomes less so the more they greedily take from it. They feed off sweet-tasting fungus, and then creepers, but these in turn disappear as the beings differentiate in appearance and the more beautiful ones become conceited and arrogant. Then they feed off quick-growing rice, gathering it each day as they need it. But through laziness, they start to gather a week's supply at a time, so that it then ceases to grow quickly, which necessitates cultivation. Consequently, the land is divided up into fields, so that property is invented, followed by theft. Here, then, is a vision of sentient beings and their environment co-evolving (or co-devolving). The beings are affected by what they take from their environment, and the environment becomes less refined and fruitful as the beings morally decline.

All this takes place according to the principle of Conditioned Arising (see pp. 33 and 124–5), in which nothing exists on its own, as each thing depends on others to condition its arising and existence. In Eastern Buddhism, the inter-relationship of all things (and thus of humans and their environment) is particularly strongly emphasized. In the *Avataṃsaka Sūtra* is an image, the 'Jewel Net of Indra', explained by Fa-tsang (643–712), a master of the Hua-yen school, as follows. In this infinite net, a jewel is placed at each knot, so that each jewel reflects every other one, including their reflections of every jewel, and so on to infinity (Cook, 1989: 214). This is seen as a simile for reality as a web of interdependence, in which each thing is 'interpenetrated' by every other. Each item is made possible by, and reflects, every other, for they all condition it in one way or another. Nothing can exist by itself, but makes its own contribution to the whole. Thus the *Sūtra* says, 'Every living being and every minute thing is significant, since even the tiniest thing contains the whole mystery.' Likewise, the Ch'an monk Sêng-chao (384–414) said, 'Heaven and earth and I are of the same root, the ten-thousand things and I are of one substance' (Suzuki, 1959: 353). Cook sees this perspective as one of 'cosmic ecology' (1989: 214).

---

[1] *D.* III.84–93; cf. Batchelor and Brown, 1992: 11–13.

In the lands of Eastern Buddhism, the traditional ideal has been one of harmony with nature. This has been particularly emphasized by the Ch'an/Zen school, in such actions as blending meditation huts into the landscape, not wasting any food in monasteries, landscape painting, landscape gardening, and nature poetry (Suzuki, 1959: ch. 11). In paintings, human beings are just one part of a natural scene, not the focus, with nature as simply a background, as often seen in Western art (Cook, 1989: 217–18). Great attention is paid to seemingly insignificant aspects of nature, for insight into them can give an intuitive appreciation of the indescribable and mysterious 'suchness' which runs through the whole fabric of existence. Such insight requires a mind in which ego-centred thought has been stilled and disciplined, but in which a natural spontaneity wells up from deep within. The seventeen-syllable *haiku* poem form is a favourite medium for the expression of such intuitions (Suzuki, 1959: ch. 7). Of the following examples, the first three are by Bashō (1643–94), one is by Kikaku (1660–1707) and one is by Jōsō (1661–1704):

(1) An old pond, ah!
    A frog jumps in:
    The water's sound!

(2) On a dry branch
    A raven is perched:
    This autumnal eve.

(3) Lice, fleas –
    The horse pissing
    By my pillow.

(4) A little frog
    Riding on a banana leaf,
    Trembling.

(5) Under the water,
    On the rock resting,
    The fallen leaves.

Such an atunement to natural phenomena is also evident in a number of the poems attributed to the early *Arahat*s in the *Thera-gāthā* (*Thag.*), a Theravāda text. A number are attributed to Mahā-Kassapa (verses 1062–70), an ascetic character claimed by the Ch'an/Zen school as the first teacher in their line. He speaks of his appreciation of the delightful rocks, 'cool with water, having pure streams, covered with Indagopaka insects' (verse 1063), resounding with elephants and peacocks, 'covered with flax flowers as the sky is covered with clouds' (verse 1068):

With clear water and wide crags, haunted by monkeys and deer, covered with oozing moss, those rocks delight me. (verse 1070)

Sāriputta affirms, 'Forests are delightful, where (ordinary) people find no delight. Those rid of desire will delight there; they are not seekers after sensual pleasures' (verse 992). That is, the enlightened appreciate nature in a non-attached, non-sensual way. Indeed, Mahā-Moggallāna speaks of his living at the root of a tree in the forest, contemplating the foulness of the body (verses 1146–52). He is also without fear of natural phenomena: while lightning flashes around the mountain, 'gone to the cleft in the mountain the son of the incomparable venerable one meditates' (verses 1167). Likewise Bhūta speaks of contentedly meditating in a cave at night, while outside the thunder rumbles, the rain falls and fanged animals roar (verse 524). In a more tranquil vein, Rāmaṇeyyaka says, 'Amidst the sound of chirping and the cries of birds, this mind of mine does not waver, for devotion to solitude is mine' (verse 49). Non-attached delight is, again, expressed by Tālapuṭa, who meditatively admires the beautiful necks, crests, tail feathers and variegated wing feathers of birds (verses 1135–6). Moreover, after rain, 'when the grove is in full flower, like a cloud, I shall lie among the mountains like a tree' (verse 1137). That is, he will be rooted and 'earthed' through strong mindfulness, while in full mastery of his formerly wayward mind. For such early wilderness-meditators, the environment could itself be a teacher, especially of constant change and impermanence. As Vimala says, 'The earth is sprinkled, the wind blows, the lightning flashes in the sky. My thoughts are quietened, my mind is well concentrated' (verse 50). The environment could also be an example – for instance a mountain as an image of unshakeability (verse 1000). Thus Mahānāma says that he is 'found wanting by the mountain with its many shrubs and trees' (verse 115). All in all, the mountain and forest environment loved by such early saints is one in which a person can develop such qualities as non-attached joy, fearlessness, energy, and full enlightenment. As Kāḷudāyin boldly affirms, 'While the wind blows cool and sweet smelling, I shall split ignorance asunder, as I sit on this mountain top' (verse 544).

Such appreciation of the forest is also found in Mahāyāna texts. Thus the poet Śāntideva praises the forest as a delightful place conducive to not clinging to anything as 'mine' (*Bca.* VIII.25, 27). In his *Śikṣā-samuccaya*, he cites the *Ugradatta-paripṛcchā* as saying that the forest-dweller should seek to be like the plants and trees, which are without a sense of self or possession (Ss. 193). He also says that if a *Bodhisattva* has to be away from the forest for a while, to teach or learn from others, he should retain a 'cave-and-forest mind' (*Ss.* 194).

While communal monastic life has always been important in Buddhism, time alone in the forests and mountains has also been so. It is an opportunity for developing certain qualities away from the support – and hindrances – posed by other humans. For all their positive potential, humans can also have many negative traits. Thus the Buddha agrees when a disciple says that humans are a deceitful 'tangle', while animals are a (relatively) 'open clearing' (*M.* 1.340–1). Consequently, a time in the company of animals and nature may be an aid to spiritual development. The Buddha's own association with and appreciation of such surroundings can be seen from the location of key events during his life. He was born under one tree, was enlightened under another, gave his first sermon in an animal park, and died between two trees. Nevertheless, he spent much of his time in and around towns and cities, teaching people. If he had been one who grasped at the beauties of nature, he would have kept clear of these.

Given all that has been said so far, it is clear that the Buddhist ideal for humanity's relationship with animals, plants and the landscape is one of harmonious co-operation. Buddhism emphasizes a disciplining and overcoming of the negativities within the conditioned nature of the human heart. Such an approach goes hand-in-hand with a friendly attitude to the environment. This can be seen in D. T. Suzuki's talk of making a 'good friend' of a climbed mountain, rather than of 'conquering' it (Suzuki, 1959: 334).

NON-HARMING OF ANIMALS

As an example of the pan-Indian value of *ahiṃsā*, or 'non-injury' (Tähtinen, 1976; Chapple, 1993), the first of the five precepts is to abstain from 'onslaught on living beings (literally breathers)' (see pp. 67–9). Its place as the most important precept is reflected in the fact that Sri Lankan villagers often sum up what Buddhism requires of them as 'not to kill animals' (Southwold, 1983: 66). While it is difficult to follow this fully, clearly a Buddhist should strive to minimize intentional injury to living beings. The law of karma backs up compassion as a motive for following the precept: it means that one *cannot* intentionally harm beings without this bringing harm to oneself at some time. Thus when the Buddha found some children molesting a snake with sticks, he said, 'Whoever, seeking his own happiness, harms with the rod pleasure-loving beings gets no happiness hereafter' (*Dhp.* 131).

The Theravādin commentator Buddhaghosa explains that it is worse to kill a human than an animal, or a larger or more substantial animal than a smaller or less substantial one (see p. 52). Among animals, it is worse to kill an elephant, which is both large and noble, and bad to kill a cow, which gives much to humans through its milk. In the monastic code of discipline, it is an offence requiring expiation if an animal is intentionally killed (*Vin.* IV.124–5). This is a lesser offence than killing a human, which requires permanent expulsion from the order, but an offence nevertheless. An offence requiring expiation is also committed if a monk uses water while knowing that it contains breathing creatures that will be killed by his action (*Vin.* IV.125); to avoid this, a water-strainer is part of the traditional kit of a monk (*Vin.* II.118). Again, it is an offence to sprinkle water on the ground if it is known that there are living creatures there that will be harmed by this (*Vin.* IV.48–9).

Animal sacrifice

An obvious abuse of animals during the Buddha's day was the killing of them as part of elaborate Brahmanical sacrificial rituals. The Buddha, along with leaders of other non-Brahmanical renunciant groups, was very critical of this, both because of the cruelty involved and because it did not bring about the objectives the brahmins hoped for. Rejecting the brahmins' view of it as a wholesome action leading to a happy rebirth, he saw it as having the opposite qualities (*A.* II.42). Such criticisms led to a great decrease in the use of animals in this way. The Buddha praised brahmins of old for not sacrificing animals – probably historically correct – and, in the *Kūṭadanta Sutta* (*D.* I.127–49), describes a sacrifice which he had himself conducted for a king in a past life. In this, no animals were killed, no trees were felled to act as sacrificial posts, workmen were not forced to help, and the only offerings were items such as butter and honey (*D.* I.141). Such a description was clearly meant as a contrast to the current mode of sacrificing! The emperor Asoka in fact banned animal sacrifices, at least in his capital city (Nikam and McKeon, 1959: 55).

Meat eating

Of course, the main reason why animals are killed is to provide food. Buddhist texts, and the actions of Buddhist leaders, have sought to discourage this. The *Mahā-rāja-kaniṣka-lekha*, addressed to a hunting emperor, says:

why do you commit such dreadful acts upon deer? Your eyes are similar to the eyes of a young deer. When the deer are startled, they look about with revolving eyeballs. Should you not therefore have compassion for these (deer)? (cited by Jamspal, *ASP.* 71–2)

The *Bodhisattva-bhūmi*, a Mahāyāna text, states that the *Bodhisattva*'s great generosity should not include giving away nets for catching animals, or a piece of land on which animals might be hunted or killed.[2] A popular *Jātaka* story (*J.* 1.145–53) tells of a king who drove two herds of deer into an enclosed park, so as to hunt them more easily. Nevertheless, when the king or his cook came to take a deer, many were still hurt and frightened in the chase. The herds' two leaders thus negotiated with the king and all agreed that there should be no chase. Each day, the single deer to be killed would be chosen by lot, and would go quietly. One day, it fell to the turn of a pregnant doe, so she appealed to the leader of her herd to postpone her turn until she had given birth. As he refused, she appealed to the leader of the other herd, known as the Banyan deer, who was the Buddha in a previous life. As he could not assign any other deer to take her place, he volunteered himself. When the king came and found him ready to die, he was astonished, for he had granted immunity to the two herd-leaders. On being told what had happened, he was so impressed by the deer's noble compassion that he spared the lives of both him and the doe. In response to the Banyan deer's requests, he then went on to spare all the other deer in the park, all deer outside the park, all four-footed beings, all birds and all fish. The deer then wandered free.

Such sparing of the lives of animals is therefore a respected ideal, known as the 'gift of fearlessness' (*abhaya-dāna*). The emperor Asoka made fifty-six official 'no slaughter' days per year, approximately four per lunar month, when no fish could be captured or sold, and animals might not be killed even in game reserves (Nikam and McKeon, 1959: 56). He gave up hunting trips – hunting being the favourite sport of Indian rulers – and went on pilgrimages instead. He banned the killing of a wide variety of non-food animals, birds and fish, and drastically reduced, then eliminated, the slaughter of animals to feed the large royal household (Nikam and McKeon, 1959: 55–6). In Sri Lanka, a number of Buddhist kings prohibited the slaughter of animals, either wholly or in certain circumstances. In China, the emperor Wu in 511 CE prohibited the use of fishing-nets, and exhorted his subjects to avoid killing beings, especially on the days dedicated to ancestor-worship. In Japan, the emperor Temmu in 675 CE restricted the use of some types of hunting devices and eating the meat of cows, horses, dogs and monkeys (Chapple, 1992: 57).

---

[2] 48b–49a; see Dayal, 1932: 175.

Meat eating in early and Theravāda Buddhism

It is often seen as surprising that vegetarianism (Prasad, 1979; Ruegg, 1980) is not more widespread among Buddhists than it is, given Buddhist teachings. In fact, the Buddha's emphasis was on the avoidance of killing. So it is worse to swat a fly – an immediate act of killing – than to eat the carcase of an already dead animal. Only in certain Mahāyāna texts is vegetarianism advocated. The position in early Buddhism, and in Theravāda lands, is as follows.

In the Buddha's day, vegetarianism was practised by Jains, though Jains see the vegetables eaten by them as containing a life-principle or soul (*jīva*). On one occasion, Jains accused the Buddha of knowingly eating an animal that had been specifically killed for him. The donor denied this, and the Buddha explained that a monk may eat meat provided it is 'pure in three respects': if the monk has not seen, heard or suspected that the animal has been killed specifically for him (*Vin.* 1.237–8). The commentary (on *Vin.* III.172) explains that, if a monk has suspicions, because of his having seen or heard of the donors hunting, fishing, or slaughtering an animal recently, he should ask about the meat and can only eat it if the being was not killed in order to feed him (*Vin. A.* 604–6; Bapat and Hirakawa, 1970: 395–6). Elsewhere, the Buddha explains that a monk receives food as a gift from a donor, and his lovingkindness for donors and other creatures is not compromised by such eating, if it is 'blameless' by being 'pure in three respects' (*M.* 1.386–71). He goes on to emphasize, though, that a donor generates much bad karma by killing a being so as to give alms to himself or a monk, through: (1) giving the order to fetch the animal, (2) its pain and distress as it is dragged with a rope around its neck, (3) giving the order to kill the animal, (4) its pain and distress while being killed, (5) the offering of the meat to a monk if it is of a type not allowable for a monk. Here, it can be noted, the evil of the act resides both in the actual actions of the killer and in the suffering of the killed.

Non-allowable food for monks, perhaps offered at times of scarcity, are: the flesh of elephants or horses, as people regarded these animals as royal emblems; dog-flesh and snake-flesh, as people saw them as disgusting; the flesh of lions, tigers, panthers, bears and hyenas, as such animals would smell the eaters and attack them (*Vin.* 1.219–20). These prohibitions were both to preserve people's faith in the *Saṅgha*, which was good for both the monks and lay people, and to protect monks from danger, a prudential, not moral, reason.

It is clear from the above that the Buddha would have frequently eaten 'blameless' meat given as alms. Thus the debate (for example Kapleau, 1981) over whether his last meal, literally 'pig-mild' (*sūkara-maddava*; *D.* II.127), was pork, or truffles dug up by pigs, is rather beside the point. It is notable that the Buddha actually resisted an attempt to make vegetarianism compulsory for monks (*Vin.* II.171–2). This was proposed by his cousin, the monk Devadatta, who is portrayed as having been proud and jealous of the Buddha's influence. In order to foment a schism, he proposed to the Buddha that all monks should both be vegetarian and follow a number of previously optional ascetic practices, such as living at the root of a tree. The Buddha refused, reaffirming that the practices were optional and meat was acceptable if it was 'pure in three respects'. Devadatta then attempted to lead his own order, under these rules, seeking to gain support from those who 'esteem austerity'. Elsewhere, such a purely external way of assessing someone's spiritual worth is seen as unreliable (*A.* II.71). Prior to his enlightenment, in his ascetic phase, Gotama had himself tried the teachings of those who taught 'purity through food', i.e. living off small amounts of only one type of food, be it jujube, beans, sesame or rice. Such externally orientated practices only made him thin and weak, though (*M.* I.80–1). The link between vegetarianism and extreme asceticism is also found in another passage, where it is included among the practices of self-tormenting ascetics, along with such things as nakedness, eating once a week, never sitting down, and pulling out hair (*M.* I.342–3). Such ascetic acts are not seen to 'purify' a person (*Sn.* 249), and meat is not what is to be seen as 'tainted fare' – breaking the precepts is 'tainted fare' (*Sn.* 242).

It is notable, above, that the Buddha did not even regard vegetarianism as an optional ascetic practice for monks. If they were given flesh-food, and it was 'pure' as described above, to refuse it would deprive the donor of the karmic fruitfulness engendered by giving alms-food. Moreover, it would encourage the monks to pick and choose what food they would eat. Food should be looked on only as a source of sustenance, without preferences. To believe that being a vegetarian is itself spiritually purifying would seem to be an example of the spiritual fetter of 'attachment to virtues and vows'. It is certainly the case that a feeling of moral superiority is a common danger among vegetarians: though it can be avoided! Likewise, vegetarians can in time become disgusted with meat, which can be seen as a form of negative attachment. In any case, as the above suggests, there are many worse actions than eating meat.

The preceding discussion is concerned with what is acceptable for a monk or nun, who must, with few exceptions, eat what is given to him or her. The considerations for a lay Buddhist are similar, but not identical. A lay person has more control over his or her food supply; ingredients must be directly obtained or bought. Lay people, within the limits of their means, make many preference-directed choices over what they eat. So for a lay person to avoid flesh-food (except, perhaps, when a guest) is not to refuse what someone has graciously offered, and not, as such, more 'picking and choosing' than is normal for a lay person. A lay vegetarian must, though, be wary of feelings of judgemental moral superiority, and negative attachment to meat. The latter is best dealt with by not refusing meat if one is someone's guest. While it is in some ways more feasible, then, for a lay person to be a vegetarian than a monk, one feature of Buddhism weighs against this leading to vegetarianism being more common among the laity. Normally, higher standards of behaviour are expected of a monk than of a lay person. If even monks are not expected to be vegetarian, a lay person might well think, 'why should I?'

In Theravāda countries, vegetarianism is universally admired but little practised.[3] There is a minority witness of vegetarians, however – such as the one-time governor of Bangkok – and most people have an uneasy conscience when they *think* about meat eating. Most lay people eat meat, though some abstain on observance days, or during periods of meditation. In Thailand, a few monks let it be known that they would prefer vegetarian food (Bunnag, 1973: 69–70). In Burma, Mahāsi Sayadaw recommends vegetarianism as the safest way for monks to ensure that their food is 'pure in three respects' (Mahasi, 1981: 45–7), and some nuns are vegetarian in periods of more ascetic practice (Kawanami, 1990: 27). In Sri Lanka, most nuns are vegetarian (Bartholomeusz, 1994: 140), many 'Protestant Buddhists' (see p. 112) have recommended vegetarianism, as does the Sarvōdaya Śramadāna movement (see pp. 225–34) (Bond, 1988: 280), and some see meat eating as hindering success in meditation (Bond, 1988: 200–4).

In general, it is seen as preferable to eat the meat of an animal which is less intelligent, and/or smaller (cf. p. 52), than the opposite. Thus it is worst of all to eat beef (in Burma prior to British colonization, it was a crime to kill a cow, as it was in the period 1960–2). It is seen as less bad to eat pork, then goat-meat or chicken, and less bad again to eat eggs. Nevertheless, eggs are always regarded as having been fertilized, so to boil or crack an egg is seen as killing a living being (Terweil, 1979: 188).

---

[3] Gombrich, 1971a: 260–2; King, 1964: 281–4; WFBR, 1983.

This means that, in Sri Lanka at least, no eggs are used in Buddhist mon-asteries, and pre-cracked 'Buddhist eggs' are sold to the middle-class pious Buddhists. It is seen as least bad to eat fish, an unintelligent form of life that needs little effort to kill. Fish is by far the most common form of flesh eaten, as is reflected in a saying on the abundance of food in Thailand, 'There are fish in the water, there is rice in the fields.' Nevertheless, the Buddhist ideal rules out even killing fish. This is expressed in one *Jātaka* story, where the Buddha in a past life is said to have been a crane who only ate fish when he found them already dead (*J.* 1.206–8).

It is clearly the case, though, that any lay Buddhist should not kill an animal for food, or tell someone else to do so. Either action clearly breaks the first precept. The question arises, though, whether buying meat from a butcher is participating in wrong action by encouraging it. One passage (*A.* 11.253) says that a person will be reborn in hell if he kills and encourages others to do so. 'Encouraging' alone is not specified as having this effect, but in any case, such encouraging would normally be seen to be of a direct form, for example 'why don't you go hunting?', or *ordering* a carcase from a butcher (Mahasi, 1981: 46). Clearly, to ask a butcher to kill an animal for one is to break the first precept. In the West, most food animals are killed in large abattoirs, and 'butchers' only sell the meat. Buddhist countries lack such large-scale slaughter-houses (they would be seen as hells on earth), and so obtaining meat is more likely to have the attendant danger of direct involvement in an animal's death. This probably helps to reduce the extent of meat eating.

To make one's living as a butcher, hunter or fisherman clearly comes under the category of 'wrong livelihood' (*A.* 11.208), to be avoided by all sincere Buddhists. Certainly one finds that, in Buddhist societies, butch-ers (slaughterers and meat salesmen) are usually non-Buddhists, often Muslims (Spiro, 1971: 45). By making a living by or from killing, they are seen as depraved people, and are often treated as outcasts. Buddhist fishermen are more common, though they have a low status in society on account of their livelihood. In Sri Lanka, the All Ceylon Buddhist Congress recommended, in 1985, that the government should not support commercial fishing through having a Ministry of Fisheries (Bond, 1988: 118). Yet, as fish are seen as a lower form of life than land animals, it is seen as less bad to kill them. The excuse is sometimes made that they are not *killed*, but just die when taken out of the water. This is evidently a case of trying to distance oneself from what is recognized as an unwholesome action. In South-east Asia, people often catch their own fish, which clearly breaks the first precept; but if a living is not made from this, it is not seen as 'wrong livelihood'.

Meat eating in Mahāyāna Buddhism

In the Mahāyāna tradition, Śāntideva had an aspiration that all should avoid meat (*Ss.* 33), and cited the *Bodhisattva-Prātimokṣa* as saying that flesh-food should not be given to a monk, but if it was, he should eat it (*Ss.* 143). Some texts give arguments for vegetarianism, such advocacy clearly having been facilitated by the climate of opinion that the Buddhist emphasis had helped to create. Jain criticism of meat eating by Buddhists may have also played its part, but the Mahāyāna emphasis on compassion seems to have been a key factor. Thus the *Mahā-parinirvāṇa Sūtra* says that eating meat 'extinguishes the seed of great compassion' (Kapleau, 1981: 34), and has the Buddha explicitly saying, 'I order the various disciples from today that they cannot any more partake of meat.' Ruegg (1980) notes that vegetarianism was first emphasized in texts, such as this, which focused on the idea of the *Tathāgata-garbha*, or Buddha-potential, in all beings. This concept is also found in the *Laṅkāvatāra Sūtra*, in which a late section has a series of arguments against meat eating,[4] and has the Buddha *denying* the scriptural idea of it being 'blameless' to eat meat that is 'pure in three respects'. Such a direct contradiction of an earlier scriptural idea is unusual in Mahāyāna texts; non-acceptable ideas are generally subverted, reinterpreted, or seen purely as a 'skilful means'. The arguments of the *Sūtra* can be summarized as follows:

1 All beings, in some past rebirth, have been one's close relative, such as one's mother, or friend. One should look on all beings as if they were one's only child, i.e. with lovingkindness, and not eat them.

2 The smell of a meat eater frightens beings and gives a meat eater a bad reputation.

3 Eating meat by Buddhists means that the *Dharma* will be spoken ill of, and the *Bodhisattva*s will lose their hearers.

4 Meat stinks.

5 Meat eating prevents progress in meditation, and leads to arrogance, as do onions, garlic and alcohol (here the influence of Hindu yoga ideas seem apparent).

---

[4] Suzuki, 1932: 211–23; 1930: 368–71.

6 The meat eater sleeps uneasily, with bad dreams (cf. that lovingkindness is said to lead to good sleep); he or she is anxious, with bad digestion and bad health. It is karmically fruitful for a *Bodhisattva* to eat grains, beans, honey, oil, ghee, molasses and sugar etc., and also healthy to do so.

7 Meat eating leads to a bad rebirth as a carnivorous animal, or a low-caste human; vegetarianism leads to a good rebirth.

8 If no meat is eaten, no-one will destroy life, as there will be no market for the bodies.

Here, various types of argument are used: an appeal to love, and to the duty of returning past kindnesses (1); prudence (2); the need to protect the *Dharma* (3); disgust (4); spiritual pragmatism (5); mental and physical health (6); karmic effect (6 and 7); and good indirect consequences of abstinence (8). The *Sūtra* concludes that it is karmically fruitful to avoid flesh-food, that the arguments defending meat eating are spurious, and that the Buddha never ate meat.

By the early fifth century CE, in the Buddhist heart-lands of Northeast India, nearly all classes but the lowest came to be vegetarian (Legge, 1886: 43). This influenced Hinduism so that, today, members of the higher castes are often vegetarian. Outside India, it is in Eastern Buddhism that Buddhist arguments for vegetarianism have had a notable effect. The emperor Wu, in 511, included a ban on meat eating among other animal-protecting legislation. This helped lead to the long-term reduction of meat eating by Chinese Buddhists, and the virtual end of meat eating in Chinese monasteries and temples (Welch, 1967: 112–13). Such a requirement for vegetarianism by monks and nuns is enshrined in the supplementary monastic code of Eastern Buddhism known as the *Brahmajāla Sūtra* (Dharma Realm, 1981; De Groot, 1893). Among pious lay people, vegetarianism has been common, being seen as an implication of either the first precept or the *Bodhisattva* vows (Welch, 1967: 365). Vegetarian feasts have been common at festivals, and when the Communist government came to laicize forcibly many monks, quite a proportion turned to running vegetarian restaurants. For Chinese Buddhists, to see Theravāda monks eating meat often comes as a shock, as it is seen as very unmonkly behaviour!

Chinese attitudes have also broadly prevailed in Korea and Japan. It is claimed that Japan was 'essentially a vegetarian country' until the middle of the nineteenth century (Kapleau, 1981: 34). Certainly, beef was not eaten. Since the opening of Japan to the West, in 1868, though,

Western meat-eating habits have gradually come to have a considerable influence. The monasteries, especially Zen ones, remain formally vegetarian, though it has been observed that trainee monks do eat meat when away from the monastery (Kapleau, 1981: 27).

In Northern Buddhism, while the tradition is Mahāyāna, the harsh, cold climate, yielding little plant protein, has meant that most people, except for some Lamas, eat meat (Bell, 1928: 217–34). Those Lamas who eat meat, though, may perform a ceremony to help the dead animal gain a good rebirth. A common livelihood is as a nomadic herdsman up on the high pastures of Tibet or on the steppes of Mongolia, so livestock play an important part in the economy of these regions. Nevertheless, people often abstain from meat on observance days – when, in pre-Communist Tibet, slaughtering was banned – and butchers are despised. The most direct method of killing an animal – with a knife – is generally avoided, suffocation being the preferred method. While Theravādins prefer to eat small creatures, the Tibetans reason that it is better to kill a few large animals (cattle, sheep and goats) than many small ones (Ekvall, 1964: 75). The fact that this fits in with the abundance of fish in Theravāda lands and cattle etc. in Tibet is surely no accident! The widespread avoidance of fish and fowl is also related to the practice of disposing of human remains by compassionately making them available to birds and fish. Tibetans are noted for their kindness to animals, and even have scruples about eating honey, for this is seen as entailing theft from bees, a view also found in Sri Lanka (Schmithausen, 1991b: 43). A similar restraint is seen in a story about the Tibetan hermit-saint Milarepa (Mi-la-ras-pa; 1040–1123). When given some meat by hunters passing his isolated cave, he used this very sparingly to supplement his existing diet of nettles. Once maggots started eating the meat, though, he stopped doing so: not out of disgust, but because he felt that clearing out the maggots and eating the meat would be stealing it from them (Evans-Wentz, 1951: 199)!

In the West, vegetarianism among Buddhists is more common than in many parts of Buddhist Asia. This is due to Western expectations of what 'non-harming' Buddhists should do, a general increase in vegetarianism in the West, along with ease of obtaining good vegetarian food, and the influence of the Eastern Buddhist model, particularly via America. In Britain, when food is offered to Western monks trained in the Thai tradition, Thais often give dishes containing some flesh, but Westerners give vegetarian ones. This is gradually having the effect of the Thais offering more vegetarian ones.

Animal husbandry

The emperor Asoka prohibited the castration or branding of animals on various holy days, as well as completely banning the killing of young goats, lambs or pigs, or of their mothers while still in milk for them (Nikam and McKeon, 1959: 56–7). In China, the *Brahmajāla Sūtra* code says that one should not sell domestic animals, or keep cats, badgers and silk worms (cf. *Uss.* 76, 82). In Theravāda countries, the 'wrong livelihood' of 'trade in flesh' is generally seen to include keeping livestock for slaughter. In rural Sri Lanka, people keep chickens and pigs for slaughter, though they may evasively refer to their goats as 'pets' (Gombrich, 1971a: 261). In Burma, there has been little domestication of animals, except as beasts of burden. The keeping of pigs and chickens has existed on a small scale, but government attempts to increase it have not been very successful (Pfanner and Ingersoll, 1962: 345), and it is rare to find a Buddhist cattle-farmer (Spiro, 1971: 45). In Thailand, around a third of people in a typical village might keep pigs and chickens, on a small scale, and there has been a modest rise in numbers of animals (for example a rise from 3.15 million pigs to 5 million between 1950 and 1970), though many people are reluctant to respond to government encouragement to keep cattle. Of those who do keep animals for slaughter, some see it as an evil occupation, but say 'I have to make a living.' Older people, who are generally more religious, are least likely to be involved in animal husbandry, even of chickens (Pfanner and Ingersoll, 1962: 355).

In the cold climate of Tibet, herding animals is a common form of livelihood, but killing them is seen as a necessary evil. It is avoided by older, more pious members of herding families, and it is preferred that an animal has a natural death, for example falling off a cliff (though this is sometimes deliberately engineered).

In Japan, a common practice is for those who live from killing animals to conduct memorial rites (*kuyō*) for them: for cows by farmers, fish by fishermen, game by hunters. These are performed as a kind of thanks, and perhaps apology, and to ease the animals on their way to a better rebirth. Such rites, though, are even performed for intimate inanimate objects such as an old pair of spectacles, and are now also carried out for pets (Hoshino and Takeda, 1987: 310).

Pest control

The elimination of pests clearly presents an ethical problem for Buddhists: Vasubandhu says that it is deluded to say that poisonous pests *should* be killed (*AKB*. IV.68d), and Asoka's edicts include a ban on the killing of vermin (Nikam and McKeon, 1959: 56). Where possible, there is often a preference for removing pests to a safe distance and then releasing them.[5] This is done with rats, mice, insects and even snakes, except the most vicious and deadly ones.[6] Nevertheless, Ingersoll (1966: 203–4) cites the opinion of a pious Thai villager, in 1960, when he heard that the government were killing some of the many stray dogs, some rabid, in Bangkok: it would be better not to kill them, and they would only bite one if it was one's karma. Likewise, Burmese villagers have been generally unwilling to assist in DDT spraying to kill malaria-spreading mosquitoes (Spiro, 1971: 45). Behaviour towards pests does vary, though. In Thailand, mosquitoes are readily killed, and insecticides are used if they can be afforded (Terweil, 1979: 191). Thais will generally kill rodents and vermin which infest gardens and paddy fields (Bunnag, 1973: 143), though Tibetans do not harm the bold rats and mice that they share their homes and monasteries with (Ekvall, 1964: 76). In Sri Lanka, insecticides are used, though with some remorse and sadness; most people – even monks – (Gombrich, 1971a: 262) will kill harmful insects, but will put up with considerable annoyance from others, and step aside to avoid treading on them (Southwold, 1983: 67–8). Richard Gombrich reports that Sri Lankan villagers, in killing small creatures such as insects, 'do not display the compunction or squeamishness sometimes found in the urban middle class' (1971a: 262). Beyond this, though, uneasiness sets in. Likewise, Barend Terweil reports that for Thai villagers, the killing of animals larger than insects 'is often accompanied with a marked discomposure' (1979: 191), though Jane Bunnag says that most in central Thailand 'appeared to feel no compunction' in killing a pig to feed their family (1973: 143).

If Buddhists do decide to kill pests, they may seek to do so in roundabout ways. For example, when a caretaker military government took over Burma in the late 1950s, it wanted to decrease the large stray-dog population in the capital, Rangoon. So as not to be too offensive to Buddhist sensibilities, only *some* of the meat put down to poison the dogs actually contained poison. This meant that it could be argued (?) that the dogs chose the poisoned pieces (and that when they did so, it was due to their past bad karma) (cf. King, 1964: 281). Similarly, in a valley of Kashmir bordering Tibet, Buddhists feel that they have to kill predatory wolves, but seek to do so in a way which obscures personal responsibility

---

[5] King, 1964: 280; Ekvall, 1964: 76.
[6] Spiro, 1971: 46, 449; Hall, 1902: 234–6; Southwold, 1983: 67.

(p. 54). In Tibet, bugs found in clothing will only be removed, not killed, though garments may be hung out on very cold nights, so that the bugs die without being directly 'killed'. Such an act is still seen to generate bad karmic results, though (Ekvall, 1964: 76). From Burma comes the example of people's ground-nut crops being ravaged by a horde of rats (Pfanner and Ingersoll, 1962: 345–6). The villagers consulted the monks, the more 'liberal' of whom said that killing the rats was an evil but was unavoidable; moreover, some of the money from the saved crop could be used for religious donations, so as to generate karmic fruitfulness and, it was hoped, counteract the evil. Most of the farmers agreed with this line of reasoning. Another possible attitude in this matter is to say that, if pests must be killed, it should be done in a spirit of lovingkindness, or, if this is seen as self-contradictory, at least lack of cruelty. In line with this, perhaps, is the Japanese practice of conducting memorial rites for dead vermin (Suzuki, 1959: 379); a company which exterminates white ants has even built a memorial tower to them at a Buddhist site (Hoshino and Takeda, 1987: 310). Sometimes a monk may seek to get round the detailed monastic rules against any participation in killing by indirectly suggest-ing to a lay person that he or she should kill a pest. Gombrich even gives the example of a monk *telling* a young temple servant to kill a cockroach when clearing out a cupboard; but the pious boy merely swept it outside (1971a: 262).

Animal experimentation

The Buddhist ideal of non-injury to animal life clearly has implications for the use of animals in product testing, and in medical research and training. The modern world 'uses' animals for these purposes in large numbers. From a Buddhist perspective, this might be seen as analogous to the animal sacrifices of ancient Brahmanism. In one case, the animals were sacrificed in the name of religion, in the other in the name of 'science' and 'knowledge'. In both cases, the *motive* is, in part at least, to bring benefit to human beings. In the West, the public mood has swung increasingly against the abuse of animals in cosmetics testing. There is also some degree of disquiet concerning the use of animals in school biology classes, where much or all of the knowledge gained could be obtained from video-tapes, slides and models. The use of animals in medical research at least has strong Utilitarian arguments in its favour. Buddhist ethics, though, is not generally based on the principle that the ends justify the means (except in certain versions of Mahāyāna 'skilful means' theory). From the traditional Buddhist perspective, it is more certain that killing an animal is wrong than that generating better drugs etc. from experiments on it is good (cf. King, 1964: 281). If the early Buddhist attitude to meat eating is applied in this area, though, it will be acceptable for a Buddhist to take drugs which others have developed using animal research. The Mahāyāna ethic would give an ambivalent answer: the precedent of vegetarianism would suggest opposition to drug-testing in that way; the principal of skilful means (see pp. 134–8) might suggest that it was acceptable, where really necessary. However, the precedents of skilful means cases only give possible legitimation for killing someone about to do a heinous act: not for killing innocent beings supposedly to help other beings. Nevertheless, the Western Zen monk Saidō Kennaway regretfully accepts that many developments in modern drugs and surgery have depended on animal dissections and experimentation. He goes on to say:

From a Buddhist point of view, anyone prepared to do this has to know and accept the karma of his actions. This would entail trying to do as little harm as possible, using alternative methods if available, killing only if absolutely necessary, treating the being with tender respect and making sure the knowledge is put to good use. (Shasta Abbey, 1980: 23)

Of course, much testing is not necessary, but arises from an atmosphere of commercial secrecy and rivalry. It might also be pointed out that many modern ills arise as the result of chosen life-styles, for example from smoking, drinking and diet. One might ask if animals should pay the price of alleviating the products of human folly (Story, 1976: 369–71). But, from a Buddhist perspective, that does not rule out compassionate help for those who thus suffer. In any case, most Buddhists would see any angry and violent means of opposition to animal experimentation, by groups such as the (UK) Animal Liberation Front, as unwholesome. Action more in line with traditional Buddhist behaviour would be to liberate animals by *buying* them from establishments that would otherwise experiment on them. Jainism and Buddhism face a similar dilemma. In India, where Jains are very active and influential in the pharmaceutical industry, animals are used for drug testing if really necessary, but are then 'rehabilitated' by recuperation facilities maintained by the laboratories; if possible, they are then released back into the wild (Chapple, 1992: 59).

As regards debate on this issue in modern Buddhist countries, information is sparse. In Thailand, graduate nurses connected to Mahidol

University, which has a 'Center for Animal Experimentation', now have bioethics courses which include a discussion of animal rights (Lindbeck, 1984: 25). Japan also uses laboratory animals, and the tension with Buddhist norms is dealt with by many companies and research facilities performing annual memorial rites to honour the animals they 'use'.[7] Among Western Buddhists, there is the Buddhist Animal Rights Group, in Britain, and the Buddhists Concerned for Animals group in America (WFBR, 1984: 73–9). The latter focuses on animal experimentation, as well as factory farming and trapping.

POSITIVE REGARD, AND HELP, FOR ANIMALS

As all sentient beings like happiness and dislike pain, however much their specific desires and sensitivities vary, the *Karaṇīya-metta Sutta* speaks of radiating lovingkindness to all types of beings (see pp. 104–5). The eleventh-century *Bodhisattv-āvadāna-kalpalatā* says 'I cannot endure the pain even of an ant' (Dayal, 1932: 199–200), and one *Jātaka* story concerns a bull who would pull one hundred carts, to win his owner a bet, only when the latter stopped using a harsh tone to get him going (*J.* I.191–3). Thus 'hard words gall even animals'.

In the nineteenth century, Fielding Hall remarked that animals were very well treated in Burma as compared to those in India. Even owner-less dogs were well fed and also very tame. He describes the Burman's attitude to animals as that of 'the gentle toleration of a father to very little children who are stupid and troublesome often, but are very lovable' (1902: 239). Yet while Buddhists are encouraged to be kind to animals, sentimentality is not encouraged, for this goes against the ideal of non-attachment. In principle, this means that lovingkindness should no less be shown to alien, 'uncuddly' creates such as lobsters than to dogs or cats.

Both humans and animals respond better to those who they feel are friendly, so that lovingkindness is seen to protect a person. Accordingly, the Buddha is said to have halted the charge of the rampaging elephant Nāḷāgiri by suffusing it with lovingkindness, so that it ground to a halt and bowed its head to him (*Vin.* II.194–6). On another occasion, he taught that the reason a monk was bitten by a snake and had died was that he had failed to radiate lovingkindness to the snakes and other wild animals (*A.* II.72–3). Even today, monks meditating in the forests of

---

[7] Hoshino and Takeda, 1987: 310; LaFleur, 1992: 145.

Plate 4. The Buddha with a devoted monkey and elephant before him, at a temple in Ko Samui, Thailand.

Thailand, Burma and Sri Lanka radiate this quality to the forest animals, including prowling hungry tigers, as a protection. There are many stories of this working (Tambiah, 1984: 86–7, 88–90).

Animals are seen as responding in a positive way to those who have a kindly presence. Once, the Buddha retired to the forest to be away from some quarrelsome monks. There, an elephant and a monkey were his companions, bringing him offerings.[8] In the 'Three Worlds According to King Ruang', a fourteenth-century Thai work, it is said that, through the emperor Asoka's goodness, pigeons and parrots brought him high-quality rice, wild rats nibbled it so as to produce white rice, bees came to make honey for him, bears brought his cooks firewood, and beautiful birds came to display and sing for him (Reynolds and Reynolds, 1982: 175)!

In the Theravādin monastic code, monks are allowed to release trapped animals or fish, if this is from compassion rather than a desire to steal (*Vin.* III.62–3). In a more positive vein, a *Jātaka* story tells of the *Bodhisattva* as a hermit who, during a drought, ensured that wild animals got water (*J.* 1.449–51). In doing this, he was so busy that he had no time to get himself food, so that the animals gathered it for him, in thanks. In the *Jātaka-mālā*, it is said that, as a boy, Gotama saved a goose which his cousin Devadatta had shot with an arrow, and went on to nurse it back to health (Chapple, 1992: 53). One famous story, from the Mahāyāna *Suvarṇa-prabhāsottama Sūtra*,[9] says that the Buddha, in a past life, even gave his body to a starving tigress that was too weak to sustain herself and her cubs, thus bringing his generosity to full perfection. In Eastern Buddhism, the *Bodhisattva* code known as the *Brahmajāla Sūtra* says: 'One should be willing to forsake one's entire body, one's flesh, hands and feet as an offering to starving tigers, wolves, lions, and hungry ghosts.'[10] Altruism towards animals can also be at a very simple level: thus it is said that it is karmically fruitful even to throw dishwater into a pool or cesspit for insects and other creatures to feed on (*A.* 1.161). The Mahāyāna philosopher Nāgārjuna also advised a king to offer food to hungry ghosts, dogs, birds and ants before and after eating, and even to have men put food at the openings of ant-hills (*RPR.* 249–50).

The Zen monk Ryōkwan (1758–1831) acted lovingly even to the lice with which he was afflicted. On early warm winter's days, he would carefully remove them from his underwear to warm in the sun, and then pop them back (Suzuki, 1959: 372)! An even more altruistic act is attributed to the great Indian scholar-monk Asaṅga (fourth or fifth century CE). For twelve years he meditated in a cave with a view to gaining a vision of the *Bodhisattva* Maitreya, the embodiment of lovingkindness. One day, frustrated at his lack of success, he saw a poor dog afflicted with a maggot-filled sore. He wished to help the dog, but not harm the

---

[8] *Vin.* 1.352–3; *Dhp. A.* 1.58–60.

[9] *Svb.* 202–40; Conze, 1959: 24–6; see also the *Jātaka-mālā* (Khoroche, 1989: ch. 1).

[10] Dharma Realm, 1981, 150; cited by Chapple, 1992: 53.

maggots. To pull them from the sore would harm them, so, with great compassion, he coaxed them out onto his warm tongue, and then was about to give them a small portion of his own flesh to feed on. At this point, the dog and maggots disappeared, and Maitreya stood where they had been: Maitreya's testing of him had elicited great love, and thus the long-awaited vision (Thurman, 1981: 22–4).

Among the charitable deeds of the emperor Asoka was the planting of medicinal herbs, and the development of wayside wells and shade-trees, for both humans and animals (Nikam and McKeon, 1959: 64). This accords with one of the duties of compassionate *Cakkavatti*: protect-ing animals and birds (*D.* III.61). One also finds 'retirement homes' for cows in Burma. Buddhist veterinary care would not naturally include the killing of an ill or injured animal, for this would still be a breach of the first precept, and is seen as not unlike killing a sick human. Buddhist compassion would urge the caring for the animal, but not 'putting it to sleep' (Schmithausen, 1991b: 46).

Buddhism also regards the liberating of animals from death as a kar-mically fruitful act, and in Eastern Buddhism, the *Brahmajāla Sūtra* code requires this. In Chinese Buddhism, particularly at the time of certain festivals or holy days, crabs are returned to the sea, birds are released to the sky, and chickens are saved from slaughter (Welch, 1967: 378–82). Livestock are sometimes released into the care of large monasteries, perhaps with contributions for their upkeep. Such monasteries may also have a pool for fish rescued from fishmongers. Unfortunately, they are not always properly fed. Liberating beings may be an act of worship to Kuan-yin, the *Bodhisattva* embodiment of compassion, or to generate karmic fruitfulness to ward off a natural disaster. Thus Hong Kong Buddhists, during a very bad drought in 1963, released sparrows, turtles, monkeys, deer, tortoises, shellfish, crabs, snakes and eels. Such liberated beings have the three refuges recited on their behalf, to help them towards better future rebirths.

In Burma, people feed the protected turtles and fish at monasteries, and it is seen as good to rescue fish from pools that are drying out, and to transfer them to a river. The freeing of domesticated animals is seen to be very karmically fruitful, and is done collectively in a special cere-mony, to protect the community (Spiro, 1971: 271–2). In 1962, the govern-ment closed slaughter-houses for three days and released 602 animals, when astrologers predicted a world calamity. Fielding Hall also tells how he went without a meal of chicken when someone bought the bird des-tined for the pot from his cook, paying over the odds (1902: 231). In Sri

Lanka, the monks of isolated communities occasionally organize a boycott of a butcher's shop, so as to save lives (Gombrich, 1971a: 260). The forest monks also look after orphaned animals such as squirrels or bear cubs (Carrithers, 1983: 291). In Thailand, a person might leave some money in their will for the dogs living in a monastery compound (Bunnag, 1973: 119), and retired draught animals are sometimes allowed to live out their days in peace (Terweil, 1979: 192). At certain festivals, people also buy birds from traders, so as to do the good deed of releasing them. An unfortunate side-effect of this custom, though, is that birds are deliberately captured for this purpose! Turtles released in monastery canals are also sometimes over-crowded and not properly fed (Burns, 1977: 25–37).

PLANTS, TREES AND FORESTS

From the beginning of Buddhism, the forest has represented the ideal place for meditation for monks (see pp. 154–5), as seen in the refrain, 'These are the roots of trees, these are empty places. Meditate, monks . . .' (see, for example, *M.* 1.118). Indeed, Theravāda monks specializing in meditation are known as 'forest monks', whether or not they actually reside in the forest (Carrithers, 1983; Tambiah, 1984). For lay people, forests may not be so inviting, but there is karmic fruitfulness in planting groves and fruit-trees for human use (*S.* 1.33). Devotion to the Buddha may also be shown by watering of, and making offerings before, the type of tree under which Gotama attained Buddhahood (*ficus religiosa*), known as *Bodhi*-trees.[11]

The Buddhist ideal of non-harming is one that extends to all sentient beings. What, though, of plants?[12] The Jains certainly thought that plants, and even minerals, contained life-principles or souls (*jīvas*) and were part of the round of rebirths. Buddhist texts, though, do not say that it is possible to be reborn as a plant,[13] or for a plant to be reborn, and later texts explicitly deny this (*AKB.* IV.36a–b). Nevertheless, the Buddha is described as having avoided harm to seed and plant life (*D.* 1.5), and there are monastic rules against harming trees and plants. It is

---

[11] Harvey, 1990b; Gombrich and Obeyesekere, 1988: 384–410.

[12] For a detailed discussion on plants and sentience in early Buddhism, see Schmithausen, 1991a.

[13] An exception is the 'Tale of *Saṅgharakṣita*', cited in the *Śikṣā-samuccaya* (*Ss.* 58–9) as referring to bad monks reborn as 'trees, leaves, flowers and fruit'. As this also has the nonsensical idea of such monks being reborn as non-organic things such as walls or mortars, though, it is of little significance.

an offence requiring expiation (by acknowledgement) for a monk to fell a tree or to ask someone else to do so (*Vin.* IV.34–5). Here, the occasion for making the rule is that a god who had lived in a felled tree complained to the Buddha. In addition, lay people complained that Buddhist monks, in felling trees, were 'harming life that is one-facultied' (*ekindriya jīva*): i.e. only possessing the sense of touch (*Vin. A.* 575), an idea found in Jainism. The Buddha thus bans the destruction of 'vegetable growths' by monks. One might speculate that the 'one-facultied life' could refer to the many small insects living on trees and plants. However, the explanation of the above rule only refers to various kinds of plants and trees, not to the insects that live on them. Indeed, the rule against monks wandering during the rainy season was made to avoid people's accusations that Buddhist monks were 'injuring life that is one-facultied *and* bringing many small creatures (literally: breathers) to destruction' by trampling growing crops and grasses (*Vin.* 1.137; my italic). Nor could 'one-facultied life' refer to the tree deity in the above passage: as the god is seen as conversing with the Buddha, he could hardly be seen as lacking all senses except touch. In another passage on tree-felling, after a reference to people's concern over 'one-facultied life', the Buddha criticizes a monk who has cut down a large tree used as a shrine, saying 'For, foolish man, people are percipient of a life-principle in a tree'[14] (*Vin.* III.156). There is also a rule against monks digging the ground or asking someone to do so (*Vin.* IV.32–3). Here, there is again reference to concern over 'one-facultied life', and then to people who 'are percipient of life-principle(s) in the ground'. In both cases, the motive of the rule seems to be to avoid offending popular sensibilities. The belief in 'one-facultied life' is not endorsed by the Buddha, but it is not actually criticized either. After a careful examination of the evidence on this in early Buddhist texts, Lambert Schmithausen holds that plants were seen as a 'border-line case' as regards sentient life, and there was no real interest in resolving the matter as a theoretical issue (1991a: 69). The *Abhidhamma*, though, lacks reference to 'one-facultied life' in its very detailed analysis of phenomena. In practice, however, plants were still included within the ambit of non-violence for monks (Schmithausen, 1991b: 6–7).

The relationship of a tree-deity to 'his' or 'her' tree is generally seen

---

[14] 'Jīva-saññino hi moghapurisa manussā rukkhasmim.' I. B. Horner, in *Book of the Discipline*, vol. 1, p. 267, translates 'For, foolish man, in a tree are people having consciousness as living beings.' While this is a possible translation, it is highly unlikely that any living being(s) within a tree would be seen as *manussā*: people or humans. It is much more likely that this refers back to the 'people' (*manussā*) who had expressed concern over 'one-facultied life'.

as a close one. In some texts, while a deity may be harmed in the process of felling his or her tree, he or she may move on to another one (*Vin.* IV.34). In one *Jātaka* story, though, such a deity is referred to as being 'reborn' (*nibbata*) in his tree, and the tree is referred to both as the deity's 'mortal body' (*sarīra*) and as his 'mansion' (*vimāna*). In this case, the god's life will last only as long as his mansion does (*J.* IV.153–6).

There are no rules against lay people felling trees (*Miln.* 266), but it is seen as an act of treachery to a friend to cut off the branch of a tree under whose shade one has rested (*J.* V.240; *Pv.* II.9, verse 3). Nevertheless, it is seen as bad form for a tree-deity to prevent his or her tree from bountifully fruiting, if this is simply because one ungrateful individual has cut a branch off it after enjoying its fruit (*A.* III.369–70). In this case, it is said that the god Sakka will summon the tree-deity to instruct the deity to 'keep tree-*dhamma*': to allow people to take from the tree's roots, bark, leaves and fruit without getting upset. If the monastic ideal is one of complete non-violence to trees, then, the lay ideal is one of co-operative harmony with them and their deities.

In a similar way, the monastic prohibition on digging the ground has some effect on lay practice, too. In Tibet, people are careful in digging the ground for fear of hurting worms etc. Likewise, in Southern Buddhist lands, some abstain from farming on observance days, to avoid injury to worms and insects. The image of the very pious lay person certainly reflects the monastic ideal. One early text (*M.* II.51–2) speaks of the behaviour of a lay 'Non-returner' saint, who was the supporter of a former Buddha:

> Ghaṭīkāra the potter, sire, is one who has laid aside jewels and wrought gold . . . does not dig the earth with a spade or with his own hands; willingly he makes a vessel from the soil of a bank that is crumbling or scratched out by rats and dogs.

Clearly, this is an ideal for an abstemious few, but it is an ideal nevertheless!

In China and Japan, there was much debate on the nature of plants and trees.[15] Mahāyāna teachings promised the enlightenment of 'all sentient beings'. Did this mean that plants, trees and the land were excluded from enlightenment, and devoid of the Buddha-nature, the enlightenment-potential? In China, Chi-t'sang (549–623), of the San-lun school, held that non-sentient beings such as plants and trees had the Buddha-nature, but as they lacked a mind, they could not actualize this potential

---

[15] LaFleur: 1973–4; Shaw: 1985.

by experiencing Buddhahood. The T'ien-t'ai monk Chan-jan (711–82), on the other hand, argued that as the Buddha-nature is the immutable mind at the base of all phenomena, even soil and dust, nothing could be excluded from Buddhahood. Certainly all could progress towards it by appropriate action, even if this were through the minute movements present in soil. In Japan, the indigenous reverence for nature fuelled the continuing debate. Ryōgen (912–85), of the Tendai school, held that plants were sentient and that their growth was a process of quiet, steady training towards enlightenment, which came when they bore fruit. Their stillness was that of a being in meditation. Shōshin (1189–1204), on the other hand, denied that plants and trees were sentient. He pointed out, moreover, that no *Sūtra* or treatise said that they could attain enlightenment. Kūkai (774–835), the founder of the tantric Shingon school, however, saw all phenomena, sentient or non-sentient, as manifestations of the body and mind of Mahā-vairocana Buddha, and thus not devoid of mind, the prerequisite for Buddhahood. Dōgen (1200–53), founder of Sōtō Zen in Japan, went even further. He saw the whole phenomenal world as not *manifesting* or *containing* the Buddha-nature, the ultimate, but as *being* it. While such Mahāyāna texts as the *Mahā-parinirvāṇa Sūtra* had denied that walls and stones had the Buddha-nature, he asserted they, like all else, *were* it. The whole changing flux of empty phenomena was nothing but the Buddha-nature, within which it was not possible to designate anything as 'non-sentient'. For him, 'There is a world of living beings in a blade of grass', as in water, air, fire, earth or a staff (Batchelor and Brown, 1992: 12). Each aspect of nature has an intrinsic value as part of ultimate reality, and to let go of oneself in full awareness of the sound of the rain or the cry of a monkey is to fathom this in a moment of non-dual awareness. As he put it:

The ocean speaks and mountains have tongues – that is the everyday speech of the Buddha . . . If you can speak and hear such words, you will be one who truly comprehends the entire universe. (Nishiyama and Stevens, 1975: 104–5)

For Dōgen as for the nature-poet Saigyō (1118–90), being in tune with nature was salvific.

CONSERVATION AND ENVIRONMENTALISM

The emperor Asoka prohibited the burning of forests without reason (Nikam and McKeon, 1959: 56), and the *Brahmajāla Sūtra*, popular in China, said that one should not set fire to hills, woodland or fields.

Nevertheless, conservation of species and habitat is not something that Buddhist cultures, in pre-modern times, have had to give much attention to, as Buddhist values have meant that the environment has not been over-exploited. Kabilsingh (1988) points out that on the small, crowded island of Sri Lanka, wildlife has not been virtually eliminated, as in many other regions of the world, this being largely due to religious sensibilities. Places such as the ancient Buddhist capitals of Anurādhapura and Polonnaruwa have acted as wildlife sanctuaries. Hunting is rare – being done by some poor people in remote areas (Gombrich, 1971a: 261) – as it is in Burma, where only non-Buddhists seem to do it (Spiro, 1971: 45). In pre-Communist Tibet, 'herds of wild blue sheep, yak, deer and flocks of migrating birds would travel with Tibetan nomads' (Kabilsingh, 1988: 19). Hunting of animals for meat occurred, but there were many extensive nature-reserves in central Tibet, especially round the capital or any monastery or sacred site (Ekvall, 1964: 76).

The situation in a number of Buddhist countries, though, is changing, because of the influence of Western values, whether in the form of consumerism, or Communist state capitalism. In Tibet, Chinese exploitation of the country's natural resources has led to much of its wildlife being killed and its forests felled. In Thailand's *laissez-faire* capitalist economy, consumerism and rapid economic change are also having a deleterious effect on the environment. In 1945, 70 per cent of the country was still forested; by 1989 it was around 15 per cent, on account of logging and the spread of agri-business, such as growing tapioca or tobacco, or prawn farms where there were once mangrove swamps. Government sanctioning of deforestation has also set a bad example for villagers, who have taken wood from remaining areas for fire-wood, charcoal, and to clear for cultivation. In the 1970s, many birds were killed by eating fish poisoned by DDT, and jungle fowl were being hunted out of existence. Even with tough penalties, there was much poaching in the forests. Every year, 50,000 birds, belonging to 40 species, were harvested from forests for food, and 375,000 birds of 350 species – including some protected ones – were used for non-food purposes (MacAndrews and Sien, 1979: 108). The 1960 Wildlife Act imposed a fine of up to $500, or one year in prison, for killing a member of a protected species, but the fine had to be doubled in 1972 as wildlife was still decreasing, partly through poor enforcement (p. 33).

Bhikkhu Bodhi, an American Theravāda monk, affirms that at the root of the world-wide 'ecocrisis' – in the form of pollution, resource depletion, erosion, deforestation – is the presumption 'that the means to

human well-being lies in increased production and consumption'
(Sandell, 1987: vi), that is, in the ideal of unlimited material 'progress'.
He refers to:

a number of assumptions specific to Western industrial society: that happiness
and well-being lie in the satisfaction of our material needs and sensual desires;
that the basic orientation of man to nature is one of conflict and struggle aimed
at subjugation; that nature must be conquered and made subservient to the
satisfaction of our desires. (p. vii)

Bodhi thus sees a need for the practical implications of the Buddhist perspective to be articulated in a new way to the leaders of Buddhist lands
currently under the sway of the Western model of development. As Klas
Sandell expresses it, the Buddhist ideal is co-operation with nature, not
domination – or passive submission to it (1987: 36). Seeking to *overcome*
external nature is likely to be an expression of human greed and attachment. Helena Norberg-Hodge (1991), who studied the traditional
Buddhist life of Ladakh, an Indian region bordering Tibet, points out
that life was 'based on co-evolution between human beings and the
earth' (Batchelor and Brown, 1992: 43), but that, since the opening up of
the area in 1974, the development of a cash economy and an influx of
tourists have subverted this balance. To help the Ladakhis reach an
appropriate accommodation with the modern world, she has aided the
setting up of the Ladakh Ecological Development Group (1983), to
introduce environmentally friendly technology such as greenhouses,
solar ovens and hydraulic rams (p. 53). While material progress brings
undoubted benefits, it needs to be tempered by the Buddhist reflections
that 'contentment is the greatest wealth' (*Dhp.* 204) and that craving is
the root of suffering. As Thich Nhat Hanh, a Vietnamese social activist
resident in France, says, 'We must be determined to oppose the type of
modern life filled with pressures and anxieties that so many people now
live. The only way out is to consume less' (Batchelor and Brown, 1992:
108). A Buddhist movement which follows such a perspective is the
Sarvōdaya Śramadāna movement of Sri Lanka. Founded in 1958, this
aims to improve the lives of rural people by awakening them to their own
powers and abilities, over against unsympathetic urban modernizers.
They aim at appropriate development, based on an economics of
sufficiency, free from 'pollution' by materialist values. Accordingly, they
concentrate on ten 'basic needs', including a clean, safe and beautiful
environment, and activities include cleaning canals and building roads,
wind-pumps and biogas generators (Macy, 1983; Batchelor and Brown,

1992: 78–86). Their camps also include environmental and reforestation schemes (Ariyaratne, 1995: 9).

Even in rapidly modernizing Thailand, wild animals and fish in the region of monasteries are often left unharmed, so that the areas have been small nature-reserves. Accordingly, Wat Phailom, near Bangkok, has the last remaining breeding-ground in Thailand for the open-billed stork, thousands of which live there in winter and autumn (Kabilsingh, 1988: 17–18). Since 1966, a programme for training monks to help in community development has included advice on the preservation of nature. Moreover, sophisticated urban dwellers have come to appreciate the isolated forest monasteries of certain meditation masters such as Ajahn Chah, in the north-east. Their visits to such places, to develop more inner peace and wisdom, undoubtedly help to build an appreciation for the forest. An active conservation movement has now developed in Thailand, involving members of the royal family, pop singers, government officials, monks, and many ordinary people, with the Wildlife Fund Thailand sponsoring Buddhism and nature conservation projects, especially to highlight Buddhist teachings which relate to nature and conservation. Relevant material includes instructions to monks to recycle old robes (*Vin.* II.291) and not to pollute water or green grass with urine or excrement (*Vin.* IV.205–6), and the ideal of having a quiet environment (*A.* v.15). The Thai-Tibetan 'Buddhist Perception of Nature Project' has distributed 3,000 books of Buddhist stories and teachings related to the environment. It will be followed by 50,000 more, to be sent to all Thai monasteries and teachers in training colleges. Audio-visual and television programmes are also planned. Similar literature is being distributed among Tibetans in India, and the project aims to expand to Korea and Japan. Its founder and co-ordinator, Nancy Nash, based in Hong Kong, says that previously, Buddhists have passively protected nature, but now they need to be more overtly active in doing so (Sandell, 1987: 73–5). Nash was herself inspired by the Dalai Lama's emphasis on 'universal responsibility'. In his 1989 Nobel Peace Prize lecture, the exiled Dalai Lama expressed his aspiration that, in future, the Tibetan plateau would become a 'Zone of Non-violence' which

would be transformed into the world's largest natural park or biosphere. Strict laws would be enforced to protect wildlife and plant life; the exploitation of natural resources would be carefully regulated so as not to damage relevant ecosystems; and a policy of sustainable development would be adopted in populated areas. (Piburn, 1990: 24; Batchelor and Brown, 1992: 112–13)

In Thailand, a major concern has been with the effects of deforestation, which has led to land erosion, hotter, shorter rainy seasons, and flooding when the rains come. In 1978, the government banned the export of much unprocessed wood, and started a reforestation project, though this has favoured quick-growing eucalyptus monoculture plantations. In 1989, the country was the first in the world to ban logging completely, stimulated by a public outcry after 350 people were killed by flooding and mud-slides, due to illegal logging. The measure was taken against the powerful vested interests of the logging industry, which then moved its activities to neighbouring forest-rich Buddhist lands such as Burma, Laos and Cambodia. The government also allows the import of timber from Malaysia, Indonesia and Vietnam.

Particular problems exist in northern Thailand, where various opium-growing hill-tribes have practised slash-and-burn agriculture, leading to forest loss and disruption of streams to the lowlands. Since the 1970s, Phra Ajahn Pongsak Tejadhammo, a forest monk, watched a tobacco company destroying much of the local lowland forest, then the locals finishing it off, then in-coming Hmong hill-tribes starting to destroy the higher, watershed forest with their slash-and-burn methods. His concern at this led him, since the early 1980s, to organize the villagers of the Mae Soy valley, near Chiang Mai, to protect the forests and help in reforestation of their now eroding land and its watersheds. The aim is to aid river-flow and irrigation and so benefit villagers' livelihood through sustainable food production. Ajahn Pongsak teaches the villagers that they depend on the forest for water, and thus food, so it is their moral duty to protect and foster it with gratitude. It should be looked on as like a second parent, with the forest animals being like the villagers' brothers and sisters. He emphasizes that a harmony with nature is the basis of true Buddhist morality, and that the healthy functioning of the forest is the key to the natural balance, which includes and benefits humankind. The forest ensures 'a healthy harmony in people's lives both physically and mentally' (Batchelor and Brown, 1992: 92). He strongly links Buddhism to respect for nature:

Dharma, the Buddhist word for truth and the teachings, is also the word for nature. This is because they are the same. Nature is the manifestation of truth and of the teachings. When we destroy nature we destroy truth and the teachings. (Bachelor and Brown, 1992: 99)

Ajahn Pongsak emphasizes that the villagers must have land to support themselves, or they will continue to destroy the forest. He urges villagers to self-help and co-operative effort, not relying on government subsidies etc. for aiding their environment. The work is based on collective decision-making, and donation of labour (as in the Sarvōdaya Śramadāna movement of Sri Lanka). By 1985, the movement involved 274 villages, had replanted half a square kilometre of forest, and was planning to replant eight square kilometres. Since then, many villagers have been involved in running a tree-nursery, terracing eroded hillsides, planting thousands of seedlings and building reservoirs and canals. By 1992, over 1,000 villages participated, with 97,000 people involved (Swearer, 1995: 128). Areas of forest land have also been fenced off for protection – which led to an attempt to prosecute Ajahn Pongsak for encroaching on government-'protected' forest! The government allows the Hmong to live on the watershed, growing subsidized cabbages instead of – it is hoped – opium. Ajahn Pongsak, though, opposes this as a too easy form of 'compassion'. He prefers bringing them down to the lowlands – where opium cannot grow – and giving them land. This will also prevent the insecticides they use from polluting water-courses.

In 1990, the UN Environmental Programme's 'Global 500 Roll of Honour' included Ajahn Pongsak – along with the Thai Prime Minister and a Thai villager who turned his land into a sanctuary for birds (Tangwisuttiji, 1990). Scores of monks in other areas are now following the example of Ajahn Pongsak, and a number of monasteries are actively acquiring land for reforestation. Ajahn Pongsak's activism has included participating in protests against allowing mining in forest areas. He is the founding head of Monks for Preservation and Development of Lives and Environment, formed in 1990. This has met at ecologically threatened sites, such as a proposed dam site in the south which would flood a large tract of ancient rain-forest. Monks participated by living in this forest, on a rota basis, to prevent this. In 1991, Phra Kru Udom Patakorn even ordained trees in the last remaining patch of ancient forest in his part of the north-east, to prevent them from being felled for a eucalyptus plantation. Unfortunately Ajahn Pongsak disrobed in 1993 because he was charged with a monastic offence entailing expulsion, but he has continued his work as an eight-precept lay person (Swearer, 1995: 128).

Thai activists have also made some contact with the Japan Tropical Forest Action Network. Japan, which has a weak, but growing, environmental movement, imports 45 per cent of the world's tropical timber, which it uses mainly as disposable plywood shuttering for concrete buildings. It protects its own forests, though, and it has a good record on pollution control, energy conservation and recycling.

In 1986, an inter-faith conference on the environment was called at Assisi, Italy. There, the (Tibetan) Buddhist representative affirmed, for example, that Buddhists should strive to protect habitats and ensure that endangered species do not become extinct (Harris, 1991: 101). In a rather sceptical tone, Ian Harris questions how deep-rooted environmentalism is in Buddhism, suggesting that it is largely in response to fashionable concerns coming from the West. Its recent rise as a self-conscious concern among Buddhists, though, can be seen as largely due to an awareness of the destructive impact of modernization – which was first experienced in the West. Harris cites *D*. III.74–5, which describes a future golden age, where humans, after a moral decline into a period of great conflict, learn to be highly moral again, and the world is prosperous. Then, 'cities and towns are so close to one another that a cock can comfortably fly from one to the next. In this perfect world, only urban and suburban environments are left. The jungle has been fully conquered' (Harris, 1991: 108). Harris sees this as a vision in which civilization is compatible with the 'total destruction of the wilderness'. And yet, in the period of conflict, people are said to have retired to the jungle and mountains to avoid killing or being killed. The implication is, perhaps, that in a highly moral society, there is no actual *need* of wilderness, not that it should be 'conquered';[16] and in any case, an urban environment may still have nature interspersed in it in semi-wild parks etc.

It is certainly appropriate, though, to question whether Buddhism has any particularly strong reasons for protecting *species*. The Buddhist concern has always been for the suffering of any sentient being, of whatever species. In an aeons-old world of change and impermanence, it is to be expected that species will become extinct (though this is happening more rapidly than usual at present). Nevertheless, each dying species consists of suffering individuals, and Buddhist concern should certainly focus on these. Buddhist principles might not strongly support saving 'the' whale, but they support saving whales! Where saving (members of) one endangered species involves killing members of another species, however, Buddhism will not be supportive. Moreover, classical Buddhist ethics would not, without being extended, see killing the last rhinoceros as *worse* than killing one when they were plentiful, or killing a cow, say. To kill a rhinoceros deliberately *so as* to try to end the species could be seen as worse, however, both because it would be a very destructive act

---

[16] Harris develops his views in Harris, 1994a, 1994b, 1995a, 1995b and 1997, while Schmithausen, 1991b and 1997 takes a somewhat more positive view on Buddhist support for environmental concerns.

and because it would offend many people. A world without a particular species is still the conditioned world of suffering beings. If the human species became extinct, then an opportunity to be born as a being capable of enlightenment would be lost – at least in this part of the universe. While the same could not be said of any other species, the higher animals at least are seen as capable of some virtue, so their loss would also hinder the spiritual progress of beings. Accordingly, for some animals, to kill one when one knows that this will push its species closer to extinction, even if this is not one's intention, can indeed be seen as a worse act than if the species were not an endangered one.

One endangered species is the tiger, partly threatened by the traditional Chinese belief that eating parts of a tiger sustains virility. Thus tigers are still imported from the dwindling numbers of India and Bangladesh into Taiwan – supposedly as 'pets'. In 1986, it was reported that Buddhist leaders there planned to buy twelve such tigers to save them from being eaten at the Chinese new year. Other endangered species are various types of whales, which the Japanese are active in hunting 'scientifically' in spite of a world moratorium. Japanese whale-hunting can be seen as the product of several factors. The fact that Japan is an island has meant that the sea has been looked to as a great food-provider. The traditional preference for sea-foods was probably also strengthened by Buddhist concerns over meat eating, for fish are seen as a low form of life. Philip Kapleau reports one whaler as saying 'If whales were like pigs or cows, making lots of noise before they die, I could never shoot them. Whales die without making a noise. They're like fish' (1981: 47) (in fact, whales in distress do make a noise: but those above water cannot hear them). With more powerful boats, and an increasing secularism, there has been much whale killing. In the post-war period, this was initially encouraged by the American occupying force, so as to help feed the starving population of Japan. Today, though, whale-meat is not much eaten, and the carcases are largely used for pet food and industrial products. To an average Japanese, killing a whale is no worse than killing a cow, though of course a pious Buddhist would not want to do either. Given the Buddhist concern for 'all sentient beings', Japanese whaling, and the Japanese emphasis on memorial rites, it is perhaps not surprising that Buddhist monks sometimes carry out memorial rites for the whales killed by whalers (Hoshino and Takeda, 1987: 310). Kapleau reports one such in 1979, put on by a Zen temple, and with government officials and executives of a large whaling company in the congregation (1981: 46–50). Unfortunately, the service did not seem to contain any discouragement of whaling, but was more like a way to salve people's consciences.

Beyond Asia, Buddhists have been active in environmental matters. In France, the Vietnamese monk Thich Nhat Hanh has set up the international Tiep Hien (Inter-being) order of meditators and social/peace activists. Among the precepts of the order is, 'Do not live with a vocation that is harmful to humans and nature' (Eppsteiner, 1988: 151). Nhat Hanh teaches his followers to use verses which remind them of their inter-relationship with the world, and their duties towards it. For example, when turning on a tap or drinking water, they should reflect:

> Water flows over these hands
> May I use them skilfully
> to preserve the planet. (Batchelor and Brown, 1992: 106)

As Thich Nhat Hanh says, 'We, ourselves, are made of non-self elements, the sun, the plants, the bacteria and the atmosphere' (Badiner, 1990: 177). In a similar vein, Stephen Batchelor says,

We feel ourselves to be separate selves in a separate world full of separate things. We feel separate from each other, separate from the environment that sustains us and separate from the things we use and enjoy. We fail to recognize them for what they are: part of us as we are of them. (Batchelor and Brown, 1992: 32)

The image of Indra's net (p. 153) is frequently alluded to by Buddhist modernists, both Western and Asian, who seek to infuse ecological activism with a Buddhist motivation based on a vision of the deep inter-relationship of all things.[17] The implicit logic, here, is that we should respect the other beings and environment that we depend on, and be aware that our negative actions towards the rest of nature go on to affect us. Those who abuse nature, in blindness to this, should be respected as human beings, but not aided.

CONCLUSION

For Buddhism, humans are a part of the community of sentient beings in a conditioned world where suffering is endemic. Humans are not seen as set over non-human nature as 'stewards', but as neighbours to other, less intelligent, sentient beings. The spiritual potential of humans means that they are to be more valued than members of other species, but that very potential is expressed and enhanced by compassionate regard for

---

[17] See e.g., Badiner, 1990: 61; Batchelor and Brown, 1992: 11, 35; Macy, 1991; Sandell, 1987.

any being. To kill or harm another being deliberately is to ignore the fragility and aspiration for happiness that one has in common with it. When it comes to indirectly causing harm to sentient beings, Buddhism's emphasis on an ethic of intention means that such actions are not necessarily blameworthy. Yet its positive emphasis on compassion means that the removal of causes of harm to beings *is* praiseworthy.

CHAPTER 5

Economic ethics

Hunger is the greatest illness . . . Contentment is the greatest wealth.

Dhammapada 203–4

Economic ethics covers a wide range of issues: types of work or business practices, the approach to work in general and entrepreneurship in particular, the use to which income is put, attitudes to wealth, the distribution of wealth, critiques of politico-economic systems such as capitalism and Communism, and the offering of alternatives to these in both theory and practice. In a Buddhist context, it also entails a consideration of such issues in relation to lay citizens, governments, and the *Saṅgha*.

LAY ECONOMIC ETHICS

In his teachings, the Buddha included advice to the laity on how best to generate and use their income, the various aspects of which are well encapsulated at *S.* IV.331–7 (and *A.* V.176–82):

1 As to how wealth is *made*, it is praiseworthy to do so in a moral way (in accordance with *Dhamma*), without violence, and blameworthy to do the opposite.

2 As to *using* the product of one's work, it is praiseworthy to use it:
(a) to give ease and pleasure to oneself;
(b) to share it with others, and to use it for generous, karmically fruitful action.

Correspondingly, it is blameworthy to be miserly with oneself or mean with others.

3 Even if wealth is made in a moral way, and used to benefit oneself and others, one is still blameworthy if one's *attitude* to one's wealth is greed and longing, with no contentment or heed for spiritual development.

These points form a useful framework for the first part of this chapter.

Right livelihood

The 'right livelihood' factor of the Eightfold Path entails that one's means of livelihood should not be dishonest or otherwise cause suffering to other living beings. 'Wrong livelihood' is trade in: weapons (being an arms salesman), living beings (keeping animals for slaughter),[1] meat (being a slaughterer, meat salesman, hunter or fisherman), alcoholic drink, or poison (*A.* III.208). Such trades, especially being a slaughterer or hunter, are socially despised in Buddhist societies, and are said to lead to a bad rebirth. Wrong livelihood is also seen as any mode of livelihood that is based on trickery or greed (*M.* III.75), that is, which entails breaking the second precept: stealing, directly or by deception. To be able to see how to increase one's wealth is fine, but to be blind to moral considerations, so as to do so 'with tricks, fraud and lies: worldly, purse-proud', is to be 'one-eyed' (*A.* I.129–30). While the early texts only give a short list of types of 'wrong livelihood', in the modern context, a Buddhist might add others to the list (Whitmyer, 1994). For example: doing experiments on animals; developing pesticides; working in the arms industry; and perhaps even working in advertising, to the extent that this is seen as encouraging greed, hatred and delusion, or perverting the truth (Saddhatissa, 1971: 52). The Western Zen teacher Aitken Roshi says that the precept against false speech implies that one should not work in a normal advertising agency, or swallow advertising lies either, thus showing complicity with lying (1984: 52).

The *Mangala Sutta* holds that a great blessing is 'work which is free from upset (*anākulā*)' (*Sn.* 262), which of course can often arise from conflict amongst employees or between employees and employer. The *Sigālovāda Sutta* says that a person should look after servants and employees 'by arranging their work according to their strengths, by supplying them with food and wages, by looking after them when they are ill, by sharing delicacies with them and by letting them off work at the right time' (*D.* III.191). In response, they should be diligent and honest, and uphold their employer's reputation. The *Ārya-satyaka-parivarta*, an early Mahāyāna text, says that a righteous ruler should censure those

who do not properly share with their wife, children, servants, maids or workers; or who make the livelihood of others difficult through overworking them or asking them to perform degrading work,

as this is 'wrong livelihood' (*ASP.* 198). While a form of slavery was countenanced by the emperor Asoka in India, in his Rock Edict XI he emphasized that slaves and servants should be treated well (Nikam and McKeon, 1959: 45). In modern times, slavery remained legal in Thailand

---

[1] The Thai monk Ven. Payutto sees this as also including controlling prostitutes (1993: 61).

prior to 1872 (Tambiah, 1976: 191–2), but it had never entailed the kind of degradation found in the Western slave trade.

Moral and spiritual qualities aiding worldly success

The early texts see success in ethical livelihoods as a boon, and see a person's moral and spiritual qualities as contributing to such success, rather than in any way hindering it. Such success-enhancing qualities include (cf. Rājavaramuni, 1990: 39–40):

(1) faith in the Buddha, keeping the moral precepts, a generous, open-handed attitude, and understanding the bad effects of the five hindrances (desire for sense-pleasures, ill-will, laziness, agitation and vacillation) (*A.* II.66–7);
(2) a moral life, free from laziness (*D.* II.85);
(3) vigilance (*appamāda*) (*S.* I.86);
(4) 'dwelling in a suitable place, association with good people, perfect application of self, and previous karmically fruitful acts' (*A.* II.32; cf. *Sn.* 259–60).

In modern South-east Asia, for example, success in this life is seen to depend on karmic fruitfulness from previous lives as well as current application and knowledge (Spiro, 1966: 1165; Nash, 1965: 162). A passage at *A.* IV.281–5 asserts that happiness and success in this life come from:

(a) the '*attainment of energy*': that is, being skilful and industrious in one's work, whatever it is, and with an enquiring mind. A similar passage at *A.* II.67 talks of 'that same noble disciple, with wealth acquired by energetic striving, amassed by strength of arm, won by sweat, in accordance with *Dhamma* (what is right and proper), and gained in accordance with *Dhamma*';
(b) the '*attainment of watchfulness*': taking care with one's possessions so that they are not lost by the action of kings, robbers, fire, water or ill-disposed heirs;
(c) *association with good, virtuous people*: so as to emulate their qualities of faith, virtue, charity and wisdom;
(d) *leading a 'balanced life'*: not being unduly elated by successes or depressed by failures. A person should also avoid both outgoings exceeding income and the pointless hoarding of wealth. Loss of wealth by looseness with women, drunkenness, gambling and friendship with evil people should be avoided.

In a similar way, the *Sigālovāda Sutta* talks of six ways of dissipating one's wealth:

Addiction to strong drink and sloth-producing drugs . . . haunting the street at unfitting times, attending fairs, being addicted to gambling, keeping bad company, and habitual idleness. (*D.* III.182)

Details of the disadvantages of each of these are then given (pp. 182–3). For example, the drunk wastes his money and he quarrels; one who wanders the streets at night leaves himself and his family unprotected; one who frequents fairs is preoccupied with finding entertainments; the gambler loses his money, makes enemies, and is not trusted; one who keeps bad company is led astray; the lazy person puts off his work, thinking: 'It's too cold' or 'it's too hot'; 'it's too early' or 'it's too late'; 'I'm too hungry' or 'I'm too full'! In such ways, a person wastes what he has already earned and fails to generate new earnings. The *Sigālovāda Sutta* also counsels caution in the use of wealth, saying that a quarter should be used for one's own ease and convenience, half for one's business or occupation, and a quarter should be saved, against adverse times (*D.* III.188). Accordingly, as being in debt is seen as stressful (*A.* III.350), being free of debt is a source of happiness (*A.* II.69–70).

Appropriate uses of income

In accordance with the above ideal of 'balance' in one's life, both a miser and one who squanders his wealth are seen as hard to satisfy (*A.* I.87). The miser is seen as one who brings cheer to neither himself nor others, but just guards his wealth, saying 'Mine!' (*J.* III.299–302). *S.* I.89–91 describes a millionaire who died intestate, after a life of eating coarse food and wearing coarse clothing: his wealth benefited no-one, and would then be taken by kings or robbers, destroyed by fire or water, or go to heirs for whom he had no affection. Elsewhere, the wealth of a rich miser is described as 'like a pool haunted by demons, where no man may slake his thirst' (*J.* I.353–4). Wealth is only of benefit if put to use, and however much one holds onto it, one will be parted from it at death. Paradoxically, the only way to benefit from one's wealth after death is by generously giving it away before one dies: for 'what is given is well saved', because of the karmic fruits this brings (*S.* I.31–2). As the Mahāyāna philosopher Nāgājuna says:

> Through using wealth there is happiness here and now,
> Through giving there is happiness in the future,
> From wasting it without using it or giving it away,
> There is only misery. How could there be happiness? (*RPR.* 315)

A. II.67–8[2] discusses the appropriate use of wealth, saying that one should seize the opportunity it offers, and should:

(a) bring happiness to oneself, one's family, friends, comrades, servants and employees;
(b) protect one's wealth against loss;
(c) give offerings to relations, guests, dead relatives and gods;
(d) give gifts to virtuous renunciants and brahmins: the best type of giving, leading to a heavenly rebirth.

Accordingly, in modern central Thailand, Jane Bunnag observed that many relationships are of a patron–client form (1973: 13) and that 'It is . . . incumbent upon a wealthy individual to support numerous clients, and other dependants, some of whom may be poor relations' (1973: 11).

Generosity is encouraged by such texts as:

Monks, if people knew, as I know, the fruits of sharing gifts, they would not enjoy their use without sharing them, nor would the taint of stinginess obsess the heart. Even if it were their last bit, their last morsel of food, they would not enjoy its use without sharing it if there was someone else to share it with. (*It.* 18)

One text says that, when people once realized the karmic fruitfulness of even a small gift, giving became widespread to 'renunciant and brahmin, to tramp, wayfarer and destitute; they provided drinking water in their courtyards, they placed seats in their gateways' (*Vv.* 1). Public works, such as the sinking of wells and the planting of medicinal plants, are also encouraged in Buddhist texts (*S.* 1.33), with the Chinese monk Puan Yinsu (1115–69) affirming that 'building bridges is a Buddha act that brings peace to men and causes heaven to rejoice' (Faure, 1991: 128). Tales of great givers of the Buddha's day, such as Anāthapiṇḍika, 'Feeder of the Poor', or the lady Visākhā, are also popular. The Mahāyāna *Upāsaka-śīla Sūtra*, which has been and remains very influential on Chinese lay Buddhism (Chappell, 1995: 2), says that a lay disciple should always stop to look after a sick stranger on the road and find a place for him to stay (*Uss.* 83). As part of the virtue of *dāna*, lay *Bodhisattva*s should engage in such social welfare activities as:

learning medicine, building hospitals, road repair, building guest houses, digging wells, planting fruit trees, building bridges, maintaining canals, protecting animals, massaging tired travellers, making shade with umbrellas, providing people with ear picks, consoling the grieving, etc. (Chappell, 1995: 8)

---

[2] Cf. *A.* III.45–6; *S.* 1.89–91; *A.* III.76–8; Saddhatissa, 1970: 143.

Helping others should not be done as a way to get a reward, though, for this is not giving, but trade (p. 10).

Buddhist giving and its socio-economic impact

Buddhists can show a considerable concern with generating karmic fruitfulness (or 'making merit') by generous deeds etc. In Theravāda countries such as Burma, Thailand and Sri Lanka, considerable time, money and effort, individually and communally, are spent on activities aimed at this, such as alms-giving, the sponsoring of ordination and *Kaṭhina*[3] ceremonies, and building a monastery or *Stūpa* (monumental shrine) (Lester, 1973: 139). For example, David Pfanner and Jasper Ingersoll estimated that in 1960, in rural lower Burma, an average of 4–6 per cent of net disposable family cash income (which averaged 1,000 Kyat, or $200 per year, then) went on such activities (1962: 348), though Melford Spiro – who may have included a broader range of activities in his estimates – found the figure for rural upper Burma in 1961 to be around 30 per cent (1971: 459). For example, parents might save for years for the ordination ceremony of their son, and spend 200–5,000 Kyat on this (Spiro, 1971: 456).[4] Thus:

The accumulation of wealth as an end in itself is not admired in rural Burma, but the accumulation of wealth for the purposes of merit-making is highly valued. (Pfanner and Ingersoll, 1962: 345)

It is no exaggeration to say that the economy of rural Burma is geared to the overriding goal of the accumulation of wealth as a means of acquiring merit. (Spiro, 1971: 459)

Manning Nash points out that in 1960s rural Burma, the rich spent more on religious activities both in absolute and in relative terms: 14 per cent of disposable income per year compared to 4 per cent for the moderately well off and 2 per cent for the poor (1965: 160). This indicates that people in Burma tend to spend what they can on such activities, after their basic needs are met. A common Burmese view is that, though the *intention*, not the amount given, is what matters, a person is wealthy because of past good karma, and also has more opportunity to make more good karma for the future (Pfanner and Ingersoll, 1962: 345). In Thailand, however,

---

[3] The donation of robes and other requisites after the ending of the annual rainy-season monastic retreat: see Swearer, 1995: 22–5.

[4] Pfanner and Ingersoll, for lower Burma, says that the average cost was $75, or 375 Kyat (1962: 348).

poorer people spend a larger proportion of their income than the wealthy (Pfanner and Ingersoll, 1962: 357). This is because Thailand's economy is more developed,[5] so that the well off tend to use surplus funds for consumer goods or investment (Bunnag, 1973: 127–8, 164–5). The less well off see their position as partly due to past karma, and so seek to help themselves by generating more good karma by giving.

While Mya Maung (1964) has claimed that the poor post-war economic performance of Burma has been due to its high expenditure on religious activities, rather than on investment, Trevor Ling argues that the devastation of the country in the Second World War and the British legacy of rural indebtedness and rice mono-culture have been important factors (1979: 107–11) – and, since 1962, we can add, so have the effects of an oppressive Marxist government. While there may be some truth in the observations that, in a country which is not short of food, people's willingness to spend on religious activities may have had some effect on the economy,

it is doubtful whether the Burmese economy which might have resulted if the money had been so channelled [into investment] would have been preferable to the majority of Burmese Buddhists. (Ling, 1979: 113)

Pfanner and Ingersoll point out that, as well as feeling that they benefit in the future by such acts, people, both individually and communally, get much immediate satisfaction and enjoyment from them (1962: 348). Robert Lester expresses it thus:

The ideal is that the monk and the layman give to each other, and that their giving promotes *both* physical *and* spiritual well-being, *both* here *and* hereafter. (1973: 156)

Thus such activities are seen as a kind of investment in happiness. In any case, money channelled to the *Saṅgha*, in being used for goods for the monastery, may still help stimulate the economy (Pfanner & Ingersoll, 1962: 357–8). The *Saṅgha* is not an unproductive drain on the economy, as some have suggested, but a focus of cultural continuity and stability, supporter of an ethically sound society. Thus:

It is not that Buddhists believe that it is more important to make pious donations than to seek economic development. Rather, they believe that such donations are the most effective way to advance social concerns. (Sizemore and Swearer, 1990: 16)

---

[5] By 1989, it was growing at 9.0 per cent per annum, the fastest growth in the world: the *Guardian* newspaper, 24 November 1989; though in the late 1990s, it took a dive, along with that of a number of other Asian countries.

Thai monks now commonly try to steer the laity's desire to give towards community development projects, such as building a school, small bridge, or hospital. Moreover, in South-east Asia generally, activities directed at generating karmic fruitfulness may be community-wide events, so as to involve the feeding of perhaps thousands of lay guests (Pfanner and Ingersoll, 1962: 348), and 'provide people with an opportunity to reaffirm and strengthen the social ties that exist between them' (Bunnag, 1973: 178).

So much for the economic and social impact of religious giving, but what of the question of whether it diverts income from helping those who are less well off? Jane Bunnag reports that, in Thailand, while karmic fruitfulness is regarded as a by-product of fulfilling social obligations such as support for kin or clients, generating it is the main motive for giving in a religious context (1973: 178). Such giving is seen as more karmically fruitful (see pp. 21–3), and this has generally meant that Buddhists are more willing to support monks or monastery-related welfare activities than to support the poor directly. This tendency is resisted, though, in the Mahāyāna *Upāsaka-śīla Sūtra*, which says that a lay *Bodhisattva* should give to the poor before 'fields of blessings' such as the *Saṅgha*, parents or teachers (*Uss.* 41; cf. 93). Giving to the former is from pity, is to eliminate the causes of suffering and to increase blessings and virtues. Giving to the latter is to repay kindness, to increase the causes of happiness, and to increase wisdom and forsake afflictions (*Uss.* 62).

In Theravāda lands, though, religious giving has a redistributive effect in various ways. Food donated to monks 'generally benefits not only the monks, but also a number of people who come to seek shelter in the monasteries', and monasteries became 'places where the destitute, orphans, and students live, obtain sufficient food, and receive moral and educational training from the monks' (Rājavaramuni, 1990: 38). In Thailand, the *wat* or monastery

provides a place of retirement for elderly men and a home for *dek wat* [boys who assist around a monastery] from poor families, as well as a hostel for country boys studying in town. Moreover, at a few monasteries, laymen who are without home and kin, or those who are chronically sick, have taken up permanent residence in the public pavilion or *sala*, and any [male] householder passing through a strange town can rest for the night in one of the local *wats*. (Bunnag, 1973: 126–7)

Moreover, as more wealthy villagers in Theravāda South-east Asia are expected to help sponsor the religious activities of the poorer ones, such as an ordination, income disparities have traditionally not built up (Pfanner and Ingersoll, 1962: 348). For Thailand, Bunnag also points to an apparent 'religious division of labour' whereby most monks come from the ranks of the less well off (1973: 48) – and after a period as monks, may return to lay life with a better education and thus improved employment prospects (1973: 127) – and the better off show their interest in religion by donation to the *Saṅgha*. Moreover, at the time of the annual *Kaṭhina* ceremonies, processions, sometimes including monk-donors, often go from urban centres to rural ones to present donations to monasteries that are less well endowed than the urban ones, which has a redistributive effect (Tambiah, 1976: 456–7).

The Buddhist attitude to wealth

For Buddhism, wealth is not evil: the important thing is how it is made and used. Yet even if wealth is made in a moral way, and used to benefit oneself and others, one should not have a greedy attitude to it:

Riches ruin the foolish, but not those in the quest of the Beyond; through craving for riches, the foolish one ruins himself as (if he were ruining) others. (*Dhp.* 355)

The virtues of contentment and fewness-of-wishes are praised, and it is said that 'contentment is the greatest wealth' (*Dhp.* 204). The highest ideal of contentment, for an ascetically inclined lay person, is perhaps expressed in the story of Ghaṭīkāra (*M.* II.45–54), said to have lived at the time of the past Buddha Kassapa. As he wished to continue supporting his ageing and blind parents, he did not become a monk, but lived as a potter who let people take his wares for free, and did not use money. Nevertheless, his open-hearted generosity inspired a king to give him a supply of food (*M.* II.54), and his 'customers' to bring him useful materials (*M. A.* III.284–5).

Whether one's wealth increases or declines, the ideal is to remain calm, and to be free of regret, provided one has attained the wealth in a moral and non-greedy way. Thus, in the Mahāyāna, the lay *Bodhisattva* fully engages in the world, but in a non-attached way. Thus the *Bodhisattva* Vimalakīrti is described as 'Though profiting by all the professions, yet far above being absorbed in them'.[6]

Generally speaking, Buddhism encourages the adoption of a 'middle way' between the extremes of:

---

[6] From the *Vimalakīrti-nirdeśa Sūtra*, as quoted by Tsunoda et al., 1964: I.101.

(a) poverty, where people have insufficient means for a becoming life: 'For householders in this world, poverty is suffering' (*A.* III.350), 'Woeful in the world is poverty and debt' (*A.* III.352), and

(b) a materialistic seeking of riches for their own sake.

Relevant to the first extreme is the following story.[7] The Buddha once walked about thirty miles specially to teach a poor peasant, who he had seen was ripe for insight. A group of well-off citizens gather to hear the Buddha teach, but he delays until the peasant arrives. When he does so, he is tired and hungry, having come directly from seeking a lost ox. Seeing that the man is in no fit state to be able to understand his sermon, the Buddha asks that he be fed with surplus alms-food. When he is fed and rested, the Buddha then teaches, and the man attains stream-entry (see p. 39) as a result. The Buddha then gives a verse which begins 'Hunger is the greatest illness' (*Dhp.* 203).

As explained below (pp. 197–8), poverty is seen as encouraging theft, general immorality and social unrest. Moreover, in a situation of poverty and conflict, it is more difficult to lead a moral and spiritual life. Circumstances which facilitate spiritual striving are that a person is young and healthy, there is no food shortage, people are friendly to one another, and the *Saṅgha* is harmonious (*A.* III.65–6).

At the second extreme, Buddhism sees material welfare as not an end in itself, but only a means to human happiness, and a support for a life of moral and spiritual development. To be ever on the look-out for 'more' is to base one's life on craving and, since one is without contentment, makes happiness impossible, for one will never be satisfied. Thus traditional Buddhist values are in tension with the values of an acquisitive, consumerist society. Bruce Morgan reports that in rapidly modernizing Thailand, though there is a general support for economic development in the *Saṅgha*, there is equally a concern

about the kind of restless, endless generation of wants and desires in a dynamic economy, never satisfied and always ascending. It is not the particular standard of living that is in question, but the style, rate and effects of continual changes in standards. (1973: 72)

It can be seen that societies at many different levels of wealth would be acceptable to Buddhism, but not a continuous striving for more for its own sake.

Russell Sizemore and Donald Swearer hold that Theravāda Buddhism, at least, 'offers a "middle way", or sees the acquisition and

---

[7] *Dhp. A.* III.262–3; Payutto, 1994: 88–9.

renunciation of wealth in a dialectical relationship'.[8] For monks, this means that while the more worthy attract more donations from the laity, their worthiness helps them to remain non-attached to it (Sizemore and Swearer, 1990: 3). For lay people:

Wealth always provides both an opportunity for a new expression and cultivation of non-attachment *and* a temptation towards the kind of anti-dhammic self-indulgence that leads to increased entrapment in the web of worldly existence. (Reynolds, 1990: 69)

To be non-attached is to possess and use material things but not to be possessed or used by them. (Sizemore and Swearer, 1990: 2)

For monks as for the laity, 'it is not the amount so much as the way the wealth is possessed and used that is subject to moral scrutiny' (Sizemore and Swearer, 1990: 17).

Economic ethics for rulers

The *Cakkavatti-sīhanāda Sutta*[9] describes a line of mythical universal emperors (*Cakkavattis*) of the past (see p. 114). Each is seen as having been a compassionate ruler, who counsels his son on how to rule, like him, according to *Dhamma*, in the sense of justice or righteousness. In one case, the son does all that his father advises, *except* giving to the needy. As a result of this failing, poverty arises for the first time for ages. Consequently, stealing arises. When a thief is caught and is brought before the emperor, he explains that he stole as he was poor: so the emperor gives him some goods with which to support himself and his family, carry on a business, and make gifts to renunciants and brahmins. When others hear of this, though, stealing only increases. The emperor therefore makes an example of the next thief by executing him. This then leads to thieves arming themselves and killing those whom they rob, so that there are no witnesses (*D.* III.64–8). The Buddha sums this up as follows:

Thus, from the not giving of property to the needy, poverty became rife, from the growth of poverty, the taking of what was not given increased, from the increase of theft, the use of weapons increased, from the increased use of weapons, the taking of life increased – and from the taking of life, people's lifespan decreased, their beauty decreased. (*D.* III.68)

Thus, a ruler who allows poverty to develop is sowing the seeds of crime and social conflict. Systemic poverty threatens law and order and

---

[8] 1990: 1; cf. Reynolds, 1990: 63–4, 68.
[9] *D.* III.58–77; see Fenn, 1996: 100–8 for a discussion of this.

thus inhibits both social cohesion and personal morality (Fenn, 1996: 107).

A related message is given in the *Kūṭadanta Sutta*, at *D.* 1.134–6. Here, the Buddha tells of a rich and powerful king of the past who wanted to offer a lavish sacrifice to secure his future welfare, in accordance with the practices of pre-Buddhist Brahmanical religion. He therefore asks his brahmin adviser, the Buddha in a past life, how to go about this. In reply, the brahmin points out that the kingdom is being ravaged by thieves and brigands. This situation will not be solved by executions, imprisonments or other repressive measures, for those who survive such measures will continue to cause problems (as often happens in anti-guerrilla measures today). He then gives an alternative plan to 'completely eliminate the plague', which involves granting grain and fodder to those who cultivate crops and keep cattle; granting capital to traders; and giving proper living wages to those in government service:

Then those people, being intent on their own occupations, will not harm the kingdom. Your Majesty's revenues will be great, the land will be tranquil and not beset by thieves, and the people, with joy in their hearts, will play with their children and dwell in open houses. (*D.* 1.136)

The king then carries out this advice and, in line with further counsel, conducts a great sacrifice, but one in which only such things as butter and oil are offered, not the lives of animals, no trees are cut down, and no one is forced to help (*D.* 1.141). While Gombrich (1988: 83) comments that this passage was meant mainly as a critique of Brahmanical sacrifice, and that he knows of no Indian king who did such things as grant capital to businessmen, the spirit of the passage still expresses a Buddhist ideal – and one which has often been cited by a number of twentieth-century Buddhists.

A key message of both the above texts is that if a ruler allows poverty to develop, this will lead to social strife, so that it is his responsibility to avoid this by looking after the poor, and even investing in various sectors of the economy. In the *Mahā-sudassana Sutta*, it is said that the Buddha, in a past life, had been a righteous king in a glorious city who established a beautiful lotus pond around which the needy were given food, drink, transport, shelter, money, and even marriage partners (*D.* 11.180). In the *Mahā-vastu*, a non-Theravādin early text, the duties of a king are said to include admitting a large body of immigrants and favouring the poor as well as protecting the rich (1.276). The Mahāyāna philosopher Nāgārjuna, in his *Rāja-parikathā-ratnamālā* (*RPR.*), advised King Udayi that he should support doctors, set up hostels and rest-houses, supply water at arid road-sides, and

> Cause the blind, the sick, the lowly,
> The protectorless, the wretched
> And the crippled equally to attain
> Food and drink without interruption. (verse 320)
> Always care compassionately for
> The sick, the unprotected, those stricken
> With suffering, the lowly and the poor
> And take special care to nourish them. (verse 243)
> Provide extensive care
> For the persecuted, the victims (of disasters),
> The stricken and diseased,
> And for worldly beings in conquered areas. (verse 251)
> Provide stricken farmers
> With seeds and sustenance,
> Eliminate high taxes
> By reducing their rate. (verse 252)
> Eliminate thieves and robbers
> In your own and others' countries.
> Please set prices fairly and keep
> Profits level (when things are scarce). (verse 254)

Robert Thurman sees such advice as outlining 'a welfare state . . . a rule of compassionate socialism' (1985: 128).

In an early Mahāyāna *Sūtra* known as the *Ārya-satyaka-parivarta* (*ASP.*), or 'Noble Discourse of the Truth Teller', which was a favourite handbook of many teachers in Tibet (*ASP.* 2), it is said that:

a righteous ruler, after attaining a realization of the impermanence of himself and his possessions . . . would use those possessions without being attached to them, while ruling over his domain. This is called the heedfulness of a ruler. (*ASP.* 187)

Stockpiles of food should be seen as neither belonging to the king, as they are produced by the people's work, nor, any longer, as belonging to the people, as the king has been 'entrusted as their sole overseer' (*ASP.* 201). Thus the *Mahā-vastu* advises that a king's duties include being circumspect, and diligent in the care of the treasury and granary (*Mvs.* 1.277). The *Ārya-satyaka-parivarta* continues:

As a ruler, he must not use inappropriate possessions or even appropriate possessions at an improper or even at a proper time if that would be harmful to the poor. Were crop failure or famine to occur to (afflict) the people, he should give them protection. He should also protect them from harm and ill caused by

robbers and thieves, armies from other states, and from each other. He should
benefit all. He should give property to the poor and lawfully chastise the wicked.
This is called the compassion of the ruler. Therefore, heedfulness and compassion are very important for the ruler. (*ASP.* 188)

The poor should be exempt from taxes if their poverty is due to factors
outside their control, such as natural calamity, theft, or pest depredation.
Those made poor by wasting their money on such things as gambling or
prostitutes, however, should have to pay their taxes but have them partly
repaid by the king, which perhaps implies that this rebate will be condi-
tional on their mending their ways (*ASP.* 202). Those who refuse to pay
taxes are not exactly *stealing*, but are doing 'an acutely nonvirtuous act
brought about by miserliness' (*ASP.* 201). A ruler who forces those who
refuse to pay taxes to do so is not stealing, but more like collecting his
wages for performing his duties (*ASP.* 201–2).

In his *Traibhūmi-kathā*, 'The Three Worlds According to King Ruang',
the fourteenth-century Thai prince Phya Lithai has a mythical *Cakkavatti*
advise other kings to collect only a tenth of the harvest in taxes, though
they should collect nothing if the people do not have enough rice, and
should not collect more taxes than their predecessors, so as not to set a
bad precedent for succeeding kings (Reynolds and Reynolds, 1982: 151).
Sufficient food should be supplied to those recruited to do service for the
ruler, or in the army, and

if you assign them to do any kind of work, assign only an appropriate amount
– do not use them too much so that they are pushed beyond what they are
willing to do. If there are any people who are elderly, do not use them – let them
do as they will. (p. 151)

Moreover, the kings should lend capital, at no interest, to subjects in need
of it for trading (p. 151–2).

The *Ārya-satyaka-parivarta* says that a righteous ruler

shall increase his treasury merely by receiving gifts, whereas an unrighteous
ruler, striving to gain wealth through cunning and all manner of deception, will
not be able to increase his treasury. (*ASP.* 211)

The moral actions of a righteous ruler mean that his country will also
have timely rains, a good harvest, no harm to crops by hail or pests, and
fewer harmful wild animals, and that malicious enemies will disappear
through the ripening of their own karma.[10]

Buddhist kings have varied considerably in the extent to which they

---

[10] *ASP.* 211; cf. Reynolds and Reynolds, 1982: 153 and *A.* II.74–6, pp. 115 and 152 above.

have lived up to the above-mentioned high ideals, but Buddhists often look to the Indian emperor Asoka as an exemplar of them (see pp. 115–17). In Sri Lanka, people also look back to medieval kings as presiding over a period of agricultural abundance based on extensive irrigation works, religious flourishing and charity. In the *Cūlavaṃsa* chronicle of Sri Lanka (Geiger, 1929), it is said of King Upatissa I (362–409) that 'For cripples, women in travail, for the blind and sick he erected great nursing shelters and alms-halls' (ch. 37, verses 182–3). Of King Mahinda II (772–92), it is said: 'The poor who were ashamed to beg he supported in secret, and there were none on the Island who were not supported by him according to their deserts' (ch. 48, verse 146). Mahinda IV (956–72 or 1026–42) is said to have

built an alms hall . . . and gave to beggars alms and couches. In all the hospitals he distributed medicine and beds, and he had food given regularly to criminals in prison. To apes, the wild boar, the gazelles and to dogs he, a fount of pity, had rice and cakes distributed as much as they would. In the four vihāras [monasteries] the king had raw rice laid down in heaps with the injunction that the poor should take of it as much as they wanted. (ch. 54, verses 30–3)

The justice of economic distribution

The obligation of rulers to seek to prevent poverty among their people raises the topic of the Buddhist attitude to the issue of 'justice' in the apportioning of wealth in a society. Russell Sizemore and Donald Swearer make the point that in Buddhism, there is more concern with the mode of acquisition and use of wealth than on the question of the justice of its distribution (1990: 2). For them, in Buddhism, moral virtue is seen to lead to wealth, and wealth is seen to be the result, and proof, of previous generosity (pp. 3–4). Nevertheless, to help the poor is seen as generating good karma, and the receipt of such help will also be karmically deserved:

when the doctrine of kammatic [i.e. based on karma] retribution is understood as an exceptionless moral explanation and justification for the present distribution of wealth and poverty in society, it undercuts moral criticism of the distribution per se. Consequently, Buddhists concerned with how to make their present society more just appeal not to a distribution of wealth corresponding more adequately to moral desert, but to the principles of non-attachment and virtues such as compassion and generosity. (p. 12)[11]

[11] Cf. Ornatowski, 1996: 202 and Ash, 1994.

Thus '*dāna* and not some concept of structural justice is the central concept in Buddhist social and political philosophy' (p. 13) and 'There are norms for redistributing wealth and visions of the well-ordered society which serve as moral strictures about the use of wealth' (p. 19).

While the above is in the main true to how many Buddhists think, it includes some unwarranted assumptions, at least as regards how faithful such readings are to the texts of Buddhism. While these certainly hold that moral virtue, especially generosity, leads to wealth as a karmic result, and stinginess leads to being poor (see pp. 15–16), it is not said anywhere that these are the *only* causes of wealth or poverty. Indeed, the fact that it is said that karmic causes are only *one* among a variety of possible causes of illnesses (see p. 23) suggests that such a view would *not* be warranted in the texts. Thus while a person's wealth and poverty *may* be due to past karma, this is only one possibility. Thus it is not right to assume that all poverty and wealth are karmically deserved. To assume that karma is an 'exceptionless moral explanation' is, indeed, to come close to karmic fatalism, which is not true to the original Buddhist vision. Thus, while appeals to generosity, non-attachment and compassion certainly *are* key persuaders for Buddhists in working for a more just society, this need not be at odds with an appeal to justice *per se*. Mavis Fenn has pointed out that, in the *Cakkavatti-sīhanāda Sutta* referred to above, there is no reference to poverty being karmically deserved,[12] and that a king reacting to poverty with sporadic personal giving is seen as ineffective: he must act more systematically and effectively by preventing poverty from becoming systemic (Fenn, 1996: 107). Moreover, this and the *Kūṭadanta Sutta* express 'views that correspond to simple notions of social justice – everyone should have sufficient resources to care for themselves and others, and to make religious life possible – and the notion that these values should be incorporated into the political system' (Fenn, 1996: 108).

Nevertheless, ideas of distributive justice may be muted by the idea that at least some poverty and some wealth are the results of karma. The notion of karmically deserved riches is seen in the fourteenth-century Thai work 'The Three Worlds According to King Ruang', where it is said that, at the time of the Buddha, the rich man Jotika could not have his riches forcibly removed by the jealous king Ajātasattu, as his riches were due to his great karmic fruitfulness of the past (Reynolds and Reynolds, 1982: 197–9). Moreover, at least in Theravāda lands, those

---

[12] 1996: 102, 121, and see Fenn, 1991.

who seek to persuade others of the legitimacy of their wealth do so by reference to some or all of: (a) the idea that it is due to their past karmically fruitful actions, (b) the idea that it was morally made, (c) the idea that it is not the result of self-indulgent craving, by demonstrating present generosity (Reynolds, 1990: 73). In fact, a rich person is seen as having a greater opportunity to do karmically fruitful actions by giving liberally to the *Saṅgha* and the community. As Phra Rājavaramuni says:

A wealthy man can do much more either for the better or for the worse of the social good than a poor man . . . acquiring wealth is acceptable if, at the same time, it promotes the well-being of a community or society. (1990: 45)

Rājavaramuni holds that as long as wealth is used for the well-being of all members of society, 'it does not matter to whom it belongs, whether the individual, community or society' (Rājavaramuni, 1990: 53). Thus, while Buddhism has no central drive towards economic equality *per se*,
(a) the well-off have an obligation to be generous to other members of the community; and
(b) rulers have an obligation to seek to avoid poverty among their people. While the *Saṅgha*'s relationship to the state has been typically one of 'cooperation and an amelioratory approach to social change, along with support for the status quo distribution of wealth' (Ornatowski, 1996: 213), monasteries have themselves traditionally had a redistributive effect, as seen above (pp. 194–5). Today, Rājavaramuni suggests that it is desirable 'to improve or modify this tradition to suit the current circumstances' (Rājavaramuni, 1990: 38).

THE MONASTIC ECONOMY

The original ideal of the *bhikkhu* and *bhikkhunī* was that of a person with a minimum of possessions living a simple life-style, supported by lay donations rather than by any gainful occupation (*D.* 1.12). The formal list of a monk's personal 'requisites', treated as his property, is as follows: an upper-, lower- and over-robe, a belt, a bowl, a razor, a needle, a water-strainer, a staff and a tooth-pick. In practice, any monk also has such articles as sandals, a towel, extra work robes, a shoulder bag, an umbrella, books, writing materials, a clock and a picture of his teacher. Such a way of life is held up as one which offers great opportunity for spiritual growth, free of the restrictions of lay life (*M.* 1.179). It is pointed out, for example, that while the sense-pleasures offered by lay life are enjoyable, to earn them, a lay person has to work hard, being affected by the extremes of weather while doing so (for example in agriculture), perhaps being affected by sadness at failure, and being bothered by worry over losing wealth, and quarrels arising from its possession (*M.* 1.85–7). The blessings of a renunciant's life are said to include blamelessly and contentedly eating that which others freely give and wandering without attachment or cares, with no possessions to lose by fire, war or theft (*J.* IV.252–3). Overall, it is suggested, sense-pleasures have more disadvantages than advantages in terms of human happiness. The values of celibacy and possessionlessness associated with renunciation are an implicit critique of the limitations within the normal social order (Fenn, 1996: 108), and emphasize the simple basic needs for a becoming human existence (Fenn, 1996: 100).

Yet monastic simplicity attracts lay donations. The virtue of a monk is seen to make him a more worthy recipient of these, and indeed the Buddha once praised the monk Sivali as chief of those who receive offerings (*A.* 1.24). In Southern and Northern Buddhism, therefore, there is a structural tension between the ascetic tendencies of the *Saṅgha* and the laity's desire to do actions which are more abundant in their karmic fruitfulness, by giving to more abstemious and ascetic monks. In Thailand, for example, a town monk with a good reputation may be given a refrigerator or even the use of a car. If he lives up to his reputation, though, he will use these with detachment (he cannot drive himself), and let other monks benefit from them. Bangkok monks may accumulate many gifts by doing rituals for the laity, or because of their activity as successful astrologers, preachers or meditation teachers. Yet these gifts of robes, cigarettes, incense, candles, biscuits or cash are often shared with disciples in the monastery and used to support the education of young monks, novices and temple boys, as well as in gifts to less well-endowed rural monasteries in a monk's home region (Tambiah, 1976: 459):

the prevailing ethic of *noblesse oblige* ensures the equitable distribution of these material goods; the more favoured a *bhikkhu* is in terms of presentation received, the more generous he is obliged to be; the lack of privacy both within the *wat* and with regard to the laity acts as a strong sanction against any monk's misuse of his personal property . . . Thus the dilemma posed by the fact that the more revered the *bhikkhu* the more he is showered with worldly goods by the householder is to some extent resolved, in that he must maintain an attitude of indifference towards material possessions and wherever possible should give them away. (Bunnag, 1973: 68; cf. p. 33)

Jane Bunnag describes a certain abbot as a respected example of such an ideal who used his money to help build a school, and supported a number of novices and temple boys with food, clothes and school equipment (1973: 72).

Monasteries themselves, generally through lay workers, have sometimes been economically active through donations, for example of land. The twentieth century, though, has seen a considerable reduction in Buddhist monastic land-ownership, as a result of confiscations by Communist governments or of land-reforms. In Theravāda lands, monastic landlordism only developed to a notable extent in Sri Lanka, where the Buddhist chronicles record many occasions when kings gave lavish gifts to accomplished monks, whether scholars or ascetics (Kemper, 1990: 155–6). Thus, between the ninth and twelfth centuries, large temples owned vast estates, which included plantations, complex irrigation schemes, the villages that depended on them, and rights over some of the labour of the villagers. There were periodic kingly reforms relating to monastic possessions, but these were not triggered by monastic wealth *per se*, which was seen as acceptable, but by lack of moral discipline or by concentration of the wealth in too few hands (Kemper, 1990: 153–61).

In China also, by the middle of the T'ang period (618–907), Buddhist monasteries were among the major land holders, through donations from members of the imperial family, the nobility and the rich (Ch'en, 1973: 126–7), by foreclosing on land mortgaged by peasants who had needed to raise income but were unable to pay off the loan, and by buying land (Ch'en, 1973: 130–1). However, in times of economic need, the state came to confiscate such land periodically (Ornatowski, 1996: 217).

Some ancient monastic codes (but not the Theravāda one) allowed surplus donations to be loaned out and interest charged, if the profit was used to promote Buddhist activities, and Buddhist monasteries may have been the first institutions in India to make such loans (Ch'en, 1973: 158–9). In China, by the T'ang period, monasteries became important agents in the economy (Ch'en, 1973: 151–73). They ran large markets, lent out seedlings and grain and a certain amount of money, and ran water-powered flour mills and oil presses. As part of the income was reinvested in such activities, this represented a form of capitalism (Ch'en, 1973: 177–8), called by Gregory Ornatowski 'communal capitalism' (1996: 219). Other income was used for repairs to monasteries, help for the destitute and hungry, and offerings to the Buddha (Ch'en, 1973: 163). Monasteries also operated hostels for monks and other travellers; no charges would be made in the case of large monasteries (Ch'en, 1973: 171–7).

Japanese monasteries also became involved in such commercial activities and trade, and in pre-Communist Tibet, monasteries were key economic institutions at the centre of a web of trading and donation relationships. Individual monks invested in such things as herds and seed-grain, but most capital was received and administered by one of a monastery's superintendents, monastic or lay. These were responsible for getting a good return from land worked by leaseholders or peasants attached to the monastery, from grazing, forest and water rights, from monastery herds, trade with China and India, bartering with herdsmen, and loans and investments.

BUDDHISM AND CAPITALISM: WEBER'S 'PROTESTANT ETHIC' THESIS

In his *Protestant Ethic and the Spirit of Capitalism* (1904, in German; 1930, in English), the sociologist Max Weber (1864–1920) developed an influential thesis that claimed that Protestant Christianity, in its Calvinist form, was a key source of values and orientations consonant with the 'spirit of capitalism'. This then led, in certain historical circumstances in Europe from the sixteenth to the mid eighteenth century, to entrepreneurial, capitalist activity, the key to the modern era. For Weber, the origin of this was the emergence, in the sixteenth century, particularly among Puritans and Calvinists, of 'reinvestment' capitalism, where profits were continually reinvested in profitable enterprises, which went beyond prior unsystematic 'adventure' capitalism. Nevertheless, in time, the economic success which this brought undermined the very ascetic virtues that had helped lead to it (Ling, 1980b: 577).

Looking at the less economically developed Asia of his day, Weber sought to show, in his *The Religion of India* (1916, in German; 1958, in English) and *The Religion of China* (1917, in German; 1951, in English), that this was because Hinduism, Buddhism, Confucianism and Taoism all lacked one of the two key ingredients of the 'Protestant ethic', these being:

(1) a 'this-worldly' or 'inner-worldly' asceticism, which emphasized disciplined, purposive, rational action in the world, with an ascetic attitude towards the fruits of such work, so that enjoyment of them could be postponed and profit reinvested, so setting off a positive economic cycle;
(2) the idea of work as having a religious significance, as a religious 'calling' akin to that of the Catholic monk.

Weber saw Buddhism as having an other-worldly monkly ideal which devalued the world and its drives, and a restriction of rational purposive activity to meditation (1963: 267), with advice to the laity too vague to be the basis of a rational economic ethic of self-discipline (1958: 199, 217–18, 222). Weber acknowledged the social welfare emphasis of the emperor Asoka's Buddhism, but oddly saw this as an historical accident not in keeping with the original spirit of Buddhism (1963: 268; 1958: 226–8). He acknowledged that, for the laity, economic activity was stimulated by the need to have a surplus to use in generating good karma, but said that this did not support capitalist reinvestment.

Weber has been criticized for focusing on the orthodox ancient forms of Buddhism and other Asian religions, as known by scholars of his day, and trying to deduce twentieth-century behavioural consequences from these. Today, scholars are also more aware of the complexities of these religions, and, moreover, there have been reform movements in them since Weber's time. Padmasiri De Silva argues against Weber that it is wrong to see Buddhism as having no positive role in changing society, for while it has its other-worldly aspects, it also has a genuine social ethic (1976: 6–7). It is only misinterpretation that makes the karma doctrine fatalistic (p. 7), and 'egolessness' does not undercut 'a healthy drive for personality integration, social reform or even nation building', and should reduce selfishness and avarice, thus aiding co-operation (p. 8). Buddhist principles are also critical of superstition, though Buddhist practice has sometimes come to include it (p. 8). De Silva thus criticizes the Weberian claim that Theravāda Buddhism has no basis for a social ethic, seeing this claim as arising from overlooking the continuity and relationship between the Buddhism of the laity, directed (mainly) at a good rebirth and life in society, and the Buddhism of (ideally) world-renouncing monks.[13]

Buddhism certainly contains an ethic of diligent work for lay people, as seen above, though, as Trevor Ling says, unlike the Puritan, 'the Burmese Buddhist views worldly pleasure as a boon to be enjoyed' (1979: 113). Thus it seems appropriate for Hans Dieter Evans to say 'Buddhism does not hinder the emergence of modern capitalist values, though it does not suggest them.'[14] In reflecting on Weber's thesis in relation to Indian Buddhism and Hinduism, Stanley Tambiah looks to Gandhi and

---

[13] De Silva, 1976: 10–17. Spiro, 1971, is a noted exponent of such a dichotomy between 'Kammatic' and 'Nibbanic' Buddhism.

[14] *Modernization in South-East Asia* (Oxford: Oxford University Press, 1973), p. 161, quoted in De Silva, 1976: 20.

the 1950s Burmese Buddhist socialism of Prime Minister U Nu, claim-ing that Indian values are not conducive to the capitalist spirit but to 'inner-worldly asceticism and the spirit of socialism' (1973: 16). Looking at Burma, he says that Weber was right, but in a way that he had not anticipated, for in Burma 'Buddhist ideas appear to stimulate and to legitimate a kind of socialist welfare politics that subordinates economic activity of the capitalist kind' (1973: 18). Ling agrees that Buddhist values 'do not find a natural expression in a capitalist economy' (1979: 111).

In Thailand, Burma and Sri Lanka, commercial roles such as those of businessmen, traders, entrepreneurs and moneylenders have tradition-ally had a low social status, especially in rural areas, through their asso-ciation with acquisitiveness and greed. In the traditional hierarchy of honour and status,[15] farmers were more respected, as they provided the necessities of life. Above them came professionals such as magistrates, civil servants, teachers and military officers, because they served the public good, and especially the king and nobility, for the same reason and because their position was seen as due to past good karma. The highest respect was given to monks and pious, generous laity. This has meant that it has been the Chinese minority who have been very active in finance and industry in Thailand, along with Thai women (Kirsch, 1975: 173–6), who cannot be fully ordained nuns (see pp. 395–8), and are under-represented in the professions. Thai men have traditionally been attracted to high-honour public-service roles, leaving women to be active in more 'worldly' economic roles. Nevertheless, the Thai *Saṅgha* has been starting to describe economic roles in more positive terms, as contributing to the public good, and male Thai resistance to commer-cial and business activity has been lessening (Morgan, 1973: 74–5).

In Tibet, there was traditionally a small middle-class trading commu-nity, which mainly exported wool (Bell, 1928: 109), yet most people in this partly pastoral society engaged in trade and bartering from time to time, and, as seen above, large monasteries traded to help support themselves (Bell, 1928: 125–6).

The fact that traders have been looked on with suspicion in a number of peasant societies where Buddhism has become established is worth reflecting on. To what extent do such suspicions originate as much from the nature of peasant societies as from Buddhism? In early Indian Buddhism, merchants were in fact among those particularly attracted to Buddhism, for its open nature in which religious outcomes were the

---

[15] For Thailand: Kirsch, 1975: 190–1 and Morgan, 1973: 74. For Burma: Maung, 1964: 760. For Sri Lanka: Ling, 1980b: 584.

result of personal efforts, as with economic outcomes in their own sphere (Gombrich, 1988: 80–1). Indeed, a greatly respected supporter of the Buddha was Anāthapiṇḍika, a *seṭṭhi* (Pali; Skt *śreṣṭhī*) or rich merchant-patron. The virtues of diligence and prudence in work which the Buddha recommended would have appealed to merchants. Commentaries on the fifth precept criticize not only intoxicants but also any irresponsible or wasteful expenditures:

The tenor is unmistakably bourgeois, and it is hard to resist the hypothesis that this attitude is closely correlated with the affinity that seems to have existed between early Buddhism and the merchant class. (Reynolds, 1990: 71)

Moreover, a passage in the *Jātaka*s (*J.* 1.120–2) seems to support entrepreneurial energy directed to investment and reinvestment. It tells of a poor man who sells a dead mouse to a tavern, for its cat, and then goes on to become rich by a series of astute investments whenever he sees opportunities for supplying goods or services. Thus it is said, 'By means of accumulation of small money, the wise man establishes himself even as by a skilful application, small particles are fanned to a fire.' Again, at *A.* 1.116–17, it is said that a rich man will invest in the business of a shopkeeper if he sees that he is both dependable and astute at making a profit, these being qualities for which there are spiritual parallels.

Gregory Ornatowski holds that the implications of key Buddhist concepts for economic ethics is 'ambiguous and depends to a large extent upon the interpretation of them within the particular sociocultural and historical situation' (1996: 201):

Buddhist economic ethics for the laity were not inherently antagonistic to the development of capitalism, but in fact supported a primitive capitalism among the merchant classes in early Buddhist India, and medieval China and Japan, seen in both 'merchant-type lay ethics' and direct economic activities by Buddhist monasteries themselves, which led to innovations in business practices and implicit support for commercial tendencies in society as a whole. (Ornatowski, 1996: 202)

In modern Thailand, Charles Keyes (1990) has traced a change from traditional suspicion of traders among the Thai-Lao people of the northeast. Since the 1950s, their way of life has changed from subsistence farming, with general equality of wealth, to one more orientated to the national and international market, and periods of work in Bangkok, leading to greater discrepancies of wealth. The north-east has traditionally been the poorest region of the country, and in a context where the government is pushing economic development for the whole country, the region has got wealthier, but not as fast as other regions (p. 181). When in

Bangkok, north-easterners have realized that, as members of a disadvantaged group, they cannot aspire to the status of an official, but can to that of a merchant, after the example of the once poor Chinese whom they see (p. 188). In changing social and economic circumstances, as previous certainties have declined (pp. 171–2), some north-easterners have thus developed 'something of a Buddhist work ethic' (p. 185) akin to Weberian 'inner-worldly asceticism' (p. 188). This is in the form of a 'this-worldly non-attachment' (p. 187), drawing on the strong valuation in the north-east given to non-attachment and the ability 'to forgo gratification in order to overcome one's base desires' (p. 186). North-easterners see themselves as stronger in detachment than other Thais, partly because they are used to dealing with tough economic circumstances (p. 189). A high proportion of north-eastern men also spend some time as monks, while women learn non-attachment in separation from children when these marry, are ordained or die, and in the rite of 'lying by the fire' for several days after they have given birth to 'dry out the womb': a form of ascetic mortification due to the heat and avoidance of solid food at this time (p. 187). Moreover, popular in the north-east is the '"dhammic group" (*mū tham*)' movement of those who seek access to the uplifting power of *Dhamma* so as to be 'ordained in the dhamma'. Members emphasize careful observance of the five precepts, including the one on alcohol (pp. 179–80), as well as thriftiness and industriousness, and de-emphasize actions leading to immediate pleasures (p. 187). Thus in most north-east villages now, some Thai-Lao families run rice-mills, transport firms and shops (1990: 173). Those running these seek to better themselves, though they acknowledge that improved worldly happiness is impermanent (1990: 186). The attitude of others to such successful entrepreneurs is ambivalent. They might greatly admire them for diligence and shrewdness, but some might suspect them of being obsessed with wealth. Yet such a charge can be countered by reference to the fact that they use their wealth, in part at least, in generous activities which are seen to be karmically fruitful (p. 183). Likewise in Sri Lanka, those in lowlands villages that have come to be involved in commerce remain suspected by some but also earn respect when their new wealth is used for acts of piety (Ling, 1980b: 584).

The case of Japan

Given the twentieth-century success of Japanese capitalism, it is appropriate to look at the background of this with the Weberian thesis in mind. During the Tokugawa period (1600–1867), Japan was very inward-looking and somewhat xenophobic, after suffering bad experiences at the hands of interfering European colonial powers. This was a time of peace after almost 400 years of civil strife. Buddhism was formally supported by the rulers, though Neo-Confucianism was the state ideology. Shōguns, or military rulers, ran society, aided by the *samurai* warrior-knight class. Society was a closely regulated, centralized state, which was felt to be needed so as to enhance national unity and strength. During this time, cities were growing in size, and commerce was developing in the new, unified, national market. Tokugawa society remained feudal in its structure, however, with an emphasis on a properly ordered social hierarchy, and respect for elders and superiors. Confucianism emphasized diligently working in one's station in life, for the benefit of the group, including descendants, dead ancestors, parents, and one's feudal lord (Duus, 1976: 171–2), and society was divided into four different, mainly hereditary, classes (Duus, 1976: 11). In decreasing order of status, these were:

(1) *samurai*: traditionally warrior-knights, but now more like civil servants in many respects. Their role was to lead, and they were seen as the group most dedicated to the good of society. The other three groups consisted of commoners:

(2) peasants: their role was to produce food, the primary necessity of life;

(3) artisans: their role was to produce various secondary necessities such as utensils;

(4) merchants: their role was to exchange things. Neither Confucianism nor Buddhism had a high regard for trading, as it was non-productive (Confucianism), and was seen to encourage greed (Buddhism).

In time, though, there developed something like a Weberian 'this-worldly asceticism' in the form of an abstemious attitude which was not aimed simply at other-worldly goals, but at success in this life, in the form of the good opinion of others, and material rewards (Duus, 1976: 172). Enjoyment was good, but not at the expense of diligence and frugality, thus the slogan 'Work much, earn much, spend little' (Duus, 1976: 171). Confucianism both encouraged production and discouraged consumption (Bellah, 1957: 109). Also from Confucianism came an emphasis on serving the group, accentuated by the *samurai* ethic of loyalty and selfless service to a person's feudal lord, and to the state. From Buddhism came an emphasis on selfless detachment, here in an active, engaged mode, as seen in the actions of Sōtō Zen monks, who were close to the people, and helped with such matters as building bridges, irrigation and draining swamps (Ives, 1992: 63). Winston King (1981) has written on the work ethic espoused by Suzuki Shōsan (1579–1655), a *samurai* who became a Sōtō Zen monk in his forties, but who was also influenced by Taoism, Confucianism and Shintō. He held that one's ordinary everyday work, whatever this may be, could be a method of practice leading to Buddhahood, if done with the proper attitude and with Buddhist teachings borne in mind. Thus, not unlike the Puritans, he sought to raise ordinary occupations to the level of spiritual practice:

Farm work itself is Buddha-action. Only when your purposes are evil is it mean and shameful. When your faith-mind is strong and secure, (your work) is the work of a Bodhisattva . . . For you to have been born a farmer is to have received from Heaven[16] an official appointment to be one who nurtures the world . . . Perform your work as a public service to the Righteous Way of Heaven . . . Producing the five cereal grains, worship the Buddha and the kami [Shintō gods]. Making the great vow to sustain the life of all men and to give alms even to insects and other such creatures, recite 'Nama-Amida-Butsu, Nama-Amida-Butsu' with every stroke of the hoe. Concentrate on every single stroke of the sickle with no other thoughts. (1981: 213)

This combines allusion to Confucian ideals and Shintō gods with Pure Land devotion to Amida Buddha (see pp. 142–3) and a Zen emphasis on single-mindedly giving oneself over to the task in hand, as a kind of moving meditation. Such an approach, of seeing one's task as supporting the community, and devoutly immersing oneself in it, was seen to help wear down self-centredness, and so conduce to enlightenment. The world was a fragile, changing place that one should not be attached to, but looking on it thus aided selfless action within it, for the benefit of all (King, 1981: 218). Working thus would ensure a rich crop yield, and the protection of 'Heaven' and the Shintō gods. Moreover, merchants should work hard, so as to convey needed goods to people, and also make a profit, provided that this was not done unfairly or greedily (p. 213).

The Jōdo Shin Pure Land school, while condemning dishonest or excessive profit, saw the work of artisans and merchants as providing the needs of others, so that:

By profiting others they receive the right to profit themselves . . . The spirit of profiting others is the Bodhisattva spirit . . . Thus Bodhisattva deeds are just the deeds of merchants and artisans. In general the secret of merchants' and artisans' business lies in obtaining confidence through Bodhisattva deeds. (quoted in Bellah, 1957: 120)

---

[16] A Confucian term, meaning the natural-moral order of the universe.

Jōdo Shin tracts influential on merchants included the maxims:

Cheerfully do not neglect diligent activity morning and evening.
Work hard at the family occupation.
Be temperate in unprofitable luxury.
Do not gamble.
Rather than take a lot, take a little. (quoted in Bellah, 1957: 119)

Such diligent work would both help the mind remain concentrated and show gratitude to Amida Buddha. The merchants of Ōmi province were much influenced by such Jōdo Shin ideas, and were well known for their diligence, hard work, simplicity of life-style, and dislike of waste (Bellah, 1957: 120–1). By such means, they often became wealthy. Thus Tokugawa Buddhist teachings encouraged in people, including merchants, great dedication and a strong will to succeed.

Towards the end of the Tokugawa period, however, there was a turning away from Buddhism and Confucianism as 'foreign' religions, and an emphasis on Shintō as the true 'national' religion. The year 1853 also saw the humiliation of Japan by being rudely awakened from its inward-looking period by American gun-boats, which came to open up Japan to American trade. This helped lead to the end of the Tokugawa regime. The re-establishment of the emperor system ushered in the Meiji period (1868–1912), when Japan opened its doors to the outside world and started to modernize rapidly, learning from the West, which it saw as a rival and threat.

There was a drive towards industrialization, directed by the state. This aimed at developing a 'rich country, strong army' so that Japan could stand its own ground against foreign powers, and redress what it saw as unequal trading arrangements.[17] Legal restrictions on the involvement of *samurai* in trade were lifted, and being deprived of their place in the previous feudal regime, *samurai* put their considerable energy into commerce and innovation. Nevertheless, Hiroshi Mannari (1996: 2–3) has shown that the percentage of business leaders from *non-samurai* backgrounds was actually 77 in 1880, and 63 in both 1920 and 1960. Thus the end of the feudal system also released non-*samurai* energy, too.

Loyalty to a person's feudal lord was transferred to loyalty to the state, focused on the emperor, its symbol (Saniel, 1965: 128). There was a wave of Shintō-inspired nationalism, with Shintō underpinning the idea of the divinity of the emperor, and Confucianism being drawn on to stress loyalty to him as father of the nation. In his *Tokugawa Religion: The Values*

[17] Davis, 1989: 308; Saniel, 1965: 133.

of Pre-industrial Japan, Robert Bellah develops a Weber-inspired analysis of how Tokugawa this-worldly asceticism and Meiji institutional changes led to the development of capitalism in a way which was analogous to its development in Protestant Europe. While European capitalism was *laissez-faire*, though, Japanese capitalism was state-directed, with loyalty to the emperor producing an overall rationality[18] to economic action which Weber had seen as necessary for successful capitalist development.

Capital was generated by the state through taxation, and while the people could not see the benefits for some time, the value of loyalty to superiors, ultimately the emperor, enabled them to work hard for the state, and future benefit, without rebelling (Saniel, 1965: 136). In time, because of a financial crisis in 1881, the state sold off some of its enterprises to influential families, so that capitalism spread further (Saniel, 1965: 139–41). Large and small private enterprises were largely run according to a family-based ethic, which encouraged loyalty to the firm, both from actual family members and those brought into the firm.

A central Japanese value, based on both Confucianism and Buddhism, is the idea of the 'return of benefits' (*hō-on*) (Davis, 1989: 307–8). As soon as a person enters the world, he or she is seen as having received 'benefits' (*on*) from *kami*, the Buddha, parents, ancestors, the country and the emperor. Later he or she receives them from village, patrons, employers and neighbours. In response to these benefits of life, nourishment, protection and guidance, the individual should respond with gratitude, love and loyalty. Confucianism saw this as a relationship between superiors and inferiors, and the individual was conditioned to obedience to superiors, from whom he or she was seen to have received various benefits. This is still at the heart of the Japanese work ethic, though Bunnag describes a somewhat similar attitude – apart from the emphasis on obedience – in Thailand, where many relationships are of a patron–client form, often based on age difference, and

the senior member is expected to provide counsel and moral guidance, as well as material assistance when the need arises; whilst the junior partner should in turn pay heed to his advice, and give more tangible evidence of his deference by acting as a general factotum for his superior. (Bunnag, 1973: 13)

Winston Davis (1989) argues that Buddhism largely contributed to Japanese modernization and development by not getting in the way: a

---

[18] Though Bellah later (1963) came to see emperor-loyalty as also containing non-rational elements which hindered economic development and full modernization and democratization, by helping to prevent a deep reorientation of social structures and values in Japan.

process of 'passive enablement' and accommodation. The Meiji restoration brought much criticism of Buddhism, for example for being other-worldly, as well as its disestablishment and some persecution. In this context, Buddhists often sought to emphasize Buddhism's usefulness to the state, through its moral exhortations, good works, and bringing of divine protection, though there were also reformers who were interested in modernization in itself, apart from its nationalistic focus in Japan. Buddhism's emphasis on social harmony helped oil the wheels of rapid social change. Its values of frugality and work as an expression of religious devotion were also useful. Not unlike Suzuki Shōsan before him, Ashari Saichi (1851–1933) said 'My work . . . *is* "Nama Amida Butsu"' (Davis, 1989: 309). Buddhists supported loyalty to the emperor, and justified such things as the war against Russia. While sympathy was expressed for the plight of workers, not much positive action was taken to help them, and poverty was often put down to bad karma. In some ways, Buddhists acted like an economically active minority such as the Jews or Mormons.

Thus, as seen above, Buddhism contains elements supportive of diligent and frugal work patterns which, under certain conditions, can respond positively to social pressure for entrepreneurial activity, if not acting to initiate such a pressure, thus overcoming Buddhism's tendency to suspect merchants and entrepreneurs of greed. Buddhism contains, though, an important emphasis on social welfare, wrongly downplayed by Weber, and holds that capitalist activity is to be justified by its benefit to the community, rather than on the grounds of purely personal benefit. This can be seen in monastic commercial activities in T'ang China, in recent developments in Thailand, and the general emphasis that wealth is acceptable if accompanied by generosity and non-attachment.

'BUDDHIST ECONOMICS'

Nevertheless, a number of Buddhist writers, primarily Theravādins, have sought to articulate a 'Buddhist economics' that is different from the capitalist or Marxist-influenced economics that have been the dominant influence on most Asian governments in the post-war era. A stimulus to many of these efforts was a short article on 'Buddhist Economics' by the Catholic writer E. F. Schumacher, an advocate of intermediate technology and critic of Western development models who had been an economic adviser in 1950s Burma. The article originally appeared in 1966, but was reproduced in his *Small is Beautiful: A Study of Economics as if People Mattered* (1973). He points out that 'modernisation', in practice, often leads to 'a collapse of the rural economy, a rising tide of unemployment in town and country, and a growth of a city proletariat without nourishment for either body or soul' (1973: 56). Accordingly, he laments that the Burmese and others had simply adopted development plans from the West, without pausing 'to think that a Buddhist way of life would call for Buddhist economics' (p. 48). He argues that for the right path of development, what is needed is 'the Middle Way between materialist heedlessness and traditionalist immobility' (p. 56), and seeks to develop such a vision by articulating an economics which he sees as implicit in Burmese Buddhist life (p. 48).

In Theravāda Thailand and Sri Lanka, the majority of monks and lay people support a somewhat conservative form of Buddhism that works with the status quo and government development efforts. Nevertheless, there are those who lament the loss of a 'Buddhistically defined moral community' through the onslaught of modernization, Westernization and secularization (Swearer, 1996: 196). Donald Swearer sees these as:

a) neo-traditionalists: fundamentalist-like movements which advocate a return to an 'idealized personal piety that either ignores or misunderstands the nature of systematic economic, social, and cultural problems and tensions'.
b) liberal reformists who engage with the problems of the modern world and seek to use creative interpretations of traditional beliefs and practices to help solve these. (1996: 196)

In Thailand, the former include Santi Asok, a rather strident sectarian movement that offers a moralistic critique of many aspects of Thai society (Swearer, 1995: 136–9), and Dhammakāya, a very successful movement that has support among political and military leaders, using the media to spread itself, and that emphasizes meditation and moral renewal (Swearer, 1995: 114–15). The reformers include those who have sought to develop and articulate ideas of 'Buddhist economics'.

In Sri Lanka, Dr H. N. S. Karunatilake, then Director of Economic Research at the Central Bank, in his *This Confused Society* (1976), has sought 'to develop an economic system suitable to the modern world based on the discourses made by the Buddha' (Karunatilake, 1976: iii), though he offers what is in places a rather idealistic vision. He sees Buddhist economic principles as having been exemplified in the reign of the Indian emperor Asoka (pp. 29, 73) and the large-scale irrigation works of past Sinhalese civilizations (p. 74). 'A Buddhist economic system has its foundations in the development of a co-operative and harmonious effort in group living. Selfishness and acquisitive pursuits have to be eliminated by developing man himself' (p. 29). Also in Sri Lanka, the psychologist and philosopher Padmasiri De Silva, in his *Value Orientations and Nation Building* (1976) booklet and *The Search for Buddhist Economics* (1975) pamphlet, has outlined what he sees as the contribution of Buddhism to social progress in various fields.

In Thailand Ven. P. A. Payutto,[19] a leading monk-scholar, has developed a vision of Buddhist economics in his *Buddhist Economics: A Middle Way for the Market Place* (1994). In this, he criticizes the tendency of modern economics to examine economic transactions in isolation from ethical considerations of the nature of what is sold, and the social and environmental impact of the transactions. He emphasizes the economic impact of unethical behaviour, such as a reluctance to invest where there is social disorder, customer dissatisfaction if shoddy goods are sold, and medical costs and poor health amongst workers if adulterated foodstuffs are sold, as sometimes happens in Thailand (Payutto, 1994: 24).

Also in Thailand, a monk who has offered innovative modernist interpretations of central Theravāda teachings, including those concerning society and economics, was the leading monk-intellectual and meditation master Buddhadāsa Bhikkhu (1906–93). Though his forest monastery was far from the centres of power, he has been influential on many college-educated people in Thailand, including judges, teachers, educators and doctors, and on the democratic student movement of the 1970s (Santikaro, 1996: 180–2). Buddhadāsa was forthright in his criticism of the 'immorality and selfishness of many modern social structures' (Santikaro, 1996: 147), and compared the wealthy of Bangkok unfavourably with the generosity of people in the countryside (Swearer, 1989: 175). While emphasizing the spiritual core of Buddhism, he felt that there was no separation between this and social concerns (Santikaro, 1996: 155), for to solve social problems, we must get at the moral defilements that are their basic cause (Swearer, 1989: 170). Thus he saw such things as hunger, illiteracy and illness as simply symptoms of a lack of true religion and moral principles in society (Swearer, 1989: 171).

Buddhadāsa felt that all religions, including Buddhism, are fundamentally socialistic, in that their founders aimed at the good of society as a whole. He thus opposed the individualism, linked to capitalism and associated 'liberal democracy', that he saw as eating away at Thai society (Swearer, 1989: 172). While opposing both capitalism and Communism, he came to espouse a kind of religious socialism that he called 'Dhammic

---

[19] Also known by the monastic title Phra Dhammapiṭaka, and formerly Phra Debvedi and Phra Rājavaramuni (see list of references under this name) (Swearer, 1995: 139).

Socialism' as the solution to society's problems – in line with Tambiah's analysis above (pp. 207–8). For Buddhadāsa, apart from 'worldly' forms of socialism in the shape of Marxism and Communism, which could be violent and malignant, there is true socialism. He saw this as being rooted in *Dhamma*, the interdependent nature of things (Swearer, 1989: 195). It draws on the fact that humans are social creatures who depend on and should help others, not acting from individualism (Santikaro, 1996: 166–69; Swearer, 1989: 173). It entails 'not taking more than one's fair share – using only what is necessary so that the rest is available for others' use', as in Buddhist teachings on contentment (Swearer, 1989: 172). It is living according to nature, taking only what we really need (Swearer, 1989: 173). Such a socialism he felt to be nothing new, but as always having been at the heart of Buddhism, which 'has an excellent and special socialist system' (Santikaro, 1996: 165–6), for he saw the administration of the *Saṅgha* as always having been socialistic and the emperor Asoka and Thai kings of the Sukhothai and Ayutthaya periods (the fourteenth to the eighteenth century) as having been genuinely 'socialist' rulers (Swearer, 1989: 192). Thus, unlike Communism and capitalism, true socialism was not foreign to the Thai Buddhist spirit. He held that:

if we hold fast to Buddhism we shall have a socialist disposition in our very being. We shall see our fellow human beings as friends in suffering . . . and, hence, we cannot abandon them. (Swearer, 1989: 195)

Moreover, he saw the concept of the *Bodhisattva* as a 'socialist' one (Swearer, 1989: 197). In the *Aggañña Sutta* (see pp. 114, 153) he saw an account of a natural socialism declining because of the start of hoarding of naturally abundant food: 'our problems began when someone got the idea of stockpiling grains and other food, causing shortages for others' (Swearer, 1989: 174). This then necessitated the election of the first king, who ruled according to 'socialist' principles (Swearer, 1989: 187–8).

Both Payutto and Buddhadāsa have influenced another key Thai liberal reformer, the lay intellectual Sulak Sivaraksa (Swearer, 1996: 215), who has also been influenced by the Vietnamese peace activist monk Thich Nhat Hanh (Swearer, 1996, 225). Sivaraksa has been described as 'a writer and publisher, lecturer, peripatetic international conferee, peace and human rights activist, founder of NGOs [non-governmental organizations], Buddhist social critic, and intellectual moralist' (Swearer, 1996: 200). He has developed an incisive critique of Thailand's rush to

American-influenced capitalist-based modernization and the materialism that it is bringing. For him, 'Modern development encourages competition and success whereas Buddhism encourages collaboration and
contentedness' (Sivaraksa, 1986: 182). While he accepts that modernization in Thailand has some potentially good aspects, in practice he feels
that it has mainly brought luxury to the few and poverty to the many,
especially farmers and urban workers (1986: xv). Rising debt has meant
that large numbers of peasants have migrated to Bangkok, where

Rampant unemployment forces many to resort to crime. Young girls work as
servants, factory workers, or are forced into prostitution. Children work illegally
in small shops under the harshest conditions. Some are even sold abroad. Men
do heavy labor for pathetically low wages. (Sivaraksa, 1992: 32–3)

Modernization has also brought pollution, urban ugliness and slums,
and cultural disintegration (1986: 20, 57–8). Sivaraksa has thus worked
to preserve and perpetuate traditional Thai culture – though he prefers
to use the older term, Siamese – but also for necessary changes in society
to enhance social justice (1986: xxiii). Like Sri Lankan writers and activists such as Karunatilake and Ariyaratne (see pp. 225–34), he looks back
to the emperor Asoka, the early *Saṅgha*, and certain pious, benevolent
kings of the past as inspiring models for a truly Buddhist society
(Swearer, 1996: 213).

The purpose of economics and a critique of consumerism

Writers in the 'Buddhist economics' mould frequently emphasize the
distinctive goal of the Buddhist approach to economics:

Buddhist economics must be very different from the economics of modern
materialism, since the Buddhist sees the essence of civilisation not in a multipli-
cation of human wants but in the purification of human character . . . formed
primarily by a man's work. (Schumacher, 1973: 50)

Economic Development must be placed against the wider background of the
need to develop a well-rounded personality and a happy human being. (De
Silva, 1975: 5)

Ven. Payutto holds that consumption should be seen only as 'a means to
an end, which is the development of human potential' (1994: 43) or 'well-
being within the individual, within society and within the environment
(1994: 35). He thus distinguishes between 'right consumption' and
'wrong consumption': the former is using goods and services 'to satisfy
the desire for true well-being', and the latter is using them 'to satisfy the

desire for pleasing sensations or ego-gratification' (1994: 41), limited only by one's ability to afford what one wants (1994: 43). Karunatilake holds that 'The present economic order is based on the thesis that permanent and limitless economic expansion is possible and desirable' (1976: 29), though for man 'no standard of living satisfies him' (p. 79). This produces a reckless use of non-renewable resources that is unfair to future generations (p. 63), and is based on recognizing craving as a fundamental axiom of economics (pp. 18, 28).

Sivaraksa thus criticizes Thailand for falling for 'the religion of consumerism', the 'dominant ethic in the world today' (1992: 3), for:

The religion of consumerism emphasizes greed, hatred and delusion. It teaches people to look down on their own indigenous, self-reliant culture in the name of progress and modernization. We need to live simply in order to subvert the forces of consumerism and materialism. (1992: 114)

There is nothing intrinsically wrong in having expectations rise, but it is harmful when people who were formerly happy are given to believe that they cannot do without a particular good. (1992: 30)

These writers thus question the very basis of a life aimed at continually increasing consumption. Sivaraksa says that as people work harder for things they do not need, they become more restless, rushing and never relaxing (1986: 44). More particularly, Schumacher says that while modern economics 'tries to maximise consumption by the optimal pattern of productive effort', Buddhist economics 'tries to maximise human satisfactions by the optimal pattern of consumption' (1973: 53). He notes that the Burma that he knew had few labour-saving devices compared to the USA, yet also had much less pressure and strain of living (p. 53). Thus, looking at the approach which emphasizes consumption,

A Buddhist economist would consider this approach excessively irrational: since consumption is merely a means to human well-being, the aim should be to obtain the maximum of well-being with the minimum of consumption. (Schumacher, 1973: 52)

Buddhist economics is the systematic study of how to attain given ends with the minimum means. (p. 53)

Likewise, De Silva holds that:

all planning for national development must go beyond pure 'maximal production' to 'optimal human development'. (1976: 36–7)

Peter Timmerman (1995), a Buddhist and director of the Institute for Environmental Studies, University of Toronto, challengingly claims that modern consumerist society is in fact 'the least materialistic culture in history' as it does not promote a careful valuing of objects, but attempts simply to use them to satisfy dreams of sexual potency, power, or image, and then discard them. In this, the 'desperate need to produce (and to consume) is driven by a kind of panic and mistrust, because it is an attempt to fill a yawning gap in existence with an endless stream of glittering objects'. A mindful approach, however, values the 'rich particularity' of things. Schumacher thus holds, on the basis of his observation of Burmese practice, that the ideal for clothing, for example, would be to use durable material, without toilsome complicated tailoring, but draping the uncut cloth round the body, and leaving time and effort free for artistic creativity in its embroidery (1973: 52).

The Thai writer Suwanna Satha-Anand, who is influenced by Buddhadāsa, holds that in Western economics,

desires are the given. It is not within the realm of economics to 'control or question' desires. It is the essence of economics to *satisfy* desires. In contrast, Buddhism seeks to *bridle* desires as a way to happiness,

for reducing one's desires makes it easier to achieve satisfaction (1995: 7). Here, Ven. Payutto usefully distinguishes craving (*taṇhā*), which is directed at attaining pleasure, from purpose (*chanda*), which aims at well-being, based on wisdom. When driven by the first, economic behaviour is unskilful, while if the latter guides it, it will be skilful (1994: 34–5). He sees modern economics as based on the assumption that people's aim is to seek happiness through the satisfaction of craving, which means that the goal is always over the horizon, as craving can never attain lasting satisfaction.

A common theme is a criticism of taking a country's Gross National Product and per capita income as the key measures of economic success. For one thing, these measures overlook the question of how goods or income are distributed (Karunatilake, 1976: 45) – 80 per cent of an increase may go to 10 per cent of the population (Sivaraksa, 1986: 59). For another, they include in their calculations unnecessary goods (Karunatilake, 1976: 40), harmful products such as armaments, alcohol, dangerous drugs and chemicals, and animal products (p. 84). As Helena Norberg-Hodge, a champion of traditional Ladakhi culture, emphasizes, a focus on GNP also registers, as positive, economic transactions which are wasteful and disruptive of traditional patterns of self-sufficiency (1991: 147). Sivaraksa holds that emphasizing quantitative measures of development focuses attention on economic factors, such as increased production, and political ones, with economists' emphasis on increased goods fostering greed, and politicians' emphasis on power fostering ill-will. Economists and politicians work together and measure results in terms of quantity, thus fostering ignorance (Sivaraksa, 1986: 57).

Critiques of capitalist and Marxist development models

Many of the writers discussed above agree in criticizing aspects of both capitalism and Communism or Marxism, while at the same time appreciating some of their elements. Karunatilake sees both capitalist and Marxist development planning as:

concerned with the purely material aspects of life, the ownership of wealth, the redistribution of wealth and what goods and services individuals should be entitled to. (1976: 23)

They thus ignore the inner development of humans as an important factor in the growth of society, so that crime and moral decline accompany economic growth (p. ii). For Buddhadāsa, both 'capitalism and communism – especially in their recent historical forms – were the same in that they are fundamentally selfish', both being only concerned with one class in society rather than society as a whole (Santikaro, 1996: 167). For him, 'Dhammic socialism' was the Middle Way which avoided the faults of both (Santikaro, 1996: 178; Swearer, 1989: 193).

To take capitalism first, this is seen by 'Buddhist economists' as having certain good points:
(1) as capitalist systems are usually democratic, they allow free choice in many matters, and thus allow freedom of religion and opportunities for self-development (Karunatilake, 1976: 22–3);
(2) they are open to Buddhist values of 'individual initiative, the obtaining of wealth by just means and the sensible spending of it for a comfortable living, for charity and helping others' (De Silva, 1976: 20), and give workers more motivation, and the avoidance of inefficient centrally directed state run industries (Karunatilake, 1976: 107–8).
On the negative side:
(1) according to a moderate view, capitalism has a tendency to 'feed on the acquisitive drives of man, his greed' (De Silva, 1976: 21); less moderately, Sivaraksa says that it is always motivated by selfishness, and so cannot be ameliorated by adding aspects of socialism to it (1986: 64). Indeed, Buddhadāsa saw it as inherently immoral (Santikaro, 1996: 166), and not even properly democratic, as it is not based on the good of all in society (Santikaro, 1996: 177);

(2) its economics does not differentiate between wants and needs (Karunatilake, 1976: 60) and assumes that human wants are endless (p. 8), with only scarcity being a legitimate constraint on their satisfaction;

(3) thus poor people's needs are overlooked while other people's wants – which may be artificially stimulated (Karunatilake, 1976: 57) – are temporarily satisfied (p. 60);

(4) it emphasizes profits, not public welfare, and emphasizes keeping wages of workers low (Sivaraksa, 1986: 60). Unless unions are strong, government officials fairly honest and efficient, and consumers' organizations on their toes, capitalists will take advantage of people (pp. 62–3);

(5) it undermines its lauded 'freedom of choice' through manipulative advertising (Sivaraksa, 1986: 63);

(6) just as much as Communism, it exploits and weakens religion (Sivaraksa, 1986: 126): 'Capitalism kills religion slowly with a neat trick without letting the religious leaders realize what is happening, while communism tries to uproot religions as if they were drugs' (Sivaraksa, 1986: 133); 'Buddhism is being killed by capitalism – slowly, to be sure' (Sivaraksa, 1986: 199).

The good points of Communism and Marxism are that:

(1) they tend to focus on essential goods and equality (Karunatilake, 1976: 24; Buddhadāsa in Swearer, 1989: 174) and so emphasize sharing (De Silva, 1976: 21);

(2) they rightly condemn acquisitiveness and exploitation of employees (De Silva, 1976: 20);

(3) in certain aspects of Marx's writings, there is a valuable humanism (De Silva, 1976: 18–29), such that a more tolerant form of Marxism could work with Buddhism: 'Marxism's courage, vision and struggle may combine with the gentleness, vitality, joy, and peaceful non-violence of Buddhism' (Sivaraksa, 1986: 208).

On the negative side:

(1) they use coercive or violent means (Karunatilake, 1976: 24; De Silva, 1976: 26);

(2) they have a tendency to breed hatred and conflict, or to use dishonest means (De Silva, 1976: 21), believing that the end justifies the means (De Silva, 1976: 29). For Buddhadāsa, they are simply the 'revenge of the worker' (Santikaro, 1996: 167);

(3) they spend too much on arms production or procurement (Karunatilake, 1976: 23);

(4) they do not allow people freedom (Sivaraksa, 1986: 53), or allow
    people to 'realize their full humanity' (Sivaraksa, 1986: 54);
(5) they are intolerant of religion;
(6) they are overwhelmingly materialistic (Buddhadāsa in Santikaro,
    1996: 167), have a materialist philosophy, and wrongly assert eco-
    nomic determinism (De Silva, 1976: 28), believing that a change in
    economic and social structures guarantees psychological change (De
    Silva, 1976: 28);
(7) they give workers little motivation, and generate inefficient centrally
    directed state-run industries (Karunatilake, 1976: 107–8).

Overall, capitalism is seen as prone to the fault of greed, but as avoiding direct hate-based coerciveness, while Communism is seen as prone
to the fault of hatred and coerciveness, while upholding a sharing ideal.
Both are different from the Buddhist 'Middle Way', and both undermine
religion, capitalism by insidious, slow corrosion, and Communism by
direct repression.

Most of the writers discussed above offer a prescription for a positively
'Buddhist economics', but space does not permit a full discussion of
these. Their main emphases, though, are implicit in their critiques of
existing economic models. Recurring themes are: simplicity and a focus
on essential needs; the avoidance of poverty; appropriate technology to
avoid high unemployment; the use of renewable resources; avoiding
harmful activities such as arms manufacture; national self-sufficiency
where possible; the use of co-operatives; the importance of rural areas
as a focus for traditional values; and the need to revitalize the rural
economy. Buddhadāsa's particular vision seems to be of a society
emphasizing co-operation and generosity, and both individual and communal energetic activity for the good of the community. By implication,
its tax system would aim at reducing income disparities. Its government
should be led by genuinely virtuous people, but could be overthrown if
it became dictatorial. Yet, it would retain its legitimacy, based on
Dhamma, even if it was unpopular in firmly opposing the expression of
people's defilements (Swearer, 1989: 172–3, 185, 193; Santikaro, 1996:
174–7). Sivaraksa sees the *Saṅgha* in its original form and in present forms
not tainted by association with power elites as the 'ideal for human
society' (Sivaraksa, 1991: 160), a 'prototype' for a 'wide-ranging counter-
civilization' which allows a reversal of 'the process of degeneration
described in Buddhist creation myths'.[20] He also advocates a kind of

---

[20] Sivaraksa, 1991: 161; here, he alludes to the *Aggañña Sutta*, on which see p. 153.

'world federalism' entailing such things as: a world parliament as an adjunct to the UN General Assembly; institutions that can tax and regulate transnational companies; economic justice between the North and the South; a taming of the global arms trade; a global disarmament administration; a permanent, strengthened international peacekeeping force, and a strengthened international judiciary (Sivaraksa, 1992: 113–15).

BUDDHISM AND ECONOMICS IN THE MODERN WORLD

In the modern world, there have been various attempts to bring a Buddhist frame of reference to bear on an actual economy and development process of a country. In lands of Southern Buddhism, this has been directed by the government in 1950s Burma,[21] in Sri Lanka a successful example of a lay-led non-governmental development movement also involves monks, and in Thailand, government development efforts came to be complemented by and added to by those involving monks.[22] In lands of Northern and Eastern Buddhism not dominated by Communism, Buddhism mostly affects economics in a less proactive way, whether as a key ingredient of simple, traditional ways of life in certain Northern Buddhist cultures (Norberg-Hodge, 1991), or as elements in the far-from-simple dynamic economies of East Asia. In the West, the Friends of the Western Buddhist Order (see p. 103) has sought to develop its own alternative economy through a string of 'right livelihood' businesses (Subhuti, 1994: 219–64). Of the above, we will discuss examples from Sri Lanka and Japan.

The Sarvōdaya Śramadāna movement in Sri Lanka

Sri Lanka underwent a colonial period under the British, and one of the elements that helped lead up to independence in 1948 was a resurgence in Buddhism. The economy remains primarily agricultural, and three quarters of the population of 17.7 million (1995) live in rural areas, the 1995 per capita GNP being $500 per annum.[23] The government has remained democratic, and government development efforts have been largely directed at the rural sector, though a 'free-trade zone' set up in 1978 has led to the garment industry becoming the country's largest

---

[21] King, 1964: 241–50, 264–7; Sarkisyanz, 1978; Maung, 1970.
[22] Suksamran, 1977; Piker, 1973; Swearer, 1973; Swearer, 1995, 118–23; Gosling, 1985; Sivaraksa, 1992: 48–50.   [23] *Small World: The Magazine of Intermediate Technology*, issue 19 (1995), 8.

foreign-exchange earner, employing 350,000 people by 1997.[24] Good progress has been made in health care and a free education system, with the life expectancy being 68 for men and 72 for women:[25]

In many ways Sri Lanka affords a model for other Third World countries, for the peasantry have been able to attain higher levels of well-being thanks to government endeavours. (Swan, 1983; 127)

Since independence, and especially since the Buddha Jayanti celebration in 1956,[26] the Sinhalese have felt that the restoration of Buddhism, and simpler ways of living, would bring prosperity, as is seen to have existed in their pre-colonial past (Bond, 1988: 106–7):

the contours of the utopian past, in which the political authority actively intervened and 'planned' for the elimination of poverty and to create general prosperity, is widely shared by prominent Buddhist monk-scholars today. (Tambiah, 1992: 108)

Accordingly, a common yearning is for an egalitarian, non-competitive, village-centred welfare-state (Tambiah, 1992: 106). Politicians have thus often preferred to build grandiose irrigation works, as in ancient times, rather than factories, which are linked to alien Western scientific materialism (Bond, 1988: 121). Some factories prefer to use intermediate technology, such as the Durable Car Company, which makes hand-crafted spare parts for the Morris Minor, a 1960s-style car still common in Sri Lanka[27] and whose owners oppose the 'planned obsolescence' mentality of car makers. Yet the impact of modern economics and urbanization have nevertheless been felt, with high unemployment among educated youth, and a communications gap opening up between the rural majority and the urban, English-educated elite.

In a study of thirty-seven monks, a cross-section of those in the university town of Peradeniya in 1983–4, Nathan Katz found that 90 per cent saw Buddhism as incompatible with capitalism but as compatible with democratic socialism, though half felt that Buddhism and Marxism were incompatible. On the free-market policies of the then government,

Half felt the free market was contrary to traditional values, while only a fifth gave it support. A good deal of concern was expressed about the rising national debt associated with free-market policies, while others were concerned about the consumerism and greed such policies seemed to invite. (Katz, 1988: 144)

[24] The *Guardian* newspaper, 7 November 1997.
[25] *Small World: The Magazine of Intermediate Technology*, issue 19 (1995), 8.
[26] Which was seen as 2,500 years after the Buddha's death, and a time for a revival in Buddhism.
[27] B. Datta, 'The Buddhist, the Businessman', *People and the Planet*, World Wide Fund for Nature magazine, 4 (1) (1995), 28–9.

Three-quarters agreed with 'Tourism has only a corrupting influence on our society' (Katz, 1988: 146).

Nearly three-quarters (Katz, 1988: 144) approved (with 5 per cent disapproving) of an important movement known as Sarvōdaya Śramadāna, or 'Sharing of Energy for the Awakening of All', movement,[28] which is also approved of by De Silva and Sivaraksa. This self-help grass-roots rural development movement seeks to foster the economic and cultural development of depressed villages by drawing on and re-emphasizing traditional spiritual and social values, and getting everyone involved in identifying, and actively working to address, needs that a village has, for example a metalled road, or a new school. It also encourages villagers to develop their own marketing co-operatives for their own products, so as to be less dependent on middle men.[29]

The movement is led by A. T. Ariyaratne, who in 1958, when a science teacher at a prestigious high school, began it by taking pupils to live and work in a remote and poor village (Macy, 1983: 13, 24). From this, hundreds of schools came to organize weekend work-camps, and the movement took off, being active, by 1973, in 4,000 of Sri Lanka's 25,000 villages (p. 25), and in 8,000 by the end of the 1980s (Bond, 1995: 5). In 1980–1, for example, it ran 3,400 work-camps (Macy, 1983: 52), and by the mid 1990s had, since its inception, recruited more than 800,000 volunteers and touched the lives of over 4 million people (Swearer, 1995: 117). It is the largest of Sri Lanka's non-governmental organizations, and has been described by Ken Jones as 'arguably the largest and most comprehensive example of socially engaged Buddhism in the world today' (1989: 25). It builds roads, wells and wind-pumps, cleans canals, operates programmes for pre-school education, vaccination, and nutrition, runs marketing co-operatives, communal kitchens, village shops and orphanages, and works with released prisoners (Macy, 1983: 21). Ariyaratne sees Sarvōdaya as working to help underprivileged people 'to assert their value as human beings and help them to share the material and nonmaterial resources in society on an equal basis with others' (1995: 11).

The movement's method is as follows (Macy, 1983: 26–7). A village invites a Sarvōdaya worker to visit it, where he or she consults with the local head monk and other leaders so as to organize a 'family gathering' of the village, usually at a temple. There, the idea of 'village awakening' is introduced, and it is suggested that the villagers organize a *śramadāna*,

---

[28] See Macy, 1983; Bond, 1988: 241–98; Bond, 1996: 121–46; Moore, 1981; Goulet, 1981; Kantowski, 1980; Ariyaratne, 1978, 1979, 1980, 1995.

[29] See Swearer, 1995: 120–3 for co-operatives that monks have led villagers to develop in Thailand.

Plate 5. A. T. Ariyaratne, founder of the Sarvōdaya Śramadāna movement, with
Professor George Bond, who researches the movement, on his right.

an 'energy sharing' work-camp to work on a project that the villagers have identified as one which will genuinely improve the village. The goal should be a realistic one, such as building a metalled road, so as to bring a sense of empowerment when it is achieved, and it is emphasized that a period of one or two months is needed to plan the project effectively. A successful work-camp gives villagers the experience of a new co-operative and dynamic way of living, working alongside each other and Sarvōdaya volunteers. The local monks, or Hindu priests, are usually actively involved, there are communal meals and three 'family gatherings' a day, at which there is discussion or talks, songs and dances (Macy, 1983: 53). As *sharing* is seen as the spirit of Buddhist *dāna* at work, there is a particular emphasis (Macy, 1983: 55–61) on the sharing:

(1) *of labour*, to help break down barriers, with all participating: men, women, young, old, people of different castes; and villagers and visiting government officials. This also brings a sense of involvement and having a stake in the project, which will encourage future maintenance of it;

(2) *of food*, drawing on contributions from all, unless they are too poor;

(3) *of ideas*, with all sections of the community being encouraged to speak up at meetings;

(4) *of language*, so that people use kindly speech, free of any pejorative forms of address, and all are addressed by family forms of address, such as 'mother' or 'younger brother'. Such mutual respect means that women feel well regarded and safe (see p. 405 and Macy, 1983: 80–3).

After a *śramadāna*, groups may be formed for youths, mothers, children, farmers or elders, and these go on to organize their own projects, such as a pre-school or marketing co-operative. This process helps a new local leadership to emerge, to counterbalance the influence of large landowners, moneylenders, merchants, and representatives of political parties.

The aims of the movement are:

(1) to take a *holistic*, integrated approach, pursuing a Middle Way between tradition and change to benefit the individual, society and the environment, blending material and spiritual improvement (Macy, 1983: 46), with the transformation of the individual and of his or her society mutually supporting each other (Bond, 1988: 263). Thus Ariyaratne says 'to change society we must purify ourselves, and the purification process we need is brought about by working in society' (quoted in Bond, 1988: 274). Thus 'Work in the world purifies individuals while it creates a better world, which in turn provides greater support for awakening' (Bond, 1988: 264);

(2) to *build a new person* by bringing about an awakening and empowerment at both an individual and communal level (Macy, 1983: 32),
using right livelihood to develop character and enhance the life of
the community (Macy, 1983: 46). One of the movement's slogans is
'We build the road and the road builds us' (Macy, 1983: 52), with a
District Co-ordinator saying 'The road we build may wash away, but
the attitudes we build do not' (Macy, 1983: 54);

(3) to be a *grass-roots* movement, with decision-making coming from
below by village people articulating their own experience and needs,
and unfolding development values implicit in their existing value
system (Macy, 1983: 20, 24);

(4) on the basis of (3), to emphasize ten *basic needs for full human welfare and
fulfilment*: safe water, a balanced diet, housing, clothing and fuel;
health care; communications and education; a clean, safe and beautiful environment; and a satisfying cultural and spiritual life (Macy,
1983: 27; Bond, 1988: 267). Ariyaratne sees these needs as 'an index
to measure the spirituo-cultural quality of life', a corollary to
Western development planners' Physical Quality of Life Index
(quoted in Bond, 1988: 282);

(5) to aim for an *economics of sufficiency*, with modest consumption, self-
reliance, and the conserving of resources and the environment
(Macy, 1983: 41–2). Thus the goal is a 'no-poverty, no-affluence
society. This is the middle path advocated by the Buddha. Such a
society need not destroy nature, value systems, or cultures'
(Ariyaratne, 1995: 16). The aim is not economic growth, which can
only ever be a means, but a right livelihood which stresses 'harmony
and the quality of life rather than ambition and working for profit
only' as in the standard Western model of development (Bond, 1988:
267).

Sarvōdaya criticizes both capitalism and socialism for focusing only on
economic activity, with the former having the fault of encouraging
acquisitiveness, and the latter as being too top-down rather than grass-
roots in its approach (Macy, 1983: 13–14, 45–6). Ariyaratne holds that:

In a free-market open economy the religious and spiritual heritage of our societies have become brushed away, leaving room for competitive and possessive
instincts of individuals to flourish. (1995: 9)

From this, he holds, come problems such as 'Alcoholism, drug addiction,
crimes, child prostitution' (p. 9). He also approves of the 1994 UN
Human Development Report in its claim that 'a new development par-

adigm is needed that puts people at the centre of development, regards economic growth as a means and not an end', and goes on to argue that decentralization is the way forward, with communications technology being used for communities to network and bypass the centres of power (1995: 12–13).

Ariyaratne looks back to ancient times in Sri Lanka when kings were inspired by Buddhism to help the people through building large irrigation works, the so-called 'temple and tank' tradition, and sees the movement as resocializing Buddhism (Macy, 1983: 17–18, 43–5). He wishes to recover the best of rural values which became overshadowed in the colonial period, when a subsistence economy based on co-operation and sharing was supplanted by an urban-centred one in which individualism and competition became more dominant (Macy, 1983: 22). Rural society and its values are seen as having come under increasing pressure in the post-independence era, with government-led rural development actions mainly benefiting landlords, rural entrepreneurs, and middle-men (pp. 22–3). Ariyaratne also holds that machines and 'machine-like men' have exterminated traditional arts and crafts (Bond, 1996: 131). Moreover, the colonial period is seen as having undermined the social roles of the monks (Bond, 1988: 250), a view previously championed by the noted monk Walpola Rāhula.

Inspiration for the movement comes partly from Quaker work-camps, and the Gandhian Sarvōdaya movement found in India (Macy, 1983: 29). Gandhian influences can be seen in the movement's emphasis on selfless service for humanity, its goal of a new non-violent social order, its emphasis on an 'economics of sufficiency' and its focus on the village as the core of this new order (Bond, 1996: 122–3). Gandhi's this-worldly asceticism, i.e. non-attached activity focused on transforming this world, present society, is also seen in the movement (Bond, 1988: 262, 275). While Sarvōdaya is clearly part of Buddhist revivalism, its leaders prefer not to call it a 'Buddhist' movement (Bond, 1988: 255–61). While based on Buddhist ethical principles, it emphasizes that these are not uniquely Buddhist, that it draws on other inspirations too, and that the movement also works with members of other religions. Yet it uses Buddhist symbols and is perceived by Buddhists as a Buddhist movement. George Bond sees it as not just a development movement, but a 'carefully planned attempt to apply the Buddhist ideals to the modern world to solve the problems of meaning and modernization' (Bond, 1988: 261).

Sarvōdaya appeals to early Buddhist texts and sees itself as recovering the social ethic of early Buddhism, so as to emphasize that Buddhism is more than its other-worldly, spiritual teachings (Bond, 1988: 242–3, 248–9). It looks to the spirit and intention of *Suttas* such as[30]

(1) the *Kūṭadanta* (see p. 198), on poverty as a cause of social unrest;
(2) the *Sigālovāda* (see pp. 97–100), on duties to others;
(3) the *Mahā-maṅgala* (*Sn.* 258–69) on thirty-eight actions and qualities which are a blessing in the world, such as self-application, self-discipline, support of relatives, contentment and patience;
(4) the *Parābhava* (*Sn.* 91–115), on actions that lead to failure in life, such as bad company, laziness, not looking after aged parents, not sharing wealth, haughtiness, gambling, adultery, and craving for power.

A favourite story in Sarvōdaya circles is that of Magha, told in the *Dhammapada* commentary (*Dhp. A.* 1.264–72). This tells how Sakka, chief of the thirty-three gods of a key heaven, attained his state on account of good deeds in a past life as Magha, a man of unstinting generosity and patience. Living in a village where people were rough and unpleasant, he determined to bring happiness to it. He therefore set to cleaning the village and then making the road smooth and even. When others saw him at work, thirty-two men gradually joined him, as he said that he was 'treading the path that leads to heaven'. The village head-man became jealous of his influence and told the king that he and his companions were thieves. When there was an attempt to have them trampled to death by an elephant, though, this failed as Magha and his companions radiated lovingkindness to it as well as to the head-man and the king. They then went on to build a beautiful rest-house at a cross-roads in the village, with women coming to be actively involved in the project, and all went on to be reborn in the heaven of the thirty-three.

The movement emphasizes that changes at the level of the individual, village, nation and world are interlinked; in 1981 it founded the Sarvōdaya Śramadāna International, concerned with both Third World development and 'maldevelopment' in industrial societies (Jones, 1989: 251). Sarvōdaya sees its mission as to

create a new global social order based on the values of Truth, Non-violence and Self-sacrifice and governed by the ideals of participatory democracy. The decentralisation of power and resources, upholding of basic duties and rights, satisfaction of basic human needs, protection and nurturance of a healthy environment, non-violent conflict resolution and tolerance of religious and linguistic differences will be given pride of place in such an order. The economic principle would be one of a sustainable (no-poverty no-affluence) society based on the sharing of resources and their prudent and mindful use. (Bond, 1995: 4)

[30] Bond, 1988: 249, 252–3.

Frank Reynolds sees Sarvōdaya Śramadāna as a reformist movement aiming at structural changes in society in the direction of greater equality, a liberal stance different from that of some conservatives who support more limited movements in the direction of greater equality (1990: 75). George Bond describes Sarvōdaya as a form of 'engaged Buddhism' (1996: 134) or a 'Buddhist social liberation movement' (1996: 121) in which the world is affirmed 'by arguing that the path to individual liberation ran through social liberation' (1996: 122). Joanna Macy sees it as a Buddhist form of 'social gospel' and a parallel to Christian 'liberation theology' (1983: 87). It expresses Buddhist teachings in a strongly social way: it is emphasized that greed, hatred and delusion can be organized at a social level, and the Four Noble Truths analysis is applied to society, with a stagnant, conflict-fraught village in place of *dukkha*, and a co-operative, harmonious village in place of *Nibbāna* (Macy, 1983: 34–7). Nevertheless, Ariyaratne acknowledges that the ramifications of the Noble Truths are not restricted to this social reading of them (Bond, 1988: 273); it is simply that Sarvōdaya focuses on mundane aspects of 'awakening' (Bond, 1988: 270–1).

Ariyaratne rejects forms of Sri Lankan Buddhism that have primarily other-worldly goals, such as many lay people's focusing on generating karmic fruitfulness for a future rebirth (Bond, 1988: 255). He emphasizes that karma is only one factor that influences people's lives, so that they should do all they can to take charge of their lives in the present (Bond, 1988: 272). He has re-orientated the traditional value of *dāna*, or giving, from primarily being support for the *Saṅgha* to being *śrama-dāna*: the gift or sharing of one's time, labour and energy, for the benefit of all. He criticizes both monastic activity aloof from society and that which is focused only on rituals which generate karmic fruitfulness for the laity (Bond, 1988: 255). Rather, people should get 'full use' of their temples in terms of drawing on their potential for social transformation (Bond, 1988: 282). The movement thus often cites a passage where the Buddha admonishes the first sixty *Arahat* monks to go in all directions:

Walk, monks, on tour for the blessing of the manyfolk, for the happiness of the manyfolk, out of compassion for the world, for the welfare, the blessing, the happiness of gods and humans . . . teach *Dhamma* which is lovely in its beginning, lovely in the middle, lovely in its culmination. (*Vin.* I.21; *D.* II.48)

In a similar way, Ariyaratne sometimes compares the Sarvōdaya approach to that of the *Bodhisattva*, who works in the world to aid the awakening of the many (Bond, 1988: 274). The movement is lay-led, but involves over 1,000 monks as workers at village level and beyond (Macy, 1983: 64). It sees itself as helping to 'restore' the wider social responsibilities of monks, lost in the colonial period, and to help broaden their understanding of the social implications of Buddhism.

Richard Gombrich, an English Buddhologist, and Gananath Obeyesekere, a Sri Lankan anthropologist, are quite critical of the movement. They hold that it reduces the demanding other-worldly path to one of this-worldly activity (1988: 246). Yet Sarvōdaya activity exists alongside an increase in 'demanding' meditative activity in Sri Lanka by both monks and laity, and Sarvōdaya has stimulated other types of demanding activity in many people who were unlikely to engage in meditation. Gombrich and Obeyesekere also regard Sarvōdaya's vision of pre-colonial village life as 'sentimental and idealized' and thus inaccurate (1988: 244). Given that most of its leaders are from the urban middle classes (pp. 246–7), its 'vision of village life and the past of Sri Lankan civilization is a projection of the bourgeoisie, a fantasy that has no social reality' (p. 250) in the form of bourgeois values that the movement seeks to spread to the villages (pp. 246–7). They also hold that many of the English-language writings on Sarvōdaya are by 'good-hearted but naive Western intellectuals who see the movement in terms of their own utopian fantasies of a benevolent social order' (p. 243). They recognize Sarvōdaya's achievements in inculcating 'a sense of Buddhist work for the welfare of others', but hold that 'the rest of the Sarvōdaya program is both naive and unrealistic, with little hope of success once the massive support from aid donors is withdrawn' (p. 245). For them, Ariyaratne's 'disembodied village has little recognition of social conflict, of the vice and folly that constitute part of our humanity' (p. 251). Yet while Ariyaratne's vision is certainly idealistic, he clearly recognizes the vices of village life and seeks to rectify these by drawing on neglected strengths that he, rightly or wrongly, sees as implicit in Sri Lankan village life. If not, his movement would be doing nothing positive, but just resisting aspects of modernization. His glowing picture of certain ancient Sinhalese civilizations certainly contains exaggerations, and is thus best treated as an inspiring vision, yet this certainly seems to be producing good results. The movement appears to have enough pragmatism to adapt to the reduction in donor support, but let us hope that this does not lead to inappropriate compromises that dull its driving vigour.

Buddhist elements in the modern Japanese economy

Since the defeat of Japan in the Second World War, it has turned its back on the project of military power which fascinated it in the first half of the twentieth century. After a difficult period of reconstruction, it has experienced a lasting economic boom. While traditional forms of Buddhism and Shintō have still been influential in the countryside, in the cities they have often lost out to secularism, though they have adapted to it in certain respects through marketing their ritual services to people. They have also lost out, in the cities, to many 'New Religions', often Buddhist-based. These address modern urban anxieties about belonging, and the quest for material security. They have dropped many traditional religious trappings, use modern means of communication etc., and are lay-led movements. The most successful has been the Sōka Gakkai, or 'Value-Creating Society', a form of Nichiren Buddhism which had a following, in 1992, of 8–10 million in Japan (population 120 million) and 1.26 million overseas converts in around 120 countries (Metraux, 1996: 365, 372).

The Sōka Gakkai (see pp. 146 and 273–4) sponsors an education system including two high schools and the respected Sōka University, two art museums, several publishing companies and a mass-circulation newspaper. It has also amassed much money and property, and has been criticized for some of its financial dealings (Metraux, 1996: 365). It runs Citizens' Livelihood Discussion Centres, which give free legal counselling and act as a channel to government for grievances on such matters as housing, social security, education and pollution. Sōka Gakkai has also sponsored a labour union and student movement which seek to synthesize capitalist and socialist values.

While the Japanese are noted for their hard work, verging on being workaholics, in 1984, the Prime Minister said that there was some concern that the Japanese worked *too* hard and left insufficient time for relaxation and spiritual matters, for 'the country's store of spiritual affluence is all important'.[31] In 1985, the Labour Minister sought to encourage workers to take more of their paid leave entitlement – in 1983, only 8.8 days of an annual 14.8 days' entitlement were taken on average[32] – so as to 'regain their human character'.[33] By 1994, it was

---

[31] The *Guardian* newspaper, 4 October 1984.   [32] In addition to twelve national holidays a year.
[33] The *Guardian* newspaper, 26 February 1985.

noted that the number of public holidays in Japan had increased to be among the largest in 'developed' countries. In 1984, the Prime Minister had floated the idea of developing a 'Net National Satisfaction Index' to monitor the happiness of Japanese citizens according to how they feel, their health, unemployment, possessions etc.[34] In fact, in a 1990 survey of the quality of life in the major cities of the world, Japanese cities came out among the top ones, though homes are of poorer quality and less spacious than in many Western nations.[35]

In the Japanese economy, employees who work in the large companies (about a third of the total work-force) are cared for very well. The companies try to give a job for life, to look after the social and physical welfare and education of their employees. In return, dedication to the firm is expected. Such an approach has its roots in Confucian family-centred ideals, Buddhist ideals about looking after employees (see pp. 100 and 188), and Japanese group-centred ethics, which springs from the needs of rice-growing agriculture. Canon,[36] the office equipment and camera manufacturer, provides extensive welfare benefits for workers, and nearly £3.5 million a year is spent on training centres and courses for them. The expression of its management philosophy has spiritual overtones: a booklet for workers says:

At Canon we are devoted to constantly to contribute [*sic*] to the betterment of society, manufacturing only the highest quality products . . . at Canon we are devoted to building an ideal company to enjoy everlasting prosperity . . . we shall co-operate to deepen mutual trust and understanding with harmonious spirit . . . our motto shall be health and happiness for personal development.[37]

While the reference to 'everlasting prosperity' sounds out of tune with the Buddhist emphasis on impermanence, the somewhat pious hopes expressed here do contain echoes of Buddhist ideals. The head of TDK declares that the inspiration for his successful company is Buddhism:

Making a profit is important, of course, but it is not the ultimate goal. Character building is much more important. At TDK we attach great importance to discovering the meaning of work. As far as valuing relationships goes, it seems to me, Japan is second to none. And at the bottom of this lies Buddhism.[38]

Of course the Japanese capitalist 'economic miracle' has been emulated by so-called 'Asian Tiger' economies of South Korea, Taiwan and

---

[34] The *Guardian* newspaper, 4 October 1984.   [35] The *Guardian* newspaper, 17 January 1985.
[36] Which used to be called Kwannon, the Japanese name of the *Bodhisattva* Avalokiteśvara.
[37] The *Guardian* newspaper, 13 December 1984.
[38] *Japan Times*, 7 December 1981, 8, as quoted in Davis, 1989: 304.

Singapore, which all share a Confucian/Buddhist value-mix, as well as by that of Thailand, which has an economically active Chinese minority. As in Japan, South Korean economic growth has been led by the government and channelled through large firms. People have worked very hard, with few welfare handouts but with support from family and from employers, if large enough. The average growth in GNP from 1962 to 1984 was 8.5 per cent.[39] Thailand has also had a similar rate of growth. Yet in autumn 1997, the growth bubble of many 'Asian Tigers' collapsed, starting with Thailand. The South Korean currency (the won) fell 50 per cent against the dollar in December 1997, so that the International Monetary Fund was called in to assist the country. An editorial in the *Guardian* newspaper (13 December 1997) stated:

The Wall Street Journal sees the whole sorry episode as an obituary to the long-termist 'communitarian capitalism' of Asia which put employees and customers ahead of shareholders and a total justification for the short-termism practised in Britain and the United States.

Whether this is the right analysis remains to be seen. High rates of borrowing seem to be a crucial factor, and a period of retrenchment is likely to be followed then by more moderate growth.

CONCLUSION

This chapter clearly shows that it is wrong to regard Buddhism as uninterested in economic issues, for the Buddha gave guidance to lay people on their economic activity. Moreover, the support of monasticism by both lay people and monastics themselves has been, and generally remains, an important part of economics in Buddhist lands. In both respects, Buddhism's emphasis is on a moral framework for economic activity, and the importance of generosity, especially in support of monastics, who help set the moral tone of society. In the modern world, Asian Buddhist lands have been affected by the twin politico-economic ideologies of Communism and capitalism. Given Communist regimes' harsh treatment of Buddhism, and their use of violence, it is not surprising that Buddhists are aware of Communism's weaknesses. While elements of the capitalist spirit are not foreign to Buddhism, its consumerist form is, and Buddhists are more at ease with capitalism when it contributes to the public good rather than just to private gain. Both Communism and full-blooded capitalism have challenged Buddhist cultures and values, thus

[39] The *Guardian* newspaper, 9 April 1986.

stimulating thought on 'Buddhist economics' as an alternative to these, especially in Theravāda lands. This has led to a variety of prescriptions which are broadly favourable to a co-operative communitarian-cum-socialist model with use of 'appropriate technology' and care for the poor. While these prescriptions can sometimes be overly idealistic or insufficiently developed, there have also been attempts to put aspects of such an approach into practice. From a Buddhist perspective, given the conditioned nature of the world and people, it is not surprising that these have all faced some difficulties, as do all human actions.

Among Buddhist lands, excluding Communist ones in which Buddhism has had minimal opportunities to affect modern society, Theravāda lands are spread around the mid-point of the spectrum running from traditional, low-income societies to high-tech rich ones, while Mahāyāna ones are, in the case of Northern Buddhism, for example Bhutan, generally at the former end or, in the case of Eastern Buddhism, generally at the latter end. At either end of the spectrum, Buddhists have not been at the forefront of those embracing modernity and its economics, but elements of Buddhism have been important in resisting or moderating its unethical aspects, or in helping to spread its genuine benefits. They have also contributed to an approach to work which values it as an arena for character building, rather than simply as a way of gaining an income.

CHAPTER 6

War and peace

Enmities never cease by enmity in this world; only by non-enmity do they cease.
This is an ancient law.   *Dhammapada* 5

Buddhism is generally seen as associated with non-violence and peace.
These are certainly both strongly represented in its value system. This
does not mean, though, that Buddhists have always been peaceful:
Buddhist countries have had their fair share of war and conflict, for most
of the reasons that wars have occurred elsewhere. Yet it is difficult to find
any plausible 'Buddhist' rationales for violence, and Buddhism has some
particularly rich resources for use in dissolving conflict. Overall, it can
be observed that Buddhism has had a general humanizing effect
throughout much of Asia. It has tempered the excesses of rulers and
martial people, helped large empires (for example China) to exist
without much internal conflict, and rarely, if at all, incited wars against
non-Buddhists. Moreover, in the midst of wars, Buddhist monasteries
have often been havens of peace.

BUDDHIST ANALYSES OF THE CAUSES OF CONFLICT

For Buddhism, the roots of all unwholesome actions – greed, hatred and
delusion – are seen as at the root of human conflicts (Nyanaponika, 1978:
50). When gripped by any of them, a person may think 'I have power
and I want power', so as to persecute others (*A.* 1.201–2). Conflict often
arises from attachment to material things: pleasures, property, territory,
wealth, economic dominance, or political superiority. At *M.* 1.86–7, the
Buddha says that sense-pleasures lead on to desire for more sense-pleasures, which leads on to conflict between all kinds of people, including
rulers, and thus quarrelling and war. As the Mahāyāna poet Śāntideva
put it in his *Śikṣā-samuccaya*, citing the *Anantamukha-nirhāra-dhāraṇī*,
'Wherever conflict arises among living creatures, the sense of possession
is the cause' (*Ss.* 20). Apart from actual greed, material deprivation is
seen as a key source of conflict, as seen in the last chapter (pp. 197–8).
    The Buddha also often referred to the negative effect of attachment

239

to speculative or fixed views, dogmatic opinions, and even correct views if not personally *known* to be true (*Sn.* 766–975; Premasiri, 1972). Surveying the intellectual scene of his day, he referred to 'the wrangling of views, the jungle of views'. Grasping at views can be seen to have led to religious and ideological wars (offensive or defensive), crusades, bloody revolutions, and gas chambers. Indeed, millions of deaths were caused, in the twentieth century, by those attached to particular ideologies which 'justified' their actions: Hitler, Stalin, the Khmer Rouge, and terrorists of various kinds.

Hatred, perhaps fuelled by propaganda at times of conflict, may spring from attachment to certain goods or issues. Though people want to live in peace, they fail to do so: they think increasingly round and round an issue until thought focuses on a particular matter, leading on to desire, and thus to dividing people into 'liked' and 'disliked', and on to greed, avarice, and thus hatred (*D.* ii.276–7). Fear, close to hatred, may also motivate evil actions, whether or not it is justified (*D.* iii.182).

Distorted perceptions which fuel conflict are clear forms of delusion. The deepest delusion, according to Buddhism, is the 'I am' conceit: the feeling/attitude/gut-reaction that one has a permanent, substantial Self or 'I' that must be protected at all costs. As part of the process of building up their self-image, people invest much of their identity in 'my country', 'my community', 'my religion', or even 'my gender'. When this 'entity' is seen as being threatened or offended, people then feel that they themselves are threatened or have been offended. So relationship with a group, which in one sense helps take a person out of ego-centric preoccupation, then becomes the basis for a group-wide 'ego' that can itself be 'offended'. Yet just as a person contains no fixed essence as 'Self', surely such conventional groupings as 'a country' or 'a community' lack any permanent essence which needs defending at all costs: note how political maps of the world change over time as boundaries move and political entities rise and fall. As regards the Buddhist community, the Buddha did not encourage his followers to feel anger at insults to it. If anyone disparaged the Buddha, the *Dhamma* or *Saṅgha*, disciples should not be angry, and if anyone praised these, they should not be elated. In either case, this would be a hindrance to clarity of mind. Rather, they should calmly assess and acknowledge the degree of truth, if any, in what was said (*D.* 1.3).

The bad influence of other members of one's community – whether of rulers or friends – is seen as another factor which may lead to conflict.

Thus at *A.* II.74, it is said that when a king acts in an unvirtuous (*adhammikā*) way, this influences his ministers to do likewise, and this influence then spreads to brahmins and householders, and on to townsfolk and villagers. That is, rot at the top can easily spread downwards through the whole of society. A flatterer can also influence one into taking, or confirm one in, bad actions (*D.* III.185–6).

SOLUTIONS TO CONFLICT

Economic means

The notion that poverty is a root-cause of crime and moral decline, as seen in chapter 5, correlates with the idea that economic measures to avoid poverty can help to prevent crime, as described in the *Kūṭadanta Sutta* (see p. 198). To the extent that economic grievances are factors in a conflict, then, this implies that addressing them can help resolve it.

Negotiation and emphasizing the mutual harm of war

The Buddha is once said to have prevented a war between the Sākiyas – members of the republic from which he himself came – and the Koliyas.[1] Both used the waters of a dammed river that ran between their territories, and when the water-level fell, the labourers of both peoples wanted the water for their own crops. They thus fell to quarrelling and insulting each other, and when those in power heard of these insults, they prepared for war. By his meditative powers, the Buddha is said to have perceived this, then flown to the area to hover above the river. Seeing him, his kinsmen threw down their arms and bowed to him, but when people were asked what the conflict was about, at first no-one knew, until at last the labourers said that it was over water. The Buddha then got the warrior-nobles to see that they were about to sacrifice something of great value – the lives of warrior-nobles – for something of very little value – water. They therefore desisted.

Over the centuries, Buddhist monks have often been used by kings to help negotiate an end to a war. Mahāyāna texts explicitly suggest that Buddhists should also try to see to it that warring parties are more ready to settle their differences. Thus the *Vimalakīrti Nirdeśa Sūtra* says, on the *Bodhisattva*:

[1] *Dhp. A.* III.254–6; *J.* v.412–14.

In times of war he teaches
Kindliness and pity
To convert living beings
So that they can live in peace.
When enemies line up for battle
He gives equal strength to both.
With his authority and power, he forces
Them to be reconciled and live in harmony.[2]

A non-violent moral stance

In a *Jātaka* story (*J.* II.400–3; cf. *J.* I.261–8), the *Bodhisattva* is said to have been a king told of the approach of an invading army. In response, he says 'I want no kingdom that must be kept by doing harm', that is, by having soldiers defend his kingdom. His wishes are followed, and when the capital is surrounded by the invaders, he orders the city's gates to be opened. The invaders enter, and the king is deposed and imprisoned. In his cell, he develops great compassion for the invading king (who will karmically suffer for his unjust action), which leads to this king experiencing a burning sensation in his body. This then prompts him to come to see that he had done wrong by imprisoning a virtuous king. Consequently, he releases him and leaves the kingdom in peace. Here, the message is that the king's non-violent stance managed to save the lives of many people – on both sides. In line with this approach are such verses as:

Conquer anger by love, conquer evil by good, conquer the stingy by giving, conquer the liar by truth. (*Dhp.* 223)

Though he should conquer a thousand thousand men in the battlefield, yet he, indeed, is the nobler victor who should conquer himself. (*Dhp.* 103)

At *J.* II.3–4, the content of the first of these is said to have been the policy of the Buddha in a previous life as a King Brahmadatta of Benares, in contrast to a king who only repaid good with good and evil with evil.

Of course, such an approach does not always save lives, and indeed it is said that the Sākiya people (see above) came to be annihilated when they did not defend themselves against aggressors. Again, in the eleventh century, when invading Muslim Turks smashed Buddhist monasteries and universities, it appears that the monks offered no resistance. Yet the non-violent response can save. A few years ago, an English Buddhist

---

[2] Luk, 1972: 89. A slightly different translation is given by Nhat Hanh, 1975: 95.

monk and his lay companion were attacked by brigands in India. The lay companion fought back and got beaten up. The monk prepared for death, by chanting, and was left alone . . . At *M.* III.268–9 the account is given of the fearless monk Puṇṇa, who told the Buddha that he was going to live and teach among the people of Sunāparanta. When the Buddha pointed out that they were fierce people, who would revile him, he simply said that he would then look at them as good people if they did not actually strike him with their hands. If they did do this, though, he would look at them as good for not hitting him with clods of earth. If they did this, he would look at them as good if they did not strike him with sticks, and so on for striking with a knife but not killing him. Finally, he said that if they killed him, this would simply bring the body, with its disgusting features, to an end. It is then said that he went on to gain many disciples among the people of Sunāparanta! In Indian history, while Buddhists were sometimes persecuted by Hindu kings, there is no record of persecution of others by Buddhists. On the other hand, neither does history seem to record any Buddhist king who did not seek to repel invaders by force! While an individual may risk his or her life by not meeting force with force, perhaps it takes a very spiritually gifted ruler to do this successfully on behalf of his or her country!

Reflections to undermine hatred and develop patience

Among the central values of Buddhism are those known as the 'divine abidings': lovingkindness, compassion, empathetic joy and equanimity (see pp. 103–9). Allied to these is the virtue of patience or forbearance (Pali *khanti*, Skt *kṣānti*), as exemplified in the *Khanti-vādi-Jātaka* (see pp. 105–7). All such values are directly relevant to defusing conflicts, and their practice will make these less likely to occur in the first place.

As part of the method of developing lovingkindness, the Theravādin commentator Buddhaghosa gives various reflections, in his *Visuddhimagga*, for undermining hatred or anger (*Vism.* 298–306). These can be seen as valuable in many contexts as methods of removing the power of these destructive emotions, and thus undermining the psychological roots of conflict. By contrast with the Christian emphasis on not holding ill-will *against* someone, the Buddhist, particularly Theravāda, emphasis is on not holding it *within* oneself, because of its harmful effects. Several of Buddhaghosa's reflections are in the spirit of: 'Whatever harm a foe may do to a foe, or a hater to a hater, an ill-directed mind can do one far-greater harm' (*Dhp.* 42). An example is:

Suppose another, to annoy, provokes you with some odious act, why suffer anger
to spring up, and do as he would have you do? If you get angry, then maybe you
make *him* suffer, maybe not; though with the hurt that anger brings, *you* certainly
are punished now. (*Vism.* 300)

That is, when someone attacks or abuses one, truly lasting harm only
arises when one reacts with anger or violence. An enemy wishes such
things as that one is ugly, in pain, without good fortune, poor, without
fame, without friends, and not destined for a heavenly rebirth. Yet
allowing oneself to be prey to anger brings these very things (*A.* iv.94).
Getting angry with others is compared to picking up a burning stick to
hit someone with, or throwing dust against the wind: one only suffers
oneself, through immediate unpleasant feelings, and future karmic
results. While the other person presents the occasion for this, such an
action is one's own, and directly harms one. Anger is conditioned by
an attack of an assailant, but it is not determined by it. There must
always be some co-operating reaction: something that one can come to
have increasing control over, by developing more self-control and
undermining the attachment to 'I' and 'mine'. Of course, this is no
excuse for abusing others on the grounds that *they* should use self-
control to avoid any annoyance on their part. Most people are not
developed enough to avoid some annoyance, so abuse will generally be
a direct encouragement for it, as well as being unwholesome for the
perpetrator.

In a more concrete way, Buddhaghosa suggests that if another is
harming one because of one's *own* anger, the wise thing to do is to put
the anger down. Or, again, if one's presence is fuelling another's anger,
it is best to get out of the way for a while, so that tempers may cool. He
also recommends one to focus only on the good qualities that an
offending person now has, or reflect that all beings must have been a
close relative or friend in one of their, and one's own, innumerable past
rebirths: so that one should now recollect their kindness (*S.* ii.189–90; cf.
Ss. 21). As past human rebirths might have been in a variety of ethnic
groups or cultures, such a reflection seems particularly relevant to situations of ethnic strife between two peoples who view each other as alien
'others'.

Buddhaghosa also suggests that one should reflect on impermanence,
and acknowledge that the mind-states of a person who has harmed one
are likely to be different now from when he or she did the harmful act
(of course, this applies even more to the actions of a past generation of
a country or group that was once seen as an enemy). Again, one can even

see an annoying person in terms of a collection of physical elements and mental processes: which particular 'part' of them is one annoyed with?? One may also reflect on the inspiring example of the Buddha in past lives, when he showed great patience at provocation, or reflect on the eleven kinds of good results of the mind-deliverance by lovingkindness (*A.* v.342), such as good sleep, without disturbing dreams, the good regard of others, a serene face and an easily concentrated mind. If all else fails, it is useful to give a gift to, or receive one from, a person to whom one is hostile.

In his *Bodhi-caryāvatāra*, the Mahāyāna writer Śāntideva has much to say on patience, which is close to lovingkindness in spirit. In a striking and thought-provoking way, he says:

Why be unhappy about something if it can be remedied? And what is the use of being unhappy about something if it cannot be remedied? (*Bca.* VI.10)

Moreover:

So when seeing an enemy or even a friend committing an improper action, by thinking that such things arise from conditions, I shall remain in a happy frame of mind. (*Bca.* VI.33)

Anger at a fool for harming others is like anger at a fire for burning things (*Bca.* VI.39). If someone strikes one with a stick on account of his hatred, it makes more sense to be angry with his inciting hatred than with him (*Bca.* VI.41). If someone harms one, just look at it as the karmic results of similar harm one has done to others (*Bca.* VI.42). Moreover, one can only be harmed by others because one's grasping has led to one's being reborn:

Both his weapon and my body are the causes of my suffering. Since he gave rise to the weapon and I to the body, with whom should I be angry? (*Bca.* VI.43)

An angry response to those who attack one is self-defeating, for by their actions, they are reborn in hell, but by patiently enduring them, one gets beyond one's past evil that karmically led to this suffering (*Bca.* VI.47–8). Moreover:

If I am unable to endure even the mere sufferings of the present, then why do I not restrain myself from being angry, which will be the source of hellish misery? (*Bca.* VI.73)

In fact, an enemy should be looked on as like a beneficial treasure, for he gives one a good opportunity for practising patience, and should be venerated accordingly (*Bca.* VI.107–11). Having thus practised patience in the face of provocation, one should share the spiritual fruits of this patience with those who attack one (*Bca.* VI.108).

Forbearance and forgiveness

In accordance with the spirit of the above, certain scriptural passages recommend the strength and transformative potency of forbearance and forgiveness. One passage concerns a conflict between the gods (*devas*) and the power-hungry titans (*asuras*) (*S.* I.220–2). Vepacitti, the defeated titan leader, is once brought before Sakka, leader of the gods, and curses him. When Sakka is not angry, his charioteer asks whether he forbears from fear or weakness, but Sakka replies: neither, I simply do not wish to bandy words with a fool. Further, he explains that the words of a fool are best stopped by responding to his anger and verbal onslaught by oneself remaining calm, not by harsh measures. This will not lead to one's opponent thinking he can take advantage of one's 'weakness', for forbearing patience (*khanti*) is a sign of real strength, unlike the deceptive 'strength' of a fool:

Worse of the two is he who, when reviled, reviles again. He who does not, when reviled, revile again, wins a twofold victory. He seeks the welfare of both himself and the other, who, having known the anger of another, mindfully maintains his peace. (*S.* I.222; *Vism.* 324)

At *S.* I.162, the same verses are used when a brahmin insults and abuses the Buddha because a relative has become a Buddhist monk. In response, the Buddha asks him what he does when he prepares food and drinks for visiting relatives, but they decline what he offers: who does the food and drink then belong to? When he replies 'those things are for ourselves', the Buddha then says that 'That with which you revile, abuse and insult we who do none of these things, *that* we do not accept. So now, brahmin, it remains with you.' He then goes on to say that he will not 'dine' with him by responding with anger to his angry words, and then gives the above verses.

At *Vin.* I.342–9 (cf. Niwano, 1977: 18–24), the Buddha tells the following story to two parties of monks quarrelling over the interpretation of a point of monastic discipline. King Brahmadatta of Kāsi conquers a weaker kingdom and later executes its former king and queen. Just before he dies, the former king says to his son, Dīghāvu, who remains unknown to Brahmadatta, 'enmities are not allayed by enmity: enmities, dear Dīghāvu, are allayed by non-enmity' (*Vin.* I.344–5). Dīghāvu nevertheless goes away to plot his revenge. By learning to sing, he attracts the attention of King Brahmadatta, enters his employ, and goes on to win a position of trust. He gets an opportunity to kill the king when the latter falls asleep on his lap when they are out hunting. Three times he draws his sword to kill the king, but three times he desists, on remembering his father's last words to him. The king then awakens, alarmed by a bad dream, and Dīghāvu reveals his identity. The king asks him to spare his life, but Dīghāvu simply asks that the king spare *his* life. They thus agree to spare each other. Dīghāvu then says:

my parents were killed by a king, but if I were to deprive the king of life, those who desired the king's welfare would deprive me of life and those who desired my welfare would deprive these of life; thus enmity would not be settled by enmity. (*Vin.* 1.348)

Brahmadatta then grants him back his kingdom, and gives him his daughter's hand in marriage. The Buddha then teaches the quarrelling monks in verses (*Vin.* 1.349), some of which are also found at *Dhp.* 3–6:

'He abused me, he beat me, he defeated me, he robbed me', the enmity of those who harbour such thoughts is not appeased.
'He abused me, he beat me, he defeated me, he robbed me', the enmity of those who do not harbour such thoughts is appeased.
Enmities never cease by enmity in this world; only by non-enmity (i.e. loving-kindness) do they cease. This is an ancient law.
And others do not know that we come to an end here; but those who know, thereby their quarrels are allayed.

All traditions of Buddhism value acknowledgement of a fault – just to oneself, or to others also – and the resolve not to repeat it (see pp. 26–8). The Mahāyāna also includes an emphasis on explicitly apologizing. In the chapter on ethics (*śīla*) of his *Bodhisattva-bhūmi*, Asaṅga states that a *Bodhisattva* should apologize for any offence he or she has caused, and should accept the properly offered apology of another (Tatz, 1986: 74, 75). In Japan, apology is much used as a way of restoring relationships, and those who apologize and confess are treated more lightly in court (LaFleur, 1992: 147).

In the Theravādin *Vinaya*, there are provisions for a formal act of *paṭisāraṇiya*: 'reconciliation', or literally 'returning to' a wrong so as to undo it. This is to be done by a monk who has scoffed at a lay person, refused or complained at his or her alms, or spoken in dispraise of the Buddha, *Dhamma* or *Saṅgha* to him or her, or caused dissension among lay supporters (*Vin.* 11.17–20). In such cases, the monk should be reproved, made to remember his offence and be accused of the offence, and then the *Saṅgha* should agree for him to go to the lay person to ask his or her forgiveness. If he feels unable to ask forgiveness, the *Saṅgha* should arrange for a competent monk to accompany him to ask on his behalf. He should try to seek forgiveness by a variety of methods if need be, in turn using the following form of words:

'Forgive me, householder, I am at peace towards you' . . . 'Forgive this monk, householder, he is at peace towards you' . . . 'Forgive this monk, householder, for I am at peace towards you' . . . 'Forgive this monk, householder, (I ask it) in the name of the *Saṅgha*.' (*Vin.* II.20)

If none of this succeeds in eliciting forgiveness, the offending monk should be made to sit on his haunches, salute the lay person with joined palms, and acknowledge his offence. Nevertheless, it should be said that, from a Theravāda perspective, if apologizing becomes compulsive for a person, it might be seen as a subtle form of self-advertising, drawing attention to 'me and my faults'.

Defusing a situation

Within the Buddhist monastic community, harmony is much valued, and systems were developed to deal with differences within it, such as disputes over matters of monastic discipline. At *M.* II.247–50,[3] the Buddha explains that there are seven ways to settle a dispute: reaching a consensus by drawing out the implications of agreed principles; majority voting if this fails;[4] overlooking monastic offences which the guilty party cannot remember committing; overlooking apparent offences committed when a person was out of his mind; setting aside an offence which has been acknowledged with the promise not to repeat it; censure of a monk who only acknowledges a serious offence under cross-questioning, after having denied it; and lastly 'covering over with grass'. This final method is to be used if the two parties have taken to open quarrelling. A wise monk should be selected from each side, and each of these should acknowledge the faults of himself and his own party in acting in such an unseemly way. This can draw a veil over such lesser offences, though not any serious ones. The commentary sees this as like covering

---

[3] Cf. *Vin.* II.93–104 and Nhat Hanh, 1987: 74–9, citing '*Mvkh.* 10 and Sseu Fen Lin (T. 1428)'.

[4] Consensus is the preferred method, but otherwise majority voting may be used. This should not be done over a trifling matter, though, or if it is known or thought that 'those who profess non-*Dhamma*' are in the majority or the (local) *Saṅgha* will be split on the matter (*Vin.* II.84–5).

over excrement with dry grass, so that someone can walk over it without becoming soiled. Nhat Hanh refers to another version of this method, called 'covering mud with straw', from a different source. Two respected senior monks are chosen, and one speaks on behalf of each of two monks. They each say something to de-escalate the feelings of those involved, by helping monk A understand monk B:

Then the other high monk says something to protect the other monk, saying it in a way that the first monk feels better. By doing so, they dissipate the hard feelings in the hearts of the two monks and help them accept the verdict proposed by the community. (Nhat Hanh, 1987: 77)

Such procedures, of course, would work best within a community of like-minded people, who share agreed objectives. Nevertheless, some features might be applicable to other kinds of conflict. The avoidance of 'divisive speech', part of 'right speech' (see pp. 38 and 76), is also relevant to defusing or avoiding conflict. One who practises this is

one who reunites those who are divided, a promoter of friendships, who enjoys concord, rejoices in concord, delights in concord, a speaker of words that promote concord. (*M.* 1.288)

NON-VIOLENT REFLECTIONS ON A VIOLENT WORLD

Among Buddhist teachings and principles relevant to the use of violence are the following:
(1) the first precept (see pp. 67 and 69), i.e. the commitment to avoid intentional harm or killing of any sentient being, whether directly or by the agency of another person;
(2) the emphasis on lovingkindness and compassion;
(3) the ideal of 'right livelihood', a factor of the Eightfold Path to *Nirvāṇa*, which precludes making a living in a way that causes suffering to others. Among the specifically listed forms of 'wrong livelihood' is living by 'trade in arms' (*A.* v.177).

Given these emphases, can war and similar forms of violence ever be justified? The Buddhist path aims at a state of complete non-violence, based on insight and inner strength rooted in a calm mind. Yet those who are not yet perfect, living in a world in which others may seek to gain their way by violence, still have to face the dilemma of whether to respond with defensive violence. Pacifism may be the ideal, but in practice Buddhists have often used violence in self-defence or defence of their country – not to speak of sometimes going in for aggressive violence, like any other group of people. Ordinary Buddhists may feel that they are not yet capable of the totally non-violent response, particularly as they are still attached to various things which they feel may sometimes need violence to defend. Of course they could give these up, by becoming a monk or nun, but they may not feel ready for this level of commitment.

This said, there are a number of textual passages which reflect on war and punitive violence, seeking to subvert the 'violence is sometimes necessary' view of worldly common sense by a dialogue with the non-violent ideal. Here, the Buddha speaks as one who himself came from the warrior-noble (*khattiya*) class. In two short discourses at *S.* 1.82–3 and 83–5, the Buddha comments on two battles which arise when the evil King Ajātasattu attacks the land of his uncle, King Pasenadi, a follower of the Buddha who is said to be 'a friend to whatever is good'. In the first, Pasenadi is defeated and retreats, and the Buddha reflects on his misery:

Victory breeds hatred; the defeated live in pain. Happily the peaceful live, giving up victory and defeat. (*S.* 1.83; *Dhp.* 201)

This clearly implies that conquest results in tragedy for the defeated, which may lead to hatred and the likelihood of a desire to overcome the conqueror. In the second battle, Pasenadi wins. Capturing Ajātasattu, he spares his life but confiscates all his weapons and army. Here the Buddha comments:

> A person may plunder
> so long as it serves his ends,
> but when they plunder others,
> the plundered (then) plunder.
> So long as evil's fruit is not matured,
> the fool thinks he has an opportunity,
> but when the evil matures, the fool suffers.
> The slayer gets a slayer (in his turn),
> the conqueror gets a conqueror,
> the abuser gets abuse,
> the wrathful gets one who annoys.
> Thus by the evolution of karma,
> he who plunders is plundered.   (*S.* 1.85)

Without justifying defensive violence, this points out that the aggression often leads to defensive counter-violence, which can be seen as a karmic result for the aggressor. Such a response happens, whether or not it is justified. Thus aggression is discouraged. Yet Pasenadi, the generally peace-loving defender, is not free of censure. To spare the life of a defeated enemy is surely good, but to leave him defenceless, without an army, is seen as storing up trouble. Khantipalo comments:

The uselessness of war as a way of solving conflicts is summed up in the last two lines . . . The Buddha saw how fruitless would be Pasenadi's action in confiscating the army of his troublesome nephew. The effect that it had was to harden Ajātasattu's resolve to conquer Kosala, which he did eventually do. In our times the huge reparations demanded of Germany after the First World war is another good example – our revenge is followed by their revenge as seen in Hitler and the Second World war. (Khantipalo, 1986: 14)

Kashi Upadhyaya comments that the passages portray the peace-loving defender as only moderately good, falling short of the ideal of complete non-violence (1971: 537). Elizabeth Harris, on the other hand, says that the passages show 'an acceptance of political realities' in which, the world being as it is, 'Pasenadi's role as defender of the nation against aggression is accepted as necessary and praiseworthy' (1994: 18). Perhaps the crux of the matter is whether one who 'gives up victory and defeat' can remain a king, or would need to be ordained as a monk to pursue purely spiritual concerns to practise this ideal. The passage does not specify. Harris is certainly wrong in saying that Pasenadi's actions are portrayed as 'praiseworthy'. If anything, he is simply portrayed as acting in a limited way according to his emotions and situation. Elsewhere, Pasenadi laments to the Buddha the preoccupations of his kingly role, which encourages such things as greed and conquest. The Buddha thus helps him to refocus his mind on wholesome actions by reminding him that, like everyone else, he will grow old and die (*S.* 1.101–2).

Nevertheless, the issue remains of whether it is possible for a sincere Buddhist king, rather than a somewhat compromised one such as Pasenadi, to rule without force. At *S.* 1.116–17, the Buddha wonders whether it is possible to be a ruler who 'reigns according to *Dhamma* [justice, virtue, righteousness], without killing or causing to kill, without conquering or causing to conquer, without grieving or causing to grieve'. Before answering his own question, however, the tempter-god Māra appears to him and encourages him to be such a king himself. Wondering why Māra should so encourage him, he sees that rulers are inevitably enmeshed in sense-desires, which causes suffering, so that a liberated person could not incline in that direction. This perhaps implies that, while it is not appropriate for a liberated person to be a king, non-violent rule is still a possibility for others – though the danger of corruption by attachment to sense-pleasures needs always to be kept in mind.

In fact, the Buddha says that he had been a non-violent *Cakkavatti* ruler in the past (*A.* iv.89–90; cf. *D.* 1.88–9; *D.* iii.59):

> a *Dhamma*-king, master of the four quarters, who had established security of his realm . . . And I had more than a thousand sons who were heroes, of heroic stature, conquerors of the hostile army. I dwelt on this sea-girt earth, having conquered it by *Dhamma* without stick or sword.

This is not because a *Cakkavatti* has no army. The *Cakkavatti Sīhanāda Sutta* has such a ruler establishing his rule, after his *Cakkavatti* father retires as a monk, by going in each of the four directions with his army, with potential enemies willingly becoming his subjects and accepting his advice to follow the five ethical precepts (*D.* iii.62). Hence no violence is necessary. This is because he has first shown that he can rule according to *Dhamma* by protecting all sections of the population from crime and poverty, and consulting with religious people on what is wholesome and unwholesome (*D.* iii.61). Of course, dealing with crime implies some use of force, though not necessarily killing. Indeed, the *Aggañña Sutta* says that the first king in human society was chosen by the people so as to deal with wrong-doers: but only by his wrath, censure or banishment (*D.* iii.92).

Such, then, is the ideal of non-violent rule as expressed in the early Buddhist texts. Yet it seems to be acknowledged that this is an ideal that can be fully lived up to only by an exceptional person. Thus Harris, after an investigation of such texts, holds:

> That lay people should never initiate violence where there is harmony or use it against the innocent is very clear. That they should not attempt to protect those under their care if the only way of doing so is to use defensive violence is not so clear . . . The person who feels violence is justified to protect the lives of others has indeed to take the consequences into account. He has to remember that he is risking grave [karmic] consequences for himself in that his action will inevitably bear fruit . . . Such a person needs to evaluate motives . . . Yet that person might still judge that the risks are worth facing to prevent a greater evil. (E. J. Harris, 1994: 47–8)

If violence is then used, it is something that Buddhism may *understand* but not actually *approve of.* This can be seen in texts which tell of clever forms of self-defence. In the *Dhammapada* commentary (*Dhp. A.* ii.217–22) there is a story of a woman who is about to be murdered by her husband, whose life she had earlier saved. When she outwits him and pushes him off a cliff, a god who observes this says that women can be as wise (*paṇḍita*) as men (p. 221). As a god, rather than the Buddha or a monk says this, there is no direct approval of the violence involved in the act.

The Indian emperor Asoka (268–239 BCE) is widely revered by Buddhists as a great exemplar of Buddhist social ethics (see pp. 115–17), partly because of his emphasis on non-violence. While encouraging his people in this and other Buddhist moral norms, he himself abandoned his forebears' custom of violent expansion of the realm. Indeed, the Hindu *Manu-smṛti* (7.169–70) holds that a king should make war when he thinks that all his subjects are contented and that he is most exalted in power, with the Hindu *Mahā-bhārata* holding that there is no evil in a king killing enemies.[5] In the early part of his reign, prior to becoming a committed Buddhist, Asoka had conquered the Kaliṅga region, but his Kaliṅga Rock Edict[6] expressed horror at the carnage that this had caused. He therefore resolved to abandon such conquests – even though he was the head of a very powerful empire. He retained his army, though, and in one edict warned troublesome border people that, while he preferred not to use force against them, if they harassed his realm he would, if necessary, do so. He retained the goal of spreading the influence of his empire, but sought to do so by sending out emissaries to bring about 'conquests by *Dhamma*', that is, to spread the influence of his way of ruling and thus form alliances. The most famous instance of this was his link with Sri Lanka, where his son, the monk Mahinda, transmitted Buddhism, in its Theravāda form.

The *Ārya-satyaka-parivarta Sūtra*, an early Mahāyāna text perhaps influenced by Asokan edicts, and in turn influential in Tibet, teaches that the righteous ruler should seek to avoid war by negotiation, placation or having strong alliances. If he has to fight to defend his country, he should seek to attain victory over the enemy only with the aim of protecting his people, also bearing in mind the need to protect all life, and having no concern for himself and his property. In this way, he may avoid the usual bad karmic results of killing (*ASP.* 206–8). In war, he should not vent his anger by burning cities or villages, or destroying reservoirs, fruit-trees or harvests as these are 'sources of life commonly used by many sentient beings who have not produced any faults', including local deities and animals (*ASP.* 197; cf. 70).

THE POSITION OF THE SOLDIER

While the 'wrong livelihood' of 'trade in arms' refers to the arms-salesman and not the soldier, it clearly has relevance to the latter. Buddhist

---

[5] *Śānti-Parvam* 15.14, 15.54; Tähtinen, 1976: 91–2.　　[6] Nikam and McKeon, 1959: 27–30.

texts do not contain the idea, found in the Hindu *Bhagavad Gītā*, for example (II.37 and 32), that if one's role in society is that of a warrior-noble, then it is one's religious duty to go into battle, when called to, and that one who dies in battle goes straight to heaven (Upadhyaya, 1971: 513–37). The Buddha's attitude can be seen in one text where a professional soldier asks him whether a soldier who falls in battle is reborn in a special heaven. In response, the Buddha is silent, but when the man persists in his questioning, he explains that such a person is actually reborn in a hell or as an animal (*S.* IV.308–9). While the *Bhagavad Gītā* holds that a truly detached person can still, as a soldier, kill (v.10; III.30), the Pali Canon sees the truly detached person – a liberated person (*Arahat*) – as incapable of deliberately killing anything (*D.* III.133).

In the Theravādin monastic code, it is an offence for monks to go to see an army fighting, to stay with an army, or watch sham fights or army reviews (*Vin.* IV.104–7). Moreover, the *Suttas* say that monks should avoid talk of various 'low matters' including armies and battles (*D.* I.7, 178). The *Brahmajala Sūtra*, a Mahāyāna code for lay and monastic followers which became influential in China, holds that those who take the *Bodhisattva* vows should not take any part in war. It forbids detention of anyone, or the storing of any kind of weapons, or taking part in any armed rebellion. They should not be spectators of battles, nor should they kill, make another kill, procure the means of killing, praise killing, approve of those who help in killing, or help through magical chants.[7]

Vasubandhu, giving the Sarvāstivāda view, is very clear that when an army kills, all the soldiers are as guilty as the ones who directly do the killing; for by sharing a common goal, they mutually incite one another. Even a person forced to become a soldier is guilty, unless he has previously resolved 'Even in order to save my life, I shall not kill a living being' (*AKB.* IV.72c–d). This is not saying, note, that the guilt of any individual is reduced by being shared; all share the same guilt as would pertain to a single individual who did the killing. Yet, given the Buddhist emphasis on intention and motive, it must be said that defensive violence is less bad than aggressive violence.

Even so, in Buddhist Thailand, army officers are well respected: though this is more for their role in helping run the country than for their military prowess. A two-year national military service is required of all men (Tambiah, 1976: 489). This even includes those who are Buddhist monks, the reason being that, as short-term ordination is common and

---

[7] Demiéville, 1957: 353, citing De Groot, 1893: 46f.

easy, only long-term monks are exempt. Ex-monks are often employed as *anusasanachams* or 'chaplains' to instruct soldiers in religious and moral matters (Tambiah, 1976: 304).

Most lay Buddhists have been prepared to break the precept against killing in self-defence, and many have joined in the defence of the community in times of need. One might say, nevertheless, that any Buddhist faces a dilemma during a war. His response might be:

(1) to avoid fighting, perhaps by becoming a monk, and to encourage peace, if possible (as Buddhist monks did during the Vietnam War);
(2) to fight, but with the intention of saving his people, country or religion, rather than killing an enemy. During the Second World War, some British Buddhists remained pacifists, while others felt it their duty to fight against Hitler's Germany.

To take course (2) cannot be seen as avoiding the evil of killing, but it is less bad than aggressive killing. A Buddhist soldier may also try to dilute the evil of his killing by the performance of counteractive good actions. If conscripted against his will, he may be more afraid of killing than being killed – for to kill will lead to bad karmic consequences. For members of a government, if they are Buddhist, the dilemma is more intense. Buddhist principles would encourage the avoidance of violence, or the minimization of it if it is used (King, 1964: 278). Yet this is not always so in practice. For example, the force which the Sri Lankan government has used against Tamil rebels has sometimes been very potent, and not too discriminating.

BUDDHIST 'JUSTIFICATIONS' OF, AND INVOLVEMENT IN, VIOLENCE

Sri Lanka

Within the Theravāda, no canonical text can be found justifying violence, yet some later writings are relevant to the issue. In Sri Lanka, once known as Ceylon, a number of chronicles focus on the actions of Buddhist kings and the fate of Buddhism from its arrival on the island in 250 BCE. The most important of these is the *Mahā-vaṃsa* (Geiger, 1980), composed by the monk Mahānāma in the fifth or sixth century CE. More than a quarter of it concerns the reign of King Duṭṭhagāmaṇi (Sinhala Duṭugämuṇu; 101–77 BCE), glorifying him as the greatest of Sinhalese heroes (the Sinhalese being predominantly Buddhist, and the majority people of the island). Chapter xxv tells how he defeated Eḷāra, a non-Buddhist Tamil general who had invaded the island from South

India, and established an enclave in the north which had lasted forty-four years. While Eḷāra was not an unbenevolent ruler, and even offered some patronage to Buddhism, the *Mahā-vaṃsa* sees him as having been a threat to the health of Buddhism on the island. Duṭṭhagāmaṇi is said to have fought not for the 'joy of sovereignty', but for the protection of the Buddhist religion. His actions are therefore the nearest thing to a 'holy war' in Buddhist history, though even this can perhaps be seen as having been (delayed action) defensive.

The chronicle tells how, for protection, Duṭṭhagāmaṇi's army was accompanied by monks and by Buddhist relics on spears. Monks were encouraged to disrobe and become soldiers, one becoming a general. After defeating the Tamils, the king was distressed at the many deaths he had caused – as Asoka had been after his defeat of Kaliṅga (p. 253) – but it is claimed (xxv.108–11) that enlightened monks (*Arahats*) reassured him that

That deed presents no obstacle on your path to heaven. You caused the death of just one and a half people, O king. One had taken the refuges [i.e. were Buddhist], the other the Five Precepts as well. The rest were wicked men of wrong view who died like (or: as considered as) beasts. You will in many ways illuminate the Buddha's teaching, so stop worrying. (Gombrich, 1988: 141)

This – written many centuries after the events it purports to describe, at a time of renewed threat from South India – is a rather perverse reflection of the doctrine that it is less bad to kill an unvirtuous person than a virtuous one: for it is always worse to kill a human intentionally than an animal (see p. 52). In any case, the king was said to have sought to make amends for his actions by a life of good works of benefit to the community, before being reborn in a heaven.

Duṭṭhagāmaṇi may in fact have been the first to unify the island: even the *Mahāvaṃsa* says that not all who fought against him were Tamil, and that he had to fight thirty-two kings before reaching Eḷāra's kingdom from the far south (Tambiah, 1992: 134). Thus the chronicle's attempt to portray his actions as simply a defence of the Sinhalese nation and its Buddhism is over-played. The alignment of the Sinhalese to Buddhism and the Tamils to a threatening alien force was probably the product of a later period. There was racial and cultural mixing from an early time, and this only began to be undermined in the fifth century, when rulers of three powerful South Indian kingdoms succeeded in undermining the influence of Buddhism on Hindu society in South India, and threatened the political stability of the island's Sinhalese kingdom, generating real fear for the plight of Buddhism (Manogaran, 1987: 22–3). There were notable destructive invasions of the island by militantly (Śaiva) Hindu South Indian states in the fifth, ninth, tenth, eleventh and thirteenth centuries.

In twentieth-century Sri Lanka, an influential book arguing for the involvement of Buddhist monks in social and political matters was Walpola Rāhula's *Bhiksuvage Urumaya* (1946; Rahula, 1974). In a colonial context, this talked of Sinhalese-Buddhist 'religio-nationalism' and 'religio-patriotism' (Tambiah, 1992: 27–8), and referred to Duṭṭha-gāmaṇi's campaign against General Eḷāra as a 'crusade' to 'liberate the nation and the religion from the foreign yoke' which was arresting the 'progress of Buddhism' (Rahula, 1974: 20):

From this time the patriotism and the religion of the Sinhalese became insepa-rably linked. The religio-patriotism at that time assumed such overpowering proportions that both *bhikkhus* and laymen considered that even killing people in order to liberate the religion and the country was not a heinous crime. (p. 21)

On the *Mahā-vaṃsa*'s claim that supposed *Arahat*s had said that most of the Tamils killed were not fully human,[8] Rāhula says:

Nevertheless, it is diametrically opposed to the teaching of the Buddha. It is difficult for us today either to affirm or to deny whether *arahants* who lived in the second century BCE did ever make such a statement. But there is no doubt that Mahānāma Thera, the author of the *Mahā-vaṃsa*, who lived in the fifth century A.C., recorded this in the *Mahā-vaṃsa*. (Rahula, 1974: 22)

He holds that this shows that responsible monks of this time had accepted such an idea and that they 'considered it their sacred duty to engage themselves in the service of their country as much as in the service of their religion' (p. 22).

When Richard Gombrich interviewed Sinhalese monks in the 1960s, he found that

most (but not all) of them were reluctant entirely to accept the view propounded to Duṭṭhagāmaṇi, for they realized its incongruence with Buddhist ethics. The stereotypes are, however, too strong to be easily demolished, and least of all by historical fact. (Gombrich, 1988: 142)

When monks were asked about the ethics of Duṭṭhagāmaṇi's war, the answers varied slightly, but typical was the reply that his

killing of Tamils was sin [*pava*], but not great, because his main purpose (*paramārtha*) was not to kill men but to save Buddhism; he did not have full inten-tion to kill. But to say that he will not pay for his sin . . . is wrong.[9]

---

[8] On this issue, see also Obeyesekere, 1988.

[9] Gombrich, 1971a: 257. I would prefer the translation 'evil' to that of 'sin', as 'sin' implies an action which offends a creator God. For further information on the use of the Duṭṭhagāmaṇi legend in the context of the current ethnic conflict in Sri Lanka, see Bartholomeusz, 1999.

Only one monk said that the king was wrong in thinking that his ultimate purpose made his action right. It was wrong. Only two monks said that he did not 'sin'. One, a kindly but very unsophisticated monk, said that it had not been a 'sin' for the king to kill Tamils as they were of wrong view, since it was not wrong to kill in order to save religion. Another held that killing is not a 'sin' if it is done to defend Buddhism, as with Duṭṭhagāmaṇi (Gombrich, 1971a: 258).

Sri Lanka has often been in the news since 1983 – when there were bloody inter-ethnic riots – because of flare-ups in the conflict between the government and ruthless guerrillas fighting for an independent Tamil state in the north-east of the island (de Silva et al., 1988). The conflict is between the majority Sinhalese, who make up 74 per cent of the population, and the Tamils, who make up 18 per cent. It is mainly centred on the issues of language use, peasant resettlement areas, and regional devolution. The Sinhalese language has come to have a privileged status, and Tamil-speakers have felt that this has placed them at a disadvantage as regards education and government employment. Peasant resettlement schemes have involved the movement of Sinhalese people into once dry areas, which had been populated by the Sinhalese in earlier eras, upsetting the current population balance with the Tamils in such areas. Regional devolution for Tamil areas has been sought so as to overcome economic deprivation, though extremists have sought a completely separate state. The tensions arising from such issues have been heightened by rising population pressures and the poor economic performance of the country, though it has a good record on health and education.

The conflict also has a religious dimension. The Sinhalese are mainly Buddhists, and Buddhism is a major ingredient in their identity, because of the long history of the religion on the island, and the fact that the Sinhalese have done much to preserve and spread Theravāda Buddhism. The Tamils are mainly Hindu, but religion is not a part of their cultural identity which is emphasized. The Sinhalese Buddhists see themselves as an endangered minority protecting an ancient tradition. While they are a majority in their own country, a history of invasions by the much more numerous South Indian Tamils make them feel insecure. One leading monk, interviewed by Juergensmeyer in 1987, talked of the geographically 'tiny . . . fragile Sinhalese Buddhist Society . . . a tear drop, a grain of sand, in an enormous sea' (Juergensmeyer, 1990: 58). For a British Christian at least, an insight into this mind-set may be gained by imagining the following scenario. If an Ireland-sized Britain (cf. Sri Lanka) and the Scandinavian peninsula (cf. South-east Asia) were islands of Christianity (cf. Buddhism) facing a Europe which had predominantly turned Muslim (cf. Hinduism in India), after having once been a stronghold of Christianity, then the presence of a Muslim enclave in South-east Britain might cause some concern, especially if there had been a history of invasions from Muslim Europe! If, moreover, Christianity in a Protestant form (cf. Theravāda Buddhism) *only* now existed in Britain and Scandinavia, this would increase the concern. There is also, of course, an analogy with the situation of Judaism in Israel, where there is, again, a perceived need for a religion to have a protected territory.

After independence from the British in 1948, Sinhalese Buddhists rightly sought to revive and strengthen their culture after the colonial period, and they have also sought to overcome the colonial legacy of the Tamils being a relatively privileged minority. Yet a side-effect of building their nationalism around a Buddhist identity rooted in perceptions of past Sinhalese Buddhist civilizations has been to exclude the mainly non-Buddhist Tamils from this ideal. Buddhist values have become distorted as 'Buddhism' has become increasingly identified, by sections of the population, with the Sinhalese people and the territory of the entire island.[10] While the *Mahā-vaṃsa* has the Buddha predict that Buddhism would flourish in Sri Lanka, this has wrongly been taken by some to support a drive to restore all, and only, Buddhists to prominence (Bond, 1988: 9). This perspective has led to Buddhists exploiting their majority position and alienating Tamils, who are still perceived as a privileged minority. Sinhalese party politicians have 'played to the gallery' and made capital out of religion, producing a communalization of politics (Bond, 1988: 121–2). Often the party in opposition has objected when the party in power has made moves to address Tamil grievances. There are Buddhists who object to this, though: both the All Ceylon Buddhist Congress and the Young Men's Buddhist Association have passed resolutions for the government to revoke the party system (Bond, 1988: 118). The division of the *Saṅgha* along political lines has not helped either, though there is a swell of opinion against this.

But for extremists on both sides – including some Buddhist monks who have demonstrated against 'concessions to the Tamils' – moderates could have resolved the ethnic problem by taking into account the concerns of both sides and encouraging mutual forgiveness of past wrongs.

[10] Cf. the rise of 'Hindutva', a kind of Hindu fundamentalism, in India.

In their drive to protect Buddhism, Sinhalese Buddhists need to pay more attention to the contents of what they are 'protecting', and less to the need for a strong political 'container' for it. A re-emphasis on the Buddhist values of non-violence and tolerance is needed, as is a more pluralistic model of Buddhist nationalism (Tambiah, 1992: 125). Tambiah points out that the heavy centralization of the state is a legacy of British rule that cannot be traced back to pre-colonial times (pp. 179–80). The pre-British kingdoms were based on a 'galactic model', with a centre in dynamic interplay with surrounding kingdoms and immigrant groups, not a fixed, exclusive nation-state (pp. 174–5). He feels that the idealizing of an ancient Sinhalese past has led to an overlooking of more recent medieval and pre-colonial times in which there was 'a multicultural and pluralistic civilization with a distinctively Buddhist stamp' (p. 149).

In the late 1990s, the government of Mrs Kumaratunga has been both talking to moderate Tamils and trying to defeat the Tamil Tigers militarily. In November 1997, she also put forward a plan to give the country a federal structure, with regions having substantial powers, including over police, land and revenue. While Sinhalese nationalists and some well-known monks object to this, it is to be hoped that people come to agree to this in a referendum, for the death toll over the years is at least 50,000, military expenditure takes up a quarter of government spending, and the economy has become stunted.

South-east Asia

In Thailand, during the 1970s, people felt very threatened by Communist insurgency and the threat of invasion after the fall of Vietnam (1975), Laos and Cambodia to Communist forces. Many saw this as a grave threat to the nation, Buddhism and the monarchy: the three pillars of Thai society. Thus during the Vietnam War, there were American air-force bases in Thailand which were used to bomb Communist areas and supply-lines in Vietnam and Cambodia. In this context, Kittivuḍḍho, a popular but militantly anti-Communist monk (Suksamran, 1982: 132–57), said in a magazine interview on 29 June 1976 that killing Communists or leftists was not 'demeritorious' as

such killing is not the killing of persons (*khon*). Because whoever destroys the nation, religion and the monarchy is not a complete person, but mara (evil). Our intention must not be to kill people but to kill the Devil. It is the duty of all Thai. (quoted in Suksamran, 1982: 150; cf. Sivaraksa, 1986: 98)

Here, one sees an echo of the unfortunate *Mahā-vaṃsa* notion of humans who are not really humans. He went on to say that while he accepted that killing was against Buddhist teachings, such killing generated only little 'demerit', but much compensating 'merit', comparing this to killing a fish and then cooking it to give as alms to a monk. His interview caused a furore in the Thai press, in which he was accused of stupidly encouraging bloodshed (Suksamran, 1982: 150–1). The Supreme Patriarch rightly denounced his attempted 'justification' of killing, but appeals to *Saṅgha* authorities to discipline him for infringing the *Vinaya* produced a negative result (Keyes, 1978: 158–9). In fact, apart for one small exception, there are no *Vinaya* rules against a monk expressing any viewpoint.

Kittivuḍḍho defended himself in a speech to monks in which he said that what he had meant in the interview was that killing Communism as an evil *ideology* was not 'demeritorious' (Suksamran, 1982: 153). In a speech to army officers, though, he made it clear that it was the job of monks to kill Commun*ism*, but their job to kill Commun*ists*. In his previous speech, he had made it clear that, in the face of a grave threat to 'nation, religion and monarchy', he would disrobe to kill their enemies (p. 154). In his speech to soldiers, he said that 'to kill some 5,000 people and ensure the happiness of 42 million Thais' was legitimate, so that to do such an act would be meritorious and not lead to hell (p. 155):

If we want to preserve our nation, religion, and monarchy, we sometimes have to sacrifice *sila* (rules of morality) for the survival of these institutions.

This he saw as sacrificing a lesser good for the sake of a greater good (p. 155). In a speech on a Buddhist festival day, he went on to say that, because of Communist violence against monks,

Let us determine to kill all communists and clean the slate in Thailand . . . Anyone who wants to gain merit must kill communists. The one who kills them will acquire great merit . . . If the Thai do not kill them, the communists will kill us. (quoted in Suksamran, 1982: 155)

There were those who agreed with him, leading to an army coup in October 1976 which brought an end to three years of democracy, and saw police and right-wing mobs mounting bloody attacks on alleged 'student-leftists and communists' occupying a university (Suksamran, 1982: 157). An unfortunate era in Thai politics.

In Burma, at the popular level, there have been millenarian ideas which looked forward to a future utopia brought in by a leader variously identified as a *Cakkavatti* king (see p. 114), a *Bodhisattva*, and Setkya-Min Buddha-Yaza, 'Lord of the Weapon and Buddha-Ruler', a future king of occult powers who would overcome disorder and re-establish the rule of *Dhamma* in the world (Sarkisyanz, 1978: 90; Spiro, 1971: 172). In times of popular discontent, a charismatic person would be so identified, and lead peasant revolts against kings or the British conquerors, as happened in 1839, 1855, 1858 and 1860. Such ideas were also linked to guerrilla resistance to the British in 1886–9, a peasant revolt in 1922, and a peasant war of 1930–1 (Sarkisyanz, 1978: 90). Thus Buddhist ideals have been adapted at the popular level to sustain revolts. Yet Fielding Hall remarks that, during his time in Burma, though there were revolts, he never saw monks having anything to do with them (1902: 56–7).

In Burma, Thailand, Cambodia and Laos, various kingdoms have arisen and fallen, and there has been no shortage of conflicts between these (Ling, 1979: 135–47). In war, Buddhist temples might be destroyed, and famous Buddha images or relics taken as booty (Tambiah, 1976: 121). This was because they were seen as the source of auspicious magical power that would benefit whoever possessed them. In Burma, the eleventh century saw King Anawratā invading the southern Burmese kingdom of Thaton to get a copy of the Theravāda scriptures that Thaton refused to give, as Anawratā's kingdom was turning to the Theravāda. In 1767, Burmese forces also devastated Ayutthaya, then capital of Siam (now Thailand), destroying most of its Buddhist temples. When one reads of this devastation, one might wonder whether it is the case that, having overridden the prime Buddhist precept against killing, Buddhist soldiers may sometimes lose *all* inhibitions in war and become very violent. As a point of comparison with non-Buddhists, however, this would be unfair, as it would overlook, for example, the great violence of war in Christian Europe up to the sixteenth century or so.

The Buddhist emphasis on non-anger and harmony means that, in both Thai and Burmese society, face-to-face expressions of anger, hatred or hostility are frowned on and avoided at all costs. They are seen to show lack of self-control and equilibrium, thus:

The Siamese [Thais] are a people incapable of retaining one spark of animosity, and during my stay in Bangkok I do not remember a single instance of seeing two Siamese come to blows and seldom even to quarrel.[11]

Hostility may be avoided by humour or avoiding a potential conflict situation, or expressed in indirect ways, such as gossip, 'slip-of-the-tongue' indirect insults, or occasionally magical means of aggression (Ling, 1979: 141–3). Western observers sometimes comment that, when a Thai

---

[11] F. A. Neale, *Residence in Siam* (London, 1852), p. 148, quoted in Bunnag, 1973: 1.

person is really pushed, and does get angry, this can lead to sudden violence of an unpredictable kind. The 'suddenness' of the anger is sometimes put down to the release of repressed aggression. However, this
view may well be based on an inability to read a Thai's subtle signs of
rising anger, which any Thai would be able to read: so there is not really
a sudden 'explosion' of anger at all. The Burmese and Thais are no
more repressed than the English, though repression is more common in
Sri Lanka, where Martin Southwold sees it as perhaps contributing to
the island's high murder rate (1983: 73–4). He notes that the rate tends
to be highest in fishing communities, and wonders if this is because
Buddhist fishermen feel less disinclined to break the first precept by
killing a human when they are used to breaking it regularly by killing fish,
so that they already feel that they are evil-doers.

China

As has been seen (pp. 135–40), Mahāyāna texts contain passages which
allow killing in constrained circumstances provided it is motivated by
compassion and carried out with 'skilful means'. To what extent were
such justifications for violence reflected in the practice of the Buddhists
of East Asia? In China, the monastic rule which meant that a monk who
intentionally killed a human was permanently expelled from the *Saṅgha*
was listed as the first, rather than as the third of such rules, to emphasize its importance (Demiéville, 1957: 348). Over the ages, Buddhists
were often noted for 'shirking their military duties', and non-Buddhists
complained at the fact that Buddhist monks were exempted from con-
scription (Demiéville, 1957: 355–6).

Nevertheless, one of the main reasons why the non-Chinese people in
the north of China adopted Buddhism was to gain magical help in times
of war (Demiéville, 1957: 355); though having engaged their interest,
monks helped steer them towards more peaceful ways. Over the centuries, Chinese and Japanese military forces have used Buddhist symbols,
banners, *mudra*s and *mantra*s to empower their actions and intimidate
opponents. Vaiśravaṇa, one of the protector 'four great kings' of classical Buddhism, became, in T'ang China, the focus of tantric rites to
assure victory in battle, to protect the *Dharma*, and in Japan was the
patron deity of soldiers. Chinese and Japanese Buddhists also included
non-Buddhist war-gods in their pantheon, such as the Shintō kami
Hachimana, identified as a *Bodhisattva* (Demiéville, 1957: 376). Chinese
kings occasionally gave a 'Buddhist' justification for violence. In 581,

after Wen-ti had established the Sui dynasty, he pronounced himself a *Cakkavatti* emperor, saying 'We regard the weapons of war as having become like incense and flowers' as offerings. He took the *Bodhisattva* vows, claimed that his battles had promoted Buddhism, and was a lavish patron of Buddhism (Welch, 1972: 297).

In China, there was sporadic involvement of Chinese monks with violence:

Without ever becoming in China an essential given of history, as they did in Japan, mutinies, insurrections or organised peasant revolts, fomented or inspired by the Buddhists, were not lacking in many eras. The eras seem to have coincided, as was also the case in Japan, with weaknesses of the centralised state. When the central power slackened its control, and religion was feudalised along with society, one sees monks born of the people constituting armed bands or putting themselves at the head of bands of peasants, all often having initiated ties with a rebellious nobility or with local functionaries wanting autonomy. (Demiéville, 1957: 357)

Japan

In Japan, Buddhists intervened in the life of the nation more openly than in China; indeed, there was a connection between Buddhism and the state from the time of the coming of Buddhism to the country, in 538 CE. In the tenth century, during the Heian era (794–1185), social order began to break down, and a strong central government was not re-established until the Tokugawa era (1603–1867). In the intervening period, a feudal society developed in which clan and regional loyalties were dominant, yet the project of attaining national unity urged the parties on to attain such dominance (King, 1993: 39). This was also a time when *sōhei*, or warrior-monks, were a recognized part of national life (Renondeau, 1957; Demiéville, 1957: 369). One factor in this was the fact that monasteries were centres of power and donated land at a time of social unrest, when political power was up for grabs. Another was the fact that Japanese Buddhists came to identify strongly with one or other school or sub-school, these becoming more like sects, so that sectarian differences were far more strongly drawn than in other Buddhist countries (Demiéville, 1957: 369–70).

In the Heian era, a demanding and oppressive aristocracy put high demands for taxes and labour on the population, which sought refuge in Buddhist monasteries, which were exempt from these. Many inhabitants of the monasteries were 'monks' in name only, and were used by the monasteries to develop land donated to them. They also came to be used in armed defence of these lands against the state or the nobility, and then armed monks rebelled against their abbots, who were often of noble origin or connected to the court.[12] By 1100, all the great monasteries of the well-established, broad-based Tendai school had armies to protect their interests (King, 1993: 41). A key text of the Tendai school was the *Mahā-parinirvāṇa Sūtra*, which contains several passages allowing violence 'in defence of the *Dharma*' (see pp. 137–8). At the same time as these developments, military barons of the provinces were launching revolts against the court (Demiéville, 1957: 370). Thus feudal conflicts and clan rivalries arose in which there was fighting between sects and the imperial court, between sects and feudal lords, and between sect and sect (Demiéville, 1957: 371).

During the troubled Kamakura period (1192–1333), central state power almost completely disappeared. Rule was by military Shōguns and the *bushi*, or warrior-knight, class. The latter helped Buddhism spread to the people, however, and thus put down deep roots. Zen's meditational and ethical self-discipline, and indifference to death, helped the *bushi* to resist two attempted Mongolian invasions in 1274 and 1281 (Suzuki, 1959: 64–79). Eisai (1141–1215), founder of Rinzai Zen, gained the protection of a Shōgun at the capital Kamakura, and helped establish the long-lasting alliance between Rinzai and the *bushi*. Rinzai Zen monks began to teach some of the *bushi* knights how to be calm, self-disciplined fighters, with no fear of death. This can be seen as an example of 'skilful means', in the form of an adaptation of Buddhism to the way of life of a particular group of people. The *bushi* also appreciated Zen discipline, simplicity and directness.

The militant and nationalistic reformer Nichiren (1222–82), ex-Tendai founder of a new school (see pp. 145–6), unsuccessfully called for the government to suppress other Buddhist sects, which he regarded as undermining the Japanese nation, citing various passages from the *Mahā-parinirvāṇa Sūtra* in support of this. The school fell into conflict with the Pure Land Jōdo school, and especially its offshoot the Jōdo-shin school (see pp. 142–3).

The Ashikaga period (1333–1573) was one of almost constant turmoil, with simultaneous rule by two emperors followed by rule by rival warring

---

[12] The elite of the monasteries, known as *gakuryo* or *gakushō*, were monks proper, dedicated to study. Monastic troops were generally recruited from the other monks, known as *shuto*, as well as lay employees, known as *kokumin*. From the fourteenth century, the *shuto* outnumbered the *gakuryo* and were in turn outnumbered by the *kokumin* (Demiéville, 1957: 371–2).

Shōguns. The Jōdo-shin school became centred on fortified temples, with its armed followers, both priests and laity, acting to defend its single-minded 'true faith' in the saving power of Amida Buddha. They could be fanatical in battle, believing that they would be reborn in Amida's Pure Land if they were killed. In the sixteenth century, the school organized and led peasant uprisings and became the ruling power in one region of Japan (Demiéville, 1957: 373). This century also saw Nichiren Buddhists attacking the headquarters of the Jōdo-shin and the Tendai school.

The Tendai school continued to maintain troops, as did the Tantric Shingon school. In 1409, Tendai monks published the following, which they attributed to Ryōgen (912–85):

Without literate culture, there are no rites which show love for superiors; without arms, there is no virtue which impresses inferiors. The world is there-fore only well ordered if literate culture and arms mutually complement each other. (Demiéville, 1957: 377)

They went on to say that as, in their day, the true *Dharma* had declined, people did not respect religion. It was thus necessary for *shuto*, troops drawn from the less able monks, to prevent disorder in monastic domains, and protect against 'heretical' sects, so as to maintain the facil-ities for study and meditation (Demiéville, 1957: 377). A biography of Ryōgen from around the same time has him urging Tendai monks to take up arms to protect their true version of the Mahāyāna against 'heresies' (Demiéville, 1957: 377–8).

However, during the Ashikaga period, Zen temples were havens of peace, culture, education and art, with Rinzai Zen having a particular influence. Zen monks did not take part in armed conflicts, though they did help train *bushi* warriors, and had the protection of them when needed (Faure, 1991: 231; King, 1993: 29–32). The Zen ideal of 'no-mind' (*mushin*), of spontaneous reaction free from discriminating thought, was influential on martial arts touched by Zen, such as swordsmanship and archery. The idea that even life and death are empty, essenceless phe-nomena (cf. p. 144) also helped develop lack of hesitation, and lack of fear of death, in battle. Suzuki quotes a medieval Japanese poem on *mushin* which includes the lines,

But striking is not to strike, nor is killing to kill.
He who strikes and he who is struck –
They are both no more than a dream that has no reality. (1959: 123)

A Chinese Ch'an text of the seventh century, the 'Treatise on Absolute Contemplation', indeed, explains that there is only evil in killing if the person killed is not recognized as empty and dream-like. As long as one sees a 'person' or 'living being' standing out from emptiness, one should not kill even an ant. One who overcomes these perceptions can kill, though: in a way similar to natural events like a storm or collapsing cliff bringing death (Demiéville, 1957: 382). Yet to claim that one who truly knows emptiness can kill might well be seen as implausible: such people should also know that they themselves and their 'side' are empty too!

Bushi sometimes retired, in later years, to a more reflective life in a monastery, but while still active warriors, they would sometimes accept their bloody career as being entailed by being born into a warrior family on account of past karma. Such distorted 'karmic fatalism' was reinforced by the strong emphasis, in Japan, on loyalty to one's family and its traditions (King, 1993: 33).

Two powerful Shōguns eventually put an end to military monasteries, with the Tendai headquarters on Mount Hiei being destroyed and thousands of its inhabitants, not just monk-soldiers, killed (King, 1993: 53–4). This 'pacification' helped in the establishment of the Tokugawa era (1603–1867), when the country was unified under a military dictatorship. During this time, Japan closed its doors to all but a few traders from the outside world. In the sixteenth century, the Portuguese had brought Christianity to Japan. Some rulers had favoured it as a foil to the power of Buddhist monasteries, and had propagated it with violence. Now, it was ruthlessly persecuted as being a possible conduit of foreign influence, and struggled on as the secret religion of a few. In 1614, Buddhism was made the established church and arm of the state.

Over the centuries, the aristocratic warrior-knights had come to be known as *samurai* – originally a term for lower-class professional soldiers – rather than *bushi* (King, 1993: 125). The warriors of earlier times had been touched by Zen to some extent, but the application of Zen theory and practice to guide martial activities, and the association of the warrior with spiritual values, is primarily a phenomenon of the Tokugawa era, when Japan was in fact much more peaceful, and *samurai* had more leisure. Thus what was earlier *bujutsu*, 'martial arts' concerned with battlefield effectiveness, became transformed into *budō*, 'martial ways', concerned with spiritual and moral cultivation (McFarlane, 1990: 403), an example being *kendō*, the 'way of the sword'. In such 'ways', Zen influence can be seen in the emphasis on meditative concentration, discipline and austerity, and direct non-verbal communication between master and disciple (Shōhei, 1987: 228).

In his teaching of Zen to people already committed by birth to being *samurai*, Takuan Sōhō Zenji (1573–1645) sought to get them to think in Zen terms. On no-mind, he says in his *Fudōchi shinmyōroku*:

The mind of no-mind is the same as the . . . original mind; it is a mind free of solidification and settling and discrimination and conceptualisation and the like . . . If one is able to thoroughly practice this mind of no-mind, one will not stop on a single thing, and will not lose a single thing. (McFarlane, 1990: 407)

Such fluidity of response was, surely, of value, whether in normal life or in swordsmanship, whether in earnest or in training. Takuan was not averse to applying Zen principles to swordsmanship:

The uplifted sword has no will of its own, it is all of emptiness. It is like a flash of lightning. The man who is about to be struck down is also of emptiness, as is the one who wields the sword . . . Do not get your mind stopped with the sword you raise, forget about what you are doing, and strike the enemy. Do not keep your mind on the person before you. They are all of emptiness, but beware of your mind being caught in emptiness. (Aitken, 1984: 5)

Such ideas sound morally dangerous, but Takuan was adapting teachings to those who were already committed by birth to fighting, and he also emphasized the virtues of sympathy and human-heartedness. Whether killing or giving life, the accomplished man acts with complete concentration, and 'without looking at right and wrong, he is able to see right and wrong' (McFarlane, 1990, 411; 1994: 201). In time, Takuan's writings came to have a formative influence on many Japanese martial arts, though Confucian ethics and Shingon ritual also had their influence alongside Zen (McFarlane, 1994: 189).

   Zen became one of the influences on the warrior-ethic known as *Bushidō*, the 'way (*dō*) of the warrior (*bushi*)' (McFarlane, 1990: 403–4). This also drew on previous warrior values and Confucianism (Kammer, 1978), and emphasized such qualities as loyalty to one's feudal lord, self-sacrifice, upholding the honour of one's family name, strength, skill, fearlessness, self-control, equanimity in the face of death, and generosity of mind.[13] In the Tokugawa era, the Confucian value of learning was also emphasized, though this in part exacerbated *samurai* tendencies to look down on other social classes. At its worst, this expressed itself in the cutting down of disrespectful commoners.[14] Nevertheless, Confucian values of humanitarianism and *noblesse oblige* and Buddhist self-sacrifice also meant that the *samurai* became efficient administrators of the country, in a range of professions.

---

[13] Maliszewski, 1987, 226; Ackroyd, 1987; King, 1993: 123–56.
[14] The Japanese social system of the day was a stratified class system (see p. 211).

Then and now, serious martial arts training is generally imbued with values drawn from Buddhism, Confucianism and Taoism, and inculcates such qualities as 'humility, patience, cooperation, discipline, self-control, mental clarity and physical health' as well as facilitating 'the joy of play and non-competitive achievement' (McFarlane, 1990: 415). Stories of past heroes help convey such values, such as that of the swordsman Kami-idzumi Hidetsuna (d. 1577), who rescued a baby from an outlaw who held it hostage and was threatening to kill it. Hidetsuna disguised himself as a monk to gain the outlaw's confidence, then overcame him by *ju-jutsu* and turned him over to the inhabitants of the village for justice (McFarlane, 1994: 190, 200). Yet not all practitioners followed such values, and *Bushidō* contained several un-Buddhist elements, such as the obligation to seek revenge (King, 1993: 153–6) and a disregard for life.

From the eighteenth century a new form of Shintō began to be developed as the 'true religion' of the Japanese, different from the 'artificialities' of foreign Buddhism and Confucianism. In 1868, this culminated in a *coup d'état* which ended the Tokugawa Shōgunate, restored the emperor system, and brought in the Meiji era. Soon after, Japan opened its doors to Western influence and rapid modernization. On a wave of Shintō-inspired nationalism, Japan later fought wars with Korea, Russia and China and then, in the Second World War, America and Britain.

Buddhist schools, after being criticized and persecuted at the start of the Meiji era, came to support the government actively and contribute to the anti-Christian and anti-socialist climate of early twentieth-century Japan (Ives, 1992: 64, 67). Soyen Shaku, a Japanese abbot, reflecting in his sermons on the Russo-Japanese War (1904–5), sought to come to understand and even come to terms with violence. Here, he 'incorporates exalted Mahāyāna teachings, Zen pragmatism, and Japanese nationalism into a fascinating but perplexing mix of ideas' (McFarlane, 1986: 102). He portrayed it as a war in which Japan was unselfishly engaged against 'evils hostile to civilization, peace and enlightenment', and hoped that when Japanese soldiers died, they would do so 'with ennobling thoughts of the Buddha' (quoted in Aitken, 1985: 146). Only a few, beyond the pale of institutional Buddhism, objected to the war (Davis, 1989: 327). Both Zen and Pure Land organizations financially supported Japan's war with China (Davis, 1989: 327), and certain Zen figures supported the growing militarism of the twenties and thirties by directing Zen practice as a preparation for combat. Harada

Sogaku (1870–1961) reportedly said that a soldier should always become 'completely at one with' his work, doing whatever he is ordered to do, whether march or shoot, this being 'the clear expression of the highest Bodhi-wisdom, the unity of Zen and war' (quoted in Ives, 1992: 65): an amazing distortion of Buddhist values (and see Victoria, 1997). We also see, in 1938, a hereditary Jōdo-shin leader as Minister of Overseas Affairs, and in the Sino-Japanese conflict, Buddhist sects officially participating, under the control of the Bureau of Religious Affairs, in the 'spiritual mobilisation' decreed in 1937 (Demiéville, 1957: 373–4). In the Second World War, most Buddhist schools agreed to support the nation in its efforts. Seemingly the one exception was the Sōka Gakkai, which refused to take part in this unified front.

The *Bushidō* code became dominated by a nationalistic form of Shintō in which a total suppression of self-interest and unquestioning loyalty to the emperor were enjoined. Such *blind* loyalty went beyond what was previously expected. In *Bushidō*, the Zen contempt for death was still present, and this was drawn on in the training of Kamikaze pilots in the closing phases of the Second World War, when the Japanese were getting desperate. Together with the idea that death was preferable to the dishonour of surrender, it played its part in the ill-treatment of prisoners of war, as well as in mass suicides of captured Japanese soldiers (Ackroyd, 1987: 583; King, 1993: 211–18).

Since the Second World War, Japan has had a constitution which forbids it to have its 'defence forces' fight overseas. During the Gulf War, for example, Japanese forces were only allowed to act in non-military support roles, even though Western governments put much pressure on Japan to take a more active role.

BUDDHIST ACTION FOR PEACE IN THE MODERN WORLD

In Burma, Aung San Suu Kyi is noted for her spirited opposition to the country's oppressive Marxist-Nationalist military regime, which ignored her party's resounding victory in the 1990 elections (Suu Kyi, 1995). In Thailand, Sulak Sivaraksa (see pp. 218–19) has founded many grass-roots non-governmental organizations for peace, human rights, community development and ecumenical dialogue, and objected to coups by the army (Sivaraksa, 1986; Swearer, 1996: 198). In Vietnam, Thich Nhat Hanh helped in efforts to oppose the 1964–75 war and to aid refugees. An exile in France since the 1970s, he is a prolific writer on Buddhism and peace, and a strong advocate of 'Engaged Buddhism' (see pp. 112–13 and 185; King 1996; Nhat Hanh, 1987). Another exile, the Dalai Lama, has become a world-wide symbol of Buddhist values. As head of Tibet's 'government in exile' in North India, he tirelessly works to win back Tibetans' control of their land from the Chinese, though he steadfastly opposes the use of any violence in doing so, and urges the need for universal compassion and responsibility in an increasing inter-dependent world (Cabezón, 1996). Buddhist activists for peace are also found in Japan, Sri Lanka and Cambodia.

Peace activities of Japanese Nichiren-based schools

In post-war Japan, a number of Buddhist schools have been active in the field of peace work. The ones which are most noted in this field belong to the Nichiren tradition (see pp. 145–6), whose followers account for around 30 per cent of Japanese Buddhists. On the face of it, one would not have expected this tradition to be so peace-orientated, given that its founder, Nichiren Daishōnin (1222–82), was militant in his attacks on other schools of Buddhism as 'ruiners of the country', even asking the government of his day to suppress them. Nevertheless, he had a vision of improving the social welfare of Japan, albeit through his own 'exclusively true' brand of Buddhism.

The Nipponzan Myōhōji is a small monastic Nichiren order dedicated to working for world peace, in opposition to the arms race and nuclear weapons. Its founder, Nichidatsu Fujii (1885–1985), strongly emphasized the precept against killing and was greatly impressed and influenced by Gandhi when he met him in India in 1933 (Fujii, 1980: 45–78, 127–9). For Fujii, 'There is no taking of life which is reasonable' (p. 237), and he saw Nichiren's idea that 'Killing one to let tens of thousands live is pardonable', as in killing a ferocious king, as a dangerous principle which could too easily be used by a killer in defence of himself. Thus for Fujii, 'It is of paramount importance to seek to let multitudes live without killing a single person. Never take the lives of others, either good or evil' (p. 238). During the Second World War, in 1944, he fasted for an early conclusion to the war and an enhancement of peace (p. 326).

The Nipponzan Myōhōji order has built over sixty 'Peace Pagodas' in Japan, including ones at Hiroshima and Nagasaki, as well as two in India and one in Sri Lanka. In the late seventies, a few monks of the order arrived in the UK and became involved in marches of the Campaign for Nuclear Disarmament. In 1980, they opened the first consecrated Buddhist *Stūpa*/Pagoda in the West, at Milton Keynes (Fujii, 1980:

Plate 6. The opening of the 'Peace Pagoda' at Milton Keynes, England, built by the Japanese Nipponzan Myōhōji order.

284–91). Ones in Vienna (1983), Massachusetts (1985) and London (1985) followed, the last being an impressive 34-metre-high structure in Battersea Park, beside the Thames. As well as being active on anti-war and anti-nuclear demonstrations, they hold that the presence of Pagodas, and the spiritual power of the Buddhist relics they contain, act as beacons of peace in a strife-torn world.

In post-war Japan, many 'New Religions' have prospered or sprung up to address the religious needs of urban people. These are mostly lay-led, and a number have their roots in Nichiren Buddhism. One, the Sōka Gakkai, or 'Value-Creating Society', has been particularly successful (see p. 146). Starting as a society for educational reform in 1930, it became the lay wing of the once small Nichiren Shōshū sub-sect, though it became separated from this in 1991, as the monks of the sect found that the 'child' had become more powerful than the 'parent'. During the Second World War, the two leaders of the Sōka Gakkai were imprisoned, as they criticized the war effort and refused to toe the government line by uniting with other Nichiren sects as part of this. The leader who survived imprisonment, Jōsei Toda (1900–58), went on to say that the defeat of Japan and its plight after the war were due to its having propagated Shintō and ignored the 'true' faith of Nichiren (Metraux, 1996: 369–70, 377, 383).

In the post-war period, the Sōka Gakkai was led by Toda and then Daisaku Ikeda (1928–), who both spearheaded a conversion drive. The movement successfully addressed the needs of urban people in difficult and changing times, and grew rapidly, at first using rather aggressive conversion techniques. Since then, while still holding to the view that it has the exclusive hold on religious truth, so that it does not co-operate in *religious* matters with *any* other sect or religion, it has been open and co-operative on matters to do with the environment, peace, the arts and cultural exchange (Metraux, 1996: 392–3).

Ikeda has gone on many 'pilgrimages for peace' in which he makes proposals for disarmament or the lessening of tensions in hot-spots, or meets world religious or political leaders such as Mikhail Gorbachev to discuss matters of cross-cultural importance (Metraux, 1996: 372, 380–1).[15] The movement has arranged school exchanges with Chinese and Russian children to help break down barriers between peoples (Metraux, 1996: 377, 380), and emphasizes the idea of human rights. It keenly supports the United Nations and its High Commission for

---

[15] See, e.g., Toynbee and Ikeda, 1989, and Ikeda, 1981.

Refugees, having raised large sums of money for the latter and also inspected refugee camps in Asia and Africa (Metraux, 1996: 379–80).

The Sōka Gakkai has been very active in peace education, as it seeks to help bring about world peace. Ikeda holds that:

modern military power must be regarded as very different from the self-defense forces with which man has been familiar throughout the ages. I see no grounds for justifying military power in the world today . . . I am convinced that examples of warfare conducted for the sake of veritable self-defense are rare. (Toynbee and Ikeda, 1989: 208)

Given the nature and expense of modern weapons,

self-defense by means of arms has reached its limits . . . it is time to return to first principles . . . Our new point of departure must be the right of survival of the people of the whole world, not of one nation alone. (p. 210)

Like the Dalai Lama, the Sōka Gakkai emphasizes that the world is an inter-dependent network that must learn to work in harmony (Metraux, 1996: 377–8). It sees nuclear weapons as an absolute evil, and seeks both to abolish them and to overcome the 'diabolical' side of human nature that would wish to use them. As the mainstream Japanese education system glosses over many of the horrors inflicted by Japanese forces in China and in the Second World War, the Sōka Gakkai has sought to redress the balance by publishing a substantial series of books recording graphic portraits of the war. Its aim is to promote anti-war sentiments and ensure that Japan does not repeat its mistakes of the past. It has also mounted photographic exhibitions on the horrors of war, especially nuclear war (Metraux, 1996: 379).

Another Nichiren-based new religious movement is the Risshō-kōsei-kai. Founded in 1938, this combines faith in the Lotus *Sūtra* and Śākyamuni Buddha, honouring of ancestors, and practice of ethical aspects of the Eightfold Path and *Bodhisattva* perfections. It is also active on the peace front, and is concerned about Japanese repentance over the Second World War, which has never been decisively and fully expressed by the Japanese government. In the 1970s, members of the Risshō-kōsei-kai Young Adults' Group built a 'Friendship Tower' in the Philippines, in an effort to help make amends for the suffering the Japanese had caused there. When he was in Singapore in 1975, their leader Nikkyō Niwano happened to go past a memorial to civilians killed by the Japanese. 'We stopped the car and from the depths of our hearts prayed in front of the tower' (Niwano, 1977: 116). He has also expressed deep regret at the Japanese attack on Pearl Harbor and, when in China, for the rapacious actions of Japanese troops there in the 1930s (Niwano, 1977: 120, 138).

Individual Japanese have also worked to express their repentance for Japanese actions in the war. Takashi Nagase, who was an interpreter with the Japanese Imperial Police, is one.[16] Though he volunteered to fight in the war, and believed in absolute obedience to the emperor, the cruelty that he saw his colleagues inflicting on Allied prisoners building the Burma–Siam railway and the full death toll, of which he learnt after the war, produced a change of heart. Back in Japan, he suffered from heart problems associated with flash-backs to scenes of maltreatment, and came to vow 'to judge myself and expiate the crimes we committed during the war – which must take all my life'. By 1963, he could return to the region of the bridge over the river Kwai, in Thailand, and by 1995 had returned there eighty-six times. Since 1976, he has organized annual reunions there of former prisoners and Japanese, laid out a garden of remembrance, and endowed scholarships for the descendants of some of the thousands of Asian slave labourers left in Thailand. In 1986, he built a Buddhist temple of peace 'to comfort the dead', and has been ordained there temporarily as a monk in the Thai Theravāda tradition. He has struck up friendships with ex-prisoners, one of whom describes him as 'one of the most exceptional men I have ever met'.

Sarvōdaya Śramadāna as a force for defusing conflict in Sri Lanka

In his critique of Buddhist aspects of the ethnic conflict in Sri Lanka (p. 260), Stanley Tambiah refers to an 'idealising' of the past that focuses on (1) scriptural ideas of *Cakkavatti* kings as expressing the ideal of welfare-orientated rule (see pp. 114–18 and 197–8) and (2) chronicles seen as showing past Sinhalese Buddhist civilization as a co-operative 'egalitarian' rural society (1992: 60). Tambiah – a Sri Lankan Tamil who is a noted anthropologist of Buddhism in South-east Asia – looks with a jaundiced eye on attempts to draw on ancient ideals to shape modern society; for he sees them as too wedded to Sinhalese-only nationalism. This is not a necessary connection, though, and there are real positive elements in this vision, if they can be separated out from ethnic protectionism and triumphalism.

One movement which draws on many of these ideals, and is in fact a

---

[16] John Ezard, 'War and Remembrance', the *Guardian* newspaper, 27 July 1995, and see Eric Lomax's *The Railway Man* (London, Jonathan Cape, 1995).

force for social harmony in Sri Lanka, is the Sarvōdaya Śramadāna self-help rural development movement (see pp. 225–34). This is not a narrowly Buddhist organization, though, for it has been influenced by the ideals of Mahātma Gandhi and Quakerism. In recognition of his work for peace, its founder and leader Ariyaratne has been nominated for the Nobel Peace Prize, and awarded the Niwano Peace Prize from the Risshō-kōsei kai.

A key aim of the movement is to break down barriers between people – whether based on caste,[17] political party, wealth, age, gender, race or religion – by encouraging people to work side by side to improve local facilities. One particular emphasis is on getting women to speak up and be more active in shaping their world. By the end of the 1980s, the movement was the only organization that was able to be active in all parts of the country, as the government could not reach areas held by Tamil guerrillas (Bond, 1995: 5). Personnel from Sinhalese and Tamil areas have visited each other's areas, with Tamils visiting Buddhist temples and Sinhalese visiting Hindu ones (Burr, 1995: 14; Macy, 1983: 50). Tamils have held prominent leadership positions in Sarvōdaya, and Tamils who work with it see it as a Sri Lankan organization rather than a Sinhalese Buddhist one (Bond, 1996: 136). At Sarvōdaya work-camps, multi-religious services are held, with people of the minority religion of the area always being the first to perform their rituals (Macy, 1983: 50). Many Buddhist monks are involved in Ariyaratne's lay-led movement, but among other sections of the *Saṅgha* there are some who express hardline views against any 'concessions' to the Tamils. There are also monks who work in Tamil-dominated areas, and who have sought to help anxious and fearful Tamils contact relatives arrested by the security forces (E. J. Harris, 1998: 111–13).

Ariyaratne's vision for Sri Lanka is of a decentralized network of communities in which people work together to bring out the good qualities of themselves and others. Like most Sinhalese, though, he would not like to see the break-up of Sri Lanka into two states. His ideal is that of a nation which accommodates internal diversity, basing such positive tolerance on ideals with deep roots in Buddhism. As his inspiration also comes from Mahātma Gandhi, such ideals also have important roots in Hinduism.

During the 1983 riots, Ariyaratne immediately, but unsuccessfully,

---

[17] While there is no religious support for caste in Buddhist teachings, a mild form of caste system exists in Sri Lanka.

asked the President to announce a curfew, and went on to set up refugee camps unilaterally (Burr, 1995: 14). After the riots, the movement organized a national conference, at which 2,000 religious and civil leaders explored ways to settle the conflict. The conference produced a Sarvōdaya-influenced 'People's Declaration for National Peace and Harmony', emphasizing that 'only by non-hatred does hatred cease' and the need for 'a friendly dialogue, based on the principles of truth and non-violence' (Bond, 1995: 6). A peace march was then proposed from the Sinhalese-dominated south to Jaffna, the stronghold of the Tamil Tiger guerrillas, but though thousands began this, it was called off on government advice (Bond, 1996: 137). Shorter peace marches followed over the next few years in the central hill-country. The movement also became a key conduit for relief supplies and funds, supplied by Western donors, to refugees (Bond, 1995: 6–7). In 1994, Ariyaratne visited Jaffna in an attempt to find a solution to the ethnic conflict (Bond, 1996: 137).

The Sarvōdaya strategic plan for 1995–8 saw the movement as having a role in 'National Re-integration', addressing problems of poverty and 'unachievable lifestyle expectations' which help feed the ethnic problems, and continuing to aid refugees and orphans. This is in line with its emphasis on basic human needs, both material and cultural, avoiding poverty and consumerism. One of its three priorities is to 'play a more assertive conflict-resolution and peace-making role' (Burr, 1995: 5). Ariyaratne emphasizes that the solution to the ethnic conflict lies in education and getting the common people of both communities to unite (Burr, 1995: 14). He emphasizes that the urge to win at others' expense leads not to a win-lose situation, but a lose-lose one (Burr, 1995: 15). In line with this, the movement has planned a series of workshops, based on experiential learning, and supported by the Asia Foundation, to train 600 Sarvōdaya monks to engage in conflict management and mediation in their villages (Burr, 1995: 6; cf. McConnell, 1995). Burr reports on the first of these, at which participants started by sharing their perceptions of various sorts of 'conflict', ranked them by gravity, and then reflected on the extent to which conflict can sometimes have positive results (pp. 7–9). There was then a discussion of Buddhist perspectives on the causes of conflict, which emphasized the role of greed, ignorance, clinging to views, and poverty. It was stressed that the solution to a conflict needed a careful mapping of it, a neutral description of it, and sympathy for the needs and interests of all parties. For this, effective, active listening was needed. One also needed to be assertive, rather than aggressive or passive (pp. 10–13).

Buddhist action to heal Cambodia

After devastating American bombing in the Vietnam War, Cambodia fell victim, in 1975, to the Maoist-inspired Communist rule of the Khmer Rouge. Their avowed aim was to create an egalitarian, self-reliant agrarian utopia, free of alien influences. In practice, this meant the dismantling of the existing civilization: city dwellers were marched out to become peasants in a rigidly collectivized setting; hospitals were emptied, with only folk-medicine allowed; religious practice was punishable by death; in many sectors, family life was abolished, and where it survived, children were given authority over adults. The Khmer Rouge systematically executed those who challenged them, and those not of 'pure peasant stock'. They singled out those from ethnic minorities, those with formal education, and monks and nuns, whom they regarded as 'parasites'. Thus arose the 'killing fields' in which 2–3 million people were killed by starvation, disease, overwork, torture and execution, leaving a legacy of famine, scattered families, despair and depression (Ghosananda, 1992: ix–xi). At the end of Khmer Rouge rule, almost all of the country's 3,600 Buddhist temples had been destroyed and only around 3,000 monks, out of 50,000, had survived; many nuns had also died (Ghosananda, 1992: 7–12).

Fortunately, Khmer Rouge attacks on Vietnamese border sites meant that the Vietnamese attacked Cambodia, and with the help of some Khmer Rouge dissidents, took control of the country in 1979. The 1980s saw continuing armed conflict between the Khmer Rouge, plus nationalist forces, and the Vietnamese-installed government. In 1989, the Vietnamese withdrew, on account of UN pressure, leaving a client government in place. In 1991, all factions signed a UN-brokered peace treaty, providing for a four-faction interim government, leading up to elections in 1993. While the UN treaty attempted to bring Khmer Rouge violence to an end by including them in the process of national reconciliation, they continued their military operations, particularly from near the Thai border in western Cambodia until their impetus ran out in 1998.

A key figure working for national healing and recovery is Mahā-Ghosānanda, an influential monk who has been compared to Mahātma Gandhi and who was nominated for the 1996 Nobel Peace Prize. Dith Pran, who was the subject of the film *The Killing Fields*, says of Ghosānanda:

Although his entire family was lost in the holocaust, he shows no bitterness. He is a symbol of Cambodian Buddhism, personifying the gentleness, forbearance, and peacefulness of the Buddha. (Ghosananda, 1992: x)

Plate 7. Cambodian monastic leader and peace activist Mahā-Ghosānanda.

Jack Kornfield says that, in the twenty years he has known him, he

> has represented to me the essence of sweet generosity and unstoppable courage of heart. Just to be in his presence, to experience his smile and his infectious lovingkindness that flows from him is healing to the spirit.[18]

Ghosānanda had been ordained as a novice monk after seeing the suffering of war as the Allies attacked the Japanese in Cambodia (Rojanaphruk, 1995: 69). He went on to study in Cambodia and India, and to learn meditation in Thailand (Ghosananda, 1992: 15–16). In India, he had worked with a relief team in the 1967 Bihar famine (Gosling, 1984: 62) and had learnt skills of peace and non-violence from Nichidatsu Fujii (see p. 271), who had himself been partly inspired by the Mahātma Gandhi (Ghosananda, 1992: 15).

In 1978, after the defeat of the Khmer Rouge, Ghosānanda went to Sa-Kaeo refugee camp in Thailand and gave out pamphlets on the Buddha's discourse on lovingkindness (Ghosananda, 1992: 18). He began to build a bamboo temple, and though the Khmer Rouge running the camp warned people not to co-operate at the cost of their lives, 20,000 attended the opening. Ghosānanda recited over and over (pp. vii–viii) to the people the *Dhammapada* verse:

> Enmities never cease by enmity in this world; they only cease by non-enmity. This is an ancient law. (*Dhp.* 5)

He constantly reminded people that 'national peace can only begin with personal peace' (p. x). In line with this, he held regular weekly meetings for Buddhist, Muslim and Christian section leaders, urging them to work together for peace and reconciliation. In April and May 1980, around 120,000 refugees in this and another camp were involved in each of two days of meditation and prayers for peace. Most were Buddhists, but Christians and Muslims were also involved (Gosling, 1984: 59). A 'Prayer for Peace' which Ghosānanda has composed includes the words:

> The suffering of Cambodia has been deep.
> From this suffering comes Great Compassion.
> Great Compassion makes a Peaceful Heart.
> A Peaceful Heart makes a Peaceful Person.
> A Peaceful Person makes a Peaceful Family.
> A Peaceful Family makes a Peaceful Community.
> A Peaceful Community makes a Peaceful Nation.

---

[18] Ghosānanda, 1992: vii. These quotations are from the introduction to a book of Ghosānanda's teachings, and are not being quoted by Ghosānanda himself!

A Peaceful Nation makes a Peaceful World.
May all beings live in Happiness and Peace. (Ghosananda, 1992: 28)

Thai monks undergoing development training assisted in the building of temples in the camps and in the peace-days, and organized schools and adult education programmes (Gosling, 1984: 60). In 1980, however, the Thai military tried to push people from refugee camp Sa-Kaeo I back across the border to Cambodia, as they wanted to stop the camp being used as a support for the Khmer Rouge, and did not want it to become permanent. Knowing the hardship and dangers that a return to Cambodia would mean, Ghosānanda and others declared the camp a temple sanctuary. While this did not please the Thais, it meant that only 7,500, mostly Khmer Rouge, of the 35,000 residents, were persuaded to leave (Gosling, 1984: 67–8).

Ghosānanda has worked in and visited many Cambodian refugee camps and resettlement communities worldwide, establishing temples in each of them and helping camp leaders build spiritual, educational and cultural preservation programmes. In 1980, with Peter Pond, a Christian social activist, he formed the Inter-Religious Mission for Peace in Cambodia. They helped locate hundreds of surviving monks and nuns so that they could renew their vows and take leadership roles in Cambodian temples throughout the world. With lay support, Ghosānanda founded over thirty temples in the USA and Canada alone. He helped rebuild many more in Cambodia, and has been active in educating monks and nuns in skills of non-violence and the monitoring of human rights (Ghosananda, 1992: 20).

At the UN-sponsored peace-talks, he led a contingency of monks and urged compromise and non-violence (Ghosananda, 1992: 20). When people objected to having Khmer Rouge personnel in an interim government, he smiled and said:

We must have both wisdom and compassion. We must condemn the act, but we cannot hate the actor. With our love, we will do everything we can to assure peace for all. There is no other way. (p. 21)

Related comments of his are:

The unwholesome minded must be included [in our lovingkindness] because they are the ones who need loving kindness the most. (p. 68)

If I am good to someone, he or she will learn goodness and, in turn, will be good to others. If I am not good, he or she will harbor hatred and resentment and will, in turn, pass it on to others. If the world is not good, I have to make more effort to be good myself. (p. 54)

He cites the Gandhian non-violent ideal as aiming at

an end to antagonism, not the antagonists. This is important. The opponent has
our respect. We implicitly trust his or her human nature and understand that
ill-will is caused by ignorance. By appealing to the best in each other, both of us
achieve the satisfaction of peace. Gandhi called this a 'bilateral victory'.[19]

He sees peace-making as a slow, but steady, step-by-step process. In this,
'Reconciliation does not mean that we surrender rights and conditions,
but rather that we use love in all our negotiations', otherwise there is no
way beyond the cycle of hatred and retaliation (p. 69). On unrealistic
compassion without wisdom, he tells the story of a dragon-king who
came to give up killing. On being attacked by children, he was advised
by a *Bodhisattva* that, while remaining non-violent, he could still hiss and
show his fire if need be (p. 33)!

In the period leading up to the 1993 elections, Ghosānanda – then
sixty-nine years old – led a nineteen-day peace march from near the
Thai border, through Khmer Rouge territory, to the capital Phnom
Penh, where 8,000 joined the march. Often, the marchers were in
danger of being caught in cross-fire, and UN troops were very concerned for their safety. In the end, though, their determination and faith
won through, and the Khmer Rouge allowed them to pass unharmed,
spreading an atmosphere of peace as they went. Ghosānanda's idea is
that peace will only come to the country when people can walk the
streets and roads without fear, and with peace in their hearts.
Ghosānanda has done many marches for peace in Cambodia. In
April–May 1994, he walked 175 kilometres with 800 monks and nuns
from Battambang to Angkor Wat through the battle-stricken north-
west. En route, a monk and a nun were killed by rockets fired from
bushes while government soldiers were accompanying the march,
guiding them through a mine-field (Rojanaphruk, 1995: 67). He has
taken a leading role in the campaign to ban land-mines, both in
Cambodia and elsewhere, and led an inter-religious delegation to
support peace negotiations in Sri Lanka. He cites the Buddha's going
to resolve the Sākiya/Koliya conflict (see p. 241) as a call for Buddhists
to go into conflict situations to help resolve them (Ghosananda, 1992:
62–3).

Ghosānanda teaches the importance of the middle path of, and to,
peace, which avoids struggling with opposites such as praise and blame,

---

[19] Ibid., p. 62. Cf. Ariyaratne's implied ideal of a win-win situation, rather than seeking to win at
other people's expense (above, p. 277).

'yours' and 'mine' (Ghosananda, 1992: 37–8). His thoughts on the path to peace include:

Non-action is the source of all action. There is little we can do for peace in the world without peace in our minds. And so, when we begin to make peace, we begin with silence – meditation and prayer.

Peacemaking requires compassion. It requires the skill of listening. To listen, we have to give up ourselves, even our own words. We listen until we can hear our peaceful nature. As we listen to ourselves, we learn to listen to others as well, and new ideas grow. There is an openness, a harmony. As we come to trust one another, we discover new possibilities for resolving conflicts. When we listen well, we will hear peace growing.

Peacemaking requires mindfulness [careful awareness of the inner and outer world]. There is no peace with jealousy, self-righteousness, or meaningless criticism. We must decide that making peace is more important than making war.

Peacemaking requires selflessness. It is selflessness taking root. To make peace, the skills of teamwork and co-operation are essential. There is little we can do for peace as long as we feel that we are the only ones who know the way. A real peacemaker will strive only for peace, not for fame, glory, or even honor. Striving for fame, glory, or honor will only harm our efforts.

Peacemaking requires wisdom. Peace is the path that is chosen consciously. It is not an aimless wandering, but a step-by-step journey.

Peacemaking is the middle path of equanimity, non-duality and non-attachment. Peacemaking means the perfect balance of wisdom and compassion, and the perfect meeting of humanitarian needs and political realities. It means compassion without concession, and peace without appeasement.

Loving kindness is the only way to peace. (pp. 51–2)

CONCLUSION

This survey of Buddhism thus shows that the tradition has strong resources to draw on for conflict resolution, but that these resources and related ideals must sometimes become better known and applied more fully. Japanese Buddhists did little to stem the violent Japanese nationalism of the early twentieth century, though they are now active in promoting peace. The post-colonial period has left a legacy of instability and social readjustment in several Buddhist lands, and it is clear that, in certain quarters, there has been a danger of religious revival degenerating into exclusion of non-Buddhist ethnic groups (Sri Lanka), egalitarianism degenerating into hatred (Cambodia), and anti-colonial nationalism degenerating into xenophobia (Burma). Ironically, this is a good illustration of the Buddhist teaching that ignorance and dogmatism are at the root of much human suffering.

We see an unfortunate tendency for Buddhists to fall sometimes into demonizing their opponents in war as embodiments of Māra, or as evil-doers who are less than human. This can be seen in the story of King Duṭṭhagāmaṇi (pp. 255–6), in Kittivuḍḍho (pp. 260–1), and in several conflicts in China.[20] In Zen, there is also a danger that certain teachings can be interpreted to allow the depersonalization of enemies (see pp. 266–7). In Burma, China and Japan, we see Buddhism as an ingredient in peasant uprisings against oppressive rulers, sometimes inspired by dis-torted popularized notions of a *Cakkavatti* ruler and the coming of the next Buddha (see pp. 261–2). In general, though, failures of Buddhists to live up to their non-violent ideals can be put down to unresolved human fears and attachments aggravated by politically unstable times.

In the twentieth century, we see Buddhists struggling against the vio-lence of Communists and Marxists. While Kittivuḍḍho has advocated opposing them with violence, because of their threat to religious culture, other leaders have been non-violent in opposing them, as in Tibet, Cambodia and Burma, or in mediating between these forces and their American opponents, as in Vietnam.

We hear the voices of such people as A. T. Ariyaratne, Aung San Suu Kyi, Sulak Sivaraksa, Mahā-Ghosānanda, Nichidatsu Fujii, Daisaku Ikeda and Nikkyō Niwano, who are quietly but firmly reminding their fellow Buddhists of the profoundly non-violent and tolerant spirit of the Buddha. Thich Nhat Hanh and the Dalai Lama have strongly embod-ied this spirit both in seeking to help their own people and in writings and activities directed beyond their lands.

Among contemporary Buddhist peace activists, the Dalai Lama and Aung San Suu Kyi have been awarded the Nobel Peace Prize, and Ariyaratne, Ghosānanda and Nhat Hanh have been nominated for it. In them and others discussed above, we can see several interlocking threads. One is an admiration for Gandhi and his methods, seen in Fujii, Ariyaratne, Ghosānanda and the Dalai Lama. Though Gandhi was a Hindu, influenced by both Jainism and Christianity, his ideals and actions accord well with Buddhist values, and he has helped impress on people the efficacy of non-violent action. Accordingly, all the peace acti-vists discussed above hold firmly to both non-violence and non-anger against oppressors. Another thread is the idea of compassion for both sides in a conflict, as seen in Nhat Hanh, the Dalai Lama, Ghosānanda, Ariyaratne, Suu Kyi and Sivaraksa. Another thread is the emphasis that

---

[20] Demiéville, 1957: 358, 367; Welch, 1972: 280–1.

peace starts within the individual, and then spreads outwards, as seen in Ghosānanda, Nhat Hanh and the Dalai Lama. A thread emphasized by Mahāyānists – the Sōka Gakkai, Nhat Hanh and the Dalai Lama – is inter-dependence. We also see an emphasis on the avoidance of dogmatic clinging to views, and being open to the perspective of others, as in Ariyaratne, Ghosānanda, Nhat Hanh, the Dalai Lama, Sivaraksa and even, on the non-religious front, the Sōka Gakkai.

CHAPTER 7

Suicide and euthanasia

Whatever monk . . . should praise the beauty of death . . . he is not in communion.
Vinaya-piṭaka III.73

CONSIDERATIONS AND ARGUMENTS AGAINST SUICIDE

While Buddhism emphasizes that there is much *dukkha* in life, this can, paradoxically, help dissuade a Buddhist from giving in to despair. If *dukkha* is to be expected in life, then there is less reason to take particular problems so *personally*: as the world conspiring against one. Reflection on the idea of phenomena as not-Self can also help a Buddhist to avoid being dragged down by unpleasant experiences. Reflection on the principle of impermanence should urge him or her to realize that all bad things come to an end, sooner or later. Reflection on the principle of karma should mean that he or she is more willing to live patiently through the results of his or her own prior action – and maybe learn something about the nature of life in the process – rather than sow the seeds of future suffering by new, rash actions.

Of course, someone faced with some weighty suffering might kill himself or herself in the hope of something less intolerable after death; yet there is no guarantee that matters may not be made worse by this act. From the Buddhist perspective, the next rebirth might be as an animal preyed on and eaten by others, as a frustrated ghost, or in a hell: so suicide may lead on to something *more* 'intolerably painful' than the present life. Even in the case of a human rebirth, there are many possible forms of severe suffering.

One of the three forms of craving is craving for annihilation (*vibhāva-taṇhā*): to get rid of unpleasant situations. Where one's whole life-situation is perceived to be so unbearable that one says 'no!' to it, it may culminate in suicide. However, as it is craving which impels one through the round of rebirths, the state of mind which prompts suicide will be a crucial cause of yet another rebirth, along with its problems. So as an attempted escape from the sufferings of life, suicide is, according to Buddhist principles, totally ineffective. It will only be followed by a further rebirth, probably lower than a human one, in which the sufferings will probably continue unabated – if due to karma – and perhaps be intensified. As dying in an agitated state of mind is seen as leading to a bad transition into the next life (cf. p. 25), suicide is seen as likely to lead to a bad rebirth next time. In the Tibetan tradition, the consciousness of one who commits suicide is seen as anguished and weighed down with negative karma, so as to need rituals to aid it (Sogyal, 1992: 301, 376).

In fact, while human life contains many difficulties, to cut it short means that the potential for spiritual development which is present in a rare 'precious human rebirth' will have been thrown away (see p. 30). Not only does suicide waste this opportunity for oneself, but it also deprives others of benefits that one may bring to them. This attitude is reflected in an early text in which the monk Mahā-Kassapa was asked by a materialist why, if rebirth existed, moral people such as monks did not kill themselves to gain the karmic results of their good actions. Kassapa replies with a parable of two wives of a brahmin who had just died. While one wife had a son, who was due to inherit, the other was in an advanced state of pregnancy. To find the sex of her child, and so gain part of the inheritance for him if he was male, the latter cut open her belly. She and her child died, though. Kassapa then says that moral people 'do not seek to hasten the ripening of that which is not yet ripe', for:

The purpose of virtuous renouncers and brahmins, of lovely qualities, is gained by life. In proportion to the length of time that such a man abides here, is the abundant karmic fruitfulness that they create, practising for the welfare of the many, for the happiness of the many, out of compassion for the world. (*D.* II.330–1; cf. *Miln.* 195)

One could add that, even for a not particularly virtuous person, suicide is an act which will bring grief to friends and relatives, and so, if for no other reason, is to be avoided.

SUICIDE AND THE PRECEPTS

Is it the case that suicide is seen as breaking the first precept? As Buddhism sees acts which harm oneself as morally unwholesome (see p. 47), and suicide can be seen in this way, one would expect so. While textual discussions of the first precept rarely mention suicide, killing oneself is just as much an act of killing as killing another person, so there seems little reason to see suicide as not breaching this precept. However, the *Mahā-prajñā-pāramitā-śāstra*, attributed to the Mahāyāna philosopher Nāgārjuna, says:

> In the *Vinaya* it is said that suicide is not onslaught on a living being [*prāṇātipātā*, i.e. a breach of the first precept]. Fault (*āpatti*) and karmic fruitfulness (*puṇya*) result respectively from wrong done to others (*para-viheṭhana*) or benefiting others (*para-hita*). It is not by caring for one's own body or killing one's own body that one acquires karmic fruitfulness or commits a misdeed. That is why it is said in the *Vinaya* that suicide is not a fault of onslaught on a living being, but it is sullied by delusion, by attachment, and by hate.[1]

This alludes to a *Vinaya* passage as saying that suicide is not a breach of the first precept, though no such passage has been traced. However, it still accepts that suicide is an unwholesome act, as it is associated with the roots of unwholesome actions. Thus in the Tibetan tradition, while the first precept only applies to killing others, as the basis of the precepts is not causing harm to others, suicide is nevertheless seen as one of the gravest bad actions (Yuthok, 1995: 46, 48), as serious as murder (Mullin, 1987: 148).

David Evans argues that the first precept concerns not depriving someone of life when this is something they value, which is not the case in suicide (1987: 98). Admittedly, the general rationale for the precepts is: don't do to others what you would not like them to do to you (*S.* v.353–5). Yet this does not allow, for example, the masochist to go round hurting others as he does not dislike pain. He clearly has to learn to like himself more, by developing lovingkindness to himself. Similarly, if someone does not value his own life, this does not allow him to go round killing others. The precepts' rationale, then, has to be taken in the context (a) of what people generally don't like and (b) learning to have lovingkindness for oneself, overcoming ill-will (associated with craving for annihilation) to aspects of one's existence.

The seriousness with which the Buddha in fact viewed suicide can be seen from the following monastic precept, one of the few entailing 'defeat' (*pārājika*) in the monastic life, i.e. permanent expulsion. This particular rule was made in the context of two events. The first is that of some monks killing themselves, or getting another to kill them, after having misunderstood the implication of a sermon of the Buddha on the 'foulness of the body': that inside the skin it is rather unattractive, and not worthy of being the object of attachment (cf. *S.* v.320–2)! The

---

[1] K12, p. 149a, translated from E. Lamotte's French translation, 1949: 740–2. See Lamotte, 1987: 106 for a slightly different English translation. Lamotte, in a footnote to 1949: 740–2, refers to various passages in it of relevance to the issue of suicide. A parallel is found at *Uss.* 171.

second event was that of some bad monks persuading a layman to kill himself, so that they could seduce his wife. They 'praised the beauty of death' and argued that, as a good person, he would have a good rebirth. He thus deliberately ate bad food until he died (*Vin.* III.72–3). The rule that these two supposed events is said to have led to is as follows:

Whatever monk should intentionally deprive a human being of life, or should look about so as to be his knife-bringer, or should praise the beauty of death, or should incite (anyone) to death, saying, 'Hullo there, my man, of what use to you is this evil, difficult life? Death is better for you than life', or who should deliberately and purposefully in various ways praise the beauty of death or should incite (anyone) to death: he is also one who is defeated, he is not in communion. (*Vin.* III.73)[2]

This rule clearly concerns murder, assisting someone in suicide, or inciting or praising suicide. Lamotte (1987: 105), in commenting on this, notes that it is not said that suicide itself is an offence, and that therefore there is nothing wrong with it from the point of view of Buddhist ethics. This seems a wrong conclusion, though. The relevant rule concerns an action that will lead to expulsion from the monastic *Saṅgha*. If someone has killed themselves, this question does not arise.

Nevertheless, Demiéville reports that in the *Vinaya* of the Mahīsāsakas (Taishō 1421, II, 7b–c), the Buddha, before giving the above pronouncement, says that suicide is a grave offence, just falling short of a full offence entailing defeat (1957: 350). The text continues (8a) by saying that, when some friends suggest that a sick monk lets himself die, so as to be reborn in heaven, he replies that suicide would prevent the continued cultivation of the holy life, and in any case, he might still recover to practise it in his present life. Again, some badly injured lay people refuse to kill themselves, saying that the suffering undergone in the world teaches one to cultivate the action of the Buddhist way (Demiéville, 1957: 350–1).

Is an unsuccessful suicide attempt a monastic offence, though?[3] At *Vin.* III.82 in the Theravādin *Vinaya*, an account is given of a monk who, 'tormented by dissatisfaction (*anabhiratiyā*)' – which seems to relate to sexual desire[4] – climbs Vulture's Peak and falls down a precipice, clearly in an attempt to kill himself. Though he survives, he kills someone else

---

[2] The *Bodhisattva-bhūmi* also says that the *Bodhisattva*'s generosity should not include giving someone an instrument for suicide or self-torture (49a; Dayal, 1932: 175).

[3] Cf. Wiltshire, 1983: 130.

[4] As explained by *Vin. A.* 467; also, at *Vin.* II.110, a monk actually cuts off his penis because of such torment!

through landing on him. The monk then wonders if he has committed an offence entailing expulsion, as he has killed someone. This is seen as inappropriate, though, presumably because there was no intention to kill the other person. The Buddha then says 'Monks, one should not cast oneself off ('na . . . attānaṃ pātetabbaṃ'). Whoever shall cast (himself) off, there is an offence of wrong-doing.' That is, not an offence entailing defeat, but something approximating to one, of which there are two grades: a grave offence and an offence of wrong-doing, the latter being the less serious. The following case, of some monks who accidentally killed someone by throwing a stone off Vulture's Peak, is dealt with in exactly the same way. This suggests that the offence, in both cases, was seen as one of culpable carelessness regarding the safety of others, and that in the first case, the offence did not reside in its being a case of attempted suicide.

Now, a possibility is that there is no monastic rule specifically on an attempted, but failed, suicide because monastic rules only relate to actions which succeed in their aim.[5] However, this is not always so. At *Vin.* II.76, if a monk aims to kill a man by digging a pit for him to fall into, while he is only defeated if the man dies, he is still guilty of a grave offence if the man is hurt, and of an offence of wrong-doing if he falls in and is unhurt.

Nevertheless, as stated, the above rule says that one should not throw oneself off a cliff, and in fact the phrase 'na . . . attānaṃ pātetabbaṃ' can also mean, more generally, 'one should not kill oneself'. *Miln.* 195–7 in fact cites this rule in arguing that virtuous people should not kill themselves, as they deprive the world of the benefit that they can bring to it. The commentary on *Vin.* III.82 (*Vin. A.* 467) says:

(1) And here, not only is (oneself) not to be cast off, also by whatever other means, even by stopping eating, one is not to be killed: whoever is ill and, when there is medicine and attendants, desires to die and interrupts his food, this is wrong-doing, surely.
(2) But of whom there is a great illness, long-lasting, (and) the attending monks are wearied, are disgusted, and worry 'what now if we were to set (him) free from sickness?': if he, (thinking): 'this body being nursed does not endure, and the monks are wearied', stops eating, does not take medicine, it is acceptable (*vaṭṭati*).
(3) Who (thinking) 'this illness is intense, the life-activities do not persist, and this special (meditative) attainment (*visesādhigamo*) of mine is seen as if I can put my hand on it' stops (eating): it is acceptable, surely.

---

[5] As suggested by Damien Keown in an e-mail letter of 13 November 1995.

(4) Moreover, for one who is not ill, for whom a sense of religious urgency (*saṃvega-*) has arisen, (thinking) 'the search of food is, indeed, an obstacle: I will just attend to the meditation object', stopping (eating) under the heading of the meditation object is acceptable.

(5) Having declared a special (meditative) attainment, he stops eating: it is not acceptable. (numbers added)[6]

This extends the prohibition on throwing oneself off a cliff to any method of suicide, even a 'passive' method such as self-starvation (1), as used by Jain saints. It does, however, allow that some instances of self-starvation are acceptable. It is acceptable when one has no time to collect food because one is inspired to practise a meditation intently (4), but not if one has already attained a specific meditative state and thinks one need do nothing more (cf. *A.* IV.22) (5). It is not acceptable if one is ill, but help is to hand (1). It is acceptable in two other cases of illness: when there is a severe, long-lasting illness, and a monk allows himself to die so as not to trouble those who attend on him (2), and where there is an intense illness, the person is clearly dying, and he knows he has attained a meditative state he had been aiming at (3). Here, self-starvation is seen as acceptable when it is because it is an unintended side-effect of a more important task (4), when it is part of a compassionate act (2), or when death is already imminent and further eating would be futile, not even allowing the completion of a meditative task (3).

Early Buddhist literature also includes discussions of a few cases of those who are frustrated at not attaining Arahatship and thus cut their throats, but who attain Arahatship at the last minute by managing to attain full insight as they watch the process of dying, perhaps accompanied by remorse at their unwise act. It seems that these cases are not such as to make suicide in any way acceptable, though (Keown, 1996). Mahāyāna literature also contains examples of: (1) *Bodhisattvas* giving up their lives to save others, including a family of starving tigers (Conze, 1959: 24–6; Khoroche, 1989: 8; *Ss.* 24–8, 37–8, 51), and (2) people burning themselves alive as an act of worship (Kato et al., 1975: 305–7). The first can be seen as praising heroic altruism, not 'suicide', while the second can be seen as a rather unguarded way of urging the complete dedication of one's life to a higher ideal: though a few in China took it literally (Yün-hua, 1965). The Chinese tradition also includes examples, influenced by Confucianism, of a person killing himself as an act of protest so as to try compassionately to bring about an improved situation in society: again,

---

[6] Cf. the Chinese translation of the Pali *Vinaya* commentary, as translated by Bapat and Hirakawa (1970: 327–8).

of no great relevance to normal suicide scenarios, though the Vietnam War period saw some famous examples of Buddhists burning themselves to death that broadly fit into this tradition (Nhat Hanh, 1967: 9, 37–8, 118–19; Rahula, 1978: 114).

EUTHANASIA

From a Buddhist perspective, death is the most important and problematical 'life crisis', as it stands at the point of transition from one life to another. Within the limits set by a person's previous karma, his or her state of mind at death is seen as an important determinant of the kind of rebirth that will follow (see p. 25, and Sogyal, 1992: 224). Buddhism thus supports many of the ideals of the hospice movement, directed at helping a person to have a 'good death' (de Silva, 1994). Thus a San Francisco Zen Center has offered facilities for the dying since 1971, and it started a full-scale training programme for hospice workers in 1987.[7] In the UK, the Buddhist Hospice Trust was formed in 1986 to explore Buddhist ideas related to death, bereavement and dying, and develop a network of Buddhists willing to visit the dying and bereaved, if requested. The ideal is to die without anxiety regarding those one leaves behind (*A.* III.295–8) and in a conscious state which is also calm and uplifted. Thus it would be preferable not to die in a drugged, unconscious state. To die in a calm state, free of agitation, anger or denial, and joyfully recollecting previous good deeds rather than regretting one's actions, means a good transition to a future life. Clearly it is best to *know* that one is dying, for then one can come to terms with death and talk to one's family freely about it, with an open and mutual sharing of feelings, uninhibited by a desire not to talk of the coming death.[8] In Buddhist cultures, family and friends of a dying person do their best to facilitate a 'good death'. Buddhist monks may be invited to chant calming chants, to help inspire a tranquil and joyful state of mind. Some of the chants (those known as *parittas* in Southern Buddhism) are seen as having a protective effect, and, if a person is not seen as certain to die, they are regarded as aiding recovery. The dying person will also be reminded of good deeds that he or she has done in his or her life, so that he or she can rejoice at these, contemplating goodness (Terweil, 1979: 256). Monks

[7] T. D. Schneider, 'Accidents and Calculations: The Emergence of Three AIDS Hospices', *Tricycle: The Buddhist Review*, 1 (3) (Spring 1992) 78–83.

[8] Sogyal, 1992: 177–8. Nevertheless, doctors in Japan often act in a paternalistic or authoritarian way, and so do not inform patients that they are dying (Becker, 1990: 553).

may also be fed on his or her behalf, so that he or she approaches death while sharing in a karmically fruitful act. In Northern Buddhism, a person will be read the *Parto Thötrol* (*Bar-do thos-grol*), commonly known as 'The Tibetan Book of the Dead', as he or she approaches and passes the point of death. This is to guide him or her through the experiences undergone in the between-lives period, so as to help him or her overcome lingering attachment to his or her body and family, and enable him or her to gain liberating insight into the processes of life and death, or at least to avoid an unnecessarily bad rebirth. In Eastern Buddhism, Pure Land Buddhists may put a painting of Amitābha Buddha at the foot of a dying person's bed, and place in his or her hands strings attached to Amitābha's hands. This is to help the person to die peacefully with the thought of being drawn to Amitābha's Pure Land.

'Euthanasia', which is derived from the Greek words *eu* and *thanatos*, literally means a 'good death'.[9] As defined by the *Concise Oxford Dictionary* (1976), it means 'Gentle and easy death; bringing about of this, esp. in case of incurable and painful disease'. Though dying while receiving care and comfort in a hospice might be seen to come logically under the definition, this is not how the term is normally used, for it is seen to apply to cases involving the sick where death is the intended result of some action or inaction, hence the terms 'active euthanasia' and 'passive euthanasia'. Active euthanasia is intentionally hastening death by a deliberate positive act, such as giving a lethal injection. Passive euthanasia is intentionally causing death by a deliberate omission, such as by withdrawing food, including intravenously administered nourishment, or withholding or withdrawing medical treatment which would otherwise have delayed death (cf. Hämmerli, 1978: 191).

Whatever the means of euthanasia, it can also be differentiated as regards the nature of the volitional involvement of the person who dies as a result of it (cf. Keown, 1995a: 168–9):

1 *Involuntary euthanasia* would be that carried out against the wishes of the patient. This was done by the Nazis against psychiatric patients and other 'inadequates' and is universally condemned. It is simply equivalent to murder.

2 *Voluntary euthanasia* occurs where the patient requests the action, which is then taken by a doctor, or where the doctor provides the patient with the means of ending his or her life, which is a case of assisted suicide.

---

[9] In Japanese, the word for 'euthanasia' is *anrakushi*, which in Buddhism is actually another name for the Pure Land (Becker, 1990: 550).

3 In what one might call *pre-voluntary euthanasia*, a patient makes a 'living will' to the effect that, if he or she becomes mentally incapable in the future then, under such and such medical conditions, he or she would want his or her life terminated. Where the medical conditions are such that the patient can justly be seen as dead when the action is taken, however – for example turning off an artificial ventilator if it is inflating the lungs of a corpse (see below) – this is not actually a case of euthanasia.

4 In *non-voluntary euthanasia*, the patient is not capable of either agreeing or disagreeing to termination of his or her life – because of being in a coma, being in an advanced state of Alzheimer's disease, or being an infant with a brain abnormality – and the decision to end the life would have to be taken by doctors in consultation with relatives, perhaps with the permission of the courts. As with the last type, this type of euthanasia raises the issue of the criteria by which a person can be pronounced 'dead', which will be discussed below. Any action performed on a body that can justly be called dead is not any kind of euthanasia.

Buddhist reasons for rejecting euthanasia

Active euthanasia is generally resisted by the medical profession and by public opinion – though it is accepted, if technically illegal, in The Netherlands[10] – but some are willing to countenance some forms of passive euthanasia. As Buddhism sees intention as crucial to the assessment of the morality of an act, however, it would not differentiate between active and passive means if these were intended to cause or hasten death. The Buddha's strong condemnation of a monk or nun praising or aiding a suicide (see p. 289) is here relevant. To kill a person deliberately, even if he or she requests this, is dealt with in the same way as murder. As is pointed out by Damien Keown (1995a: 170), one who follows the first precept 'does not kill a living being, does not cause a living being to be killed, does not approve of the killing of a living being' (*D.* III.48). To request that one is killed would be to 'cause a living being to be killed', and would thus break the precept. This would be the case

---

[10] And in 1994, the Michigan Commission on Death and Dying recommended that it be made legal in Michigan, if a terminal patient was likely to die within six months, and it was the patient himself or herself who initiated the action leading to death (the *Guardian* newspaper, 28 April 1994). In December 1994, Oregon introduced a Death With Dignity Act, under which doctors can prescribe a lethal dose of drugs to a terminally ill patient who is of sound mind and asks for this (the *Guardian*, 6 December 1994). The northern states of Australia also came to allow doctor-assisted suicide, but then the federal government over-ruled this decision.

even if the request were in the form of a 'living will'. If a doctor is requested to administer euthanasia, this does not absolve him or her from responsibility for the act of killing. In the case of a prior 'living will', there is not even any certainly that the patient, though now unable to communicate, has not changed his or her mind. The Buddhist emphasis that there is no permanent Self (see pp. 36–7) entails a recognition that people's views and intentions are often very changeable.

Now, voluntary euthanasia for one in intense pain is often referred to as 'mercy-killing', especially if it is a case of active euthanasia, and some argue that this should be allowed for humans as for animals.[11] Buddhists, though, are reluctant to carry it out even for animals (see p. 173). It might be thought that the Buddhist emphasis on compassion would allow such an act, yet several episodes from the *Vinaya* show that this is not the case (cf. Keown, 1995a: 60–4, 171–3). In all of these, the monks involved are held guilty of an act entailing defeat in the monastic life. In the first, monks 'out of compassion' praise the beauty of death to a sick monk so that he takes some undisclosed measure and dies (*Vin.* III.79). The commentary (*Vin. A.* 464) says that they urged him to die so as to gain a good rebirth as the result of his virtue, so that he stopped eating and so died. In the second case, involving a condemned man, the executioner kills him quickly after a monk asks him to, so as not to prolong his pain and miserable period of waiting (*Vin.* III.86). The third case involves the case of a man whose hands and feet have been cut off. When a monk asks the relatives looking after him if they want him to die, and they agree, he prescribes the feeding of buttermilk, which makes the man die (*Vin.* III.86).

In all such cases, the motive for the act can be seen to have been compassion, yet the act is still condemned. Here, Keown makes a useful distinction between motive and intention, as made in the courts (1995a: 62). Motive concerns the ultimate aim of an action, while intention concerns the more immediate goal of an action, an objective on the way to attaining an ultimate aim. Thus one who kills to obtain an inheritance has the motive of obtaining money, and also the intention to kill. Keown sees the above cases as showing that Buddhism has life as an ultimate value, or 'basic good', and that it should never be sacrificed even in the name of another such value, friendship or compassion. This means that to have compassion as a motive, but to intend death in the process, is unacceptable. This is one way of looking at the matter, though a Mahāyānist

[11] Stephen Levine (1992), a Buddhist meditator who has done much work with the dying, supports voluntary euthanasia under certain circumstances.

might argue that sometimes 'skilful means' implies that it is acceptable to kill if the motive is compassion (see pp. 135–8). However, Mahāyāna scriptural cases of 'compassion killing' are always to prevent the victim committing some evil deed against others: they are to prevent suffering to others, and also bad karma being generated by the victim. Such cases do not fit the euthanasia scenario.

In any case, perhaps a better way to interpret the Buddhist attitude to 'mercy-killing' is as follows. An action is unwholesome if it is rooted in greed, hatred or delusion (p. 46). Here, 'rooted in' can be seen to refer to an action's intention, to its motive or to both together. To advocate death on the grounds of compassion would be seen as an unwholesome act rooted in delusion, so that the compassion involved was unwise. The *Abhidharma-kośa-bhāṣya* (*AKB.* IV.36c–d) says that killing may arise from a variety of roots, including ignorance.[12] Examples of the latter are animal sacrifice and killing one's aged or sick parents, as the 'Persians' do. A note to Pruden's translation of the text (*AKB*, pp. 735–6) cites the *Vibhāṣā* (p. 605c16) as saying a certain people of the West thought it a good act to kill a parent if he or she was decrepit or in pain so that he or she would attain new organs and a painless life. This clearly implies that it is delusion to try to end suffering by killing the person who is suffering. Indeed, the *Upāsaka-śīla Sūtra* says that if one gives one's parent a weapon to kill himself or herself, or kills one of them at his or her orders, the atrocious offence of killing a parent is still committed (*Uss.* 179).

Why is killing a person in pain an act based on delusion? In the case of the sick monk, the commentary explains that more proper advice is: 'as the paths and fruits have arisen, it is not surprising you are virtuous: therefore do not be attached to residence etc., setting up mindfulness in respect of the Buddha, *Dhamma*, *Saṅgha* and the body, develop heedfulness in attention' (*Vin. A.* 464; cf. Bapat and Hirakawa, 1970: 326). This suggests that a person should use the process of dying as an opportunity for reflection, so as to see clearly the error of attachment to anything which is impermanent, be it the body, other people, possessions, or worldly achievements. Dying presents the reality of the components of body and mind as impermanent, *dukkha* and not-Self in stark form; it is thus an opportunity for gaining insight into these. An enforced death cuts short this opportunity.

In Theravāda Buddhism, it is also commonly seen that 'no act of

---

[12] The others being greed, hatred and false views. Killing because of the last, which would include suicide and killing someone who wanted to die, would clearly be rooted in the view that a person is annihilated at death.

killing can be carried out without the thought of ill-will or repugnance towards suffering' (Ratanakul, 1988: 310). In the case of 'mercy-killing', a doctor's motive of compassion is good, but it is mixed with aversion to the patient's pain, which disturbs the doctor, so that 'Subconsciously he transfers his aversion to the suffering to the one who embodies it' (p. 310). Taniguchi, drawing on Theravāda texts, also says that if a mother in severe pain asks her son to end her life, and he does so, they share the delusion that death is the only way out, and the son is motivated by attachment to his mother and aversion to her pain.[13] For such reasons, Pinit Ratanakul reports that in Thailand there is a growing consensus that euthanasia, active or passive, is morally unjustifiable (1990: 27). He nevertheless observes that, as in the West, nurses 'reported instances of lethal overdoses being given, of no-code orders [i.e. not to resuscitate] being written, of withdrawal of life-support systems or orders to withdraw treatment' (1986: 219). Though he says that such practices conflict with traditional Thai Buddhist values, he gives insufficient details of the contexts of such acts to give a proper moral assessment of them.

There is also the question of whether killing a sick person will actually end his or her suffering. For one thing, there is no guarantee that even a good person will have a pleasant rebirth in his or her next life, as there may be a backlog of bad karma to catch up with him or her (see p. 25). For another, if the suffering of a sick person is due to karma, then killing him or her is unlikely to end the suffering, as the karmically caused suffering will continue after death until its impetus is used up. Thus, it is better to deal with the suffering here and now, while one still has a human rebirth and can deal with the suffering better. However, it is not held that all suffering or illness is due to karma, for it may arise from: winds, bile, phlegm, a combination of these, change of season, stress, suddenly, *or* from the maturing of karma (see p. 23).[14] As regards death and karma, the Theravādin commentator Buddhaghosa says that death may be (1) due to the natural ending of a normal human life-span,

---

[13] Shoyu Taniguchi, 'A Study of Biomedical Ethics from a Buddhist Perspective', MA thesis, Graduate Theological Union and Institute of Buddhist Studies, Berkeley, Calif., 1987, pp. 90–3, cited in Florida, 1993: 43.

[14] Lesco cites several Tibetan sources, including the medical doctor Yeshe Donden, to the effect that Tibetans see all feelings and illnesses as ultimately due to karma, whatever the immediate causes for their arising (1986: 53–5). However, this may simply be based on the idea that one can have human illnesses and feelings only if one is reborn as a human, which is due to karma, rather than meaning that karma is the specific cause of all illnesses. In the Yogācāra school of Mahāyāna philosophy, though, *all* experiences are seen as arising from specific karmic 'seeds'. In the Chinese tradition, Chih-i's *Great Concentration and Insight* lists various causes of disease, only one of which is the maturation of karma (Ikeda, 1994: 69–70).

or (2) due to the natural ending of the karma-determined life-span of a particular individual, or (3) an 'untimely (*akāla-*) death', for example by being murdered, due to karma which disrupts the normal life-span (*Vism.* 229; cf. *Kvu.* 543–4). This implies that all death, except of those who are very old, is due to karma. The *Sutta* passage which says that all illnesses are not due to karma, however, could be seen to imply that some premature deaths are not due to karma. Indeed, the *Karma-prajñapti-śāstra* (ch. xi, as quoted at *AKB.* II.45b) says that death occurs because of the exhaustion of karma leading to life, to objects of enjoyment or to both, or because of not avoiding a cause of harm, for example excess food. That some deaths have nothing to do with the results of karma is also implied by *Miln.* 150–4. This discusses the efficacy of *parittas*, Buddhist chants which are seen to have the power, in certain cases, of curing illnesses and so of saving a life. They do not work when a person is coming to the natural end of his or her life term, or when the illness is due to karma (p. 151); they only work for one who is in his or her prime and who has faith (p. 154). This admits that one in his or her prime might die even though he or she is not due to do so from karma, for want of the curative properties of such a chant.

If not all illness and death is due to karma, what follows? Firstly, that an illness should not just be passively accepted, as a 'just' result of karma. Doctors and relatives should do what they can to save a patient. Where an illness is clearly terminal, it then becomes likely, though not certain – particularly in the very old – to be due to karma. If it is due to karma, hastening death by euthanasia will not end the suffering involved, as karma will cause it to continue after death. If it is not due to karma, it is still important for the patient to 'see the death-process through', to learn from it. The case of those who are unconscious and so perhaps cannot 'see the death process through' will be discussed below.

Of course, one might say that it could be the patient's karma to die by euthanasia. This could, in principle, be the case – but it no more excuses euthanasia than a murder's being due to the victim's karma excuses the murderer. Wise compassion, then, should not include euthanasia.

Nevertheless, a Buddhist consideration which might be seen to support voluntary euthanasia is the importance of dying in a good state of mind: calm, conscious and so able to see the death process through (Becker, 1990: 553–5). *If* someone *knew* for certain that he or she would die soon, and that he or she would be in increasing pain, only maskable by drugs that rendered him or her unconscious, then he or she *might* choose to go sooner in a good state of mind, in which he or she could be reasonably calm, and learn from the death process, than later in a prolonged unconscious or pain-agitated state. Yet the dichotomy is, at least nowadays, becoming a false one. When morphia was used as a pain-killer, it could quite easily render the patient unconscious. There are now pain-killers which minimize this, so as to allow a state which is neither unconscious nor pain-agitated, but a semi-conscious state from which a person can be roused (Hämmerli, 1978: 192). Pain will still be experienced to a degree, and the drugs may cause nausea and eventually lead to final unconsciousness,[15] but to cut this short by euthanasia will abort a learning experience, albeit a difficult one. Moreover, if the person was *not* in fact bound for death in the near future, euthanasia would be throwing away the potential of human life. Keown also makes the fair point that 'Although it is important to die as mindfully as possible, it must be recognised that many people die peacefully, naturally and unconsciously in their sleep, without, one imagines, their spiritual progress being greatly hindered thereby' (1995a: 185). That is, while it is not good to die in an agitated state, dying while unconscious still avoids this. Moreover, at *S.* v.369–70, it is said that a person well practised in spiritual qualities, even if he or she dies while bewildered by the teeming bustle of a city, will gain a good rebirth.

It is clear, then, that on Buddhist principles, euthanasia is unethical and inadvisable. This does not entail, though, that completely self-administered euthanasia, without the help or connivance of another party – i.e. suicide in the case of a difficult illness – should be *illegal.* Indeed, of Buddhist countries, only Sri Lanka, because of British influence, criminalizes attempted suicide. In the case of Channa, a spiritually frustrated monk set on killing himself (*M.* III.263–6), the *Arahat* Sāriputta does what he can to dissuade him, but neither he nor the Buddha, on hearing of this, seeks to prevent Channa from carrying out his plan, since he is set on it and of sound mind; in the event he does so, but manages to become an *Arahat* while dying (Keown, 1996). Suicide (if followed by rebirth) is unethical, but a person still has a right to do unethical actions. He or she should consider, though, that his or her actions may well have a devastating effect on relatives and friends, which gives additional reasons for not doing them.

A relevant case, here, is that of Elizabeth Bouvia, who in 1983 asked the California Supreme Court to be allowed to die by starvation while

---

[15] My thanks to my research student Liz Williams, an ex-nurse, for pointing this out.

receiving pain-killers and hygienic care. She was a twenty-six-year-old who was suffering from cerebral palsy and quadriplegia, with hardly any motor control, and who felt 'trapped in a useless body' (Nakasone, 1990: 72). After long and serious reflection, she felt that any option but death would be unfulfilling. The court refused her request, on the grounds that she was not terminally ill, that her death would be devastating for her parents and other disabled people, and that she could not ask a doctor to abandon the duty of care enjoined by the Hippocratic Oath (Nakasone, 1990: 72). Here, Buddhist principles would mean that it would be a wrong action on the part of a non-terminal patient to starve herself to death (above, p. 290, (1)). It is less clear whether it would be wrong for doctors to let her starve, if treatment for pain was being administered. If the patient could feed herself if she wanted to, and was of sound mind, then perhaps she should be allowed to die. If she could feed herself, though, she would have been less likely to want to die. The problem, here, was that she was completely dependent on others feeding her. This meant that she wanted others to kill her, by removing her feeding, rather than to allow her to kill herself. This would be asking them to commit an unethical act, and one which it is perfectly acceptable also to make illegal.

Cases of non-intended death

While Buddhist principles entail that genuine cases of euthanasia are unethical, this does not mean that cases which might be mistakenly viewed as euthanasia would be unethical. In one such type of case, death occurs as the result of an action, but is not the intended aim of the action. There are several scenarios which come under this description. The first relates to pain-relief for the terminally ill. Where the pain is intense, pain-relieving drugs might gradually kill the patient. As the body develops a tolerance to the drug, the dosage has to be increased gradually, and may reach a toxic level, so that the patient dies from the drug (Hämmerli, 1978: 192). In such a case, Keown (1995a: 175) points out that there is a useful distinction to be made between intention and foresight. One may know that a side-effect of one's action may be a certain result, but unless one's aim is to attain that result, one does not intend it. For example, one may know that driving a car will kill insects, but if one does not drive so as to kill insects, this is not one's intention. That such a distinction is recognized in Buddhism is perhaps shown by a case in the *Vinaya*. Here, a sick monk dies as a result of medicine given by other monks (*Vin.* III.82–3). They are held to be guilty of no offence if they did not mean to cause his death, but of a grave offence, just short of one entailing defeat, if this was the intention (*Vin.* III.82–3). Death as the unintended side-effect of pain-killers is seen by Van Loon (1978: 76–7), Barnard (1978: 208) and Florida (1993: 46–7) as an acceptable case of 'passive euthanasia', though it seems preferable to reserve the word 'euthanasia' for cases where death is the intended aim, as explained above.

In another scenario, a patient might rightly feel that he was tying up scarce medical resources, or bankrupting his family with high medical bills. He might therefore, from compassion to others, *freely choose* to forgo the means of further life (Ratanakul, 1988: 312), as in the *Vinaya* commentary case mentioned above (p. 290, (2)). Of course, it is very important that a person would not feel pressurized by others to perform such an altruistic act. If this were the case, the pressurizers would in effect be committing murder. If a terminally ill person simply could not face eating, then it would be the duty of others to help him eat, and provide intravenous feeding if necessary.

In another scenario, in the advanced stages of a disease, for example cancer, there is the question of continuing with an excessively burdensome treatment if it is painful and not expected to produce a cure, so as to be futile or pointless.[16] The patient, or his doctor in consultation with him, might decide that another round of chemotherapy was just not worth it, as it would detract from the quality of the remaining life term, and would not actually prevent death. To continue treatment, here, would be 'to cling desperately to a life that is ending or to flail against the forces of impermanence' (Anderson, 1992: 41). Sogyal Rinpoche affirms that:

Life-support measures or resuscitation can be a cause of disturbance, annoyance, and distraction at the critical moment of death . . . In general there is a danger that life-sustaining treatment that merely prolongs the dying process may only kindle unnecessary grasping, anger, and frustration in a dying person, especially if this was not his or her original wish. Relatives . . . should reflect that if there is no real hope of recovery, the quality of the final days or hours of their loved one's life may be more important than simply keeping the person alive. (1992: 372)

Kalu Rinpoche has said that a terminal patient who himself chooses to be taken off a life-support system is doing an act which is karmically

---

[16] Cf. Keown, 1995a: 176; Hämmerli, 1978: 192–3; Barnard, 1978: 205–8.

neither bad nor good (Sogyal, 1992: 374). Yet as this would probably have to have been by a previous 'living will', it would have to have been *very* carefully worded, and there is the danger that it no longer expressed the patient's current wishes.

Dr Elizabeth Kübler Ross, who has done much work with the dying, lists five stages that those approaching death go through: (1) shock and denial, (2) anger, (3) bargaining with God and fate, (4) depression and (5) acceptance.[17] Buddhist counselling for those approaching death is to aid the acceptance process and teach them to let go (cf. *M.* iii.258–62); to be aware of the feelings of fear, anger, denial, despair etc. that come up, but not to cling to them, and not to cling to the dying body, life or relatives (*S.* v.408–10). Meditation practice schools a person in letting go, and thus prepares him or her for this; indeed, there are meditations on the inevitability of death (for example *Vism.* 229–39). Dying, though, is a time when a person *has* to learn to let go, even if he or she has not yet done so. The more attached a person is, and the more he or she denies his or her impending death, the more difficult it will be for him or her and his or her relatives. To develop acceptance of the process, as the natural ending of a conditioned phenomenon, is to prepare for an easier passing away. As expressed by Jacqui James, a Buddhist meditation teacher who helped her mother through the last two weeks of her dying from cancer:

Learning how to die properly is all about learning how to let go, learning how to watch the natural ebb and flow of all things, learning that life is a process of continual beginnings and endings, continual birth and death. When you see this cyclical movement clearly then there is no more fear of death. When you have learnt *that* not only have you learnt how to die but you have also learnt how to live. (James and James, 1987: 150)

The Amaravati Buddhist Centre, near Hemel Hempstead, England, is a place where some people are now going to die in good surroundings. In the case of a nun who died there, the other nuns who attended her said that it was a privilege to be in the same room as her, as she had learnt to be at peace with her coming death, and exuded a radiance of spirit that was uplifting to share in (Sucitto, 1988). The Thai monk Mettānando also tells of a lady who was riddled with cancer and extremely agitated as a result. After she was taught a simple meditation, she became happy, and survived for six months rather than the two months that doctors had given her. She then died happy and at peace,

[17] *On Death and Dying* (New York, Macmillan, 1970), pp. 38–137, cited in Ikeda, 1994: 97–8.

making a considerable impression on the doctors and nurses who observed her (1991: 208).

Where treatment of a terminal illness is futile, the non-administering of treatment might give up a chance to delay slightly death due to natural causes, but it would not hasten it – make it happen more quickly than it would have happened naturally without treatment – and death would not be the aim. It would thus involve neither suicide nor murder, and would be morally acceptable. The South African heart doctor Christiaan Barnard sees such a case as one of passive euthanasia, but as acceptable (1978: 208–9, 211), as does Florida, particularly if there are additional factors, such as the family being bankrupted by treatment, and a shortage of hospital beds in the locality (1993: 44). Now, while withholding treatment would prevent the delay of death, as in passive euthanasia, unless its *intention* was to thus cause death, it does not come under the full definition of passive euthanasia given above. This also seems to be the opinion of Kübler Ross. She opposes all euthanasia, which she refers to as 'mercy killing', but finds it acceptable to allow a patient to die in peace if he or she is beyond medical help (1989/90).

Regarding such a case, Taniguchi, articulating a Theravāda view, says: 'If one chooses to die or refuses life sustaining medical treatment, one must be motivated by aggression towards one's state of suffering, or be passionately attached to pleasant states, or be deluded that death is a way to avoid suffering.'[18] This might be true if treatment was refused when it could do some good, but it need not be otherwise. The Thai doctor Pinit Ratanakul also holds that even when a terminal patient refuses extraordinary treatments, so that he dies, this is an unwise act which prevents bad karma 'running its course', so that it does not continue into the next life (1988: 309), and the Dalai Lama holds that it is best to face suffering, which is karmically caused, in the present, human life, where one is better placed to bear it than in, say, an animal rebirth (Sogyal, 1992: 375). This is an argument not about morality, though, but about the wisdom of an act. Here, three points can be made. Firstly, it is not certain that all illness or death is due to karma (see pp. 297–8). Secondly, ideas about karma are not usually seen to imply that pain-killers should not be taken because this 'interferes' with the flow of karmic results. Thirdly, allowing a disease to run *its* course without (futile) treatment is hardly interfering with the flow of karmic results.

---

[18] Shoyu Taniguchi, 'A Study of Biomedical Ethics from a Buddhist Perspective', MA thesis, Graduate Theological Union and Institute of Buddhist Studies, Berkeley, Calif., 1987, pp. 89–90, cited in Florida, 1993: 42.

Thus, in the case of a severe terminal illness, where death will soon come anyway, avoidance of futile treatment would be acceptable. Indeed, the *Vinaya* commentary (above, p. 290, (3)) even sees it as sometimes acceptable for a person in such circumstances to stop eating. One can see such a case as one where neither the motive nor the intention is to die, but to be peaceful, and thus better able to compose oneself during a dying process which is already under way irrespective of what anyone does or does not do. The Dalai Lama gives some degree of support to this:

if a dying person has any chance of having positive, virtuous thoughts, it is important . . . for them to live even just a few minutes longer . . . If there is no chance for positive thoughts, and in addition a lot of money is being spent by relatives simply in order to keep someone alive, then there seems to be no point. (Anderson, 1992: 41; Sogyal, 1992: 372)

This would support non-treatment, but only where treatment would make it difficult to have 'positive, virtuous thoughts'.

What of the avoidance of futile and/or expensive treatment when this is non-voluntary? Ratanakul raises the case of deformed infants – who of course may be severely mentally impaired – and says that it is morally unacceptable to Thai Buddhists to withhold treatment from them or allow them to die (1990: 27). In Japan, also, infants with severe brain abnormalities are sometimes cared for for years at the wish of loving parents (Becker, 1990: 545). Clearly, it is unacceptable to remove feeding from such infants. Anything should also be done which would *improve* their condition or maintain a viable state of health. Thus a child with Down's Syndrome, for example, should be given every help. Where a child's condition is such that he or she would be constantly battling with infections or other medical complications, and this would be painful and expensive and tie up scarce medical resources, then perhaps he or she should be allowed to die – for example by not having infections treated – if this is what the parents want.

Another scenario for avoidance of futile treatment is that of the non-resuscitation of a terminal patient who has a heart-attack (cf. Keown, 1995a: 174–5). While non-resucitation would be acceptable if it was what the patient wanted, perhaps in a prior 'living will', it would probably also be acceptable if he had not expressed himself on the matter, if he were clearly already in the terminal phase of his illness. To die amidst the unnecessary techno-frenzy of a hospital 'crash' team is surely a disturbing experience! Non-resuscitation would be unacceptable if the patient had affirmed that he *did* want to be resuscitated. It would perhaps also be immoral to resuscitate a genuinely terminal patient who had said that he did *not* want to be resuscitated. Hämmerli suggests that a doctor who insists on prolonging the life of a hopeless case as long as possible may in fact be treating his own guilty conscience, so as to appear a 'good' doctor (1978: 182), and Barnard sees this as possibly a case of selfishly not wanting to appear a failure (1978: 204).

The question of the criteria of death

Another type of case in which an action would be acceptable as no intentional killing occurs would be that in which the action can be seen to occur after the patient has died. This, then, raises the question of the criteria for being 'alive' and being 'dead'. The type of scenario which particularly raises this issue is that of a patient in a 'persistent vegetative state' (PVS). Here, a person is in a coma as the neocortex of his or her brain has been damaged. If this continues for a long time, the damage may be regarded as irreversible. If the brain-stem of the person is undamaged, however, the person can breathe unaided (though artificial respiration may be added as an aid) and digest, his or her heart will beat (though help may be needed in regulating it), and his or her body will retain certain reflexes such as dilation of the pupils and, usually, swallowing, yet the senses do not seem to work, and no voluntary movements are made (cf. Keown, 1995a: 160; Mettānando, 1991: 210). If someone is permanently without any sign of conscious awareness and the ability to make decisions, however, two questions arise:
(1) is the patient still a 'person' with value?
(2) is the patient alive?
Some would regard the life of a human who is 'not a person' as without value, so that it is not unethical to kill him or her. Buddhism, however, does not see the value of life as residing in personhood (Keown, 1995a: 27–30). This is shown by the fact that animals and humans in the womb have value and should not be killed. Some Buddhists would still say that a life without volition (Van Loon, 1978) or awareness/sentience[19] would be without value. Yet even were one to accept these criteria, which are debatable,[20] there seems no way of knowing that, in the inner recesses

[19] Geoffrey Redmond (of the Foundation for Developmental Endocrinology, Cleveland, Ohio), 'Application of the Buddhist Anatma Doctrine to the Problems of Biomedical Ethics', paper given at the conference of the International Association of Buddhist Studies, Paris, 1991, pp. 19–20, 22, 33.
[20] See Keown, 1995a: 32–7, 143–4, 160–1. Such criteria would also seem to give scant grounds for not killing a person who was unconscious and insentient under anaesthetic!

of a patient's mind, these qualities are not present, albeit in an attenuated form. Buddhism accepts many meditative states in which consciousness behaves in non-ordinary ways. It also accepts 'formless'
rebirths, where consciousness is not accompanied by any kind of body.
It is therefore hard to be sure that physical tests will always be able to
detect existing states of consciousness. Indeed, the remaining consciousness may be reflecting on the dying process, preparing for death, so as to
attain as good a rebirth as possible (Mettānando, 1991: 210). Indeed,
Vism. 554 says that, as a person is dying, there is a phase in which the eye
and other sense-organs stop working, but the sense of touch, the mind-
organ and the vitality-faculty remain 'in the heart-basis alone' and consciousness is in the process of preparing for death.

Is a patient in a PVS alive, then? It seems that, by Buddhist criteria,
he or she would be. Keown (1995a: 145–58) has a good review of the relevant textual material. Two passages (*S.* III.143 and *M.* 1.296) affirm that
a body is dead and 'will-less (*acetanan*) like a log of wood' when it is
without three things: 'life (*āyu*), heat and discriminative consciousness
(*viññāṇaṃ*)'. It is explained that 'life' and heat depend on each other, like
the light and flame of a lamp, and that the five sense-organs depend on
heat (*M.* 1.195). The 'life-activities' (*āyu-saṅkhāras*) are not states that are
felt, otherwise one would die in the meditative state of the 'cessation of
identification and feeling' (*M.* 1.296).[21] This is a state attained by
advanced meditators in which all functions of the mind shut down, and
on the way to attaining it, breathing ceases (*M.* 1.296 and 301). Unlike a
dead body, which has no life or heat, and has the sense-organs 'wholly
dis-integrated', a person in the state of cessation still has life and heat,
and his or her sense-organs are 'clarified'. It is left ambiguous whether
consciousness still occurs in this state, and the different Buddhist schools
had different opinions on this. In his study of the state of cessation, Paul
Griffiths sees it as a state in which a person may seem dead (*M.* 1.333;
Vism. 380), as he or she does not breathe and 'heartbeat, blood pressure,
body temperature and metabolic levels in general have all fallen to a very
low level', and mentally, a person is in a state which Western medical
observers might liken to a profound cataleptic trance (1986: 10–11). It lasts
for up to seven days (*Vism.* 707).

The above shows that Buddhism holds it possible to be in a state in
which there is no breathing, and no detectable mental activity, and yet

---

[21] Though the *Vibhaṅga* says that it is sometimes associated with feeling (*Vibh.* 125), just as it is sometimes associated with consciousness (p. 131).

be alive. A persistent vegetative state is not the same as the state of cessation, but shares some of its qualities. One difference is that a person
continues to breathe, unaided, in the PSV. Buddhism would clearly not
regard one in such a state as dead, then, and to remove intravenous or
tube feeding from such a person would be to kill him or her.

A famous case of this type was that of Tony Bland, who in 1989 was
crushed in a football stadium disaster and was in a PVS. In 1993, the UK
House of Lords ruled that the food provided to him by a tube was a form
of futile treatment, and could legally be withdrawn, even though this
would lead to his death. He then died in a heavily sedated state (Keown,
1995a: 159–68). This was in accord with the recommendations of the
1988 euthanasia report of the British Medical Association, which
opposed active euthanasia, but accepted that futile treatment, which it
saw as including artificial means of feeding, could be removed from terminal patients.[22] Keown (1995a: 162–4), however, rightly disputes
whether feeding could be regarded as 'futile treatment'. Firstly, he points
out that feeding, even if done by nurses, could not be seen as medical
treatment unless it was of a kind specifically selected to cure an illness,
which it was not. Even if it were regarded as 'treatment', its only possible aim was to sustain life. As it was succeeding in doing so, it could not
be seen as 'futile treatment', i.e. treatment which was not attaining its
goal. In a somewhat similar case in 1995, the Irish Supreme Court
decided that a woman who had lain in a coma for twenty-three years
could have her feeding-tube removed, even though she was not in a PVS
but could still recognize people. The grounds were that feeding by tube
was an intrusive and unusual method of feeding which interfered with
the integrity of her body.[23] Yet the view of a dissenting judge in the
Court seems correct: the action was intended to cause death by starvation. If someone cannot feed himself or herself, it is the duty of others
to help him or her, by whatever means.

To say that a patient in a PVS is alive, and should not be starved to
death, is not to say that extraordinary medical means should be used to
keep him or her alive indefinitely. A patient in such a state is very prone
to infections. As Keown argues, 'it does not follow that there is a duty to
go to extreme lengths to preserve life at all costs' (1995a: 167). Such a
person could be seen as beyond medical help, so that any *medical treatment*
would be futile, as it could not restore health. If relatives wished medical
complications such as infections to be treated, they should be, unless

[22] The *Guardian* newspaper, 6 May 1998.   [23] The *Guardian* newspaper, 28 July 1995.

resources were genuinely not available. If not, the condition should go untreated, which could well result in the patient's death.[24]

What, though, of patients whose brain-stems have died, so that they cannot breathe unaided (which those with live brain-stems *usually* can), and are without any reflexes: are they then to be regarded as dead, so that no action can be seen as 'killing' them any longer? Keown (1995a: 151–8) argues that brain-stem death should be taken by Buddhism as the correct criterion of death. He points out that *Vin.* III.73 defines killing as the 'cutting off' of the vitality-faculty (*jīvit-indriya*)' and that *Vin. A.* II.438–9 specifies this as the physical vitality-faculty rather than the mental one, which in any case depends on it (1995a: 148). The commentary on *M.* I.296 identifies 'life (*āyu*)' with this material vitality-faculty (*M.A.* II.351), and the Abhidhamma defines this as:

That which, of these material states, is life (*āyu*), persistence, continuance, last-ingness, movement, upkeep, keeping going, vitality, vitality-faculty. (*Dhs. sec.* 635)

Buddhaghosa says that it 'has the characteristic of maintaining conas-cent types of matter. Its function is to make them occur. It is manifested in the establishment of their presence' (*Vism.* 447). It is identified with 'vital breath' (*prāṇa*) (*AKB.* IV.73ab), but clearly not with the physical breath, for as 'life', it is seen as occurring from the moment of concep-tion, because of past karma (*AKB.* II.45b). It is thus clearly not identified with any organic structure or function, such as breathing, but as Keown says, seems to denote 'the basic biological processes of life' (Keown, 1995a: 149). As 'life' and heat are compared to the light and flame of a lamp, they can be seen as two processes which keep biological processes 'burning', i.e. functioning.

Keown refers to the meaning of *prāṇa* in Buddhist medicine, and in Buddhist-influenced Ayurveda (Indian traditional medicine) as ranging 'from the gross physical process of respiration to the flow of subtle energy which was thought to regulate the internal functioning of the body' so as to regulate 'respiration, heartbeat, swallowing, digestion, evacuation, menstruation, and many other bodily functions. In this capacity it seems to be closely related to the autonomic system' (1995a: 149).[25] He goes on (p. 151) to cite Mettānando (1991: 204) as saying 'This

---

[24] Cf. Mettānando, 1991: 209–11, though he only talks of withholding treatment, including life-support, if resources are needed for others in intensive care.

[25] In Tibetan Buddhist thought, consciousness is said to be mounted on the *prāṇa*s or winds which circulate through many channels in the body (Sogyal, 1992: 248–9).

group of interrelated bodily functions attributed to the *prāṇa* we now recognize as bodily functions maintained by the nuclei of the brainstem.'
While Keown holds that, as 'life' and heat always occur together, so permanent loss of body-heat seems to be 'the only empirical criterion
offered by the early sources as a means of determining death' (1995a:
151), he concurs with Mettānando in taking brain-stem death as signifying the end of life. Mettānando sees this as entailing that *prāṇa* and consciousness have gone (1991: 206), and Keown sees it as meaning that
there is no body-heat, presumably as he sees the brain-stem as its cause
(1995a: 152). Keown holds that early Buddhist texts see that 'death is the
irreversible loss of the integrated organic functioning which a living
organism displays' (1995a: 155), as when *M.* 1.296 says that death involves
the 'dis-integration of the sense-organs'. At death, often referred to as
the 'break-up of the body', the operation of the sense-organs 'is no
longer co-ordinated as it would be in a living, self-regulating organism'
(1995a: 156). He regards the brain-stem as carrying out such a 'co-ordi-
nating function', without which 'the organism ceases to be a unified
whole and can no longer survive', even if components can survive a
while longer: the heart continues to beat for up to an hour (1995a: 155),
and remains alive for an hour or so even after this stops, and the skeletal
muscles live for another six hours (Barnard, 1978: 201). Thus irreversible
brain-stem death is the criterion for determining that death – an end to
integrated organic functioning – has occurred, this being simultaneous
with consciousness leaving the body (Keown, 1995a: 158). Keown does
not actually identify 'life'/'vitality-faculty' with the brain-stem, but sees
it as closely related to it.

CONCLUSION

Overall, it can be seen that Buddhism regards human life as a precious
quality that should not be thrown away by suicide, and maintains that
people should not incite or aid others to kill themselves. Euthanasia scenarios present a test for the implications of Buddhist compassion, but
the central Buddhist response is one of aiding a person to continue to
make the best of his or her 'precious human rebirth', even in very
difficult circumstances, rather than prematurely ending this. The adage
'where there is life there is hope' is appropriate, though 'where there is
human life, there is opportunity to reflect and learn' is one which
Buddhism might emphasize. At a certain point in terminal illness,

though, it may be appropriate to abstain from futile treatments that reduce the quality of life on its last short lap. It may also be appropriate to deal with mounting pain in such a way that death is a known but unintended, and unsought, side-effect of increasing dosage of drugs. Any help for the dying that does not include the intention of bringing death is acceptable.

CHAPTER 8

Abortion and contraception

Hard to gain is a human rebirth. *Dhammapada* 182

EMBRYONIC LIFE

Before discussing abortion, it is appropriate to examine Buddhist views about the nature of life in the womb. In Buddhism's rebirth-perspective, human life is not seen as something that gradually emerges as an embryo develops.[1] Consciousness is not regarded as an emergent property of this process, but is itself seen as one of the conditions for it to occur, as expressed in a passage from the Theravādin collection of *Sutta*s:

'Were consciousness (*viññāṇaṃ*), Ānanda, not to fall into the mother's womb, would the sentient body (*nāma-rūpaṃ*) be constituted there?' 'It would not, Lord.' 'Were consciousness, having fallen into the mother's womb, to turn aside from it, would the sentient body come to birth in this present state?' 'It would not, Lord.' (*D.* ii.62–3)

Thus the flux of consciousness from a previous being is a necessary condition for the arising and development in the womb of a body (*rūpa*) endowed with mental abilities which amount to sentience (*nāma*, literally 'name'): feeling, identification, volition, sensory stimulation and attention (*S.* ii.3–4). The monastic code recognizes human life as starting at conception; for the minimum age for full ordination, twenty (*Vin.* i.78), is reckoned from then, not from leaving the womb:

When in his mother's womb, the first mind-moment has arisen, the first consciousness appeared, his birth is (to be reckoned as) from that time. I allow you, monks, to ordain one who is aged twenty from being an embryo (*gabbha-vīsaṃ*). (*Vin.* i.93)

The Theravādin commentary on a similar passage at *Vin.* iii.73 (*Vin.* A. 437) explains this time as 'from the first relinking mind (*paṭisandhi-cittaṃ*)'

---

[1] Below, 'embryo' or 'foetus' will be used equally for the being in the womb at any stage of development, even though there is a usage in which 'zygote' means fertilized egg, 'embryo' refers to the womb-being for the first eight weeks, and 'foetus' refers to the being after eight weeks.

(cf. *Vism.* 499), with the commentary on the above *D.* II.62–3 passage (*D. A.* 502) also using this term for the consciousness which falls into or enters the womb.[2] 'Relinking' mind or consciousness is a commentarial term for the consciousness which connects to a new life, immediately after the end of the previous one (*Vism.* 460, 554). It is equivalent to 'arising' (*uppatti*) mind, which in the Theravādin canonical Abhidhamma is described in the same way (*Ps.* 1.312–13) and is said to be accompanied by all the other personality-factors, including feeling (*Vibh.* 411).

Modern biological knowledge shows that there are two key events at the start of life:

(a) *fertilization* of the ovum by a sperm, which takes place in the oviduct or Fallopian tubes, normally five minutes to an hour after intercourse (Keown, 1995a: 78);[3]

(b) *implantation* of the fertilized egg in the lining of the womb, which takes place six or seven days later, by which time there are over a hundred cells; the egg takes eight or nine days to complete its attachment (Keown, 1995a: 76–7).

At what point would Buddhism see 'relinking' consciousness as arising? On this, a key early text describes the three conditions which must all be met for a human life to start:

> If there is, here, a coitus of the parents, *and* it is the mother's season, *and* a gandhabba is present: it is from the conjunction of these three things that there is descent of the embryo [and not if only the first, or only the first and second, condition is met]. Then, monks, the mother for nine or ten months carries the embryo (*gabbham*) in her womb with great anxiety for her heavy burden. When it is born, she feeds it with her own life-blood . . . that is to say, mother's milk. (*M.* 1.266)

Here, there must both be the appropriate physical conditions of sexual intercourse at the right time of the month, and also the presence of a *gandhabba*. The latter term indicates a being who is ready to be reborn (*M. A.* II.310). While the developed Theravāda view is that '*gandhabba*', here, is just a way of talking of the instantaneously transmitted consciousness of a person who has just died, as they accept no between-lives interlude, the Sarvāstivādins – and also the Mahāyānists – saw it (Skt *gandharva*) as the name for a between-lives being (*AKB.* II.4, 10, 13–15, 40). Indeed, even in the Theravāda collection of *Sutta*s, there is a small but substantial body of evidence to support the idea of such a between-lives

---

[2] See also *Ps.* 1.52; *Vism.* 528, 600.

[3] After fertilization itself, when the sperm penetrates the outer layer of the ovum, about twenty-four hours later the two sets of twenty-three chromosomes fuse together (Keown, 1995a: 82).

state, with the *gandhabba* as a kind of mutable, restless 'spirit' seeking out a new rebirth to 'fall' into (Harvey, 1995: 98–108).

What, though, is one to make of 'descent of the embryo' (*gabbhassāvak-kanti*)?[4] It clearly does not refer to the exit from the womb at birth – for the above passage sees this as coming later. Could it be alluding to 'descent' of the fertilized ovum to implantation? This seems ill supported by the above passage, for no literal 'descent' need be meant. *Avakkanti* has an alternative form *okkanti*, and the verbal form of this, *okkamati*,[5] is used of 'falling' asleep (*Vin.* 1.15). The word can also mean simply 'enter'. Damien Keown thus seems right when he holds that in modern terms, 'we have every reason to locate the descent of the intermediate being at fertilisation' (Keown, 1995a: 78), this being a very clear point of origin, from which everything else follows (Keown, 1995a: 79).

ABORTION AND BUDDHIST PRINCIPLES

Given the Buddhist view of embryonic life, it is not surprising that causing an abortion is seen as a serious act:

When a monk is ordained he should not intentionally deprive a living being of life, even if it is only an ant. Whatever monk deprives a human being of life, even (*antamaso*) down to destroying an embryo (*gabbha-pātanaṃ upādāya*), he becomes not a (true) renouncer, not a son of the Sākiyans. (*Vin.* 1.97)

The penalty for a monk intentionally causing an abortion is permanent expulsion from the *Saṅgha*:

Whatever monk should intentionally deprive a human being of life . . . he is also one who is defeated [in the monastic life], he is not in communion . . . *Human being* means: from the mind's first arising, from (the time of) consciousness becoming first manifest in a mother's womb until the time of death, here meanwhile he is called a *human being*. (*Vin.* III.73)

Such passages from the Theravādin *Vinaya* have their counterpart in the Sarvāstivādin *Vinaya* used in Tibet, which clearly forbids monks' and nuns' involvement in abortion (Stott, 1992: 173–4, 181). While these passages pertain to monks and nuns, rather than lay people, the rules which

---

[4] *Gabbhassa avakkanti* in the citing of this passage at *Miln.* 123. The meaning can be either 'descent' (*avakkanti*) 'of the embryo' or 'into the womb', as *gabbha* can mean 'embryo' or 'womb' and the ending -*assa* could mean either 'of' or 'to'. The commentary (*M. A.* II.310) favours the former meaning, which makes sense, given that the passage goes on to use *gabbha* to clearly mean the embryo.

[5] The future form of which is used on consciousness 'falling' into the womb at *D.* II.62–3, quoted above.

entail expulsion if broken cover serious matters, and it is clear that, here, causing an abortion is seen as a case of murdering a human, a serious breach of the first of the five precepts applying to all lay Buddhists. David Stott, speaking on behalf of the Tibetan tradition, argues strongly that abortion is wrong, going against both Śrāvakayāna ethics and the Mahāyāna emphasis on compassionate cherishing of all beings. He thus holds that it is bad to have an abortion, perform one, or advise someone to have one (1986: 15).

As with all aspects of Buddhist ethics, intention is a key factor. This can be seen at *Vin.* III.83–4, on a series of cases where a woman asks a monk for an abortive preparation, either for herself or a rival co-wife.[6] If he accedes to her request, then:

(a) if the child dies, he is defeated, even if he is remorseful;
(b) if the child does not die, but the mother does, this is a grave offence (lesser than defeat), entailing temporary suspension: this must be because this result was not that intended by the monk;
(c) the same applies if neither die;
(d) if both die, 'ditto (*pe*)': this must surely refer back to the judgement in case (a), defeat, rather than in cases (b)–(c), as the child dies, as intended;[7]
(e) if he simply tells her how to cause an abortion by crushing or scorching, and the child dies, he is defeated.

In case (e), the commentary says that the monk is not defeated if the child is aborted, but by the woman using a different method from the one he recommended, or by a different person applying that same method to the woman.[8] Here again, as in (b), the woman does not carry out what the monk had told her to do, so the offence is less serious.

A key reason why Buddhist principles treat abortion as such a serious matter is that human life, with all its potential for moral and spiritual development, is seen as a rare and precious opportunity in a being's wandering in the round of rebirths (see p. 30). For a being to gain a foothold in a human womb and then be killed is to have this rare opportunity destroyed. Now it might be said: as all rebirth is due to past karma (see, for example, *Miln.* 128), might not a being with the karma for a human rebirth simply find another human womb if aborted from another? This

---

[6] On monks' involvement in medicine, see Keown, 1995a: 1–5.
[7] McDermott, 1998:166–7 argues for this reading, and a personal communication from Damien Keown supports it. Note that the format of the text is rather abbreviated at this point. If any judgement other than defeat were intended here, the commentary would surely have discussed it, which it does not.　　　[8] *Vin. A.* 468–9; see also Bapat and Hirakawa, 1970: 328.

is possible, but should no more 'excuse' abortion than the killing of an adult who might then be reborn as a human. In any case, the state of mind in which a being dies can affect its next rebirth (see p. 25), and the trauma of being aborted might lead to anger and fear in the foetus, meaning that it would have a less good rebirth than it was previously heading for, thus losing the opportunity for a human rebirth for some time. Now, being aborted might well be itself due to a foetus's past karma, but again, this should no more excuse abortion than saying that if a person murders an adult, this is acceptable as the death is due to the adult's past karma.

Given the seriousness of abortion, it is not surprising to find certain passages outlining its karmic results. A *Jātaka* story (*J.* v.269) thus refers to abortion-mongers in a hell, along with matricides and adulterers. In the *Petavatthu*, there are two stories of jealous elder wives causing younger ones to miscarry or abort (one at two months, the other at three months).[9] In both cases, the women falsely swear that they did not do it, and go on to be reborn as ill-smelling ghosts on account of the deed and the lie. They also suffer in having to devour their own children, as they had sworn that they would if they were lying in their oaths (*Pv.* 1.6, 7).

Relevance of the age of the foetus

In law, it is often the case that abortion is permitted on certain grounds on foetuses of a certain age. In England and Wales, abortions can be carried out up to 28 weeks (though foetuses can survive from 23 weeks), while France only allows them up to 10 weeks. What is the Buddhist view in this area? In the above story, the karmic result is the same whether the foetus is two or three months old, and McDermott sees this as evidence that the age of an aborted foetus is not seen by Buddhism as affecting the seriousness of the act (1998: 160–1). Keown also holds that causing the death of a foetus is as grave an offence as killing an adult (1995a: 93), and Stott holds that a foetus is:

not a 'partially souled' being nor a 'potential' being but an embodied sentient being, however small. It would thus be difficult for any Western Buddhist to make the claim that the smaller the foetus, the less serious the abortion. (1992: 176)

Yet there is some ambiguity in the textual evidence. It is clear from *Vin.* III.73 that causing an abortion is seen as a case of murder, and the

---

[9] See Reynolds and Reynolds, 1982: 98 and *Dhp. A.* 45–53.

commentary on *Vin.* 1.97 (see p. 313) says that the offence is committed even if the foetus is only in its first phase, as a *kalala* (*Vin. A.* 437–8), said to be like a drop of oil on a hair tip (*S. A.* 1.301). Yet *Vin.* 1.97, by using the word 'even', implies that, just as killing an ant is the least serious case of killing an animal, so killing a foetus is the least serious case of killing a human. Of course, even this is seen as a serious offence – which actually entails the same *monastic* punishment, expulsion, as any other killing of a human[10] – yet this does not prevent other acts of murder from being more *morally* serious.

Trevor Ling, on the basis of a study of views in Thailand and Sri Lanka, says:

In general it can be said that in Theravāda Buddhist countries the moral stigma which attaches to abortion increases with the size of the foetus. This is an aspect of the general Buddhist notion that the seriousness of the act of taking life increases with the size, complexity and even sanctity of the being whose life is taken. It is relatively less serious to destroy a mosquito than a dog; less serious to destroy a dog than an elephant; it is more serious to take the life of a man than of an elephant, and most serious of all to take the life of a monk. It would thus be less serious to terminate the life of a month-old foetus than of a child about to be born. (1969: 58).[11]

Here, there is probably an allusion to the commentarial passage at *M. A.* 1.198, as quoted on p. 52. Keown argues that the *size* criterion in this passage only applies to animals, not humans, for whom degree of virtue is seen as crucial (1995a: 96, 99). He argues that all human *life* is seen as equally valuable, but that extra virtue gives additional value to a person, too (p. 97). However, the passage in question does acknowledge that it is morally worse to kill some animals than others – even though the same *monastic penalty* applies – and worse to kill some humans than others.

Now, in the case of foetuses, they may be the reborn form of beings of greater or lesser virtue, but as this cannot be known by a person contemplating an abortion, this cannot be a relevant consideration for assessing his or her degree of fault in an abortion. The age/size of a foetus is, broadly, knowable, and while the above passage does not apply the size criterion to humans, it *does* say that the intensity of bad motive, and of the means used, make the act worse. Now, to abort a foetus at five

---

[10] Also at *Vin.* iv.124–5, dealing with the killing of animals, the punishment only varies according to such matters as intention and foreknowledge of the monk, with no discussion of killing of different kinds of animals.

[11] Apart from this, he cites a Thai non-Buddhist popular belief that the *khwan* or spirit is only properly established in a child three days after birth, making it properly 'human' (p. 58).

months – by inducing contractions – arguably does entail more forceful means than to do so at, say, two months, by scraping out the uterus. This would mean that the act of the abortion*ist* would be worse when the abortion was later – and also the act of the woman requesting the abortion *if* she knew that more violent means were to be used. In any case, with a later abortion, the woman would have a more developed relationship with the foetus, which would mean that her motivation to have an abortion at this stage would probably have to be more intense, and perhaps perverse, in order to go through with the abortion.[12] Thus on these two grounds, rather than on that of size *per se*, a later abortion would be worse than an earlier one, though an early one would still be a serious act. Both these points are contained in a statement of Dr Pinit Ratanakul, who holds that Thai Buddhists

believe in the uniqueness and preciousness of human life irrespective of its stages of development . . . To destroy any form of human life will yield bad karmic results . . .

The gravity of these results depends on many factors, such as the intensity of the doer's intention and effort, as well as the size and quality of the being that was killed . . . In the case of induced abortion, the stages of the development of the fetus aborted influence the degree of the karmic consequences for those who perpetrate abortion. These different stages also imply different degrees of the potential of the fetus which itself influences the weight of the karmic consequences. (1998: 56)

He thus sees Thai women's preference for earlier rather than later abortions as appropriate. While this preference *may* be partly because a late abortion is more difficult to hide from others, that is not the only consideration.

So, it is clear that Buddhism sees abortion as akin to killing an adult human, but that does not mean that all such acts are equally bad. As a parallel, note that in American law, murderers may get different sentences, depending on the circumstances and motive of the act. Those who kill in self-defence or in war are also treated differently. Thus there can surely be degrees of badness in abortion as in other forms of intentional killing.

Nevertheless, it is clear from *Vinaya* passages quoted above that deliberate abortion is *always* worse than killing an animal, which would

---

[12] Saying this would seem to imply that it is worse to kill someone with whom one has a positive relationship – a relative or friend – than a stranger. Though this is never exactly spelt out anywhere, the fact that it is seen as a terrible act to kill a *parent* intentionally might be seen to imply that it is also particularly bad, though to a lesser degree, to kill any relative.

include killing, say, an elephant, seen as a noble animal in Buddhism, or a chimpanzee, which is nowadays seen as the most developed of animals. As I think that there are Buddhist grounds for saying that an abortion becomes worse according to the age of the foetus, so we could say that abortion is not *as* bad as killing a newborn baby – though in the last few months of pregnancy, the difference may be minimal. We could thus say that the evil of an abortion lies somewhere between the evil of killing a chimpanzee and the evil of killing a baby, other things being equal.

Robert Florida argues that it is less bad to abort a younger foetus as this entails inflicting less pain, the degree of suffering caused being the criterion of how bad an action is (1998: 16). He goes too far here, though, for Buddhism would still object to killing someone painlessly. That someone feels pain in being killed is only *part* of the evil of killing,[13] though when a killing entails more pain, it is appropriate to see it as worse. As regards the extent to which foetuses suffer, scientific evidence sees this as starting to occur at twenty-three weeks or earlier, as indicated by a huge surge in hormone stress level.[14] While Buddhist texts see pain as entailed at any stage in the womb (*Vism.* 500) and some sense of touch as present from the beginning (*Vibh.* 413; *AKB.* 11.14b), it seems valid to say that a more developed foetus would be *more* sensitive to pain, so that a later abortion would accordingly be *worse* if the foetus were not anaesthetized.

The fact that the killing of even very young foetuses is against Buddhist ethics has implications for fertility treatments and embryo research. *In Vitro* Fertilization, or IVF, entails fertilizing an ovum outside the womb, using the sperm of the husband or a donor, then placing it in the womb to grow. Stott holds that, while this might be acceptable in Buddhism in theory, in practice it is unacceptable, as it involves fertilizing up to ten ova, and implanting only the 'best' one or ones. The rest are discarded or used in research, i.e. killed, or frozen for later use, with a real risk that this will kill them. He holds that a Buddhist could only, with a good conscience, take part in the procedure if all the fertilized eggs were implanted, even those with a potential handicap, for 'a handicapped being is as valuable as a non-handicapped one' (1986: 13–14). However, no IVF centres operate using these conditions, and there is no guarantee that doctors would follow a couple's wishes (Keown, 1995a: 137).

Doctors envisage that research on embryos might lead to improved

---

[13] Keown, 1995a: 35–6 appropriately argues against taking sentience as the 'essence' of a living being, yet goes too far in apparently seeing the degree of pain inflicted as irrelevant to assessing the evil involved in a killing.   [14] The *Guardian* newspaper, 8 July 1994.

contraceptives, alleviation of genetic abnormalities, infertility treatments, and cures for hereditary and other diseases. Yet such research involves killing many embryos, and destroying the human life of the very young to benefit others, or even, in some cases, to lead to further abortions of foetuses with newly detectable abnormalities (cf. Keown, 1995a: 119). As Stott says:

Since when has Buddha advocated the killing of one being for the benefit of another? One might as well argue that one should kill a rich man to make oneself and others happier. Such 'compassion' is, of course, not the limitless compassion without partiality that Lord Buddha teaches. (1986: 14)

Now, the Mahāyāna does envisage certain scenarios in which killing is allowable as a 'skilful means' to prevent further death (see pp. 135–8). Yet in such cases, most texts are *very* careful in delineating the special circumstances in which this is possible, and only concern the killing of someone who is himself involved in great killing. In the case of a foetus, it is an innocent bystander, so it would be inappropriate to use classical 'skilful means' arguments to justify abortion.

Possible grounds for abortion

In the various legal systems of the world, and in debate on the issue, a variety of reasons are accepted, or rejected, as grounds for a legally acceptable abortion. These can be grouped together in the focus of their concern:
(1) *a threat to the mother's physical health*:
    (a) if continuing the pregnancy will lead to the death of the mother;
    (b) if continuing the pregnancy will harm the physical health of the mother, but not cause her death;
(2) *a threat to the mother's mental health*:
    (a) arising from the fact that the pregnancy is due to rape or incest, or where a minor is pregnant;
    (b) if the pregnancy will threaten the mental health of the mother because of an existing medical condition;
(3) *problems with the foetus's health*:
    if the foetus is malformed or has a serious medical condition, such as being HIV-positive;
(4) *socio-economic factors*:
    (a) entailing a financial strain on the woman;
    (b) entailing a strain on support for existing children;

(5) *a woman's 'right to choose':*
    the woman has the 'right to choose' to have an abortion if she wishes,
    as she has a right to decide what happens to her own body;
(6) *the needs of society:*
    if the country is over-populated, abortions have their part to play in
    reducing this problem.

Some of these grounds are seen in the 1967 UK Abortion Act, which
accepts abortion on grounds of

risk to the life of the pregnant woman, or of injury to the physical or mental
health of the pregnant woman or any existing children of her family, greater
than if the pregnancy were terminated

or if

there is substantial risk that if the child were born it would suffer from such
physical or mental abnormalities as to be seriously handicapped.

What are Buddhist considerations relevant to these 'grounds', given
that it has been argued above that some abortions can be worse than
others, depending on circumstances and related intention, so that an
abortion might sometimes be seen as a very regrettable 'necessary evil'?
What if the life of the mother is threatened by the pregnancy? In classical Hinduism, causing an abortion was strongly condemned, *except*
where it was necessary to save the life of the mother (Lipner, 1991: 60),
and Keown holds that in such a situation, 'it seems certain that
Buddhism would share the view of Hindu jurists that it was morally permissible' (1995a: 193). In Sri Lanka, this is the only ground for a legal
abortion. Nyanasobhano, an American Theravādin monk,[15] in an
article strongly arguing against abortion from a Buddhist point of view,
also holds that it is acceptable on such a ground, though if it is simply to
reduce some medical risk to the mother, things are less clear cut.
Abortion in such a case would still be unwholesome to some extent, but
this would be mitigated by the circumstances, as in killing from self-
defence (1989: 26–7). A similar view is found in the Tibetan tradition,
where His Holiness Ganden Tri Rinpoche holds that, where the life of
the mother is definitely at stake, abortion is permissible, but not if there
is just some implied threat to the mother's mental health.[16] This reasoning seems apt, though ancient Theravādin texts do not envisage the possibility of abortion for medical reasons, seeing abortion as generally
carried out by a married woman who was pregnant by a lover, or a

[15] Leonard Price, ordained 1987.   [16] Lesco, 1987: 217, citing an audience in September 1985.

jealous woman wishing to prevent her co-wife from presenting their husband with an heir (McDermott, 1998: 170).

Now, one way of thinking through the relevance of possible grounds for abortion is to use what one might call the 'baby and chimpanzee test'. As I have argued above that the evil of abortion is somewhere between the evil of killing a baby and killing a chimpanzee, then:

(1) *If* there are any circumstances which would mean that killing an infant would be a 'necessary evil', then this would imply that this would be so for an abortion on parallel grounds;

(2) in circumstances which would *not* 'justify' killing an infant but *would* or *might* justify killing a chimpanzee, abortion in a parallel case *might* be seen as a 'necessary evil'.

Now, if there were constrained circumstances, perhaps in a tragic accident, where saving a woman's life meant having to do something which killed her baby, then this might, tragically, be acceptable – though the woman might altruistically choose to save her child. Thus abortion to save the life of a mother would, as a parallel, be a tragic necessity.

If a woman's illness could be cured by killing a baby for one of its organs, would this be justifiable? No. Would it be justifiable if it was a chimpanzee that was being killed (if its organs could be made genetically acceptable to a human body)?[17] If the illness was not a fatal one, surely 'no', on Buddhist grounds. If the illness might be fatal, then 'perhaps', especially if no other species was a possible donor. Thus an abortion to prevent damage to a woman's physical health would only be a 'necessary evil' if the illness might be fatal.

What of rape? In the restrictive Thai law on abortion (1956), abortions are permitted only on grounds of a threat to the mother's life or a serious threat to her physical health, or in the case of rape – which also covers cases where the woman is under thirteen, or under eighteen in the sex trade, or over eighteen if she is in the sex trade against her will (Hall, 1970: 122). On the matter of rape and abortion, the texts have nothing to say – though the fact that cases of abortion due to rape are never mentioned is itself interesting. Nyanasobhano, while acknowledging the horror of pregnancy due to rape or incest, and the bravery needed to continue with such a pregnancy, implies that this is an 'extra mile' that a woman might altruistically tread, in consideration for the innocent child within her (1989: 23–4). In a similar light, Philip Lesco says:

---

[17] Whether or not this is actually possible is not relevant: one is considering a hypothetical case so as to sharpen up one's ethical thinking.

Does her suffering justify the taking of the human life within her as the means of resolving the problem? The Buddhist would argue against this, basing the position on the high value placed upon the human rebirth. (Lesco, 1987: 216)

Shoyo Taniguchi argues against abortion on many Buddhist grounds, and she holds that to allow abortion on the grounds of rape or incest, 'where violence initiates life, is to allow another kind of violence towards another individual' (Taniguchi, 1987: 78).

What might the 'baby and chimpanzee test' suggest? If a trauma drug could be developed by injecting a baby with a substance, then extracting a product of this from the baby after it had been killed, would this be justified if it could partially alleviate a woman's trauma from being raped and made pregnant, even if the baby used was an abandoned one of the rapist's? Surely not. What if a chimpanzee were used, rather than a baby? Well, on the one hand, trauma is not a fatal condition. On the other hand, a woman pregnant from rape will continually be reminded of the rape and rapist by the pregnancy, and hatred for the foetus may ensue. The case is one of a potentially grave threat to mental health. A grave threat to mental health might lead to a kind of psychological 'death' (which itself might raise the risk of suicide), so killing a chimpanzee, or the foetus, *might* sometimes be a 'necessary evil' in such a case.

What of other cases of a threat to the mental health of a pregnant woman: could this justify killing a baby? No, surely. What of a chimpanzee? If there has been no rape, there will not be a nine-month reminder of a trauma involved. If the threat to mental health would arise after the birth of the child, the child can be adopted, so there would be no justification for killing, whether of a chimpanzee or a foetus. If, though, the woman's mental health would also be severely threatened if she gave up the child for adoption, then abortion *might* be a 'necessary evil'.

What of cases of foetuses that are somehow damaged? Lesco holds that as a 'meaningful life' for children with Down's Syndrome or spina bifida is possible, Buddhism is strongly against aborting such individuals (1987: 216). Taniguchi argues that such a person may be a very worthy one, asking the rhetorical question: 'Which is more qualified as a human, a severely handicapped person full of loving-kindness (*mettā*) or an Olympic gold medallist full of jealousy and greed?' (1987: 82). One might add that, given that Buddhism sees suffering as a part of any life, a factor in seeking to abort an impaired human being might be simply a desire only for the 'perfect' and to hide from unpleasant, but real, aspects of life.

Pinit Ratanakul reports that when Thai women are informed that they are carrying a foetus with some abnormality, it is usual to carry the baby to full term, babies with Down's syndrome rarely being aborted (1998: 58–9). He regards this as being because they see the baby's handicap as due to both its and their own bad karma – which would follow logically from Buddhist principles – and have no wish to increase their bad karma by having an abortion. Another factor is the preference for letting the bad karma of the child exhaust itself in the present, rather than allowing it to lead on to further problems for it (Ratanakul, 1998: 59). Those who go on to care for their handicapped children hope that their nurture, and other good actions, will help overcome the bad karma of both the child and themselves. Nevertheless, some women, having avoided the evil of abortion, go on to abandon their newborn babies at the hospital; 70,000 were so abandoned in the years 1992–4, with a number of these being children of HIV-positive mothers, though in some such cases the baby is aborted (Ratanakul, 1998: 59). In fact, only around 30 per cent of babies born to HIV positive mothers register in tests as infected with the virus, and this reduces to 12 per cent by the time the babies are eighteen months old, the higher figure being due to effects of the mother's, rather than the baby's, infection.[18]

Dr Somsak, vice-chairman of the Thai Medical Council, though, reports that 'in more cases than not, women who contract German measles while pregnant choose to have an abortion, to avoid giving birth to a blind baby who might also be deaf and with a defective heart'.[19] Here, one relevant consideration *might* be that, though Buddhism sees a human rebirth as a rare and precious opportunity for spiritual development, to be *fully* 'precious', one needs all one's senses, in a context supportive of spiritual growth (see p. 30). Thus, while it is still bad to abort a baby if it has defective senses, it might be seen as less bad than if this were not the case. Lesco also considers cases of foetuses with Tay-Sachs disease, for which life outside the womb will only ever be of a short duration. Given this scenario, he holds that abortion could be seen as a form of euthanasia (1987: 216). Yet Buddhist principles do not support any genuine case of euthanasia (see pp. 294–300), and seem rather to indicate allowing the birth of such babies and giving support in their limited life.

As regards the 'baby and chimpanzee test', if we ask whether it would be justified to kill a baby which was itself malformed or with a serious medical condition, the answer, on Buddhist principles, must be 'no',

[18] *Bangkok Post*, 2 May 1990 and 5 June 1994. My thanks to Louis Gabaude for all citations from this newspaper and from *The Nation*. [19] *Bangkok Post*, 5 June 1994.

though perhaps one can avoid extreme methods of keeping it alive. What of a chimpanzee in the same scenario? I would say that the same reasoning applies. So aborting a damaged foetus would not be a 'necessary evil'.

What of cases of pregnancy posing a financial burden on the mother and any existing children? Would it be justified to kill a baby to reduce the economic strain on a family? No. Would it be justified to kill a family's chimpanzee on such grounds? No, though it might need to be found a new home. So abortion on socio-economic grounds is not justified. Stott argues that it is not 'compassionate' to have an abortion carried out on such grounds, asking how it is morally permissible to kill another being because one is unhappy or poor (1986: 14–15). Likewise, Nyanasobhano says,

The fact that we are suffering now does not make us immune from future harm if we do harm to someone else. We cannot, in the long run, get out of suffering by causing more suffering. (1989: 19)

Buddhist principles entail that it is the karma of the foetus and the karma of the mother that bring them together, and it is best to accept the responsibility that this entails, rather than forcefully rupturing this link, sweeping away something that is unwanted. Moreover, killing a foetus not only harms it, but will sow the seeds for more suffering for the mother than she sought to avoid by having an abortion.

If a poor family had a newborn baby dumped on it, would it be right to kill it? We would surely say 'no': it can be passed on for adoption, provided the family does not choose to look after it. Why would the same not apply to a child from an unwanted pregnancy? Of course, giving up a baby for adoption brings its own pains, in the form of wondering, over the years, what is happening to it. Yet it would seem odd if the life of a child and the happiness of adoptive parents were outweighed by this. In any case, the child from an unwanted pregnancy may come to be accepted and loved, as everything is subject to change, and if not, adoption is still an option (Nyanasobhano, 1989: 21). Moreover, one could see giving up a child for others to adopt as a form of *dāna*, or giving, to them. It can also be noted here that Buddhist monasteries and nunneries have often looked after orphans. Against a view that says it is 'unfair' to allow a child into the world under certain circumstances, Buddhism would say: it will be born in some shape or form anyway, soon, according to its karma. So it is better to do the best one can for it in the circumstances it is already heading for.

What of the woman's 'right to choose' an abortion, based on the idea that she has a right to do what she wants with her 'own' body? Buddhism, with its emphasis that there is no Self which can be found as 'owner' of mental and physical processes, would dispute this:

This body, monks, is not yours, nor does it belong to others. It should be regarded as (the product of) former karma, effected through what has been willed and thought out. (*S.* II.64–5; cf. *Dhp.* 62)

Taniguchi thus says:

If a woman can claim the woman's right to the use of her body in the case of abortion, saying 'a fetus belongs to me, because it is in my womb, therefore, I can do whatever I want to do with it', she can also claim the right to the life of her one-day-old . . . In reality, this is not so. (Taniguchi, 1987: 78)

That is, a foetus is not just 'a part' of a pregnant woman, but another living being, 'temporarily housed in the body of another', as Keown puts it (1995a: 106), whose life must be properly considered, not just swept aside by a 'right to choose'. To do that could be to act from all three of greed, hatred and delusion, the three roots of unwholesome action:

Greed, that is passionate attachment, would lie behind a person's considering only their own interests or pleasures in the situation. It would also solidify the notion that an 'I' owned the foetus and could do with it what 'I' would. Hatred would motivate one to strike out to eliminate the perceived cause of discomfort, the foetus. Delusion might cloud one's understanding and lead to denial that the foetus is a living being. (Florida, 1991: 41–2)

If it is argued that the woman's interests should always outweigh that of her foetus, Buddhist principles would say: but because of the karmic results of abortion, it is not actually in the woman's long-term interests to have an abortion, unless the circumstances prompting it are extreme. As Nyanasobhano says, 'A woman might convince herself that an abortion is justified in her case, but she cannot convince the law of kamma (karma)' (in NIBWA, 1988: 9). Apart from any longer-term karmic results, the woman may, as a result of the abortion, be harmed through haemorrhaging, sterility or infection, or the guilt, self-accusation or depression which may develop. To return to the 'baby and chimpanzee test': would it be justified for a woman simply to choose to kill a baby or chimpanzee, because of her difficult circumstances? No, surely. So, again, the 'right to choose' does not justify an abortion.

As regards using abortion as a means of reducing a country's over-population, this seems a drastic measure when compared to using contraception. In Communist China, the 'one child policy' means that

women are sometimes given abortions against their will. This combines
murder of the foetus with assault on the mother, and is surely a barbaric
practice. To use the 'baby and chimpanzee test': would it be right for a
woman to kill a baby so as to help reduce a country's over-population?
No. Would it be justified for her to kill a chimpanzee if the chimpanzee
population were seen as too high? No. Even though elephants are sometimes culled/killed on such grounds, population, at least in the case of
humans, can be controlled by contraception (though this needs to be
made easily available). So population control does not justify abortion.

Thus, on Buddhist ethical principles, abortion could be seen as a 'necessary evil', in the cases of:
(1) a real threat to the life of the mother;
(2) a possible threat to the life of the mother;
(3) rape causing great trauma,
(4) the alternative being a mentally ill woman further traumatized by
    having to give up her child for adoption.
Cases (2)–(4) would need careful medical/psychological assessment. The
woman would have the right to choose against medical advice *not* to have
an abortion, but not to choose to have an abortion where the medical
grounds were insufficient. In cases of psychological assessment, of
course, she would herself be involved in ascertaining the grounds. The
later the abortion, the worse it would be, though ground (1) above might
entail a late abortion.

CONTRACEPTION

If Buddhist principles counsel strongly against abortion, what is
Buddhism's attitude to contraception? Ling found that in both Thailand
and Sri Lanka, Buddhists felt that a population increase which was out
of proportion to availability of food would lead to poverty and crime
(1969: 54). In Thailand, for example, contraception has been widely
taken up. In Bangkok, there is a restaurant called Cabbages and
Condoms which helps fund family-planning activities, and family-
planning education has included blowing up coloured condoms on the
*klong*s (canals) of Bangkok. A 1968 study found 71 per cent of married
women of child-bearing age in favour of contraception (cited in Ling,
1969: 57). Stott also cites the Tibetan Lama Khenchen Thranggu
Rinpoche as saying 'I see no great fault in preventing conception' (Stott,
1992: 174).

In fact, Buddhism does not say that people should 'go forth and multiply', just as it does not see marriage as a religious rite. Yet given the nature of human drives, it is expected that, however much Buddhism holds up a celibate, monastic ideal, there will be no shortage of people who wish to marry and have children. Given that contraception prevents a human life rather than destroys it, as does abortion, Buddhist objections to contraception are limited.

Nevertheless, some forms of 'contraception' in fact work by (1) preventing the implantation of a fertilized ovum, rather than (2) preventing ovulation or fertilization. They are thus agents of an early abortion. In the first category, the 'morning after' pill is an obvious abortifacient, but the Intra-uterine Device (IUD) or coil also acts mainly by impeding implantation. Most 'pills' combine a low dose of oestrogen, which *may* prevent fertilization, but also contain progestogen, which prevents any fertilized ovum from implanting. In the second category come the high-dose oestrogen 'pill', the condom, the diaphragm, the rhythm method, sterilization, vasectomy and the male pill, if it is developed (Stott, 1986: 18; Keown, 1995a: 122–3). Stott therefore sees methods of the first group as objectionable on Buddhist grounds.

The extent to which Buddhists actually worry about 'contraceptives' which cause early abortions varies. W. F. Wong reports that the informed Buddhist view in Sri Lanka is that the IUD and the 'morning after pill' are unacceptable on these grounds.[20] Yet Ling reports that, when Buddhist medical research workers in Thailand were acquainted with the fact that the IUD/coil might cause the early destruction of a fertilized ovum, they did not think that its use should be discontinued (1969: 58). In fact, a 1965 study in Thailand found the IUD (Lippes-loop) to be the most popular contraceptive (77 per cent), followed by some form of the pill (13 per cent) and condom (9 per cent).[21] By 1967, though, twice as many women were using the pill as were using the IUD (Ling, 1969: 57). It thus seems that as birth-control methods have become more widespread there, a preference for the pill over the IUD has developed. Nevertheless, the IUD is still widely used. This is surprising, but is perhaps based on health concerns about the pill, concern that condoms *can* be unreliable, and the thought that a very early abortion is preferable to a later one. On the other hand, it might be based on a

---

[20] 'Re: Contraception, Abortion and Buddhism' posting on 'Buddha-L' Internet forum, 8 November 1995, citing 'a group discussion with a Professor of Buddhism from Sri Lanka'.

[21] Planning Committee for the International Conference on Family Planning Programs, Geneva, August 1965, *Family Planning and Population Programs* (Chicago and London: University of Chicago Press, 1966), p. 98.

line of reasoning which says: many fertilized ova do not implant anyway; certain medical conditions can make this more likely; using the IUD is akin to deliberately setting up such a medical condition. Yet the problem remains that, as an intentional human act, this should not be free from ethical assessment.

Only occasionally do Buddhists express concern over contraception proper, but on not very strong grounds (Ling, 1969, 1980b):

(a) it encourages promiscuity: but it is surely preferable to abortion;
(b) it allows the proportion of non-Buddhist ethnic groups in a country to rise, as with the Tamils in Sri Lanka (cf. pp. 258–60): but this is a judgement based on little evidence, made in a conflict-charged atmosphere;
(c) it prevents more beings from attaining a human rebirth: but if over-population is the result, the conditions for existing humans to develop spiritually would be reduced; in any case, the human population is still rising.

ABORTION IN BUDDHIST CULTURES

Among Tibetans

Tibetan Buddhism has preserved the Indian Buddhist view that abortion is the taking of a human life and is thus wrong. Philip Denwood says on it:

nowadays all peoples from Tibetan-speaking areas regard it with horror as the killing of a living being which has done no wrong. It is hard to see what incentive there would have been for it – there was no pressure of population and I doubt if it was known as a technique for saving the mother's life.[22]

David Stott reports that, from anecdotal evidence from lay people and religious authorities among Tibetan refugees in Nepal and India, abortion is not practised 'to any extent' in the community, despite its being legal in India (Stott, 1992: 177). Stott also affirms that, without exception, the various Tibetan authorities he asked held that abortion was 'unvirtuous' or 'expressly forbidden' (1992: 174, 180). In 1978 Lama Lodo, when in San Francisco, said the following to someone who reported that a friend was considering an abortion:

The best thing for you to do would be to try to talk her out of the abortion because it is an act of profound negative consequences to kill a human being.

---

[22] Personal communication, 19 July 1983.

A human being's body is so precious that it would be better if you talk her into having the baby and then putting it up for adoption.[23]

Around 1985 in the USA, Dharmadhatu, the organisation of the influential Tibetan Lama Chogyam Trungpa, planned to start a Buddhist adoption agency, and formed a Family Services Council to encourage women to consider alternatives to abortion, such as adoption (Spring Wind, 1986: 172).

Nevertheless, spiritual help for those who have had an abortion is seen as appropriate by Tibetan Buddhists. Stott holds that one should be compassionate to them, as they will eventually suffer pain and anguish: 'we must cherish both those who commit the sin of abortion and their unborn victims, as we cherish ourselves' (1986: 15). He goes on to advocate a method of self-purification for those who have had an abortion, using the power of sincere confession (cf. pp. 27–8; Stott, 1986: 15). Such a purification would not work, however, if one had previously *planned* to have an abortion and then to purify oneself; for the regret and resolution never to have an abortion again, which are part of it, would be insincere (1986: 15). Ven. Sangye Khadro, an American nun ordained in the Tibetan tradition, has likewise suggested such a method as a way to heal the pain and guilt after an abortion (NIBWA, 1988: 13–14), and Sogyal Rinpoche recommends such actions along with dedicating the karmic fruitfulness of good deeds to the baby's future enlightenment (Sogyal, 1992: 376).

Lands of Southern Buddhism

In Sri Lanka, where abortion is only legal if the mother's life is at risk, Ling found a more frequently expressed objection to abortion, and a less unanimous acceptance of contraception, than in Thailand (1969: 57–8). For example, the Sarvōdaya Śramadāna rural development movement is radically opposed to abortion (Macy, 1983: 86). Nevertheless, there are some moves towards 'liberalizing' the law to allow it on the grounds of a threat to the woman's physical and mental health.[24] The law does not seem to have been changed, though. In Burma, Jane and Manning Nash claim that children are rarely born out of wedlock 'because either a pregnancy means a marriage, or abortion is a common resort' (1963:

---

[23] Lama Lodo, *Bardo Teachings* (Ithaca, N.Y.: Snow Lion Publications, 1987), p. 41, as quoted in Keown, 1995a: 103.
[24] R. J. Cook and B. M. Dickens, *Abortion Law in Commonwealth Countries* (Geneva: World Health Organisation, 1979), p. 75, 86.

252). Abortion, performed by midwives pressing the foetus till it dies, 'is frequently practised as preferable to a forced marriage of young people' (p. 265), given that marriage is seen to involve a loss of autonomy for both partners. Beyond this, little other information is available on abortion in what is otherwise a strongly Buddhist country. It is worth noting the remark of Melford Spiro, though, who says that the 'distinction between what is good from the ultimate perspective of religion (*lokuttara*), and what is necessary from the relative perspective of worldly existence (*loki*), permeates . . . Burmese attitudes' (1971: 450).

In Thailand, if an unmarried woman becomes pregnant, this is not welcomed, though most often the child is born and accepted into the family, or the woman is married to the father, if he is agreeable (Hanks and Hanks, 1963: 442). Trevor Ling reports a 1968 study of 960 women of child-bearing age in which 91.8 per cent were in favour of abortion if it was needed to save the life of the mother, 95.6 per cent against it simply as a means of limiting family size, and 12.7 per cent in favour of it for unmarried women (1969: 57–8). The existing 1956 Thai law on abortion is rather restrictive (see p. 321), yet it is ill enforced, and there have come to be many illegal abortions. A 1981 estimate for Thailand gives around 300,000 abortions per year, whether legal or illegal, in a population of around 50 million, i.e. around 6 per 1,000 population. As Keown points out, this means that abortions in Thailand were 'running at some 50 per cent higher than the number in the USA for the equivalent number of citizens' (Keown, 1998: 4). The rate was also about double that for England and Wales, which had around the same population as Thailand then.[25]

Comparative abortion rates are given using various scales: per 1,000 population; per 1,000 women of child-bearing age; and as a ratio to 1,000 live births. In 1981, abortions in Thailand amounted to 37 abortions per 1,000 women of child-bearing age (Florida, 1998: 23). In the same period, figures for some other countries were: Canada 11.1; USA 24.2; Hungary 35.3; Singapore 44.5; Japan 22.6 officially, but probably between 65 and 90; USSR 181 (Florida, 1998: 23). If we look at the Thai abortion rate per 1,000 live births, a different picture emerges, though. In 1981, abortions ended 10 per cent of pregnancies in Thailand (Florida, 1998: 23), which if we guess that 10 per cent of pregnancies ended in miscarriage, means a rate of around 125 abortions per 1,000

[25] Based on the fact that there were 102,677 legal abortions in England and Wales in 1977 (the law was radically changed in 1967), climbing to 170,463 by 1989 (from *The Observer* newspaper, 5 January 1997).

live births, while in the USA, in 1976, there were 312 abortions per 1,000 live births.[26] This suggests that, while the crude abortion rate per 1,000 population is higher in Thailand than in America, this is because, while Thai women are less likely to terminate a pregnancy than American women, they have a higher rate of pregnancy. This suggests that if Thai women's relative reluctance to terminate a pregnancy remains, while their use of contraception increases, the abortion rate per 1,000 population will fall. We see, in fact, that the 1994 Thai figure was considerably lower, for the Thai Medical Council reported that there were around 100,000 abortions in Thailand then,[27] compared to 174,000 that year in England and Wales.[28]

A 1993 study of abortions in 200 Thai hospitals showed that only 8 per cent of the 2,351 abortions were legal, and that in 65 per cent of cases, they were done by traditional birth attendants, not doctors.[29] In urban centres, a high proportion of those having abortions are young and single, reflecting the heavy social stigma attached to being an unmarried mother, but prostitutes have a low abortion rate (Odzer, 1998) and, overall, most abortions are had by married rural women (Florida, 1998: 23–4).

In 1981, the Thai Parliament debated a bill to 'liberalize' the existing abortion law, motivated by the desire to avoid health risks from illegally performed abortions, to allow abortion (up to twelve weeks) on grounds of:

(1) danger to the mother's mental health;
(2) expected physical deformity or mental retardation of the child;
(3) social or financial reasons;
(4) failure of a prescribed contraception (WFBR, 1981: 24).

Those who opposed the bill – who included Buddhists, Roman Catholics and Muslims – held that it would lead to abortion on demand. In September 1981, the bill was passed by the lower house (79 for, 3 against, with 219 abstentions), pending consideration by the upper house. In December, however, this rejected the bill by 141 to 1, in response to strong campaigning by various religious groups and individuals (WFBR, 1981: 52). The lower house chose not to raise the issue again in the Parliamentary agenda.[30]

As of 1981, no medical practitioner had been prosecuted under the existing law (Florida, 1998: 24), though this changed in 1994, when

---

[26] *The Observer* newspaper, 5 January 1997.   [27] *Bangkok Post*, 9 January 1992.
[28] *The Observer* newspaper, 5 January 1997.   [29] *Bangkok Post*, 30 June 1994.
[30] *Bangkok Post*, 30 February 1982.

several clinics were raided after aborted foetuses were found dumped by a roadside. At the same time, the government sought to improve sex education, and improve facilities for caring for babies of women who could not look after them.[31] At the time, there was much debate in Thai newspapers on abortion. Ratanakul thus affirms that the high rate of illegal abortions is becoming a matter of urgent concern to Buddhists (1998: 53). He holds that:

Thai Buddhists do not condemn those women whose life situations make the decision to abort seem unavoidable. There is a concern for the dilemmas women face with unwanted pregnancies, the results of poverty, immaturity, contraceptive failure or severely defective fetuses and maternal health threats, yet there is a refusal to isolate abortion simply as a matter of a woman's reproductive choice. (1998: 63)

For Thais, abortion is discussed not in the language of rights – to life or choice – but of 'benefit and harm, with the intent of relieving as much human suffering in all its states, stages and situations as circumstances allow', with an emphasis on reducing the circumstances leading women to feel that they need to have an abortion (Ratanakul, 1998: 64–5).

After an abortion, Thai women tend to be full of remorse and sorrow, and try to ease their psychological pain, and aid the dead foetus, by doing actions generating karmic fruitfulness, and sharing this with their short-lived child (Ratanakul, 1998: 57). There are no specialist rituals for doing this, as in Japan (see below), as this would be seen as drawing attention to the abortion and perhaps partially validating it (Florida, 1998: 25–6), but general rituals such as feeding monks, releasing captured birds, or making donations to temples or charities are used. Given that Buddhism does not encourage brooding guilt, it is useful that such actions ease the minds of the women to some extent.

Lands of Eastern Buddhism, especially Japan

In the People's Republic of China, abortion law is controlled by the Communists, whose 'one child policy', to ease population pressures, means that abortions are sometimes compulsory and unwanted. In Japan, there is a very liberal abortion law, and there has been much discussion on how Japanese Buddhists relate to abortion, notably Robert LaFleur's *Liquid Life: Abortion and Buddhism in Japan* (1992).[32] In Japan, ethics is derived from Confucianism, Buddhism, Shintō and, now, secular influences. Confucianism has traditionally attached much

---

[31] *The Nation* Thai newspaper, 27, 28 and 31 May 1994.   [32] See Tanabe, 1994 for a critical review.

importance to the family and correct social relationships, Shintō has been concerned with nature, ritual purity and strengthening the nation. Classical Buddhist ethics is thus only one of the factors affecting the moral outlook of Japanese Buddhists.

After Japan's defeat in the Second World War, a baby-boom developed as soldiers returned to their families, so that there was a fear of over-population at a time of great economic hardship. Many babies were unwanted, so that there was a sudden rise in abortion and infanticide (LaFleur, 1992: 135). Concern over the population rise, backed by doctors' concern over the dangers of illegal abortions, led to the passing of the 1948 'Eugenic Protection Law' (Hall, 1970: 261). Supported by all political parties, this allowed abortion in the first five months[33] on various grounds, including the 'health of the mother', which could be interpreted as mental health (LaFleur, 1992: 135). A 1949 law went on to allow abortion on economic grounds (Hall, 1970: 261), and a 1952 amendment then allowed doctors complete discretion in the matter, without a need to justify their decision to any government authority (LaFleur, 1992: 135). Abortion thus became easily and cheaply available in the most permissive abortion system in the world (van der Tak, 1974: 30). Abortion became the preferred means of birth control, and abortion on demand, though technically illegal, was available.

Reported abortion numbers climbed from 246,104 in 1949 to a peak of 1,170,143 in 1955 (Hall, 1970: 262), though under-reporting, due to private doctors wishing to avoid tax, meant that this represented a real figure of between 1,755,000 and 4,330,000 (van der Tak, 1974: 31), i.e.:

(1) a 1955 rate of 13.1 (real 20 up to 48) per 1,000 population (van der Tak, 1974: 31), compared to 6 per 1,000 for Thailand in 1981;

(2) 676 (Hall, 1970: 262), or perhaps 2,000 (van der Tak, 1974: 31), per 1,000 live births in 1959), compared to around 125 in Thailand in 1981, and 312 in the USA in 1976.[34]

Thus perhaps two-thirds of healthy foetuses were being aborted in Japan in 1959! Bardwell Smith, writing in 1988, gave a conservative estimate of 1 million abortions a year in Japan: about three times the rate for the UK and a third higher than the USA rate at the time (1992: 70). Japanese women had often had two abortions by the time they were 40, this being most likely prior to marriage or once two children had been born (1992: 71).

Yoshio Koya points out that, in 1954, only 27 per cent of women who

---

[33] The *Guardian* newspaper, 27 January 1996.   [34] *The Observer* newspaper, 5 January 1997.

had had abortions had practised contraception (1954: 288), though abortions started to decline after 1960 as contraceptive use increased (van der Tak, 1974: 31). By 1971, 53 per cent of women reported current contraceptive use, of whom 73 per cent used condoms and 33 per cent the rhythm method, with the pill and IUD practically unavailable because of medical opposition on the grounds of their side-effects (van der Tak, 1974: 33–4),[35] or perhaps doctors' fears over losing income from performing abortions (LaFleur, 1992: 136). Moreover, naivety about contraceptive methods is not dealt with in schools on account of reluctance to discuss sexual matters (on which Confucianism has, traditionally, been very coy), so ignorance in this area persists (Smith, 1992: 71). Women are reluctant to use a diaphragm, as it would probably be fitted by a male gynaecologist (Smith, 1992: 70).

LaFleur argues that a factor in Japan's high abortion rate is the way in which Japanese people have come to think of foetuses, drawing on popular ideas of 'returning' them, which had already crystallized in the Tokugawa era (1603–1867). LaFleur holds that 'many Japanese, especially in modern times, prefer to be somewhat imprecise about the "preexistence" of the fetus or newborn', but they have a 'vague sense' of it as coming from some sort of previous life (1992: 26). The idea of 'return' fits in with this preferred imprecise view, and implies a period of waiting to come into this world later, perhaps in the same family (p. 26). 'In that sense the aborted fetus is not so much being "terminated" as it is being put on "hold", asked to bide its time in some other world' (LaFleur, 1992: 27). Such a view is, of course, in great tension with classical Buddhist ideas of the rarity and preciousness of human rebirth. Likewise, popular views of the status of the foetus are potentially at odds with classical Buddhist views on this. A key term, here, is *mizuko*, 'water-child' or 'water-children', which is used to refer to a miscarried or aborted foetus, though it originally also applied to a stillborn child or one who died soon after birth (Hoshino and Takeda, 1987: 308; LaFleur, 1992: 16, 23). The term suggests a being whose 'status is still in flux' – its viability in this world still being in question (LaFleur, 1992: 29): as a *mizuko*'s form has not yet 'solidified' in the world, it is seen as acceptable to 'return' it to a formless state (p. 24). Traditionally, parents might hope for a return of the child after a temporary repose in a kind of *mizuko* limbo, or perform rituals to aid the *mizuko* to a better world among the ancestors and *kami*, or in a Pure Land among

---

[35] The government finally allowed the sale of oral contraceptives in 1999 (the *Guardian* newspaper, 3 June 1999).

Buddhas (p. 27). The idea of a *mizuko* as a being-in-flux need not jar with classical Buddhist notions, if it simply reflects the idea of impermanence and the special perils facing a foetus or young baby. Yet to the extent that the idea allows a deliberate 'return' of a foetus, it is in great tension with classical Buddhist ideas. Accordingly, Keown comments that 'No doubt the *mizuko* concept has more significance than Western folk-tales about child-bearing – such as that babies are brought by a stork – but perhaps not *that* much more' (1998: 207).

We find, in fact, that while Japanese women have frequent recourse to abortion, a significant number of them go on to experience emotional problems, sometimes years later (Smith, 1992: 68). This is partly exacerbated by the decline of the traditional family in urban Japan, so that the individual must increasingly deal with such matters without wider support.[36] Even women who have no initial regret at an abortion later feel sadness, a need to mourn, and perhaps guilt (Smith, 1992: 72). Since around 1975, Buddhist priests have popularized rituals to help deal with these feelings, and people have increasingly sought these to 'assuage the guilt or alleviate the distress they are feeling about abortion' (LaFleur, 1992: 4).

The rites are known as *mizuko kuyō*: a memorial service (*kuyō*) for a *mizuko*. These seek to nourish and aid the spirit of the aborted foetus or stillborn child, and thus console the mother and perhaps also the father (Smith, 1992: 73). Elizabeth Harrison describes such rites as intended

to appeal to an appropriate deity to provide for the well-being of the dead, to transfer merit to the karmic account of the dead child so that he or she may proceed more quickly to a felicitous rebirth, and to appease the dead so that they might become a benevolent influence in the lives of their living family. (1998: 93)

The rite may be performed once, monthly, or on the anniversary of the death, individually or, more commonly, as part of a rite for many *mizuko* (Smith, 1992: 73). Increasingly, the rites are moving inside the temples, with priests officiating to a congregation of 'parents' (LaFleur, 1992: 149). Forms of the rites vary, but they include the chanting of *Sūtra*s on the perfection of wisdom and to the compassionate *Bodhisattva* Kannon, and songs of praise to the *Bodhisattva* Jizō. A mortuary tablet is also inscribed and placed in a shrine at the temple or at home. Other features are sermons and counselling.[37]

---

[36] Smith, 1992: 67; cf. Hoshino and Takeda, 1987: 315.
[37] Smith, 1992: 74; for further details, see Brooks, 1981: 123–5.

Jizō (Skt Kṣitigarbha) is seen as a *Bodhisattva* who has vowed to help humankind until the next Buddha, Maitreya, teaches on earth. He is seen as a guardian of travellers, of those in trouble, and women and children. He is particularly seen, in Japan, as looking after dead children, especially those who have died young (LaFleur, 1992: 45), who in medieval Japan came to be seen as languishing in a kind of limbo state for a period of time (LaFleur, 1992: 58, 63–4; Brooks, 1981: 123). Offerings are made to the Buddha on behalf of the child and an image of Jizō or of an infant is bought and placed in a special part of the temple grounds; coloured bibs will be attached to the image on the anniversary of the death (Pye, 1983: 27). LaFleur points out that, as Jizō is shown as a shaven-headed monk, he looks childlike, so that his statue is explicitly seen to represent both the aborted foetus and its *Bodhisattva*-protector (LaFleur, 1992: 8, 53). Families come to wash the statues and to offer flowers, and also toys, as a way of communicating with the dead child (pp. 9–10). The statues may also be dressed in raincoats, baseball jackets or knitted shawls (Brooks, 1981: 125).

For some temples, fees for *mizuko kuyō* rituals have become a useful means of support as other income reduces. While some temples offer such rituals with reluctance, others see them as performing a useful function, both for the bereaved and for the temples themselves (Smith, 1992: 68). For the Hase-dera temple in Kamakura, such rites have come to be its major activity: by 1983 its cemetery had around 50,000 Jizō statues for *mizuko* (LaFleur, 1992: 3–4). Some 'temples' – really just cemeteries or memorial parks – have also opened which perform only *mizuko kuyō* rites, almost entirely for aborted foetuses (pp. 5–6). These operate in a somewhat commercial way, selling Jizō statues which, perhaps two feet high, are arrayed in rows, and one can even pay for the rite to be performed on one's behalf (p. 149).

Mizuko kuyō rites seek to deal with guilt by apologizing to the dead foetus. Sometimes at temples to memorialize *mizuko*s, people place brief letters of apology (on wooden pallets) to their *mizuko*. As, in Japan, apology is much used to restore relationships, and apology and thanks shade into each other, so the attitude to *mizuko* can be seen as a mix of apology and thanks for vacating its place in the womb (LaFleur, 1992: 147). Letters written to the dead foetus as part of the rite say, for example, 'My baby, I am sorry. You came just too early for us', or 'Please forgive your foolish father . . .' (Brooks, 1981: 122–3). Some feel that the practice is only a start towards making up for what they have done (Harrison, 1998: 114). Yet some women now just perform the rite as it has become

Plate 8. A Japanese cemetery, with statues of the *Bodhisattva* Jizō dedicated to aborted or stillborn babies.

the 'done thing' (p. 112), and while a large number of women who have had abortions participate in *mizuko kuyō* rites, they are still a minority (Harrison, 1998: 112).

Along with offering apology and assuaging guilt, another reason for the popularity of *mizuko kuyō* is to deal with fear. From Shintō comes the idea that the neglected dead can feel *urami*, bitterness or malice (Brooks, 1981: 135), so as to be dangerous and want to wreak revenge, *tatari*, on the living (LaFleur, 1992: 54). Combined with Buddhist ideas about the karmic results of abortion, this means that women often see an earlier abortion as the cause of later repeated illness, financial troubles, or family tensions (Smith, 1992: 78). *Mizuko kuyō* rites are seen to transform the child from a potentially threatening unsettled spirit into a benign protector, with a place among the family ancestors – a concern coming from Chinese Confucianism (Smith, 1992: 82). Anne Brooks cites a Dr Suzuki as saying that only 10 per cent of those practising *mizuko kuyō* did so from fear, but she felt that this was too low an estimate (1981: 136).

From the mid 1970s, advertising of *mizuko kuyō* rites has helped arouse criticism, in the media and elsewhere, of temples indulging in crass commercialism which exploits the fears of women (LaFleur, 1992: 138; Harrison, 1998: 97), as well as heightening guilt feelings (LaFleur, 1992: 162). At the Purple Cloud temple in Chichibu city, which specializes in the rite, Jizō statues cost £1,125, with an annual upkeep charge of £31.[38] Brooks cites an advertisement which, after referring to the diseases and other problems caused by the spirits of aborted foetuses, had an order form for Jizō statues, priced from $8 to $700 (1981: 140). In questioning forty-three professional men such as professors and journalists, LaFleur found support only for simple, inexpensive rites for the foetus, with no opposition to the existing abortion law (1992: 164–6).

Mainline temples only started doing the rites in the mid 1970s, when parishioners asked; for otherwise they would have gone to new entrepreneurial temples. Yet they are sensitive to the above criticisms. The Jōdo and Jōdo-shin Pure Land denominations have been extremely reluctant to perform the rites, being particularly critical of the notion of the foetus seeking revenge, which they see as in tension with Buddhist ideas (LaFleur, 1992: 163–4); indeed, a major Jōdo-shin sub-sect put up roadside messages condemning *mizuko kuyō* (Harrison, 1998: 98). Likewise Ochiai Seiko, a newspaper correspondent and wife of a Jōdo-shin priest, regards *mizuko kuyō* as un-Buddhist, being more like an exorcism to ward

---

[38] The *Independent on Sunday* newspaper, 12 September 1993.

off foetal reprisal. Yet she opposed any suggestion of reforming the abortion law as right-wing illiberalism. She felt that life, including that of foetuses, animals and rice, should be respected, but that the process of living entailed that 'it is necessary for us to go on "taking" the lives of various kinds of such beings' (LaFleur, 1992: 170).

On the other hand, Domyo Miura, a leading priest of the tantric Shingon school, and first chairman of the Japan Buddhist Society, promotes the *mizuko kuyō* rite but does not see it as mitigating the seriousness of abortion itself:

even before a child comes into the world, Buddhists regard it as a life from the very instant when consciousness is born . . . Out of billions of sperms one unites with one ovum, life starts. (quoted in Keown, 1995a: 110)

For him, the concept of a foetus as a 'water-child' does not justify abortion (Keown, 1998: 207–8). Likewise, the Purple Cloud *mizuko kuyō* temple, discussed above, sees abortion as wilful and unnatural (LaFleur, 1992: 171), with serious karmic effects (p. 223), and wants the abortion laws tightened up (p. 169).

Japanese Buddhist organizations, though, do not generally go in for stating public 'positions' on social issues (LaFleur, 1992: xiii). LaFleur holds that most mainline Buddhist denominations seem to support legalized abortion (1992: 192): they 'tolerate, and make moral space for, abortion' (p. 195). He cites a 1995 review of his book by Noriko Kawahashi,[39] in which she says that she discussed the review with some Sōtō Zen monks. These differed in their opinions. One said it was a 'sin' (*tsumi*) for a woman to take the decision about abortion into her own hands, while an older monk felt that LaFleur had got it about right in suggesting that the tradition allows Buddhists to think of abortion in terms of suffering rather than 'sin' (LaFleur, 1995: 194).

In 1978, the Japanese Buddhist Federation pointed out that, while Buddhists have not, in general, voiced any criticism of abortion (p. 137), the *Abhidharma-kośa* states that 'life is there from the moment of conception and should not be disturbed for it has the right to live'.[40] Yet it said too that, while Mahāyāna Buddhism advocates respect for life, it also 'teaches that it is inevitable for man to sacrifice some forms of life in order to protect and nourish himself':[41] farmers have to kill pests, for instance. It went on to say that 'one should accept reality with all of its

---

[39] *Cross Currents*, 13 (1995) 371–8.
[40] Japan Buddhist Federation, *Understanding Japanese Buddhism* (Tokyo: Kyodo Obun Center Co., 1978), p. 162, cited in Brooks, 1981: 133.   [41] P. 158–9, cited in Brooks, 1981: 137.

contradictory demands as one's *karma*. At the same time, however, one should continue to reflect on the universal principle and strive for the ideal.'[42] Brooks sees the *mizuko kuyō* rite as a way of mediating between practicality and the ideal, in a way which is characteristic of Japanese Buddhism, which emphasizes state of mind and attitude rather than the morality of overt behaviour (1981: 138).

Indeed, LaFleur sees the apologies which are part of *mizuko kuyō* as helping people to 'retain their sense of their own humanity', so that they can see themselves as caring and sensitive (1992: 155). Thus the *mizuko kuyō* rites

make it possible for many Japanese to tolerate the practice of abortion and still think of themselves as moral and even 'sensitive' – both individually and collectively . . . That is, through this ritual their moral options are not limited to either categorically forbidding abortion or, at the exact opposite pole, treating the fetus as so much inert matter to be disposed of guiltlessly. (LaFleur, 1992: 58)

The language of the ritual clearly does not treat the foetus as a thing, and 'parents' show their 'softness' by offering such things as pinwheels and other toys, as well as sweaters to keep the Jizō statues 'warm' (pp. 158–9). LaFleur points out that Japanese people do not usually use euphemisms for a foetus such as 'foetal tissue': they acknowledge that it is a child, even when planning to abort it. So the clash with the first precept is not hidden by such wording (LaFleur, 1992: 11). Using the *mizuko kuyō* rite, 'a woman is free to acknowledge any feelings of bonding that have developed within herself. Such feelings need not bar her from deciding to have an abortion' (LaFleur, 1992: 213). These may be partly why Buddhists in Korea (Tedesco, 1998) and Taiwan, where generally relaxed attitudes to abortion are also found, are starting to adapt the Japanese practice of *mizuko kuyō*.

Reflecting on the Japanese situation on abortion, what is one to make of the gap between theory and practice, which is also seen, to a lesser extent, in Theravāda Thailand? This might look like, but is not, hypocrisy, which is acting in a way that is the opposite of what you *tell others* to do. Here, though, the point is that, in admitting that abortion is wrong, a right view of things is held to, and this is itself a form of wholesome action: wholesome mental action (see p. 57). To have an abortion is clearly unwholesome physical action, and may also entail unwholesome verbal action, but it is less bad than having the abortion and denying that it is an unwholesome action, as this would then involve wrong view, a

---

[42] P. 166, cited in Brooks, 1981: 138.

form of wrong mental action (see p. 48). While this reading of the situation is rational in terms of Buddhist principles, it should be noted that the approach it outlines has a different emphasis from that in Indian-based *Vinaya* (monastic discipline). Here the emphasis – for those who choose to become monks or nuns – is on overt physical and verbal behaviour that is in line with agreed norms. While this is clearly part of a way of life intended to train the mind, the monastic code does not concern itself with views or beliefs,[43] even if expressed verbally. Yet both approaches, here, share in accepting that one's views must be genuinely held, and cannot be compelled, and the *Vinaya* does not denigrate the importance of right view: it is just that, as a kind of legal code, it does not focus on it.

Mizuko kuyō, then, is a good practice inasmuch as it accepts that abortion is wrong (as well as seeking to help the dead foetus), yet this element must be preserved if the ritual is to have any real Buddhist worth. The rite may also be beneficial in helping those who have had an abortion 'to come to terms with any unfinished business the experience leaves in its wake' (Keown, 1998: 213). Yet to expect the rite to wipe the karmic slate completely clean, rather than to weaken the bad karmic effects, would be to expect too much of ritual. For a person to plan to perform it, as a ritual 'fix' after having had the abortion that it will 'apologize' for, would be to undermine the sincerity of the apology and regret. Anne Brooks reports that among those who conduct *mizuko kuyō* rites, some sincerely teach devotees Buddhist ethical teachings, while some just offer a ritual route to averting problems and gaining peace of mind (1981: 138–40). As a way to deal with guilt over an abortion, the rite needs to be handled carefully. It is good to recognize a past unwholesome action as unwholesome, yet if this is done to the extent of stimulating heavy guilt and self-hatred, this would be to stimulate agitated 'restlessness and unease', one of the hindrances to spiritual development (see p. 61). The important thing is remorse for a past wrong and a determination not to repeat it. As for people who stimulate reflection on a past abortion making money from those who then decide to have a *mizuko kuyō*, this is questionable: if people *wish* to make a donation or *want* to buy a Jizō statue, that is perhaps acceptable, but it should be up to them, and this should be made clear. Brooks in fact feels that the practice of families erecting individual Jizō statues tends to foster commercialization (1981: 141).

---

[43] With one exception: the view that there is nothing wrong with sensual desire: see p. 55 n. 27 above.

ANTI-ABORTION BUT PRO-CHOICE? THE RELATIONSHIP BETWEEN MORALITY AND LAW

To point out the position of Buddhist ethics on abortion is not the same thing as saying that those who agree with these principles should seek to ensure that the law of their countries completely enforces such ethical principles. In Buddhist countries, while there have been and are certain legal restrictions on the killing of animals, which clearly breaks the first precept, these are limited. Butchers are not sent to prison. Likewise, though selling alcohol offends against the principle of 'right livelihood', doing so is not banned in any Buddhist country. Again, attempted suicide is generally not illegal. This is because the relationship between morality and law is not a straightforward one-to-one match.

In most countries, Buddhist or otherwise, there are actions seen as unethical, such as various forms of lying, which are not illegal. There may also be certain legal offences which many people see as ethically neutral, and some may be seen as morally praiseworthy, such as illegal demonstrations against oppressive regimes. The extent to which a country encodes the ethics of its people in law is a matter for debate, and this involves a consideration of the function of law, i.e. social norms backed up by punishment by the state if they are infringed.

Philip Lesco holds that Buddhism is both 'pro-life' and against 'attempts to legislate individual morality' (Lesco, 1987: 217), and the female Western Zen teacher Rōshi Jiyu Kennett says:

I personally would never have an abortion, and I will *never* agree to legislation that abolishes abortion whilst *never* ceasing to try to dissuade other women from having abortions. To legislate against abortion would leave too many women in danger of death. If suicide did not get them, the quacks would. (1978: 17)

A character called Sunyata, in the *Newsletter on International Buddhist Women's Activities*, after arguing strongly against abortion on Buddhist grounds, goes on to say that it should not be made illegal:

Ethics cannot be imposed on others; morality has little meaning unless there is a choice involved. The purpose of ethics is to avoid killing and suffering, so there is no benefit in women dying at the hands of backyard abortionists if abortion was made illegal and doctors had to turn them away. (NIBWA, 1988: 12)

Helen Tworkov argues for a 'pro-choice/anti-abortion position' (1992: 62). She quotes a female American Zen priest as saying both that the idea of abortion 'makes me sick' and that she would still vote 'pro-choice' on the issue. Tworkov goes on:

In the past year, the American Buddhist women I spoke with (from all different lineages) agreed that abortion may sometimes be necessary but is never desirable, and should never be performed without the deepest consideration of all aspects of the situation. This came from women who said that they themselves would, under no circumstances, ever have an abortion, from women who could imagine circumstances under which they would consider abortion, and from women, like myself, who had experienced an abortion. All of us are currently committed to a pro-choice ballot. (1992: 63)

She says that after her own abortion, in 1960, she denied that a life had been taken, but in time, partly through becoming a Buddhist, she saw that this was not so. It was a serious matter, and yet women should be allowed a choice over it.

So far the views of some Western Buddhists. What of Asian ones? What do we find when we look at Buddhist-influenced pre-modern law? Of all Buddhist countries, Burma has had a traditional legal literature most strongly influenced by Buddhist norms (Huxley, 1995a: 49–50). In Sri Lanka, no traditional law-texts survive, and caste was the basis of dispute settlement and social organization. In Thai and Khmer traditions, the king was seen as the primary source of law. In China, Buddhism could only marginally influence the existing legal tradition. Surprisingly, Tibet's laws were much less influenced by Buddhist ideas than Burma's, perhaps because it took its law from Central Asian states to its north (Huxley, 1995a: 55).[44] In Burma, as elsewhere in South-east Asia, the main types of law texts were:

(1) *Rājathat*: the less ephemeral of a king's commands (Huxley, 1995a: 48), which included general guidance to the judges in the royal courts (Huxley, 1997: 75).

(2) *Dhammathat*: 'customary law' (Huxley, 1995a: 52), which gives guidance on unofficial dispute settlement, especially at village level (Huxley, 1997: 74). In the form of digests of law for popular consumption, its rules 'should be obeyed because they are as old as human society, or because they are universally acknowledged as correct because they are implicit in the Buddha's dhamma' (Huxley, 1997: 73). Indeed, they were seen as 'editions of the age-old law text which is written on the walls at the boundary of the universe' (Huxley, 1995a: 52).[45]

(3) *Pyatton*: *Jātaka*-type stories of clever judges or reports of cases

---

[44] Though French reports that Buddhist ideas affected the way the law was applied (1995: 114).

[45] One seventeenth-century Burmese view was that *rājathat* takes precedent over *dhammathat* in regard to disputes over property, life and injury to humans (Huxley, 1995b: 74–5).

(Huxley, 1995a: 49) which give 'helpful legal information' in the form of non-binding precedents (Huxley, 1997: 78).

The *dhammathat* texts were often composed by monks (Huxley, 1995a: 48), especially those expert in monastic discipline (p. 53); indeed, the *Vinaya* is often quoted from in South-east Asian legal literature, and its reasoning style is influential on law (Huxley, 1997: 70–1). Both in Burma and elsewhere in South-east Asia, it is notable that 'no sharp distinction was made between law, morality and good behaviour. Law texts [of any of the above three types] are often bound together with Jatakas and other works on ethics and *politesse*' (Huxley, 1997: 81).

In spite of the strong Buddhist influence on traditional Burmese law, Andrew Huxley, an expert in this field, can find no ruling on abortion in it.[46] He speculates that this may be because abortion did not 'threaten the king's peace . . . nor does it lead to a claim for compensation to be mediated at village or suburb level', and so came under the remit of neither *rājathat* nor *dhammathat*. All Burmese kings used the rhetoric of enforcing Buddhist morality, but few went to the lengths of Alaungpaya (c. 1755) and Badon (c. 1790), who outlawed the slaughter of animals, and it seems that Badon even imposed the death sentence for alcohol or opium use. That the law books do not seem to mention abortion implies that, however much this was seen as against the first precept, it was not regarded as a matter that the king's law or customary law needed to concern itself with. So far then, there seems to be support for the 'anti-abortion, pro-choice position'.

In Thailand, one 1978 study found that the majority of people saw abortion as immoral, yet also held that the abortion law should be liberalized to allow it on socio-economic grounds and for a broader range of medical reasons.[47] In 1981, when Parliament was debating liberalization of the law, a poll of monks found that 75 per cent held that the bill was immoral, yet 40 per cent felt that it should pass, with only 40 per cent opposing this (12 per cent of nuns thought that it should pass and 78 per cent that it should not).[48] While such a mismatch of views might seem surprising, there is a logic to it. On the one hand, Buddhism is clear that

---

[46] Personal communication.

[47] Referred to in The Population Council, *Abortion in Thailand: A Review of the Literature* (Bangkok: The Population Council Regional Office for South and East Asia, 1981), p. 91, as cited in Florida, 1998: 24.

[48] Amongst others, 65 per cent of workers saw the bill as immoral, though 66 per cent agreed with it, the figures being 38 per cent and 85 per cent for businessmen-traders. On the other hand, 50 per cent of students and lecturers did not think the bill immoral and 81 per cent supported it, the figures for doctors and nurses being 42 per cent and 87 per cent (WFBR, 1981: 30).

abortion is an unwholesome action; it also holds that to deny that an unwholesome action is unwholesome is itself a potently unwholesome action (see p. 57). On the other hand, Buddhists may be concerned about the suffering of women having botched illegal abortions which threaten their health, with only the wealthy being able to afford safe abortions.

Given both of these facts, it is not surprising that Buddhists sometimes both acknowledge that abortion is immoral and also want the abortion law liberalized. For the Buddhist women who have abortions, the above logic also means that it is less bad to have an abortion when this is acknowledged as being unwholesome than to have one believing that there is nothing wrong with doing so.

Yet in 1981, there were Buddhists arguing against reform of the Thai abortion law. The monk Sobhonganaphorn argued that morality was universal and based in nature, not a variable man-made matter, so man-made law should not flout it (WFBR, 1981: 21). The editor of the *World Fellowship of Buddhists Review*, however, while admitting that those involved in abortion must face its karmic results (WFBR, 1981: 33), held that one cannot force absolute morality onto people in dire circum-stances (WFBR, 1981: 35); while an editorial in the *Bangkok Post* argued that to impose religious ideals on a society could lead to extremes, as was occurring then in Iran (WFBR, 1981: 29). In 1994, the monk Somchai Kusalacitto held that abortion, including abortion of damaged or ill foe-tuses, was wrong, but that:

There are times when people choose to commit a sin in exchange for something better or more righteous . . . They have the right to make their own decisions on what to do so long as they are willing to accept the Karma or outcome of their actions.

He went on to say that the social conditions that led to unwanted preg-nancies should be addressed.[49] At the same time, Dr Vithoon Eungprabhanth said 'Doctors who choose to commit sins to help others should have the right to do so. At the same time, those doctors who are afraid of committing sins must be allowed to pursue their beliefs.'[50]

However, one problem with the above is that Buddhist ethics seems to treat abortion as being as serious as murder, and it is normal for legal systems to make murder illegal, so as to protect people. Why, then, do Buddhists tend to treat abortion as an immoral action which should not be against the law in all cases, unlike murder? This perhaps springs from

[49] Quoted in *The Nation* Thai newspaper, 13 June 1994.   [50] Ibid.

seeing the role of government and law as one of ensuring peace in society. Abortion does not threaten social order in the same way that murder does – especially as, in Buddhist countries, there are no violent conflicts between pro- and anti-abortionists, as in America. Thus, while a Buddhist would expect the karmic results of abortion to arise in the future, she may see less need for legal punishment to follow from the act. Thus the support for liberalizing the law, or the lax enforcing of the existing law, as occurs in some countries.

Yet what view on the proper relationship between law and morality do we find in Buddhist texts? The *Aggañña Sutta* describes early human society as gradually increasing in immorality and disorder until the people choose their first king to punish wrong-doers (*D.* III.92; see p. 114). In the *Cakkavatti-sīhanāda Sutta* (*D.* III.58–79; see p. 114), an ideal ruler is said to revere *Dhamma*, in the sense of moral norms and compassionate justice, and to rule only in accordance with it. He should both prevent crime and advise people on what is moral and immoral. One such *Cakkavatti* ruler is said to have been loved by his people as a father, and to have loved his people as a father does his children (*D.* II.178). These passages suggest that the job of a ruler or government is to prevent immorality descending into disorder and to encourage morality, if not rigidly enforce it. The emperor Asoka (268–239 BCE) was inspired by such ideals (see p. 115), and sought to rule justly. While placing some legal restrictions on the killing of animals, he felt that careful reflection and meditation were better means to moral improvement than legal compulsion (Nikam and McKeon, 1959: 40). Nevertheless, he strongly encouraged non-violence in his subjects, and saw his role as including that of encouraging them in various facets of following *Dhamma*, in the sense of morality and spiritual development (Nikam and McKeon, 1959: 33–4). Government should thus have a moral dimension, though compelled morality is not the ideal. How much is it good for people to let them get away with bad actions, though?

One Mahāyāna text, the *Suvarṇa-bhāsottama Sūtra*, or 'Supreme *Sūtra* of Golden Light', suggests that a ruler should err on the side of restrictions, if anything. In a section giving advice to kings, it says:

For the sake of suppressing what is unlawful, a destroyer of evil deeds, he would establish beings in good activity in order to send them to the abode of the gods. (*Svb.* 135)

If he overlooks an evil act, a king does not exercise his kingship according to the duty for which he was consecrated by the lords of the gods . . . He is called king because he acts in various ways in order to demonstrate the fruition and fruit of acts that are well done or ill-done . . . He must not knowingly without examination overlook a lawless act. No other destruction in his region is so terrible. (*Svb.* 141–2)

For when a king overlooks an evil deed in his region and does not inflict appropriate punishment on the evil person, in the neglect of evil deeds lawlessness grows greatly, wicked acts and quarrels arise in great number in the realm. The chief gods are wrathful . . . Unfavourable winds will blow . . . Crop, flower, fruit and seed will not properly ripen. Famine will arise there where the king is neglectful . . . Through the anger of the gods his region will perish. (*Svb.* 135–7)

Thus quarrels, war, death, famine etc. will arise, while ruling according to *Dharma* will please the gods. Here, a king must not let crime go unchecked as this will lead to social disorder, and thence to other problems as the gods are upset by this. He should also impress on people that actions have karmic consequences.

Chapter 6 of the *Ārya-satyaka-parivarta*, or 'Noble Discourse of the Truth Teller',[51] also has some interesting things to say here. This early Mahāyāna text, perhaps influenced by Asoka's edicts (*ASP.* 8, 46), has the *Bodhisattva* Satyavādin advising a king on state policy. In this, he emphasizes that a righteous king should be compassionate, but he criticizes the too easy compassion of a Prince Abhaya:

If a ruler is too compassionate, he will not chastise the wicked people of his kingdom which will lead to lawlessness and, as a result, the king will be unable to remove the harm done by robbers and thieves. (*ASP.* 228)

As with the *Sūtra* of Golden Light, the mistake of lax punishment is specified, here, as social disorder. Yet the 'Discourse of the Truth Teller' does not just see the king as having the role of preventing social disorder. As with the other sources cited above, it sees the king as having a role in improving the morality of his people:

Rulers . . . are called pleasing ones (rāja) in that they (are responsible for) maintaining the happiness of people, causing them to be good. (*ASP.* 180)

His compassion includes 'chastising the wicked' (*ASP.* 188), and this implies compassion for evil-doers in an attempt to reform them. In punishing people, his aims should be to convince them not to neglect their obligations (*ASP.* 188–9) so that they 'might become good persons again' (*ASP.* 200). Just as the *Cakkavatti* mentioned above looks on his subjects as

---

[51] See pp. 199–200. Jamspal holds that it was composed some time between the second century BCE and the first century CE, and says that it was a favourite handbook of many teachers in Tibet, such as Tsong kha pa, particularly in their advice to rulers (*ASP.* 2, 46).

like his children, so the righteous ruler should punish wrong-doers in a like spirit to that of a father disciplining a wayward son:

Everything is done in order to remove their faults with the wish: 'I should train them to prevent the arising of faults.' This is the way a ruler gets tough. (*ASP.* 191)

A righteous ruler 'with compassion should root out wicked people just as a father disciplines a son'. He should view the wicked as sick, and 'like a doctor a ruler should not get angry with them but rather make effort to remove their faults' (*ASP.* 209). Such passages imply that punishments by the state have, at least in part, the function of moral reform.

This *Sūtra* includes amongst evil-doers in need of punishment 'slaughterers, bird killers, and pork sellers' (*ASP.* 193). That is, people who in many societies would not be targeted for punishment, but who go against Buddhist ethics. Nevertheless, the recommended 'punishment' for such people, here, is only one of being chastised and warned not to continue in their actions (*ASP.* 194). While those from Western liberal democracies might see even this as an attempt to impose morality on people, Buddhism would say that there are certain objective moral standards: morality is not just a matter of opinion. Nevertheless, any punishment should be motivated by compassion for the wrongdoer.

If the law seeks to prevent social disorder and encourage moral reform, it also seeks to protect people. Thus the 'Discourse of the Truth Teller' says that the righteous king, in compassion, 'should also protect them from harm and ill caused by robbers and thieves, armies from other states, and from each other' (*ASP.* 188). Should his remit extend to the protection of unborn foetuses? Perhaps someone might say that these are not yet 'members' of the society that a king rules and seeks to offer protection over? Yet no-one would seriously argue that a baby, not being a *full* member of society, should not be given full protection. So why should a foetus not be offered protection, given that human life is seen to start at conception? A righteous ruler should offer some degree of protection even to animals in his realm (see p. 114), so why should even greater protection not be offered to human foetuses?

The above shows that the 'anti-abortion/pro-choice' position of Tworkov and others does not sit too well with the views of a number of Buddhist texts, which see the state as having a *moral* function which is not only that of ensuring social peace. Tworkov's view may be partly due to her being an *American* Buddhist, because of America's tradition of a strong separation between church and state, a notion which is foreign to many Buddhist lands. That some countries with large Buddhist populations have lax abortion laws, or laxly enforced ones, is to be regretted, on Buddhist grounds.[52] Buddhist principles suggest that the state should do what it can to persuade people to give up evil. It is true that Buddhism has never advocated making all immoral actions illegal, as doing so might itself threaten social order, as well as removing genuine moral choice from people. But for Buddhism, non-illegal immoral killings, at least in peacetime, have involved animals, not innocent humans. Should protecting innocent humans be outweighed by the fact that this would upset some people and reduce their choice? On Buddhist grounds, the answer is surely 'no'.

In a war, if this is a genuine defensive one, killing of humans might be seen as an evil which is legal as it is necessary in order to protect innocent lives and social order. There are no parallels here for abortion, though, for with abortion innocent life is being taken and there is no real threat to social order.

Perhaps the only possible ground for abortion where it might be acceptable to be more 'liberal' in law than in Buddhist ethics is in the case of a foetus which is badly impaired. While Buddhist principles would counsel against an abortion here, it does not seem appropriate to compel a woman by law to have such a child. This is not on the grounds of 'compassion' for the child, but on the grounds of compassion for the woman.

But what of the consequences of making abortion illegal on all but the grounds summarized on p. 326, with the addition of the case of badly impaired foetuses? The problem is that women will have illegal abortions on other grounds, and that these may be performed by 'quacks' who damage the women's health or cause their deaths. Here, the issue is not unlike the question of whether hard drugs should be legalized, to prevent drug-related killings arising from the high price of illegal drugs, and to prevent AIDS deaths due to sharing dirty needles. Yet in this case, (a) it is possible to make clean needles available without legalizing hard drugs and (b) those killed in drug-related killings are not innocent of relevant fault, as is a foetus. For a closer analogy, we need to

---

[52] When abortion laws are fairly restrictive but are not enforced, the 'law' becomes, in effect, a publicly declared standard of morality, rather than law proper, but this brings the law into disrepute as it is no longer treated *as* law. Here, either better enforcement, as is now happening in Thailand, or liberalization, or both, seems best.

return to the 'baby and chimpanzee test' (see p. 321). If it were found that people were dying because of side-effects of a particular way of killing babies, should killing babies be legalized, so that people could have easy access to less dangerous means? No. What if it were unwanted chimpanzees, not babies? Surely, we would have to ask: why are people killing chimpanzees? Thus the moral answer to dangerous illegal abortions is not a liberal abortion law, but resources for easily available contraceptives, with encouragement to use these, and good adoption and fostering services. Even with a liberal abortion law, resources would be needed to fund easily available abortions, or people would still go to quacks on financial grounds. Of course, there will be countries where contraceptives are not yet easily available on account of people's inability to afford them. While it should be a priority to make them available and affordable (or free), until they are, enforcement of laws on abortion should not be done harshly.

CONCLUSION

We can thus conclude the following:

(1) the Buddhist scriptural tradition is clear in its opposition to abortion. It considers abortion as worse when the foetus is older and when the reason for considering an abortion is weaker. It always considers it as worse than killing an animal in parallel circumstances;

(2) Buddhist principles indicate that those having abortions should recognize their action as evil to some degree, otherwise it will be an even worse action;

(3) Buddhists are more willing to condemn abortion on moral grounds than to oppose legalisation of it, often being more permissive in practice than in their outlook;

(4) yet classical Buddhist textual views of the function of law and government do not support the spirit of 'abortion is wrong but should be allowed by the law'.

We have seen that Buddhists have accommodated themselves to abortion to varying degrees, and that there are those who argue that the not infrequently permissive practice of Buddhists is the best ground on which to base a 'Buddhist position'. The trouble with this is that a classical Buddhist idea is that people's moral practice declines over the ages, and permissive practice on abortion could simply be seen as a sign of this, not of any true expression of Buddhist principles.

It is clear, at the very least, that the great majority of Buddhists agree that abortion is killing a human being, and is an evil that should be avoided, other things being equal. A crucial issue, though, is *how* evil is it, and what 'other things' can come to outweigh this evil, so that abortion comes to be seen as a 'necessary evil' in certain circumstances? It seems that in Japan and Korea, almost any grounds for abortion have been seen to make it a 'necessary evil'. At the opposite end of the spectrum are Tibetan Buddhists, Sri Lankan Theravādins, and a number of Theravādins in Thailand. In between comes a sizeable body of opinion in Thailand. The position in Burma has been that, in pre-colonial times at least, abortion was not liable to punishment, and there is some evidence of its currently being accepted in society, if not widely practised.

The absence of angry demonstrations outside abortion clinics in any Buddhist countries is perhaps partly to be explained by the fact that Buddhism sees anger as a destructive, unwholesome emotion, even so-called 'righteous' anger. In America, there have even been abortion clinic workers who have been killed by anti-abortionists. At a theoretical level, one might wonder whether Mahāyāna 'skilful means' reasoning could even be used to justify such an action. Such a 'justification' could be along the lines: the doctor is engaged in killing many beings, so to kill him would be to save them and save him from the evil of killing. Yet the argument does not work: the killing of an abortionist would be an action which would incite outrage, fear and anger, and the hardening of positions on the abortion issue, which would not be conducive to real reflection and change. Even if this were not the case, the kind of advanced *Bodhisattva* who could do such an action, the very opposite of normal Buddhist ethics, without great spiritual danger, is extremely rare.

The approach to abortion most in tune with central Buddhist principles would be:
(1) encouragement of reflection on the value of human life;
(2) encouragement of responsible use of contraception, so as to minimize the chances of women even having to consider an abortion;
(3) encouraging the non-use of 'contraceptives' which actually cause early abortions, and the development of more effective contraceptives which do not do this;
(4) encouragement and support for adoption services, with 'giving up' a child for adoption being seen as a form of *dāna*;

(5) support for legal abortion only where the case for its being a 'necessary evil' is strong (see p. 326), or where the foetus is badly impaired;

(6) compassion for those who have had an abortion by provision of some kind of ritual to alleviate their psychological pain, encourage an expression of sincere regret and attempt to benefit the dead child spiritually.

CHAPTER 9

Sexual equality

To one for whom the question arises, 'am I a woman or am I a man in these matters?' . . . to such a one is Māra fit to talk!   *Saṃyutta Nikāya* I.129

'Sexual equality' covers a range of issues on which religion can have a direct or indirect bearing:

(1) access to religious teachings and practices, and encouragement to follow them;
(2) images of men and women's spiritual potential;
(3) opportunity with regard to specialist religious roles, and status within them;
(4) status, authority and respect within the family;
(5) equality of legal status with regard to such matters as inheritance and divorce;
(6) access to educational and other resources, and encouragement to use them;
(7) opportunity with regard to work and earnings;
(8) opportunity with regard to political power and rights;
(9) the actual achievement of equality as allowed/facilitated by a religion or culture.

These are affected by the way a culture construes the differences between men and women: with how biological differences of sex are used as a basis for a set of differing expectations and characterizations of 'male' and 'female' genders. In most cultures, any sexual inequality is usually at the expense of women; thus the issue is generally focused on the status of women. Nevertheless, some feminists have questioned whether 'equality' with men is always the appropriate goal for women to seek, if it simply means equal access to a world where the rules are set by men.

In the West, while feminism and its precursors have brought about valuable changes to the position of women, feminism not infrequently leads to dogmatic viewpoints being taken up, both *between* feminists and non-feminists and *within* both 'camps'. This can lead to 'clinging to views' – holding to particular views with attachment and indignation –

353

which Buddhism has always been wary of, although Buddhists have not always managed to avoid it. Whatever debate there is on the status of women among Buddhists, the ideal should always be to assess critically both one's own existing views and those of others, so as not to be swayed simply by either habitual and/or traditional attitudes or by newly fashionable viewpoints. The bottom line, from a Buddhist perspective, is whether a particular idea, attitude or practice conduces to an increase or decrease – for both men and women – in such qualities as generosity, non-attachment, calm, kindness, compassion, clarity of mind, and awareness of, and insight into, the nature of mental and physical states. The aim, then, is true human welfare, judged by criteria that are not regarded as gender-specific. The extent to which this inclusive goal needs to take account of real differences between men and women has, and does, receive different answers from Buddhists.

Before examining the situation of women 'in' Buddhism, it is worth pointing out that as Buddhism has evolved over many centuries, its many forms have existed in a variety of cultural milieux. The views and behaviour of Buddhists have been influenced not only by Buddhism, but by other traditions such as Hinduism or Confucianism, as well as by such factors as particular traditional kinship systems or, of course, their own psychological limitations.

WOMEN IN EARLY HINDUISM

What of the position of women in the culture which preceded Buddhism and developed alongside it in India? In the *Veda Saṃhitās (c.* 1500–1000 BCE), there were a few little-worshipped goddesses among many gods; there were probably some women among the poet-seers who composed the texts, and perhaps some among those trained to sing sacrificial hymns. Women were greatly honoured as mothers, and were permitted considerable freedom of movement by their menfolk.[1] As Vedic religion developed, the *Brāhmaṇa*s were composed (1000–700 BCE) as guides to complex rituals seen to have a controlling power over the cosmos. Priestly specialists were now needed, who required a special education away from home. This was only given to males of the brahmin class; their sisters only received it if their fathers had the requisite knowledge. A son was seen as necessary to perform the funeral rite for a father, so that he could win the heaven world, and for rites to

---

[1] Young, 1987: 60–4; Jhingran, 1989; Dewaraja, 1981: 6.

benefit male ancestors. There were thus rituals to prevent the birth of a girl, for daughters tended to be seen as an unwelcome burden until they were married, which was their duty (Jhingran, 1989: 92). A wife came to be seen primarily as a child-bearer and as subservient to her husband and his parents. Thus, as the Vedic religion became increasingly dominated by the brahmin priests, women's status decreased. In the mystical, ascetic texts known as the *Upaniṣads* (700–200 BCE), there is reference to a few women debaters, such as Gārgī, but asceticism was generally seen as a male preserve, and ascetics often saw women as temptresses.

From the fifth century BCE, Buddhism and Jainism came to have considerable success, and Brahmanism went on the defensive, seeking to become more popular by drawing in cults of various Indian deities. The brahmins also developed a number of texts, known as *Dharma-śāstras*, to regulate the life of society in accordance with their developing norms. In these, one can see the status of women continuing to decline. Perhaps the most influential of the religious law-books was the *Manu Smṛti*, the 'Laws of Manu',[2] dating from around 100 CE, which clearly codified a developing tradition. In it, women were prohibited from reading the sacred Vedic texts, and could not perform sacrifice or worship without men (Dewaraja, 1981: 6–7). While it was held that the honouring of women pleased the gods, and that families did not prosper without their happiness (III.55–7), nevertheless, 'a woman is never fit for independence' (IX.3), even in her own house (V.147). She must be protected by (IX.3) and be subject to (V.148) her father, then her husband, then her grown-up son. This was partly because women were seen as highly sexed and ever ready to seduce men (IX.13–18), though other Hindu law texts prescribed tougher penalties for adultery by a man than by a woman (Jhingran, 1989: 96). A woman's religious duties were simply those of serving her husband and looking after the home (II.67). She should always obey him (V.151) and revere him even if he was adulterous or devoid of virtues (V.154). A man could divorce his wife (IX.81), but a woman had no right to divorce her husband.

Such brahmin ideals were followed to varying extents by Hindus, especially those of higher castes. By the Gupta period (320–540 CE), Hinduism was regaining considerable strength in India. Given that Buddhism had less interest in regulating the specifics of lay life, Hindu

---

[2] Selections on women are given in S. Radhakrishnan and C. A. Moore (eds.), *A Source Book in Indian Philosophy* (Princeton, N.J., Princeton University Press, 1957), pp. 172, 189–92.

ideas inevitably had an effect on ordinary Buddhists, though they were resisted to varying extents.

THE EFFECT OF BUDDHISM

Buddhism's emphasis on individual karma lessened the need for *sons* to perform a man's funeral rites. A person's destiny after death was due to his or her *own* karma, perhaps with a little help from that shared with him or her by others, male or female. In general, the Buddhist era was one in which women 'commanded more respect and ranked as individuals. They enjoyed more independence, and a wider liberty to guide and follow their own lives' (Horner, 1930: 82), so that women's position was one of 'approximation to equality with men'.

From a Buddhist perspective, there was no reason to feel gloomy at the birth of a daughter. When King Pasenadi was downhearted at the birth of a girl to Queen Mallikā – later to lead her husband to be a Buddhist (*M.* II.106–12) – the Buddha said:

> Indeed, a woman of a certain sort is better than a man, lord of folk:
> Wise, virtuous, revering her husband's mother, a devoted wife.
> The man born of her is a hero, ruler of the regions,
> Such a son of a good wife is one who advises his realm.   (*S.* 1.86)

Here, the Buddha gives a statement which skilfully combines an elevation in the status of women – a 'wise, virtuous' woman may be better than a man – and a comforting statement to the king about getting a worthy grand*son*! Nevertheless, early Buddhism did not just look on women as child-bearers, and marriage was not their only aim. To be an unmarried adult woman was a legitimate role, and women might also become Buddhist nuns. It is said that the faithful laywoman should encourage her beloved only son to emulate the best laymen or monks, and her beloved only daughter to emulate the best laywomen or nuns (*S.* II.235–6).

Miss I. B. Horner (1930: 287–8) summarizes the elements of sexual equality that are found in the early Buddhist texts:
(1) The Buddha is said to have won enlightenment for the sake of monks, nuns, laymen and laywomen (*S.* 1.196), and to have taught *Dhamma* to all four.
(2) The virtues and vices of all four groups are said to have an analogous effect on the persistence or disappearance of Buddhist knowledge and practice (*A.* III.247). Thus the *Saṅgha* is 'illuminated' by a monk,

nun, layman or laywoman who is 'accomplished in wisdom, disciplined, confident . . . practising according to *Dhamma*' (*A.* 11.8), and
the same set of virtues or vices leads to hell or heaven for a man or
woman (*A.* v.283–7).

(3) Women may have both the same spiritual limitations and the same
spiritual powers as men.

(4) Nuns may develop to the same extent as monks.

(5) The Buddha said that he would not die until he had monks, and
nuns, and laymen, and laywomen who could teach *Dhamma*, 'establish it, expound it, analyse it, make it clear' (*D.* 11.104, 113).

(6) The Buddha gave the same teachings to both sexes, and sometimes
went out of his way to teach women.

At *D.* 11.96–7, the Buddha refused a meal invitation from some proud and
rich young men, as he had already accepted an invitation from the
courtesan Ambapālī, which he honoured even when the young men
objected. Ambapālī was later ordained and became an *Arahat* (*Thig.*
252–70).

THE SPIRITUAL POTENTIAL AND ACHIEVEMENT OF WOMEN

The historical Buddha's perspective on the spiritual potential of women
is usefully described by Alan Sponberg as one of 'soteriological inclusiveness' (1992: 8–13). This does not assert, as such, the social equality of
men and women, but that the spiritual path is equally open to both, for
sex and gender differences are 'soteriologically insignificant' (p. 9).
Sponberg sees this attitude as probably 'the most basic and also the most
distinctively Buddhist attitude regarding the status of women' throughout Buddhist literature (p. 8). This relatively revolutionary attitude,
though, was complemented, in early Buddhism, by what Sponberg calls
'institutional androcentrism' and then by what he calls, more conten-
tiously, 'ascetic misogyny' (see below, pp. 379–83).

Female Arahats

That the Buddha agreed that women could become *Arahat*s is seen from
his overview of his disciples' achievements, there being 'far more than
500' in each of the following categories: (1) monks who are *Arahat*s, (2)
nuns who are *Arahat*s, (3) celibate laymen who are Non-returners, (4) celibate laywomen who are Non-returners, (5) laymen who are without
doubt and perplexity (i.e. are Stream-enterers), (6) laywomen who are

without doubt and perplexity.[3] His pre-eminent nuns, and their qualities, were (*A.* 1.25): Mahā-Pajāpatī Gotamī – the Buddha's aunt and foster-mother (chief of nuns of long standing); Khemā (great wisdom); Uppalavaṇṇā – who was raped in the forest after she became an *Arahat* (*Dhp. A.* II.48–51) (psychic power); Paṭācārā (monastic discipline); Dhammadinnā (*Dhamma* teaching); Nandā (meditation); Soṇā (energetic striving); Sakulā (the divine eye); Bhaddā Kuṇḍalakesā – once a free-lance debater (*Dhp. A.* II.217–26) and personally ordained by the Buddha (*Thig.* 109) (quick higher knowledges); Bhaddā-kapilānī (memory of past lives); Bhaddā Kaccānā – seen as the Buddha's ex-wife (*A.A.* 1.198) (great mastery of higher knowledges); Kisā Gotamī – whom the Buddha had cured of grief at the death of her child (*Dhp. A.* II.270–5) (wearer of coarse robe); Sigālamātā (released by faith).

In the Pali Canon, the *Therīgāthā* consists of seventy-three sets of verses attributed to 102 early nun *Arahat*s.[4] Among the attainments referred to are those of thirty nuns who gain the 'threefold knowledge' during the three watches of the night, as the Buddha had done (*Thig.* 120). The nun Sumedhā recalls that, prior to her ordination, she had been acknowl-edged as 'Virtuous, a brilliant speaker, having great learning, trained in the Buddha's teaching' (verse 449). Not wanting to be married to a king, she had had great detachment, and a desire to escape the round of rebirths: 'Either there will be going forth (ordination) for me, or death; not marriage' (verse 465). She goes on to compare sensual pleasures to vomit (verse 478), a butcher's knife (verse 488), delusive dreams (verse 490) and a pit of coals (verse 491). When the king came to her, she threw down the hair she had just cut off, as a consolation for him (verse 514).

Some female *Arahat*s saw themselves as having begun to develop spir-itually even while in an unhappy marriage. Thus Muttā says:

I am well-released, properly released by my release by three crooked things, by the mortar, pestle, and my crooked husband. I am released from birth and death. (*Thig.* 11)

Another, unknown nun is simply happy to be beyond such a marriage:

Well-released, well-released, properly released am I from the pestle. My shame-less man, even his sunshade etc. (disgust me). My pot gives forth the smell of water-snake. (*Thig.* 23)

---

[3] *M.* 1.490–1; cf. *M.* III.277; *Ud.* 79; *S.* 1.33. See pp. 39–40 on *Arahat*s, Non-returners and Streamenterers.
[4] See *Thig.* and *Thig. A.* Discussed in: Horner (1930: 162–210), Murcott (1991) and Blackstone (1998).

The nuns were ordained for a variety of reasons, though, not just to escape such marriages. According to Horner, at least thirty-two were unmarried, eighteen had clearly been married, three of whom had been widowed (1930: 173–4), and a number were ordained because of grief, especially at the loss of a child (p. 194).

Among the early *Arahat* nuns, at least thirty looked to Paṭācārā – who had lost her two children in tragic circumstances (*Dhp. A.* II.264–5) – as their teacher (*Thīg.* 117–21). Of other great teachers who are nuns, Dhammadinnā answers an array of questions from her ex-husband on subtle points of doctrine, with the Buddha then praising her answers as the ones he would have given (*M.* I.299–305). Khemā, said to be 'widely learned, a brilliant speaker', addresses a famous passage, to a king, on a Tathāgata as being 'deep, immeasurable, hard to fathom as is the great ocean' (*S.* IV.376). Sukkā laments that the men of Rājagaha, as if drunk, do not attend to her teaching *Dhamma* but the wise drink it up (*Thīg.* 54–5). *S.* I.128–35 gives verses attributed to a number of nuns, such as Vajirā, who likens the five personality factors to the parts of a chariot: a famous simile later taken up in the *Milindapañha* (pp. 27–8).

Of particular interest are the verses of Somā. On going deep into a wood, the tempter-god Māra comes to her to make her afraid and so desist from meditation. Māra insinuates:

That vantage-ground (i.e. Arahatship) to be attained by sages is hard to win. With her two-finger-intelligence, no woman is able to attain that.

Somā recognizes Māra, though, and replies:

What (difference) should a woman's state (*itthi-bhāvo*) make, when the mind is well concentrated, when knowledge is rolling on, when she rightly has insight into *Dhamma*? To one for whom the question arises, 'am I a woman or am I a man (in these matters)?' or 'what indeed am I?'. To such a one is Māra fit to talk! (*S.* I.129; cf. *Thīg.* 60–2)

Māra therefore knows that she can see through him, and slinks off. This passage in some ways parallels that of Māra's tempting of Gotama just prior to his enlightenment. In Somā's case, specious doubts arise concerning a woman's ability to attain spiritual states, but she conquers them by seeing the irrelevance of gender: what matters is appropriate spiritual practice and insight. Likewise, Māra unsuccessfully tries to tempt other nuns as follows: you should enjoy sensual pleasures and 'be not a woman who regrets too late' (*S.* I.128); have you come to the wood, alone, looking for a man (p. 130)?; you are beautiful and should enjoy yourself with a young one such as he (p. 131); are you not afraid of 'the wiles of seducers'? (p. 131); don't you want to be reborn? (p. 133); who made the human form? (p. 134).

The *Therī-apadāna*, a late Theravāda canonical text on the lives and past lives of the nuns whose verses are given in the *Therīgāthā*, contains many stories which Jonathan Walters sees as unmistakably combating 'misogynist attitudes that continued among Indian Buddhists' (1995: 114). He translates material from the text on Mahā-Pajāpatī Gotamī, the Buddha's foster-mother and the first nun, which focuses on her, aged 120, passing away into final *Nirvāṇa* at death. In this she, referred to simply as Gotamī, is portrayed as paralleling the Buddha, Gotama (1995: 117), both having a 'great final *Nirvāṇa*' (verse 75). To the Buddha, she says: 'But by your nurturing was reared my flawless dharma-body' (verse 32), and to the not-yet enlightened Ānanda, who helped her persuade the Buddha to ordain women, she says:

> That state which is not seen by elders [senior monks]
> nor by non-Buddhist teachers
> is witnessed by some Buddhist girls
> when they are only seven. (verse 66)

However, she says to the Buddha:

> It is thought, chief of the world,
> that women are all flawed.
> If there should be some flaw in me,
> compassion-mine, forgive me. (verse 44)

The Buddha goes on to say:

> Yet still there are these fools who doubt
> that women can grasp the truth.
> Gotamī, show miracles,
> that they might give up their false views. (verse 79)

She then says that she has the six 'higher knowledges' (verse 78), as had the Buddha and certain other *Arahat*s, and shows the first of these by rising into the air, multiplying her form, diving into the earth, walking on water, flying etc. (verses 80–90), and the fourth by telling of her deeds in past lives (verses 95–119), with the Buddha's confirmation. The 500 nuns she was ordained with also display their psychic powers (veses 120–3). Gotamī then goes through the same series of meditative states that the Buddha is to do on his death, before passing into final *Nirvāṇa* (verses 145–8), at which there is an earthquake and flowers fall from the sky (verses 148–9), as at the Buddha's death. The Buddha then says:

The Buddha's great nirvāṇa, good,
but not as good as this one:
Gotamī's great going out
was positively stellar. (verse 173)

Know this, O monks, she was most wise,
with wisdom vast and wide.
She was a nun of great renown,
a master of great powers.
She cultivated 'divine-ear'
and knew what others thought. (verses 183–4)

Mahāyāna images of female spiritual perfection

While Arahatship is the spiritual goal of the Theravāda, the Mahāyāna
aims at becoming a *Bodhisattva* and then a Buddha. In perhaps the earliest extant Mahāyāna text, the *Aṣṭasāhasrikā* Perfection of Wisdom *Sūtra*
(*c.* 100 BCE–100 CE), the perfection of wisdom (*prajñā-pāramitā*) is
praised as the 'mother' of all Buddhas (Conze, 1973: 31, 172). *Prajñā*,
which is grammatically feminine, is analytically based intuitive liberating insight into emptiness (see pp. 124–5) . When this is developed, it acts
as the basis for the 'birth' of Buddhahood.

While the 'feminine' perfection of wisdom gives birth to
Buddhahood, this requires other qualities, too; for wisdom is also seen
to give birth to and nourishes lesser levels of realization (Cabezón, 1992:
185). For the *Bodhisattva*, on the path to becoming a Buddha, though,
compassionate skilful means (*upāya kauśalya*) is needed as well as wisdom
(Lamotte, 1976: 126–7). In Mahāyāna and especially Vajrayāna thought,
such skilful means, and also the compassionate aspiration to
Buddhahood (*bodhi-citta*), is envisaged as male, akin to a father, as a complement to the feminine wisdom.

From around 400 CE, female holy beings gradually came to appear
in Mahāyāna texts and then art, such as the Perfection of Wisdom
personified as a female *Bodhisattva* (Conze, 1967: 243–60), and they
became particularly popular in tantric Buddhism (see pp. 141–2) and
thus in the lands of Northern Buddhism. Here, a very important figure
is Tārā, the 'Saviouress': a *Bodhisattva* said to be 'mother of all the
Buddhas' (Williams, 1989: 236–8). Among her twenty-one forms, the
'Green' and 'White' ones came to be some of the best-loved deities in
Tibet (Beyer, 1973). They are seen as graceful, attractive and approach-
able, and as ever ready to care tenderly for those in distress.

Plate 9. A popular print from Sri Lanka, showing the Buddha returning to earth from a heaven after teaching his dead mother the *Abhidhamma*, a complex compendium of analytical wisdom.

Plate 10. An image of Tārā, the 'Saviouress', in the courtyard of a temple in Kathmandu, Nepal.

From 700 CE, some Indian tantric texts added female consorts of the heavenly Buddhas and *Bodhisattvas* (Conze, 1967: 82). In any such couple, the female was known as the *prajñā*, or 'wisdom' partner, and the male symbolized (skilful) 'means' (*upāya*): skilful compassionate action, facilitated by the more passive wisdom symbolized by the female partner. The ideal was for a practitioner to unite these two qualities, to a very high degree, in his or her own person, so as to produce the great bliss of enlightenment. This, in turn, was symbolized, in Tibet, by pairs of holy beings in sexual union, known as *yab-yum*, or father-mother, forms. In some forms of tantric practice, lay practitioners would actually perform sexual yoga with a partner, in a very self-controlled way, to manipulate and transform the sexual energies, as a means to spiritual development (see pp. 141–2).

Commenting on the Mahāyāna's incorporation of the feminine principle, Edward Conze says (1967: 81):

The Mahāyāna believed that men should, in their meditations, complete themselves by fostering the feminine factors of their personality, that they should practise passivity and a loose softness, that they should learn to open freely the gates of nature, and let the mysterious and hidden forces of this world penetrate into them, stream in and through them. When they identify themselves with the Perfection of Wisdom, they merge with the principle of Femininity . . . without which they would be mutilated men.

Here Conze is specifically discussing the early Mahāyāna valuing of the perfection of wisdom, but his remarks equally apply to later tantric notions of male and female as symbolizing a spiritual complementary pair. Sponberg sees the latter perspective as one of 'soteriological androgyny' (1992: 24–8). Here, sexual/gender differences 'are acknowledged as provisional, as not ultimately real, and they are further affirmed as potentially powerful means of soteric transformation' (p. 25). Both sexes are seen as having 'masculine' and 'feminine' traits, and both sets of complementary traits are seen as 'essential to the ideal state, a state of androgynous integration' (p. 25). Thus a male must draw on and develop repressed 'female' energies, and vice versa, to transform them and remove their destructive potencies (pp. 25–6). This would be done, for example, by working with a *yidam*, a chosen deity who would be vividly visualized and then mentally identified with (Harvey, 1990a: 261–4). A man might be assigned a *yidam* who was female, just as a woman might be assigned one who was male.

Sponberg holds, though, that the ideal of androgynous integration seems to have been mainly for the benefit of men (1992: 28), as might be inferred from the Conze passage quoted above. Women were not excluded, though. Of the eighty-four famous tantric masters (the *Mahā-siddhas*) of India (eighth to twelfth centuries), mostly lay practitioners, four were women (Ray, 1980), and tantric masters such as the Indian Nāropa and the Tibetan Marpa had wives or consorts who were also accomplished tantric masters (Willis, 1989: 69).

Some tantric texts, on the level of practice known as *Anuttara-yoga*, say that it is possible for a woman to become enlightened in one lifetime (Tsomo, 1988: 42). They also emphasize that all women should be respected, as some may be *ḍākiṇīs* (p. 84). *Ḍākiṇīs* are a type of female *yidam* who are seen as playful but, when the dynamic energy they represent is blocked in a person, also wrathful (Allione, 1986: 41–2), often being shown dancing upon a male figure (see Allione, 1986: 25–46). Tibet has many stories of their appearance to practitioners at crucial moments in their lives, so as to issue an incisive challenge to their fixed ideas and superficial understanding (Allione, 1986: 37; Willis, 1989: 63–5). The Tibetan translation of *ḍākiṇī* is *Khadoma (mKha' 'gro ma)*, which means something like 'Sky-goer': that is, one who, through wisdom, is at home in emptiness, and who creates openings for people to deepen their wisdom, and develop in a more rounded way (Willis, 1989: 61–2, 66, 73). In art, such beings are often shown wielding a knife with a crescent-shaped blade and a hook on it (Allione, 1986: 32–3). The hook represents saving compassion, while the blade symbolizes their power to cut up ego-centred delusions. In the Dzog Chen (rDzogs-chen) teachings of the Tibetan Nyingma (rNying-ma) school, *ḍākiṇīs* are seen as guardians of teachings hidden by the great teacher Padmasaṃbhava, regarded as their founder, and also as demanding guides to those who may rediscover these.

Padmasaṃbhava (eighth century) said of Yeshe Tsogyel (Ye-shes mTsho-rgyal), one of his two main consorts:

The human body is the basis of the accomplishment of wisdom, and the gross bodies of men and women are equally suited. But if a woman has strong aspiration, she has higher potential.[5]

This, even though she claimed:

I am a woman – I have little power to resist danger. Because of my inferior birth, everyone attacks me . . . If I have wealth and food, bandits attack me . . . Because I am a woman, it is hard to follow the *Dharma*.[6]

This first-generation Buddhist may well, though, have been saying this mainly to help her win certain secret teachings from Padmasaṃbhava.

In India and Tibet, the most popular *Bodhisattva* has been Avalokiteśvara, embodiment of compassion, who was seen as male. In China, however, where he was known as Kuan-yin, 'he' gradually came

---

[5] Willis, 1989: 17, quoting Dowman, 1984: 86.
[6] Willis, 1989, 96, quoting Tarthang Tulku, 1985: 105.

to be portrayed as female (Reed, 1992; Paul, 1979: 247–80). This may
have been because the Chinese saw compassion as a 'female' quality.
Other factors may have been a female allusion in his *mantra*, his association with Tārā, and the fact that, from the fifth century, some of 'his'
popular incarnations were female. 'He' may also have merged with a
pre-Buddhist goddess thought to care for mariners. In time, Kuan-yin
came to be seen as an all-compassionate 'mother-goddess', the most
popular deity in all of China. In several of the legends of her incarnations, she acts in a way that rejects the Confucian emphasis that women
should marry (Reed, 1992: 167–8). As the princess Miao-shan, she
becomes a nun, to the great anger of her father, but goes on to cure his
blindness and give him spiritual insight (which is a Buddhist way of
enacting the Confucian value of respecting parents). In another legend,
she has men compete for her hand in marriage by learning many verses
from the Lotus *Sūtra*; she then dies before the winner can marry her.
Kuan-yin was thus called on by women to save them from unwanted
marriages or from sexual attacks. Married women also called on her to
aid difficult child-births, and to gain a son, which increased their power
within the Confucian-dominated family ethos.

Also in China, a popular idea in a number of schools was that of the
'Buddha-nature': a Buddha-potential latent in all, male or female. This
notion is strongly expressed in the 'Lion's Roar of Queen Śrīmālā'
(*Śrīmālā-devī Siṃhanāda*) *Sūtra* (*c.* 250–350 CE; Paul, 1979: 281–302). This
concerns the teachings of the wise *Bodhisattva* daughter of King
Prasenajit (Pali Pasenadi): the same daughter whom the king had initially
lamented over for not being a boy (see above, p. 356)!

The Chinese Ch'an (Zen) school particularly came to emphasize
sexual equality, in contrast to the prevailing Confucian social ethic which
saw men as clearly superior. The Ch'an ideal, based on the idea of all
sharing the Buddha-nature, and on the emptiness of worldly distinctions
(Levering, 1982: 20), can be seen in Ta-hui Tsung-kao's (1089–1163) statement:

For mastering the truth, it does not matter whether one is male or female, noble
or base. One moment of insight and one is shoulder to shoulder with the
Buddha. (Levering, 1992: 139)

His description of one of his most successful laywomen students is as
follows:

Can you say that she is a woman, and women have no share (in enlightenment)?
You must believe that this matter has nothing to do with (whether one is) male

or female, old or young. Ours is an egalitarian Dharma-gate that has only one flavour. (Levering, 1992: 139)

Here, one sees a strong echo of the verses of Somā in the Theravādin *Sutta* collection (see p. 359). Yet such teachers saw enlightenment as for the exceptional person with great determination and courage: a 'great hero (*ta-chang-fu*)', which term had clear masculine connotations in Chinese culture (Levering, 1992). Indeed, the above-mentioned monk said of another laywoman disciple:

When you look at her you see a woman, but this is like the action of a man (*chang-fu*), and she is able to complete the affairs of a great hero (*ta-chang-fu*). (Levering, 1992: 149)

Thus a woman was seen as able to attain the same spiritual level as a man could reach, but doing so required her to excel in qualities particularly associated with men.

However, one should not forget that Zen also has its more gentle, 'feminine' side, such as the tea ceremony (Wawrytko, 1991: 267–8). Moreover, the openness of enlightenment to both men and women is a recurrent theme in Ch'an and Zen. While this was often more rhetoric than reality, lay followers particularly seem to have advocated equality, as seen in stories in which the daughter of the famous Layman Pang outwits her father (Faure, 1991: 244). The founder of Sōtō Zen in Japan, the renowned Dōgen (1200–53), argued that, as women could be enlightened, men should be prepared to have such women as their teachers, otherwise they showed that they did not understand the *Dharma*. He asked 'By what right are only males noble?' (Wawrytko, 1991: 273):

What demerit is there in femaleness? What merit is there in maleness? There are bad men and good women. If you wish to hear the *Dharma* and put an end to pain and turmoil, forget about such things as male and female. As long as delusions have not yet been eliminated, neither men nor women have eliminated them; when they are all eliminated and true reality is experienced, there is no distinction of male and female. (Levering, 1982: 31)

Levering explains that in saying this, though, Dōgen was not challenging the accepted position of women in Confucian-influenced Japanese lay society (1982: 30). In practice, it also seems that he had few female disciples (Faure, 1991: 244), whatever the reasons were for this. While even his spiritual egalitarianism came to be neglected in later Japanese Zen (Uchino, 1986), it has been taken up again in Western Zen (Shasta Abbey, 1981).

GENDER, REBIRTH AND THE STATUS OF WOMEN

To return to the Indian cultural sphere, what, though, is the traditional Buddhist understanding of sex differences and their significance? In the *Abhidhamma* literature, which carefully details the nature of mental and physical processes, there is only said to be a specific kind of differentiation between men and women at the physical, not mental, level: the subtle qualities known as the female-faculty and male-faculty. The first is defined as

That which in a female is feminine appearance, feminine characteristic, feminine behaviour, feminine deportment, femininity, being feminine. (*Dhs.* 633)

with an exactly parallel definition of the male-faculty. Both are seen as types of invisible material form (*Vibh.* 72) and as being present from the moment of conception (*Vibh.* 414–15). In the Theravādin commentaries (*Asl.* 321), 'appearance' etc. are seen as the *products* of the two faculties, which are like their seeds. Gods of the lower heavens, still within the 'realm of sense-pleasures', still have the sexual faculties, but those of the higher, '(elemental) form' level of *brahmā* gods lack them (*Vibh.* 418; *AKB*.ii.12b–c). Yet the Sarvāstivādins, and perhaps Theravādins saw these beings as still being 'male' through having at least the body shape and voice of a male (*AKB.* ii.12b–c). For both schools, though, both men and women can be reborn in their next life at this level.

While the *Suttas* occasionally refer to the general 'mind-set' (*citta*) of a man or woman (see below), the *Abhidhamma* does not detail any *citta*, here meaning a specific mind-state, particular to either men or women. It thus implies that any difference between the psychology of men and women pertains to the particular *mix* of mental states that tend to occur in them. Moreover, in a late part of the Pali Canon, it is said that each of the five personality-factors is 'not a female, not a male, not a Self, not what pertains to Self' (*Nd.* ii.280). That is, there is no permanent woman-essence, man-essence or Self in the changing physical and mental processes making up a 'person'. This is partly because it is accepted that sex can change during a person's life (*Asl.* 322).

Between lives, sex is *generally* seen to remain the same, but this is not invariably so. In the *Vimānavatthu*, on heavenly rebirths, when the gender is specified by the text or its commentary, it is always the same. The *Petavatthu* (ii.13) discusses the case of a woman said to have been a queen 86,000 times; yet she had not always been a woman: 'you were a woman, you have been a man, and as an animal also you were born' (verse 12).

Similarly, it is said to be hard to find a being who, in some past life, has not been one's mother, or who has not been one's father, or brother, sister, son or daughter (*S.* II.189; cf. *Thīg.* 159).

Thus, sex can change from life to life – but for what reasons? The above *Petavatthu* story continues by saying that the woman, having developed a mind full of lovingkindness and 'faded out the mind-set (*citta*) of a woman', was reborn in a *brahmā* world, i.e. beyond sexual differentiation (verse 19), though at *J.* III.93–4, a being of much good karma from a *brahmā* world is reborn as a woman who becomes an ascetic with the *Bodhisattva*. At *D.* II.271, a male god, Gopaka, says that he *had* been a woman, Gopikā, but by faith in the three refuges, and carefully fulfilling the precepts, 'having faded out the mind-set of a woman and developed the mind-set of a man', he was born in his present male form. He contrasts his state with that of three not very good monks, whom (s)he had supported, who were now reborn in a much lower heaven serving the higher gods. He thus says,

> While as for me – see the difference!
> From household life, and female, I
> Am now reborn a male, a god,
> Rejoicing in celestial pleasures! (*D.* II.273)[7]

At *Thīg.* 400–47 (cf. *J.* v.232–9), a male adulterer is reborn in a hell, then as three kinds of animal who were castrated, as a hermaphrodite human, a troublesome co-wife, and finally as a woman rejected by several husbands (who was then ordained and became an *Arahat*). Such passages demonstrate that gender *is* seen as changeable, but that it is regarded as remaining the same, as if by force of momentum, unless: (1) some specific redirection of the mind is made to this end (see *Asl.* 65), or (2) the fruition of karma makes it particularly appropriate that there is a gender change. They also suggest that there is a difference between transcending sexual differentiation, as in the Brahmā worlds, and losing it, as with being a hermaphrodite.

If there is a suggestion that a female rebirth is not quite as good as a male one, this may well be due to the idea that there are five particular forms of suffering that a woman, but not a man, undergoes: (1), 'at a tender age, she goes to her husband's family and leaves her relatives behind', (2) menstruation, (3) pregnancy, (4) giving birth, and (5) 'she waits upon a man' (*S.* IV.239). Of these, the middle three are biologically

---

[7] See Schuster Barnes, 1987: 259 for a Mahāyāna text in which this 'Gopaka' says that sexual differences are empty of inherent reality.

set, while the first and last are culturally based. The passage does not say that these *should* be so, but simply that they were the case in the society of the Buddha's time – as they have been in many others. One could broaden this to say that, given certain physical pains involved in being a woman – indeed, in the past, child-birth was not infrequently life-threatening – and given that many societies have not treated women equally with men, rebirth as a man might be seen as preferable. Thus a nun who had previously lost a child says:

The state of a woman has been said to be painful by the charioteer of men-to-be-tamed [the Buddha]; even the state of being a co-wife is painful; some, having given birth once, even cut their throats. (*Thig.* 216–17)

Of course, of the five forms of suffering particular to a woman, a nun who has never married is only subject to menstruation.

The Indian brahmin background of the most famous Theravādin commentator, Buddhaghosa (fifth century CE), is perhaps an influential factor on his saying that 'the male appearance is higher (*uttamaṃ*), the female appearance is lower (*hīnaṃ*)' (*Asl.* 322). He also says that, among precious things or 'treasures',

(1) Sentient ones, such as elephants, are 'considered foremost', when compared to insentient ones such as gems, as they are adorned with them as ornaments.

(2) Among sentient treasures, humans are foremost, as they use animal treasures as conveyances.

(3) Among the human treasures, the man treasure is accounted foremost as 'the woman treasure performs service for the man treasure' (*Khp. A.* 178).

Of course, this overlooks the fact that women's serving men is simply a cultural factor. It is not surprising, though, that Buddhaghosa regards rebirth as a man as established by strong wholesome actions, and rebirth as a woman as established by weak wholesome actions. As regards the case of a person coming to take on physical characteristics of the opposite sex during life, strong unwholesome action is the cause of a man coming to look like a woman, while weak unwholesome action is the cause of a woman coming to look like a man (*Asl.* 322).

In later Theravādin literature, the idea of a female rebirth as a less good one seems to be expressed. In the *Jātakas*, the wise princess Rujā says that she will be an honoured female for the next six lives; then, 'I shall be born as a son of the gods, with great power, a male deity, the best in a divine body' (*J.* VI.239, commentarial section). The *Dhammapada* commentary, story 3.8, incidentally says (1.327) that a woman will be reborn as a man by good works and resolving that the karmic fruitfulness of her actions should lead to such a rebirth; also, that a wife who treats her husband well will be reborn as a man. Further than this, the Sarvāstivāda school taught that a woman who attained the 'path of seeing', i.e. stream-entry, would no longer be reborn as a female (*AKB.* IV.21a–b).

Among Mahāyāna texts, the '*Sūtra* on Changing the Female Sex' says that a woman has more greed, hate and delusion than a man (Paul, 1979: 308). In the 'Questions of the Daughter Pure Faith', Pure Faith asks the Buddha how to be no longer reborn as a female. While the text implies that a woman of sufficient insight would not ask such a question, the Buddha tells her how to attain her aim, by avoiding such things as envy, and being devout, giving up attachment to home and family, and developing indifference to her female body (Schuster, 1981: 36–7). In the *Bodhi-caryāvatāra* (X.30), aspirations for beings to be free of misfortunes include one that women achieve rebirth as men, but also that those of higher status – by implication men – be without conceit. The *Sūtra*s on Amitābha Buddha's Pure Land (c. 200 CE) (see pp. 142–3) say that it will be populated only by male humans and gods, but faith will allow one who is currently female to be reborn there (Paul, 1979: 169–70).

VIEWS ON SPIRITUAL STATUSES UNATTAINABLE BY WOMEN

Of the three focuses of devotion in all schools of Buddhism, the first (the Buddha) is male, the second (*Dhamma*) is neuter and the third (the *Saṅgha* of those who have fully or partially attained *Nirvāṇa*) consists of both males and females. On the gender of a Buddha, the pre-Mahāyāna texts (*M.* III.65–6; *A.* I.28) say that it is impossible for:

(1) a female to be an *Arahat* who is (also) a Perfectly and Completely Awakened One (*sammā-sambuddha*): i.e. a full Buddha, one who rediscovers the Path after it has been lost to human society, and shows it to others (*M.* III.8);

(2) a female to be a *Cakkavatti* king: a compassionate and just emperor of a huge realm (see p. 114). In many respects, such a person is seen as the secular counterpart of a perfect Buddha: at his birth, Gotama could have been either, and he said that his remains should be dealt with like those of a *Cakkavatti* (*D.* II.141)

or for any female to attain the state of:

(3) a Sakka: ruler of the thirty-three gods of the pre-Buddhist Vedic pantheon (in which he is known as Indra), a decisive and very active god

who makes frequent appearances in the *Jātakas* to aid virtuous beings;

(4) a Māra: an evil, tempter god who uses his power to keep people attached to the rounds of rebirth, and thus repeated death;

(5) a Brahmā: in the realm of (elemental) form, there are sixteen heavens, the third of which is that of a Great Brahmā (*Vibh.* 424–5): a type of god full of lovingkindness and compassion (*D.* 1.249–51), who has influence over a thousand, or up to a hundred thousand world-systems (*M.* iii.101–2). Nevertheless, such a being is prone to conceit and the delusion that he is eternal and a creator of worlds (*D.* 1.18). Sometimes, the beings in all the form realms are referred to as *brahmās*. The Theravādin commentary (*M. A.* iv.123), though, makes it clear that only *brahmās* in the restricted sense, i.e. Great Brahmās, are meant here. It goes on to say that while *brahmās* are neither male nor female, a human male can be a Great Brahmā in his next life, while a woman cannot.

Here, various key cosmic positions (sometimes known as the 'five ranks'), both the worst and the best, are seen as unattainable by a female. The key qualities of the excluded positions seem to be: (1) compassionate leadership in the discovery and teaching of key knowledge, (2) compassionate rule of a huge realm, (3) decisive leadership and action for good, (4) leadership in evil and (5) power linked to kindness (and conceit). Overall, it is implied that females do not go to the extremes of attainment as do men, and, as seen in all of the above exclusions except (4), cannot combine compassion with great power. While, in the *Karaṇīya-metta Sutta* (*Khp.* 8–9), a mother's love for her only child is taken as a key example of lovingkindness, the radiation of this type of feeling is recommended to *all* beings, without exception.

Nevertheless, it is still seen as possible for a woman to be an *Arahat*, a ruler, or a god, or be reborn in most of the elemental form heavens. In the *Jātakas* (*J.* 1.201), when some men try to exclude some women from the good deed of constructing a meeting hall, a friendly carpenter helps them to be included, for 'excepting the world of Brahmā, there is nowhere bereft of womankind'. Yet the exclusion of women from certain activities is sometimes portrayed as understandable. Thus the Buddha, when asked why women did not (at that time, in India) sit in court, engage in business or go abroad, says that it was due to their being angry, envious, greedy, of weak wisdom (*A.* ii.82–3). Yet as the questioner here is Ānanda, who is frequently shown to be very helpful to women (Horner, 1930: 295–300), the exchange has less the flavour of a put-down than a question out of sympathetic concern, even if it now sounds patronizing.

While the early texts countenance the possibility of a woman ruler, later texts of the pre-Mahāyāna schools do not seem keen on the idea. A commentarial passage in a *Jātaka* (*J.* II.326) says, 'Where women rule, the seeing lose their sight, the strong grow weak . . . virtue and wisdom fly', though this is not necessarily seen as the fault of women themselves. In another story (*J.* I.154–5), a stag is killed by hunters through following an attractive doe to a dangerous area, though she had warned him. The *Bodhisattva*, having watched this, says (canonical section), 'Woe to the man pierced by the arrow-shaft (of desire)! Woe to the land where women are leaders! And they are also blamed who go under the sway of women!' The *Jātaka*s even recognize that some women deserve to rule but are stopped by cultural norms. In the (non-Theravādin) *Mahā-vastu*, a tigress wins a competition to be king of quadrupeds by winning a race. Because the animals would not have a female king, as 'Everywhere males are king', they say that the one she chose to marry would be king (*Mvs.*II.69–72).

Buddhist texts have a variety of views on the question of whether a female can be a *Bodhisattva*, a compassionate seeker of perfect Buddhahood. In the Theravādin *Jātaka*s, on the Buddha's previous lives as a *Bodhisattva*, he is never female, whether as a human, animal or god (Jones, 1979: 20). On the ascetic Sumedha's resolve to strive for Buddhahood, a canonical *Jātaka* verse (*J.* I.14) and the canonical *Buddhavaṃsa* (*Bv.*ch. II, verse 59) include 'attainment of the sexual characteristic (*liṅga-sampatti*)' and will-power among the qualities needed for this resolve to succeed. The *Jātaka* commentary sees this as meaning that a *Bodhisattva* has to be male, and of heroic resolve, being prepared to swim across a huge ocean, if he had to, to attain Buddhahood (Warren, 1896: 14–15). Thus a female, while still in a rebirth as a female, cannot become a *Bodhisattva* and then a Buddha. Yet in the context of Theravāda Buddhism, this is in practice hardly a restriction, as Buddhas are seen as *extremely* rare individuals. The key goal is to become an *Arahat*, which is open to women.

The Mahāyāna, which encourages most to follow the *Bodhisattva* path to full Buddhahood, does generally accept that women can be *Bodhisattva*s – with texts often addressed to both 'good sons' and 'good daughters'.[8] There are different opinions in the texts, though, as to how

---

[8] Though the latter are only usually included when both are addressed (Paul, 1979: 107).

far along this path they can progress while still female. One of the most restrictive is the '*Sūtra* on Changing the Female Sex', which says that a woman who awakens to the thought of enlightenment 'will not be bound to the limitation of a woman's state of mind', and thus be reborn (?) male from then on (Paul, 1979: 175–6). On the other hand, Asaṅga's *Bodhisattva-bhūmi* holds that a *Bodhisattva* may be a female for the first third of the long *Bodhisattva* path, his brother Vasubandhu seeing this as lasting up to and including the seventh of the ten *Bodhisattva* stages, after which a *Bodhisattva* is irreversibly bound for Buddhahood (Paul, 1979: 212–13). The present Dalai Lama, though, holds that even such an idea of restriction on female ability was probably just due to past social influences on Buddhism (Tsomo, 1988: 42).

Not infrequently, women recognized as *Bodhisattva*s are said to be magically transformed into men, prior to further progress.[9] The best-known example of this is in the *Saddharma Puṇḍarīka Sūtra*, or Lotus *Sūtra*,[10] which reached its final form around 200 CE. Here, the eight-year-old daughter of a dragon king[11] is said to have great knowledge, understanding and resolve, and faultless practice. In a moment, she attains the state of an advanced *Bodhisattva*. A male *Bodhisattva* then points out that the *Bodhisattva*-path is very hard and long, so how could a young girl have done this? An *Arahat* then says that, while still female, she cannot become an irreversible *Bodhisattva*, one certain to become a Buddha (in the Sanskrit version of the text); or alternatively a Buddha, one of the 'five ranks' (see p. 372) (Chinese text). After the Buddha immediately accepts a gift from the girl, she likewise immediately changes into a male *Bodhisattva* and then a Buddha, to the amazement and edification of everyone present. In commenting on this episode, scholars of the Chinese T'ien-t'ai school, which saw the Lotus *Sūtra* as the highest expression of truth, held (1) that for a woman with deep insight into emptiness, change of sex is not necessary in order to attain Buddhahood, or (2) that the dragon king's daughter was already a tenth-stage *Bodhisattva*, on the very brink of Buddhahood. They thus held that a woman could attain Buddhahood in her present life (Paul, 1979: 282–4; Schuster Barnes, 1987: 125). The Ch'an/Zen school saw the above episode as showing that sudden enlightenment was possible for anyone with appro-

---

[9] Ibid., 23, 134; Lamotte, 1976: 169, n. 37; Schuster, 1981.

[10] Pp. 251–3 of the Kern translation (1884), from Sanskrit, pp. 212–13 of the Kato et al. one (1975), from Chinese. See also Paul, 1979: 185–90 and Schuster, 1981: 42–4.

[11] *Nāgas*, snake or dragon deities, were seen to have preserved the Perfection of Wisdom *Sūtra*s taught by the Buddha until humans were ready to receive these teachings.

priate insight (Levering, 1982: 24–5; Schuster Barnes, 1987: 126–7). The story was not seen to show that the girl had to become a male before becoming a Buddha, but that, already having attained Buddhahood through sudden insight, she then went on to manifest a male form (Levering, 1982: 26–7, 31).

Other Indian texts discussed by Diana Paul (1979: 190–211, 232–6) and Nancy Schuster (1981: 31–46) have young girls of great wisdom being challenged to change sex. At first they say that this is not necessary, and then do so anyway, but in the process make such remarks as: 'I formerly had a female body, having the nature of emptiness, it was not real . . . Contrary views of that body arise from discrimination' (Paul, 1979: 198). They say that enlightenment is attained by neither a female nor a male, for 'it' is not something to 'attain' at all (Schuster, 1981: 31–5), or that if one cannot attain Buddhahood in a female body, one cannot attain it in a male body either, for the thought of enlightenment, and the seeing of emptiness, is neither male nor female (Paul, 1979: 232–6).

In these texts, the notion that a female cannot be an advanced *Bodhisattva* or Buddha is being played with and critically examined. It is clear that a woman can go on to become such a being. On the one hand, there is no need to transcend the female sex to reach spiritual excellence; on the other, the wise see no reason to be attached to it, by refusing to change it. For one thing, doing so helps liberate men from their doubts about the spiritual potential of females. For another, to change sex illustrates that it has no fixed, inherent existence. This is more clearly shown in the sixth century CE *Vimalakīrti-nirdeśa Sūtra* (Paul, 1979: 230–2; Lamotte, 1976: 169–72). Here an irreversible *Bodhisattva* goddess, when challenged by a male *Arahat* to change her sex, says that she has sought 'femaleness' for twelve years, but has not found it, for it is empty, an illusion. She then uses her magical powers to exchange forms with the *Arahat*, and asks him: why don't *you* change *your* female form? Lastly, she emphasizes that being male or female is only a matter of appearances and convention, for no *dharma*s (phenomena) are either male or female. 'Maleness' and 'femaleness' are not essential ingredients of people, but relative and conditioned states or labels.

Alan Sponberg sees this approach as expressing an ideal of 'nondualistic androgyny' (1992: 24). Over against doubts concerning women's spiritual abilities, which were strongly articulated in contemporary Hindu texts, and seem to have had currency among some Buddhists, these texts argue that, for those who understand emptiness and the consequent 'sameness' of all phenomena, distinctions of sex have no relevance to the

Bodhisattva-path (Schuster, 1981: 54–6). While it remains true that all the named Buddhas in Mahāyāna texts are actually seen as male, Tibetans now generally see Tārā (see p. 361) as a fully fledged female Buddha, as they also do Vajra-yoginī and Sarasvatī (Tsomo, 1988: 84). In one account, it is said that Tārā had once been a princess who made the *Bodhisattva* vows. When monks advised her to take the form of a man, she replied that there is no such thing as a 'man', 'woman', 'self' or 'person'. She then vowed that, as there were few female *Bodhisattvas*, she would remain female in all her lives as a *Bodhisattva* (Beyer, 1973: 65; Willson, 1986: 34).

IMAGES OF WISE AND WAYWARD WOMEN

The *Jātaka* stories (see p. 9), which are full of heroes, heroines and villains, contain both positive and negative images of women. It is clear that many of the stories were taken up from a floating fund of Indian folk-tales, and, in this process, attitudes which were not always Buddhist came to be included.

A number of Theravādin *Jātakas* concern virtuous or wise women. Story 194 (*J.* II.121–5) tells of a woman who saves her husband from a scheming and cruel king by calling on the gods to help, through the power of her own virtue; Sakka comes to the rescue. In story 519 (*J.* V.88–98), a virtuous woman cures her husband of leprosy by drawing on the truth-power of her statement that she loves only him. In story 544, a sixteen-year-old princess teaches *Dhamma* to her father to prevent him from believing the teachings of some ascetics of wrong view (*J.* VI.232–41). In story 66, a queen skilfully cures an ascetic of lust for her by showing him the various weighty responsibilities of married life. In story 539 (*J.* VI.64), a wise girl counsels a queen to let her ascetic husband wander alone: while two bangles on one arm knock together and make a noise, a single one does not: thus it is better to be on one's own. In story 419 (*J.* III.436–8), a man intends to kill the wife who had previously saved him from death, in order to take her gold jewellery. Knowing of this, she pretends to bow to him and manages to push him off a cliff. The verses say, 'A man is not always clever; here and there women are clever (*paṇḍitā*) and attentive' (p. 438). Unlike in the previous stories, this woman's wisdom brings no benefit to a man! Wise women also appear in the *Dhammapada* commentary. Story 13.7 concerns a sixteen-year-old weaver's daughter, who is the only person among the people of Ālavi to take heed of the Buddha's sermon on the need for meditation on death.

Three years later, the Buddha keeps his audience waiting while he waits for her, so that he can test her understanding. She then becomes a Stream-enterer.

In the Theravādin *Jātaka* collection, the sections most focused on women are the 'section on women' (*J.* 1.285–315) and the *Kuṇāla Jātaka*, story 536 (*J.* v.424–56). The former contains ten stories, numbers 61–70, though only eight actually concern women. The latter stands out as particularly misogynous, being a string of stories purportedly given to monks incited by their former wives into being discontented. It talks of the untrustworthy and fickle nature of women, of their embracing men only to get their money, and their unfaithfulness to their husbands, though it includes eight reasons for a woman to despise her husband, for example his drunkenness, stupidity and neglect of her (*J.* v.433). Bollée, in his translation of this *Jātaka*, notes parallels to misogynist verses in the Hindu *Mahā-bhārata* (1970: 119–21), and also various Hindu parallels to sub-stories within it (for example pp. 150–1). Indeed its form is atypical for a *Jātaka*, as it consists of a *series* of stories, has some canonical *prose*, and has verses other than canonical ones. Bollée holds that most of the verses of the *Kuṇāla Jātaka* are not Buddhist. Moreover, it is a *Jātaka* that has not been much portrayed in Buddhist art or other literature (p. 166), and neither a roughly parallel *Jātaka* in Chinese (p. 129) nor a thirteenth-century Sinhalese text which uses aspects of it (p. 131) is misogynous.

In a few of the other *Jātaka* stories, negative aspects of women are focused on to various extents. Stories 6, 61, 63 and 193 tell of vain or treacherous women, with the message that this is to be expected of all women. As stories of bad men do not attribute their evil to their being men, it can be seen that the *Jātaka*s are generally cast in a man's 'voice', in which women are 'other'. Stories 64, 65 and 130 see women as full of wiles, with 64 saying 'Don't be glad if you think "she likes me"; don't be sad if you think "she doesn't like me". The state of women is hard to know, like the path of fish in water!' (*J.* 1.300). Stories 62 (prose part, *J.* 1.293) and 199 (prologue, *J.* 11.134) generalize that women are unfaithful to their husbands, with stories 120 and 130 giving notable examples of this. The sensual, worldly nature of women is emphasized in story 402, which says that women can never have enough of 'intercourse, adornment, and child-bearing' (prose, *J.* 111.342), with story 120 (prose, *J.* 1.440) saying that 'women never tire of sex, it is the nature of (their) birth'.

The message that 'they can't help it', though, is used to counsel that husbands should not be angry at their wayward wives: stories 65

(*J*. 1.301–2) and 191 (*J*. ii.114). The message that women make themselves available to any man, like a road (story 65), is countered by a passage in the *Abhidharma-kośa-bhāṣya*, which says that a man breaks the third precept through delusion if his sexual behaviour is based on the view that women are just to be used (*AKB*. iv.68d). Moreover, in story 534, the view of women as unfaithful is countered by the *Bodhisattva* saying that women should not be censured, for 'as great beings, women are born in the world', and as mothers, they are the source of life and breath to a man (verses, *J*. v.368).

In his survey of the Theravādin *Jātakas*, John G. Jones (1979: 81–116) cites twenty-four (4.4 per cent) as explicitly addressed to monks who wished to disrobe in order to marry or remarry (p. 81), such stories painting a negative picture of life with a woman (see, for example *J*. v.209–10). Jones also cites another nineteen stories (3.5 per cent) which see women as unfaithful, untrustworthy and fickle etc. He also refers (p. 100) to fourteen stories with a more positive image of women. However, the negative depiction of women in some *Jātakas* is not something that the Theravādin tradition emphasized. Of the thirty-five *Jātaka* stories which are specially selected in the canonical *Cariyā-piṭaka*, on the various perfections of the *Bodhisattva*, only one of Jones' 'offending' forty-three is included (no. 443, at Cp. ii.4), and here, the story is not actually misogynous. In the *Dhammapada* commentary stories, the strain of negative thought on women in the *Jātakas* is ignored except for story 18.5 (text, iii.348–9), which has the message that a man should not be angry with his wife for adultery. While it is not to be denied that there is a strain of negative imagery on women within the *Jātakas* – which Sponberg (1992: 18–24) refers to as 'ascetic misogyny' – it should be noted that the 1895 English translation (as used by Jones, but not above) exaggerates this to some extent.

One can see the *Jātakas*, when they are particularly depicting or discussing women, as:

(1) warning monks tempted to break their vows of celibacy that it is not worth it;
(2) warning laymen not to be distracted by their wives' actions from coming to listen to Buddhist teachings;
(3) helping laymen not to take any failings of their wives personally, and thus not to be angry with them;
(4) to support an ideal of mutual support within marriage, unless one partner – usually the male – wishes to be ordained;
(5) giving positive role-models for women, as virtuous, wise women who

support the ideal of renunciation of family life, for those who wish to pursue it.

ASCETIC WARINESS OF THE OPPOSITE SEX

The Buddha often emphasized the overcoming of desire for and attachment to sensual pleasures (see p. 89): an ideal which is at the basis of the Buddha's founding of a celibate *Sangha*. In this, for example, monks should look on women as if they were mothers, sisters or daughters (*S. IV.*110–11). At *A. III.*68–9, the Buddha tells his monks that there is no sight, sound, smell, taste or touch so enticing and distracting as that of a woman, so that he who clings to any of these grieves for a long time. He then goes on to say that, in whatever posture or action, a woman 'persists in overpowering a man's mind (*cittaṃ pariyādāya tiṭṭhati*)'. Women are thus to be seen as a 'snare of Māra', such that it is safer for a monk to sit down with a poisonous snake, or a man with a sword, than sit down alone with a woman, particularly if he is without mindfulness. Accordingly, it is said that woman is the 'stain' of the holy life (*S. 1.*38), and the following discussion is found:

Lord, how are we to act towards women?' 'Do not see them, Ānanda.' 'But if we see them, how should we behave, Lord?' 'Do not speak to them, Ānanda.' 'But if they speak to us, Lord, how should we behave?' 'Practice mindfulness, Ānanda.' (*D. II.*141)

It is also said that a monk should not teach *Dhamma* to women, without the presence of a learned man, in more than five or six sentences in one session, though this could be expanded if they asked questions (*Vin. IV.*20–3).

Nevertheless, just as there is nothing like the sight, sound, scent, taste or touch of a woman to 'persist in overpowering a man's mind', exactly the *same* is said of the effect of a man on a woman, in the very first *Sutta* of the *Aṅguttara Nikāya* (*A. 1.*1–2). Thus such texts are not to be seen as expressing misogyny, but as warnings to celibates to be wary of the attractions of the opposite sex. It is unfortunate that the Pali Text Society translation of *A. III.*68–9 (above) wrongly says that a woman '*will stop to ensnare the heart of a man*' instead of that she, through her sight etc. 'persists in overpowering a man's mind', because of *his* attachment to the female form. Sponberg (1992: 20–1), Schuster Barnes (1987: 257, n. 1) and Paul (1979: 54, n. 14) all use this incorrect translation. Paul (1979: 6–7) also holds that a passage at *S. 1.*124–7, in which 'Māra's daughters' –

craving, discontent and attachment – fail to tempt the Buddha with the various beguiling female forms they take, shows a 'prototype of woman as evil'. If this were so, then Māra's being male would show a 'prototype of man as evil'. But Buddhism does not see either as inherently evil. Schuster Barnes (1987: 110–14) has a good critique of the incorrect notion that Buddhist asceticism led to monks 'despising' women.

The stories of temptations of Māra to certain nuns quoted above (p. 359) show that they were as liable to sensual distractions as monks. The nearest one gets to misogyny in such passages is perhaps in one where the Buddha is said to tell his monks that womankind has five disadvantages, like a black snake: 'she is unclean, bad-smelling, timid, fearful and betrays friends'; like such a snake, she is also angry, grudging, deadly poisonous – for 'she mostly has strong attachment', a forked tongue – for 'she mostly indulges in back-biting speech', and betrays friends – for 'she mostly commits adultery' (*A.* III.260–1). Here, ascetic wariness about the opposite sex becomes a focusing on purported unattractive features of it.

The overcoming of distractions posed by the opposite sex was seen as a form of heroic strength, for monks or nuns. This is shown by *A.* III.89–93, which compares five types of warriors and monks. Just as a warrior may give up at the sight of the dust raised by an approaching enemy, or his flag, or his sound, or on being struck, or is victorious, so a monk may disrobe when he hears of some beautiful girls, or when he sees them, or on being railed at and scorned by a woman, or when a woman deliberately cuddles up to him; or he remains mindful, even if a woman cuddles up to him. Likewise, when a man tries to seduce a nun, she says, 'it is not fitting, sir, that a man should touch a woman who has gone forth' (*Thig.* 367). As he is so entranced by her eyes, she takes one out and gives it him, to shock him out of his attachment to her body (*Thig.* 396).

The *Vinaya* certainly refers to weaker monks making various attempts to get round the rule against abstinence from sexual activity, for example keeping a female monkey to have sex with (*Vin.* III.21), or having intercourse with a wooden doll (*Vin.* III.35–7). There is also reference to a monk agreeing to have sex with a woman when she 'assures' him that she alone will make all the necessary movements (*Vin.* III.36), and to a monk speaking lewdly to some women (*Vin.* III.128). That is, monks are not seen as helpless victims of temptresses, but as having the potential for plenty of weaknesses themselves! Moreover, if the texts have more warning to monks than to nuns to be careful as regards the opposite sex, this may well have been partly because alms-givers were generally women, and thus monks had more meetings with the opposite sex (cf. *M.* 1.462, *A.* III.259).

As regards Mahāyāna texts, Diana Paul gives translations of two texts which she sees as portraying women as 'sexually uncontrollable' (1979: 3) and 'diabolical' tempters of monks (p. 8). She thus sees the texts as showing 'extreme prejudice' against women (p. 10) from the supposedly resentful monks who composed them (p. 6). In fact, the first text (Paul, 1979: 11–25), the *'Sūtra* of the Buddha Teaching the Seven Daughters', betrays no such attitudes. In it, the Buddha simply points out that wise women do not get attached to their appearance, for they know that this fades with age and ends with death. He also warns women against jealousy, as this is a frequent reason for their being reborn in hell. His audience then 'not as male or female, were ecstatic' (Paul, 1979: 22–4). The second text is the 'Tale of King Udayana of Vatsa' (Paul, 1979: 25–50). This concerns a king who nearly kills a very virtuous wife on account of the slander of her by a jealous co-wife. On realizing his mistake, he goes to the Buddha, ashamed of his deed, and asks him to explain fully the 'flattery and deceit . . . the faults of women, their obsequiousness and their lying and treachery' (p. 29), for women influence him to do things leading to hell. The Buddha replies that, to understand the faults of women, the king must first know men's faults, which lead them to be perplexed by women. He describes men as having four such faults:

1 They have insatiable desire for women, such that they do not frequent monks and brahmins and do not cultivate moral and spiritual states (pp. 29–35). Being like hungry demons, they are shackled to women through their desire, and consequently do evil. Such men are seen as like dogs on heat. It is said that 'women can ruin the precepts of purity . . . causing one to go to hell' (p. 31). In cavorting with prostitutes, or having affairs when they are already married, men generate suffering for themselves. Such men are foolish and confused as, intoxicated by desire, they turn away from wisdom and virtue.

2 They turn against their parents when they marry (pp. 35–7; cf. *S.* 1.176).

3 They vainly pass their time, doing evil, not realizing that life is short (pp. 37–9). In this, they are confused by desire, and act in cruel ways.

4 When rich, they lavish money on women, being submissive to them through desire, and do not give to monks or brahmins (pp. 39–49). Intoxicated by desire, they race towards women like hogs towards mud, but these bewilder and deceive them, and can be pitilessly cruel. It would

be better for a good man to be seized by a killer than to be close to a woman. A woman's external beauty hides inner (physical) impurity, of blood, bones and mucus etc., so that women are more detestable than a dead dog. But 'fools are bound to the appearance of women'. Through flattering men, women catch them like a fisherman using a net. But fools still commit adultery, and assault women, and thus generate future pain for themselves in hell. The Buddha complains that even those who have heeded his teaching sometimes fall away because of lust.

Paul sees the above as a 'vituperative polemic against women' by 'monks who projected their own insecurities and weaknesses onto women', being jealous of them as powerful competitors for people's attentions (1979: 26). Yet the above passages could just as easily be read as a survey of the suffering generated through men's actions being dictated only by their sexual desire, and women selfishly exploiting their power to sexually attract men. In this regard, both men and women can be at fault.

Clearly the passage discussed by Paul does contain a strong dose of ascetic unromantic realism about the unattractiveness of much of the human body. Early texts likewise have contemplations on body components – in oneself and others – and rotting corpses, to undercut sensual desire and attachment (*M.* 1.57–9). But such considerations apply equally to both male and female bodies. Thus, after describing the 'unclean' nature of a woman's body, so as to undermine male lust, Nāgārjuna says:

> Since your own body is
> As filthy as a woman's,
> Should not you abandon
> Desire for self and other? (*RPR.* 165)

Admittedly, the unattractive features of the body are often described in the texts as those of a female body, or just a body of unspecified sex. This is probably because monks were more numerous than nuns, and had a greater role in handing on the texts. Describing negative features of the *female* body is an appropriate medicine, a skilful means, for a celibate male who is having difficulty dealing with lust. It should be understood in this practical context, and not be taken personally by female readers. In fact, as male lust is often directed at a male's fantasy-influenced constructed image of a woman, reflections on the unattractive features of the body can simply be seen as a way of deconstructing this *image* in a man's mind. The emphasis on unattractive features of a *female* body may perhaps also be because men have a somewhat greater tendency to be attracted to the *appearance* of a female body than women have to be attracted to the *appearance* of a male body, rather than such factors as a sense of humour and the sound of the voice.

In any case, to emphasize, in certain contexts, the unattractive aspects of the body beneath its surface attractiveness is in no way to look down on either a female or a male person. The early texts encourage the development of lovingkindness to all beings (for example *S.* v.119; cf. *Vism.* 382), and in fact genuine friendliness to a member of the opposite sex may be facilitated precisely by *not* seeing him or her in terms of his or her sexual attractiveness.

One can, though, see a continuity, in the Mahāyāna passages referred to above, with some of those on women in the *Jātaka* stories. As many Buddhist texts are addressed to men, the negative features of women get over-emphasized. When this happens, Sponberg may be right in seeing a convergence with a concern for purification from pollution that has its roots in pan-Indian ascetic traditions with pre-Buddhist origins (1992: 22). The *Śikṣā-samuccaya* contains a passage, for example, which says that hindering someone – man or woman – from being ordained leads a man into such rebirths as being blind, an outcast, a hermaphrodite, a woman, a dog or a snake (*Ss.* 73–4).

The Mahāyāna, though, also contains texts which seek to undercut the idea that the body is intrinsically impure. Candrakīrti often cited a passage in the *Dṛdhādhyāśaya-paripṛccha Sūtra* which says that, just as it would be foolish to contemplate the impurity of a woman conjured up by a magician, so it is for a person to contemplate the impurity of anything that does not truly exist: for everything is empty of inherent existence (Sponberg, 1992: 23).

THE ORDINATION OF WOMEN

A Buddhist *Saṅgha* of nuns (*bhikkhunīs*) was founded by the Buddha five years after his enlightenment. The issue is dealt with in Theravāda texts at *Vin.* ii.253–83 and A. iv.274–80 and discussed by Horner (1930: 95–161), Khantipalo (1979: 133–8), Nattier (1991) and Sponberg (1992: 13–18).

Prior to there being a Buddhist order of nuns, one had existed in Jainism (see *Thig.* 107–11), a slightly older religion. The Jain order, though, for both men and women, was more solitary and less organized than the Buddhist one. Moreover, by the first century CE, Jainism had split into the 'White clad' (Śvetāmbara) and 'Sky clad' (Digambara) fraternities

(Basham, 1967: 291), with the latter (whose monks wear no clothes) actually denying that women were capable of liberation (see Jaini, 1991). As
regards other precedents, Buddhist texts also refer to a few women religious wanderers (*M.* 1.305) and free-lance debaters.

In the Theravāda *Vinaya* (Pali texts on monastic discipline), discussion
of the issue starts by referring to Mahā-Pajāpatī Gotamī, the aunt and
foster-mother of the Buddha (see p. 360). She comes to the Buddha and
asks him to allow women to be ordained. The Buddha replies, 'Be
careful, Gotamī, of the going forth of women from home into homelessness.' She asks twice more but receives the same reply each time. She then
goes away, crying, and then she and her companions shave off their hair
and don yellow monastic robes, to show their sincerity and determination. They then follow the Buddha to another place, arriving dirty, with
swollen feet and in tears. They meet Ānanda, the Buddha's faithful attendant monk. When Gotamī explains why she is crying, Ānanda says that
he will ask again, on her behalf. Asking three times, he receives the same
reply as she had. He then changes his tack and asks,

Now Lord, are women, having gone forth from home into homelessness in the
Dhamma and Discipline proclaimed by the Perfect One, able to realize the fruit
of Stream-entry, or of Once-returning, or of Non-returning, or of Arahatship?
(*Vin.* 11.254)[12]

To this, the Buddha replies that they can indeed attain these states of
sanctity (see pp. 39–40). Ānanda then says that, because of this, and
because Gotamī had been the Buddha's foster-mother, it would be good
if the Buddha would grant ordination to women. The Buddha then
agrees, on condition that the nuns accept eight 'important rules (*garu-
dhammā*)' (*Vin.* 11.255: discussed below), which they do.

The Buddha's apparent hesitation on this matter is reminiscent of his
hesitation on whether to teach at all (*M.* 1.168–9), as he at first thought
that no-one else would understand the profound discovery he had made
at his enlightenment. In both cases, he only agrees once good reasons
are cited: some 'have little dust in their eyes' and will understand; women
can attain advanced states of insight. While the ordination of women
was not a complete innovation, I. B. Horner comments that it was considered unusual at the time, and was made in the face of the 'dead
weight' of public opinion (1930: 110), so that 'What Gotama did for
women shines as a bright light in the history of freedom' (p. 113).

[12] *Dhp. A.* 1.115 says that Mahā-Pajāpatī, at a time prior to the death of her husband and her request
for ordination, was already a Stream-enterer.

The Buddhist tradition actually sees it as impossible for the Buddha not to have agreed finally to Gotamī's request. The Buddha says that the holy life instituted by him would have been incomplete without nuns undertaking to practise *Dhamma* (*M.* 1.491–3). Some of the thirty-two characteristics that Gotama's body was said to have had, from birth, are seen as indicating that, if he became a Buddha, he would be popular among and loved by monks, nuns, laymen and laywomen (*D.* III.167–8). Again, the Buddha is portrayed as knowing, soon after his enlightenment, that he would have an order of nuns (*D.* II.113). Descriptions of past Buddhas at *D.* II.4–7 mention the names of their two chief male disciples, but do not specifically refer to any female disciples. However, the *Buddhavaṃsa*, a late canonical text, gives the names of the two chief nun disciples of each (for example *Bv.* II, verse 214), and the names of Gotama Buddha's chief nun disciples are 'predicted' (III, verse 15). Given that the outline of a Buddha's life is seen as following a set pattern, this implies that the founding of an order of nuns was regarded as a set part of such a life. A Buddha is thus destined to have spiritual 'daughters' as well as spiritual 'sons'.

The *Vinaya* passage on the start of the nun's order continues with the Buddha saying (once Gotamī had withdrawn; p. 256) that, but for the ordination of women, the 'holy life' would have lasted long, and 'true *Dhamma*' (i.e. the highest level of practice of Buddhism, prior to any decline: cf. *Miln.* 132–4) would have lasted a thousand years; now it would only last for five hundred years (but for twice as many people). He then backs this up by comparing a religious order with women in it to: (1) a household with many women and few men in it, which easily falls prey to robbers, (2), a rice field that does not last long, because of an attack of mildew, (3), a field of sugar-cane that does not last long, because of an attack of red-rust. That is, he is portrayed as seeing the monastic *Saṅgha* as less strong and healthy by admitting women to it. He then says that he has instituted the eight important rules for nuns as a precaution against future problems. Buddhaghosa's Theravādin commentary, here, sees the eight special rules as ensuring that the 'true *Dhamma*' *will* last a thousand years, with Buddhism as a whole lasting five thousand years.[13]

E. J. Thomas (1949: 110), though, questions the historicity of aspects of the Pali account of the ordination of nuns, as this is said to be five years after the Buddha's enlightenment, and just after the death of his

[13] *Vin. A.* 1291, translated in Tsomo, 1988: 261–2.

father (*Thig. A.* 141; Rhys Davids and Norman, 1989: 72). However, the *Vinaya* account implies that Ānanda was the Buddha's attendant at the time, though he is not said to have been appointed formally as attendant until twenty years after the enlightenment, which would also be too late for the death of the Buddha's father. A further point, made by Liz Williams,[14] is that at *M.* III.253–5, Gotamī is described in a way indicating that she is a lay person – as following the five lay precepts – in a passage which continues with the Buddha talking to Ānanda of gifts given to both the *Saṅgha* of monks and the *Saṅgha* of nuns. If the nuns' order existed when Gotamī was still a lay person, then the account which includes her being the first nun is cast into doubt;[15] though the conflict may arise from *M.* III.253–5 consisting of two originally separate passages being put together in one text.

The Sarvāstivādins, in their *Madhyamāgama*, and the Dharmaguptakas, Mahīśāsakas and Haimavatas, in their *Vinaya* texts, give an account close to that of the Theravādins (Nattier, 1991: 29). All these monastic fraternities were heirs of the Sthaviravādins of the first schism (around 315 BCE), who disagreed with the Mahā-sāṃghikas on certain matters (Nattier, 1991: 30–2). While surviving texts of the latter fraternity are meagre, none of them contains an account of the founding of the order of nuns, even the *Mahā-vastu*, which contains much miscellaneous story material that might have included it. Jan Nattier thus holds that the account as we have it is later than the first schism. Alan Sponberg sees the account, particularly the relatively elaborated Pali version, as a mythicized account of the processes of mediation surrounding the founding of the nuns' order, a result of reconciliation and compromise between different factions of the *Saṅgha* (1992: 13–16). He dates the account between 200 and 237 BCE, after the Sarvāstivādins and Vibhajyavādins (parent body of the Theravādins) split, but before the Mahīśāsakas split off (1992: 32–3). Given that the Sarvāstivādins broadly share the account, though, such a late date seems implausible. Moreover, the above argument for it being later than even the first schism rests only on the lack of evidence in Mahā-sāṃghika texts, of which few survive. No school using a monastic code of this school has survived; monastics of Southern, Northern and Eastern Buddhism all use codes from the Sthaviravādin schools.

Diana Paul (1979: 80–7) gives the translation of an account of the

---

[14] One of my research students.
[15] A strange echo between the two conflicting passages, though, is Ānanda's reference, in identical words, to the ways in which Gotamī had looked after Gotama as his foster mother.

ordination of nuns from a fragment of a Sanskrit text, *possibly* of the Mūla-Sarvāstivādin school. In this, the account is given in the first person, by the Buddha (which is odd for an early Buddhist text). The Buddha at first refuses ordination for women, except for Gotamī. He then agrees to allow it for other women too, after Ānanda asks him, but there is no reference to the spiritual potential of women, or to Gotamī's having been the Buddha's foster-mother. Here, the Buddha's agreeing without there being any further argument seems odd. The Buddha first says that it is unsuitable for women to be ordained, giving the similes of a family with few women in it etc., then gives the eight important rules as a preventative measure which will allow ordination. Sponberg (1992: 32–4) sees this as an earlier version than the Pali one. However, a contin- uation of the text (at Paul, 1979: 92) refers to newly ordained nuns as having three 'supports': robes, alms-food and medicine. There is no ref- erence to the root of trees as home, for while this was allowed in the early period of the nuns, they came to be prohibited from living in the forest, for their own safety (*Vin.* II.278). This suggests that the text is not a par- ticularly early one.

The Theravādin account of the beginnings of the nun's order (*Vin.* II.253–83) *also* refers to three supports for nuns (p. 274), though in a passage which comes *after* others which show that the nuns' order had already been in existence for some time when *they* were composed. Nevertheless, Hirakawa has argued that the content of the eight chief rules shows that they were not formulated when the Buddha first gave ordination to women, but later.[16] The different traditions of monastic discipline do not completely agree, for example, on what the six rules for a probationary nun, referred to in one of the eight, are (Tsomo, 1988: 256).

The most likely reason for the Buddha's caution over ordaining women – if we take the Theravāda account at face value – was concern over the danger of sexual relations between monks and nuns, if they were to be in close association. In this topic, it is worth noting a passage at *M.* I.306, on renunciants and brahmins who hold that 'There is no fault in pleasures of the senses' and so take their sexual pleasure with girl wanderers, saying that 'Happiness is in the young, soft and downy arms of this girl-wanderer.' Their view, that sense-pleasures are no 'stum- bling-block' for a monk or nun, is, in fact, the only actual *view*, as opposed to overt behaviour, for which a monk can be condemned (if he

---

[16] 1982: 37, as cited in Tsomo, 1988: 224.

persistently makes it; *Vin.* IV.133–6). Given the centrality of celibacy to the monastic life, then, the danger of sexual relations could indeed be viewed as a 'mildew' etc. in the *Saṅgha*. Moreover, women were themselves regarded as strongly orientated towards sex and having children (see p. 402). In any case, given the importance of the *Saṅgha*'s being above suspicion, a focus of devout, uplifting respect for the laity, male and female, any excuse for scandal-mongering had to be avoided. The eight rules can thus be seen as a guard against even suspicion of sexual relations among monastics, as well as a way of promoting and preserving the integrity of the order of nuns as a group independent of the secular world, except through material support.

The first special rule is that 'A nun who has been ordained (even) for a century must greet respectfully, rise up from her seat, salute with joined hands, do proper homage to a monk ordained but that day' – a rule also found among those for Jain nuns (Jaini, 1991: 20). After accepting this rule, it is said that Gotamī, via Ānanda, later tries to get the Buddha to relax it (*Vin.* II.257–8), so that the monks and nuns would greet each other (by bowing etc.) simply according to the length of time in the *Saṅgha*, as is the case among monks, and among nuns. The Buddha refuses, though, saying that other sects, with less concern for guarding their discipline, did not allow the greeting of women, so how could he? This reply seems to suggests that this rule arose mainly as a wish not to go too much against the grain of the current views of the relationship between men and women. It is interesting, though, that *Vin.* II.262 adds a rider to the rule: a monk is *not* to be formally greeted by nuns if he has flirted with, or tried to seduce, a nun. In any case, the important thing might be seen as the fact that there was a clear way of deciding who bows to whom in the *Saṅgha*, as bowing is beneficial to all who do it. Juniors should always bow to seniors, and members of the 'junior' order – i.e. that which was established later – should bow to members of the senior one. Even among monks, one who bows to a senior might still be more spiritually advanced than him, for it is said that even a Stream-enterer lay person will bow to a monk who is an ordinary person (*Miln.* 162): so order of bowing is not the same as order of spiritual advancement.

The sixth special rule was 'When, as a probationer (*sikkhamānā*), she has trained in the six (probationary) rules for two years, she should seek ordination from both *Saṅgha*s.' The category of being a probationer only applied to women, who had to follow the first five of the ten precepts of a novice (which include celibacy: see p. 88) plus not eating after noon. Having shown herself worthy of ordination, a woman had to be ordained as a nun by a group of nuns and then the ordination had to be confirmed by a group of monks. Monks only needed to be ordained by monks. In the original ordination ceremony, a woman was asked if her mother and father had given permission for the ordination (as for monks), not her husband. Later, though, it became an offence (requiring expiation) to ordain a woman without her husband's permission (*Vin.* II.271; *Vin.* IV.334–5). There is no necessity to ask if a prospective monk has his wife's permission, though it is common to ask anyway, out of a sense of social obligation. Another relevant point, here, is that if a nun left the *Saṅgha* to join a non-Buddhist sect, she could not be reordained later, whereas a monk could be, after a four-month probationary period (*Vin.* I.69).

Overall, the eight special rules show that the nuns always had to show formal respect to the monks, were dependent on them for a number of ceremonies, and were under their protection. This implies that, in some ways, there are parallels between their relationship and the Buddha's view of the proper relationship of men and women in marriage. This can be seen in the case of the *Sigālovāda Sutta* advice on marriage (see p. 100):

(1) while a man should hand over authority to his wife, the monks are the source of authority in monastic matters, but delegate it to the nuns:

(2) while the husband should not disparage his wife, and should give her clothes and jewellery, monks should respect nuns and share with them their greatest possession: *Dhamma*, by teaching them;

(3) if treated well by her husband, a wife will run the household well; if taught well by the monks (and by other nuns), nuns will practise well;

(4) while both a husband and wife should be faithful, both monks and nuns should be faithful to the monastic discipline, especially celibacy.

As Jampa Tsedroen, a German nun in the Tibetan tradition, sees it, in the Buddha's day, women were not used to making independent decisions, but looked to men for guidance and protection. To have made the nuns independent of the monks would thus have been impractical and made the nuns vulnerable. Thus the Buddha sought to ensure that the nuns gained knowledge and advice from the monks (Tsomo, 1988: 47–8). As an alternative to seeing analogies between the monk–nun relationship and marriage, one might see it as akin to that of protective elder brother to younger sister (Kabilsingh, in Tsomo, 1988: 226). Such a view is tenable as the monks are sometimes said to be spiritual 'sons' of the Buddha (*D.* II.84), with the nuns as his 'daughters' (*Thig.* 336; cf. 46).

Alan Sponberg (1992: 13–18) speaks of the position of nuns, under male authority, as showing an 'institutional androcentrism' in Buddhism. He argues that social acceptability was a key concern to the *Saṅgha*, given that it depended on material support from lay society. Monks and nuns had to be sufficiently separated to give no excuse for accusations of improper conduct between them, but not so separate that the nuns became an autonomous group of women uncontrolled by some male authority, which was unacceptable to society at large (p. 17). Perhaps one sign of this is the fact that only a fully ordained monk can split a *Saṅgha*: not a nun, a novice, or a lay person (*Vin.* II.204; *Miln.* 108; *AKB.* IV.100a–b). Thus, 'For all its commitment to inclusiveness at the doctrinal level, institutional Buddhism was not able to (or saw no reason to) challenge prevailing attitudes about gender roles in society' (Sponberg, 1992: 18).

Indeed, it seems that monks were not always happy with the fact that the Buddha had ordained nuns. At the first council, convened just after the Buddha's death, Ānanda is held to account on various matters, including having made efforts to attain the ordination of women, this being said to be an 'offence of wrong-doing' (a minor offence). While he does not himself see it as an offence, he acknowledges it as one, out of faith in the *Arahat* monk elders of the council (*Vin.* II.289). The council consisted of 499 *Arahat* elder monks – no nuns – selected by Mahā-Kassapa (the most senior monk), with Ānanda, who became an *Arahat* on the eve of the council, as an important final member (*Vin.* II.285–6). Mahā-Kassapa had been praised by the Buddha as excelling in the quality of shaking off inner defilements by careful attention to monastic discipline (*A.* 1.23), and had a great concern that the *Saṅgha* be healthy and long lasting, emphasizing that a contented, abstemious life was the key to this and its ability to produce *Arahats* (*S.* II.194–224). He was a very ascetic monk who loved the simple life in the forest, away from the crowds (*Thag.* 1051–62) – and where nuns were not allowed to dwell. Moreover, on one occasion, he had to be asked three times by Ānanda to go and teach the nuns (*S.* II.215). In short, he seems to have had little to do with the nuns, and was concerned lest the foundation of their order might have a bad effect on the persistence of good discipline and spiritual realization.

In her introductions to her translations of the *Vinaya*, the *Book of the Discipline*, I. B. Horner points out:

Life for the nuns was probably harder than it was for the monks. In spite of the sympathy with which their troubles were met, they were to some extent discriminated against. (vol.v, p. xiv)

Fairly frequently, the monks had a lesser penalty than nuns, for the same offence. (vol. III, p. xxxviii)

A great number of women are traditionally held to have flocked to the Order of nuns. It is conceivable that they were generally regarded as of poorer quality than the monks, and therefore there had to be a severer testing in order to weed out those who had entered without having a real vocation. (vol.v, p. xiv)

For nuns, there are four extra offences entailing expulsion from the *Saṅgha*: with sensual intent, touching a man anywhere between collar bone and knee or going to a rendezvous with him; not making known that another nun has broken a rule entailing expulsion; and persistently imitating a monk suspended for bad behaviour (*Vin.* IV.211–25). Of course, the fact that nuns have more rules to follow (311 in the Theravādin *Vinaya*, against 227 for monks) is a product of the fact that they have to follow all the rules for monks along with those particular to themselves.

One measure of the status of women is the amount of karmic fruit-fulness (or 'merit': *puñña*) that is said to accrue from giving alms to nuns. Such karmic fruitfulness is said to vary in proportion to the virtue and holiness of both the recipient and the donor (*M.* III.256). This, in turn, is probably due to the extent of positive, joyful intention which tends to accompany acts of giving, this being the greater when the donor and/or recipient is/are particularly virtuous. At *M.* III.256–7, the order of karmic fruitfulness from giving to different sections of the *Saṅgha* is, in decreasing order, as follows:

Both *Saṅgha*s with the Buddha at their head.

Both *Saṅgha*s after the Buddha's death.

The whole *Saṅgha* of monks.

The whole *Saṅgha* of nuns.

A number of monks and nuns specified by the *Saṅgha*.

A number of monks specified by the *Saṅgha*.

A number of nuns specified by the *Saṅgha*.

Here, nuns always come after monks at any level of generality, though there is more karmic fruitfulness in giving to all the nuns rather than a limited number of monks. The slightly lesser karmic fruitfulness accruing from gifts to nuns can best be seen as a reflection of the male-centredness of Indian society in the Buddha's day. In that situation, there would be more joy – in a man or woman – in giving to a male monastic than a female one.[17] Of course, the same reasoning would imply that in any modern society which was not male-centred, this would not be the case.

---

[17] Note that, at *Vin.* II.268, if a layman or laywoman bequeaths goods to 'the *Saṅgha*', they belong to the monks, not nuns. If a nun makes such a bequest, though, the goods belong to the order of nuns.

NUNS AND OTHER FEMALE RELIGIOUS ROLES IN
BUDDHIST CULTURES

Ancient India

In accordance with the above, it appears that it was harder for nuns to get alms than for monks. At *Vin.* IV.175–6, it is said, in relation to a starving nun, that 'Women obtain things with difficulty' (as at *Vin.* III.208). It is also stated that nuns should not ordain new nuns every year, as there was not enough accommodation for them (*Vin.* IV.336). The relative difficulty of nuns getting alms seems to have persisted in India. In the *Bodhi-caryāvatāra*, an eighth-century CE text, Śāntideva includes the aspiration 'May nuns be materially sufficient, abandon quarrelling (with each other) and be unharmed' (*Bca.* x.44). Moreover, the idea of female renunciation, if this involved leaving young children, was frowned on. Thus in the *Jātakas*, the *Bodhisattva*, as an ascetic who has left his children in the care of relatives, mildly rebukes his ex-wife for having gone off to be an ascetic without thought of them (*J.* III.376–83). Elsewhere, though, there is no censure when the *Bodhisattva* leaves his wife, once she has given birth to the child she was carrying, to become an ascetic (*J.* II.139–41).

In the early period, the nuns nevertheless seemed to have flourished. In the edicts of the emperor Asoka (268–239 BCE), there are a number of references to nuns, and their status can be seen from the fact that his own daughter became a nun, Saṅghamittā. Nuns were also numerous and well supported up to around 300 CE, though they appear only rarely in Mahāyāna *Sūtras* (Paul, 1979: 79). Respected women in Mahāyāna texts are usually laywomen, towards whom certain texts are specifically directed (Tsomo, 1988: 101, 175).

After 300 CE, nuns' numbers seemed to drop, as evidenced by the much smaller number of inscriptions recording donations to Buddhist temples etc. by nuns,[18] and the fact that the records of Chinese pilgrims visiting India in 399–400, 629–43 and 671 CE do not mention many communities of nuns in their accounts. The 671 report (of I Ching) also says that nuns did not receive the same material support as monks (Falk, 1980: 209–11). As Hinduism reasserted itself, Hindu social norms for women, which may have gradually influenced Buddhists, would have led to reluctance to support women who renounced their expected roles as wives and mothers. That Buddhists nevertheless sought to resist this

[18] From donations given them by the laity, or by the laity on their behalf.

trend is shown, for example, by the sixth-century Tamil epic *Maṇimēkalai*. This undercut existing Hindu ideals of romance, and argued for Buddhist ideals, through the story of a courtesan's daughter who resisted suitors and became a nun (Richman: 1992). Historical and archaeological records show that nuns probably existed in India till the general demise of Buddhism there, in the tenth or eleventh century (Kabilsingh, 1991: 30). Nevertheless, it can be seen that the order of nuns came to lose its original prestige and creativity as it faded into relative historical obscurity (Sponberg, 1992: 18).

Lands of Eastern Buddhism

In Eastern Buddhism, Confucian strictures on the behaviour of women meant, for example, that Chinese nuns had to live in isolated localities. Nevertheless, the order of nuns was very successful in China, and China, Taiwan and Korea are the only places where fully ordained *bhikṣuṇīs* (Pali *bhikkhunīs*) still exist. In China, nuns were sometimes quite influential in both religious and political matters, which may have been due to the fact that the organizational structures of monks and nuns were always separate in China (Paul, 1979: 80). The *Pi-ch'iu-ni chuan* records the biographies of sixty-five eminent nuns over the period 317–516 CE (Tsai, 1994; Conze et al., 1954: 291–5), including those excelling in asceticism, meditation, faith and teaching, or scholarship and teaching (Schuster Barnes, 1987: 124; Schuster 1985: 93–6). Some wrote commentaries and treatises, though no such work known to be by Chinese women has survived. Moreover, no-one added to this early record of nuns, in the way that similar records of eminent monks were added to (Schuster Barnes, 1987: 130).

The popularity of becoming a nun may have been partly because it offered respite from the low status of women in secular society (Welch, 1967: 392), though this effect did not seem to lead to the popularity of nuns in a Hindu-dominated India. At various times, the number of monks and nuns in China has been recorded, as shown in table 1:

Table 1

Year	Nuns	Monks	Ratio	
729	50,358	75,524	1:1.5	(Ch'en, 1973: 85)
1221	61,240	397,615	1:6.5	(Ch'en, 1964: 401)
1930	225,200	513,000	1:2	(Welch, 1967: 412–14)

The low ratio of nuns to monks in 1221 may reflect the rising influence of Neo-Confucianism. While the number of monks and nuns in Communist China is now much lower, as it is in Communist Vietnam, the Chinese order of *bhikṣuṇī*s is strongly established in Taiwan, where members outnumber the monks (around 6,500 to 3,500): with greater affluence, families no longer have a financial need to have a son looked after at a monastery. Taiwan's biggest monastery is largely run by the nuns, who outnumber the monks there by three to one. Taiwan can in fact be seen as the main stronghold of Buddhist *bhikṣuṇī*s in the world. The nuns have the same opportunities in Buddhist education as the monks, and the same responsibilities in teaching. They are also involved in social and medical work, teaching in schools, Buddhist colleges and universities, and working in Buddhist publishing ventures (Tsomo, 1988: 121–3, 179, 189–94). The Chinese order of nuns is also found to some extent in countries which include Chinese populations, such as Malaysia, Indonesia, Singapore and Thailand. In South Korea, the *bhikṣuṇī* order is also strong and active: it is the mainstay of day-to-day Buddhism, with the nuns also being strong on monastic discipline and meditation, and having good educational facilities (Tsomo, 1988: 134).

Insufficient *bhikṣuṇī*s reached Japan from Korea ever to ordain Japanese *bhikṣuṇī*s, so Japanese nuns have only been novices following ten precepts, plus the *Brahmajāla Sūtra Bodhisattva*-precepts that the monks also followed (Tsomo, 1988: 129). From at least the seventeenth century, nuns did not have a high status, having been unable to live in proper temples (only remote hermitages), to conduct funerals in their own right, or be recognized as Zen masters. Nevertheless, at least one, Ryonen Gensho (1646–1711), attained renown for both her artistic and her spiritual achievements (Spring Wind, 1986: 180–7). Education for nuns was minimal, but this started to change with the modernization of the country in the Meiji era (1868–1911), which led to nuns petitioning for improvements in their status in the 1920s and 1930s. Restrictions gradually started to be lifted, and this accelerated in the more liberal climate since 1945 (Uchino, 1986). Today, the nuns are not formally ordained as novices, but just follow the *Bodhisattva*-precepts, are celibate, and do not drink alcohol or eat meat.

In the pre-modern period, Japanese monks no longer followed the ancient monastic code of a *bhikṣu* (Pali *bhikkhu*), but only the *Bodhisattva*-precepts. Following a government decree in 1872, they, but not nuns, increasingly began to marry. After a period of celibate training, they become married priests. At first, the status of their wives was low, but in the more recent liberal climate, they have received more recognition and have come to be allowed to take on certain priestly duties – a change that the celibate nuns, who undergo much more training than they, are not too pleased with. There are around 2,000 celibate nuns, most of whom live alone, running their own temples; some have assistants. They do not receive support from their sect organizations, but depend on their parishioners, fees for such things as teaching the tea ceremony, savings, family support, and some help from their Buddhist teacher. Training institutes for them exist, but there have not, until recently, been many new nuns coming forward; contemporary two-children families are not very willing to let one go to be ordained. Consequently, most nuns are quite old (Tsomo, 1988: 124). There are now some university-educated young ones, though.

Lands of Southern Buddhism

In Southern Buddhism, the *Mahā-vaṃsa* chronicle (ch. 34, verses 7–8) refers to a royal donation to 60,000 monks and 30,000 nuns in the first century BCE. While the order of *bhikkhunīs*, following 311 precepts, long flourished there, it came to die out in 1017 CE, after a disastrous invasion.[19] In principle, it could have been reintroduced from Burma, where it existed till at least the thirteenth century (Gombrich, 1988: 168), probably being ended there because of Mongol attacks on the region. Nevertheless, while the ordination line for monks was reintroduced into Sri Lanka from Burma in 1070 CE, that for *bhikkhunīs* was not reintroduced. In Thailand, and neighbouring Laos and Cambodia, it seems never to have been established.

A Theravādin 'nun' is now a woman who in general permanently keeps the eight or ten precepts of a devout lay person (see pp. 87–8), though these nuns are not accorded the status of *sāmaṇerīs*, female novices, who used to keep the ten precepts permanently.[20] They are known variously as *dasa-sil-māṇiyō* ('ten-precept-mothers': Sri Lanka), *thela-shin* ('possessors of the precepts': Burma) or *mae jī* ('honoured mothers who are ordained': Thailand). As with a monk, the head is shaved, a Pali name is taken and a robe is worn: white, yellow, brown or pinkish-brown according to country and whether eight or ten precepts are followed. The nuns' status, though, is ambivalent, for they are not

[19] On Theravāda nuns in ancient India and Sri Lanka, see Khantipalo, 1979: 128–65.
[20] On contemporary Theravāda nuns, see Kabilsingh, 1991: 36–66, 87–93; Khantipalo, 1979: 153–63; Tsomo, 1988: 109–11, 138–49, 229–32, 262–6.

officially counted as members of the monastic *Saṅgha*, but as pious lay women (*upāsikā*). In Thailand, they are not under the auspices of the Department of Religious Affairs, and do not pay reduced fares on public transport, like monks; and yet, like monks, they are not allowed to vote (nor can they vote in Burma). As more karmic fruitfulness is seen to be generated by giving to a more virtuous person, and monks follow more moral/monastic precepts than the nuns, lay donors are less willing to support nuns than monks (Kawanami, 1990: 25). The number of Theravādin nuns has been increasing during this century, however. In Sri Lanka, there are now about 3,000 (to around 20,000 monks), which represents around 0.06 per cent of Buddhist females. In Thailand, there are roughly 10,000 nuns (to around 250,000 monks, during the rains retreat, when many men are ordained temporarily), which represents around 0.04 per cent of females. In Burma, there are around 25,000 nuns, about 0.14 per cent of females. Around sixty Theravāda nuns now also exist among recently (re-)converted Buddhists of Nepal, and they take an active part in teaching and spreading Buddhism there (Tsomo, 1988: 138–9).

In Thailand, nuns tend to do domestic chores around the monastery, and manage its finances, with less time than monks for study. They receive rather patchy support, though the development of a nuns' Institute in 1969 has been helping to improve facilities for them and upgrade their status. In Burma, nuns are better respected and supported, with more time for study than in Thailand. Some are eminent scholars and others are very experienced meditators. In Sri Lanka, the status and activity of nuns have increased during the twentieth century as part of a revival in Buddhism, so that it is no longer true that most nuns are aged.[21] Since the 1980s, they have developed an organization increasingly like that of the monks. In many respects, eight-precept nuns act like novices, and ten-precept ones like monks. Both are much respected by the laity. Their time is spent in study and meditation, and in serving the laity much as monks do. Yet, on account of their simple life-style and their meditation, they are often seen by the laity as more virtuous than city and village monks, though not forest-dwelling monks (Bloss, 1987: 23–4, 27). Recently educational facilities for nuns, which have not been good, have started to improve (Kabilsingh, 1991: 89).

---

[21] Bartholomeusz, 1994 and 1992: 43–61; Bloss, 1987: 9–17; Gombrich and Obeyesekere, 1988: 274–95.

Some lay activists, especially among the urban elite in Sri Lanka, hope that the Theravādin *bhikkhunī (and sāmaṇerī)* ordination-line can be re-established. However, that would require ordination by both a group of ten properly ordained *bhikkhunīs* and a similar group of monks (*bhikkhus*). It is therefore necessary to find a community of *bhikṣuṇīs* (Sanskrit equivalent of Pali *bhikkhunīs*) from Eastern Buddhism who come up to Theravādin standards on ordination-line and discipline. The monastic discipline that such nuns follow is not a 'Mahāyāna' code (though they also follow an additional Mahāyāna code), but that of the Dharmaguptas, one of the early schools closely allied to the Theravāda. The Chinese ordination-line, in fact, partly derives from some nuns brought by sea from Theravāda Sri Lanka in 429 and 433 CE (Conze et al., 1954: 291–3; Khantipalo, 1979: 151–3). Some claim, though, that in Chinese and Korean tradition, nuns have generally been ordained by monks alone (Tsomo, 1988: 248–9).

In 1971, a Thai eight-precept nun, Voramai Kabilsingh, was ordained as a *bhikkhunī* in Taiwan, but the Thai *Saṅgha* sees her, at best, as a Mahāyāna *bhikkhunī* (Kabilsingh, 1991: 48–54; Spring Wind, 1986: 202–9). However, in 1974, the President of Sri Lanka, William Goppallawa, declared that the government would support the re-establishment of a *bhikkhunī* order, a concern which was helped by the presence in the country of the German nun Ayya Khemā and her outspoken support for re-establishment (Bartholomeusz, 1994: 147). A register of nuns was started in 1984, and in 1988 a minister proposed rules to unify female renunciants and also create an order of lay nuns. In 1985, the government sent a representative to study the Chinese nuns, and asked monks and scholars to submit views on the possibility of re-establishing the *bhikkhunī* ordination-line (Tsomo, 1988: 114). Nevertheless, most monks and even lay nuns are wary of a threat to the integrity of Theravāda Buddhism if ordination comes from Mahāyāna nuns (Bartholomeusz, 1994: 147, 181).

In America, Sri Lankan Theravādin monks of Los Angeles have been impressed by the enthusiastic interest of American women in Buddhism (Bartholomeusz, 1994: 187). In 1988, with the help of Mahāyāna nuns of various traditions, a Thai lawyer (in May, at the LA Buddhist Vihāra) and five Sri Lankan nuns (December, Hsi Lai temple) were ordained as *sāmaṇerī*, or novices, as a first step towards ordaining *bhikkhunīs* (Bartholomeusz, 1994: 181, 186–7). At the second ceremony, Ayya Khemā also became a *bhikkhunī*. Nevertheless, older monks in Sri Lanka contested the ordinations, especially that of Ayya Khemā. In March 1998, there was also a *bhikkhunī* ordination in Sri Lanka itself, at a monastery in Dambulla, but this has also been seen as invalid by senior *Sangha* leaders on the island.[22]

For the *bhikkhunī* community to be formally restarted – which I certainly hope will happen – the agreement of senior monks in Theravādin countries would be required, which would be difficult at present to attain. Some monks may fear that donations to them will decrease if there are also *bhikkhunīs* for the laity to support. Many senior monks in Sri Lanka also refer to the canonical passage which has the Buddha initially holding back from ordaining women (see p. 384; Bloss, 1987: 22). Also, many nuns may prefer their present status, in which they are more independent of monks than they would be as *bhikkhunīs* (Bloss, 1987: 19; Bartholomeusz, 1992: 51). In Sri Lanka, most nuns already see their monastic vocation as equal to that of monks, or even superior (Bartholomeusz, 1994: 190).

Demands and agitation by women are likely to be counter-productive. For *bhikkhunīs* to exist, their discipline will require an ongoing working relationship with monks. Change will come slowly. At present, a minority of senior Sri Lankan monks do support the ordination of women (Bloss, 1987: 22). Balangoda Ānanda Maitreya (1896–1998), who was perhaps the most respected monk on the island, was sympathetic (Gombrich and Obeyesekere, 1988: 302), though he opposed formal re-establishment of the Theravādin *bhikkhunī* order from Mahāyāna nuns as too contentious. Rather, the nuns should follow all the *bhikkhunī* precepts even if they cannot be formally ordained as *bhikkhunīs* (Bartholomeusz, 1994: 168–9). Among more junior monks, though, Katz found in 1983–4 that 22 of the 37 he asked in the university town of Peradeniya were supportive. Even among the eleven who did not support it, there was often a feeling that it was a shame that it could not be done (1986; 1988: 147). Such monks are likely to form a nucleus of those who come to accept the ordinations now being carried out. In Thailand, also, the young educated monks who act as secretaries to very senior ones are more open to the idea of full ordination for women. In time, they may come to take up senior posts themselves (Kabilsingh, 1986: 147). Improved education for existing eight- and ten-precept nuns will also facilitate the recognition of them as worthy of higher ordination as *bhikkhunīs*.

[22] *Yasodhara: Newsletter on International Buddhist Women's Activities*, 14 (3) (April–June 1998), 11. By fifteen months later, there were around 150 *bhikkhunīs* at Dambulla, according to the *Guardian*, 14 August 1999.

Lands of Northern Buddhism

In Northern Buddhism, Tibet has a few recognized female incarnation-lines, one going back to the eighth-century Yeshe Tsogyel (Ye-shes mTsho-rgyal), consort of Padmasambhava (see p. 365), herself seen as a manifestation of the female *Bodhisattva* Vajra-vārāhī, Dorje Phagmo (rDo-rje Fags mo in Tibetan).[23] One of the incarnations was as the much-loved twelfth-century mystic Machig Lapdron (Ma-gcig Lab-sgron), founder of the Mahāmudra Chod (gCod) lineage of practice (Allione, 1986: 143–204). The current incarnation of Dorje Phagmo is among the most revered people in Tibet.[24]

Notable female saints of Tibet have generally lived as hermits and wandering practitioners, outside the main monastic centres, and have not belonged to the dominant Gelug (dGe-lugs) tradition (Allione, 1986: 14–15). The order of nuns was never properly introduced into Tibet, because of the difficulty of nuns travelling there from India to ordain them. Some monks ordained *bhikṣuṇīs* themselves in the twelfth century, but this was seen by most as an invalid form of ordination. Thus Tibetan Buddhist nuns (Tibetan *a-nis*) are not full *bhikṣuṇīs*, following the 366 rules of the Mūla-Sarvāstivādin monastic code used in Tibet, but are *śrāmaṇerikās* following the ten rules of a novice, plus twenty-six more. In the case of Mongolia, even the *śrāmaṇerikā* ordination was not transmitted. *A-nis* are thus akin to Theravāda nuns in the number of precepts that they follow, except that they are formally recognized as novices, unlike the Theravādin ones.

While families have been encouraging to sons who wished to be monks, they have often been less willing for their daughters to become nuns, preferring them to marry (Willis, 1989: 106, 122). In the harsh Tibetan climate, the physical risk to mother and child of child-birth meant that fertile women were much prized to keep the family line going. Sir Charles Bell reports that the ratio of nuns to monks in Tibet was about 1:35 (1928: 164), though Willis reports a ratio of 1:9.[25] Prior to the Chinese Communist occupation, there were 18,828 nuns in Tibet: around 0.75 per cent of the female population, probably the highest of all Buddhist lands. Of these, about 8,000 lived in large communities of over a hundred nuns, the largest housing around a thousand

[23] Dowman, 1984; Tarthang Tulku, 1985; Willis, 1989: 11–32.
[24] Miller, 1980: 155; Allione, 1986: 29–32; Willis, 1989: 104–5, 121.
[25] 1989: 100, citing T. W. D. Shakabpa, *Tibet: A Political History* (New Haven: Yale University Press, 1967), p. 6.

(Willis, 1989: 119, 163–4). While there are no figures for the number remaining there, there are around 1,930 living as refugees in India or Nepal or among existing communities there or in Bhutan (Tsomo, 1988: 151).[26]

Traditionally, the education of Tibetan nuns focused on chanting and meditation, not on Buddhist philosophy, as for the monks. Today, in the exiled community in India and Nepal, nuns are being included in logic and philosophy training (Tsomo, 1988: 152; Willis, 1989: 124–34). The Dalai Lama sees improving the status of the nuns as helping, for example, in the spread of Buddhism in the West (Tsomo, 1988: 51). He has also affirmed that, without a *bhikṣuṇī* order, Tibet cannot be considered a 'central land', that is, a Buddhist heartland (Tsomo, 1988: 41). He is therefore supportive of Tibetan nuns gaining *bhikṣuṇī* ordination from their Chinese sisters (Tsomo, 1988: 242, 267–75). A start was made in 1984, with the ordination of four of them in Hong Kong (p. 246). The Dalai Lama alone, however, cannot grant recognition of Tibetan *bhikṣuṇī*s without the agreement of other senior monks.

The aspirations of nuns of all types were strengthened by the holding of an international conference of Buddhist nuns in February 1987 at Bodh-Gayā, India, where the Buddha attained enlightenment (see Tsomo, 1988). It was organized by an American *bhikṣuṇī* of the Tibetan tradition, Karma Lekshe Tsomo, a Thai Theravāda laywoman, Dr Chatsumarn Kabilsingh, and a German Theravāda nun, Ayya Khemā (Tsomo, 1988: 49); participants came from twenty-six countries, and included the Dalai Lama. The German monk Nyanaponika, long resident in Sri Lanka, sent a message of support, as did the Sri Lankan Commissioner of Buddhist Affairs. The meeting saw the formation of Sakyadhītā, 'Daughters of the Buddha', the International Association of Buddhist Women, which is doing important work in helping Buddhist nuns throughout the world learn about each other and helping to improve their education and status.

Excluding the People's Republic of China (which includes Tibet), Vietnam, Laos and Cambodia, for which figures are not available, there are around 60,000 Buddhist nuns in the world: 38,000 Theravāda nuns; around 15,000 *bhikṣuṇī*s of the Chinese or Korean traditions; 3,000 *śrāmaṇerikā*s of these traditions; 2,000 *śrāmaṇerikā*s of the Tibetan tradition; and 2,000 Japanese nuns (cf. Tsomo, 1988: 53–4).

---

[26] For further information on Tibetan nuns, see Havnevik, 1991 and Willis, 1989: 96–134.

LAYWOMEN IN BUDDHIST TEXTS

In praising particular disciples, the Buddha includes a number of lay-women as excelling in various qualities (*A.* 1.26): Sujātā (being first to take refuge), Visākhā (giving to the *Saṅgha*), Khujjuttarā (being learned), Sāmavātī (dwelling in lovingkindness), Uttarā (meditation), Suppavāsā (giving choice alms-food), Suppiyā (nursing the sick), Kātiyānī (being of unwavering faith), Kālī (having faith even from hearsay) and Nakula-mātā (conversing intimately): at *A.* III.298, the Buddha tells the latter's husband that he is lucky to have such a compassionate wife as his coun-sellor and teacher. A similar list for laymen also includes someone who excels in teaching *Dhamma*. Among these women, Visākhā is particularly notable (see Horner, 1930: 345–61), a rich, self-assured housewife who supported and attended to the needs of the *Saṅgha* with great care, and to whom the Buddha gave a long discourse (*A.* 1.205–14). Elsewhere, the Buddha advises Visākhā to use her own judgement regarding whether or not the quarrelsome monks of Kosambī taught in accordance with *Dhamma* (*Vin.* 1.355–6). Her action also causes the Buddha to make a rule that the word of a trustworthy laywoman disciple should be listened to if she says that a monk has sat down in a secluded place with a woman and indulged in some form of sensual behaviour (*Vin.* III.187–8).

In the *Suttas*, Visākhā is a key donor, as is the man Anāthapiṇḍika, a wealthy merchant. While the latter was noted for periodic large gifts such as the buying of land for the Jetavāna monastery with a huge amount of gold, Visākhā gives more in the form of a constant supply of the daily necessities of life for monks and nuns (Falk, 1990: 132). While they are not often mentioned together in the *Suttas*, Nancy Falk has shown that in the Theravāda commentaries to the *Dhammapada* and *Jātakas*, these two become increasingly paired and paralleled (1990: 136) as 'a matched pair of "perfect" male and female donors' (1990: 139), standing 'in place of father and mother' to the *Saṅgha* of monks (*J.* III.119). Each type of giving is increasingly seen as being also carried out by the other, which implicitly denies 'that any gift is more appropriate for male or female' (1990: 138–9). Nevertheless, giving, a key Buddhist value, is often much practised by women. Indeed, in the *Vimānavatthu*, a Theravādin canonical text on the heavenly rebirths of various good people, most of the donors are female (Falk, 1990: 140).

Horner (1930: 83–94) points out that, in the early Buddhist texts, most adult women referred to (other than nuns) are married women sup-ported by their husbands. There is reference, though, to women workers among poorer people. Many worked in households as domestic slaves, along with their male counterparts. The evidence is that such people were not maltreated or overworked. They could be released by their master, for example in order to be ordained. Women also worked in agriculture, and as acrobats, musicians and dancers. Some worked as prostitutes, including some very rich courtesans.

The early texts recognized that many women gained their specific identity through marriage. Thus it is said that a fire is made known by its smoke, a kingdom by its king, and a woman by her husband (*S.* 1.41–2), probably meaning that a woman is often known as 'so-and-so's wife'. Yet one *Jātaka* story mocks the popular view that a woman is 'naked without a husband' (*J.* 1.307); for it praises a woman who saves her brother, not her husband, from a threatening king, as she can get another husband but not another brother. Nevertheless, it seems that the Buddha saw women as primarily orientated towards gaining a husband and children, and thus power in a household. At *A.* III.363, he outlines the goals and aspirations of various kinds of people. Those of nobles (*khattiyas*), brahmins and householders relate to success in their sphere of activity or work, while for women: their goal is a man; their ambition is adornment; their resolve is for a child; their desire is to be without a rival; and their fulfilment is to gain authority (*issariya*), by implication within their own marriage-based household. Of course, any of these kinds of people could go beyond these usual aims, for example by focusing on enlightenment. That a woman's 'resolve' is for a child is echoed by a passage which says that women end life 'unsated by and not opposing' sex and child-bearing (*A.* 1.78). This was said partly because giving a child to a family was a source of power, as part of the network of marital dynamics. The Buddha thus describes the five 'powers' (*balas*) of a woman as those of beauty, wealth, kin, children and moral virtue (*sīla*; i.e. keeping the precepts). With these, she dwells at home in confidence, overpowering her husband and continuing to get the better of him. Against these powers, a man can only get the better of his wife by the power of authority (or being masterful, *issariya*-; *S.* IV.246). Of her five powers, only the last is essential, both for a lasting relationship and for a good rebirth (*S.* IV.247–8). It could also allow a woman to be head of a prosperous household, for it is said that one of the reasons why a family prosper is that they 'place in authority (*ādhipacce*) a virtuous woman or man' (*A.* II.249).

Elsewhere, it is said that a monk should have the qualities of a woman with a 'lovely reputation' (cf. *A.* III.37), being 'gentle, meek, and tranquil (*upasantā*)', that is, not easily angered (*M.* 1.125–6). The valuing of such calm in a wife, and as a general spiritual quality, is also seen in relation to legends of the compassionate and powerful *Cakkavatti* kings (see p. 114). Among such a king's seven 'treasures' is his wife (as at *D.* II.175–6), who is seen to parallel the spiritual 'treasure' of 'tranquillity' (*passaddhi*; *S.* v.99). Nevertheless, it is recognized that women are not always calm: 'the power (*bala*) of children is crying, the power of women is anger, the power of thieves is a weapon, the power of kings is ruling ...' (*A.* IV.223).

In the Vessantara *Jātaka* (see pp. 63–4), the *Bodhisattva* shows his unstinting generosity by even being prepared to give away his children and then his wife. This, of course, implies that he in some sense 'owned' them. This interpretation does not seem amiss given that it is said that a woman is 'the best of possessions',[27] and the Western idea of a father 'giving' his daughter in marriage also reflects such an idea. Yet in Buddhism, all 'possession' is only a provisional, not an ultimate concept – for as all is not-Self and impermanent (see pp. 34–6), nothing can be truly 'mine' – and if a wife was seen as in some sense a possession, she had to be a willing one. Thus the Buddha says, admiringly, that one of the conditions for the prospering of the Vajjian republic is that they 'do not forcibly abduct others' wives and daughters, and do not compel them to live with them' (*D.* II.74).

LAYWOMEN IN BUDDHIST CULTURES

A history of European conflict with Islam has meant that there has long been a view in the West that 'women are benighted in Asia'. When some contemporary feminist views are added to this, strong negative expectations can be set up regarding the position of women in Asian cultures. As a point of reference, it might be borne in mind that women had few legal rights in the USA prior to the 1920s, and until 1976 had to overcome barriers to obtain credit or set up in business. Italian women had no right to divorce prior to the mid 1970s, and Frenchwomen had no legal right to control their own incomes prior to the mid 1960s (Miller, 1980: 156). Thus to assume that the West historically has a better track record on sexual equality than Asia is not necessarily correct.

Lands of Southern Buddhism

In the lands of Southern Buddhism, the good position of women in the pre-modern era was often remarked upon by Western colonial observers (Dewaraja, 1981). Inheritance laws treated sons and daughters

[27] *S.* I.43; cf. *M.* I.162, *Miln.* 192, *Thig.* 406–25.

equally, and both husbands and wives had legally recognized grounds for divorce. In Burma, Sir Guy Burgess held that, 'Unlike the Hindu wife, the Buddhist wife is considered as practically on an equality with her husband, and she generally takes an equal part in the management of the family affairs',[28] with Fielding Hall (1902) seeing the Burmese wife as very free as compared to nineteenth-century Western women. In Thailand, influence from Brahmanized cultures between the mid four-teenth and mid eighteenth centuries put women at a relative disadvan-tage compared to Sri Lanka and Burma, but this was gradually overcome in the modern period, and Thai women won the right to vote at the same time as men in 1932.

In contemporary Burma, there is a 'marked equality obtaining between the sexes' and women 'enjoy social position equivalent to men (except in some religious spheres)' (Nash and Nash, 1963: 263, 260). This is so even though women see men as superior, being able to be Buddhas, being more 'noble', having pleasanter lives, and not having to bear chil-dren (Spiro, 1971: 82–3). Around a third of the Burmese women hope to be male in their next life (Spiro, 1971: 81), with a smaller proportion hoping so in Sri Lanka (Dewaraja, 1981: 11), though in Thailand, such a view is rare, and it is seen as better to be a wealthy woman than a poor man (Hanks and Hanks, 1963: 436). In Sri Lanka, *Vipassanā* meditation is now popular among the laity, with a majority of practitioners being women, and teachers also include laywomen (Bond, 1988: 178–87, 209). Practitioners often hold that lay people have an advantage over the monks as they experience more suffering, and that 'Women have an even greater advantage than laymen, for women experience more *dukkha* [suffering] than men' (Bond, 1988: 184).

Lucien and Jane Hanks report that, while most social relationships in Thailand are structured on the basis of senior/junior or patron/client, the relationship of husband and wife is one of equality (1963: 437). Advice at marriage is for the wife to please her husband, and be gentle and understanding; the husband should love and protect his wife, and be just and considerate; there is no mention of obedience (Hanks and Hanks, 1963: 437; Terweil, 1979: 152). It is not expected that every woman should be married, at least in rural Burma, where it has been noted that the role of unmarried men or women (whether spinsters, bachelors, divorced or widowed people) has been a legitimate and

---

[28] As quoted in Lee, 1978: 266, from G. Burgess, preface to U Gang's *Digest of the Burmese Buddhist Law*, vol. III, (Rangoon, 1897), p. 132.

respected one in society (Nash and Nash, 1963). Thai parents do not have a preference for sons rather than daughters, and boys and girls play the same games. Younger children are looked after by, and obey, older ones, of either sex (Hanks and Hanks, 1963: 432, 436). Nevertheless, traditional Western ideas, with their sharper distinction between the sexes, are having an influence. The dress of young children, once almost indistinguishable for boys and girls, has become more sexually typed (Hanks and Hanks, 1963: 447).

In Southern Buddhist lands, the royal harem traditionally had a major political role. Moreover, in recent times, the first woman prime minister in the world was in Sri Lanka, Mrs Bandaranayake, widow of an assassinated political leader. Her daughter is now president of the country. In the Sarvōdaya Śramadāna village development movement (see pp. 225–34), moreover, women are encouraged to overcome their traditional shyness so as to speak up and take an active part in a village's activities of self-renewal (Macy, 1983: 79–89). In Burma, Aung San Suu Kyi, daughter of an important political leader, is head of the party which won the 1990 election, though a military junta has prevented this from taking power (see p. 270). For Thailand, Jane Bunnag holds:

as in western society, the most educated and enterprising women can also achieve positions of real power and influence, both in business affairs, and in the national bureaucracy. (1973: 14)

In rural Burma and Thailand, there is little differentiation of jobs along gender lines. Indeed, in Burma, 'men cook, wash, baby tend, sew, weave and knit. Women plant, harvest, build houses, drive ox carts, fish, keep stores, and chop wood' (Nash and Nash, 1963: 263). In Thailand, women have traditionally had a large role in trading activities (Kirsch, 1975; Hanks and Hanks, 1963: 446), from local markets to transport, construction and real-estate companies: in 1965, 90 per cent of Bangkok real estate was owned by women (Kirsch, 1975: 175). Men nevertheless tend to look down on such work as worldly and linked to greed:[29] if they can, they gravitate to high-status jobs of an administrative nature, where they outnumber women by around ten to one.

In Thailand, as is well known, there are a large number of prostitutes (Kabilsingh, 1991: 67–86; Odzer, 1998), even though Buddhism sees prostitution as an unseemly way of life and using a prostitute's services as indulging in a low form of supposed happiness. Some prostitutes see their way of life as the result of bad karma and seek to make up for this

[29] Note that in Russia, many women are doctors, but this is not seen as a high-status job!

by generosity to Buddhist temples, releasing captive birds, or making donations to children's homes or flood victims (Odzer, 1998: 41–2). The number of prostitutes greatly increased in the 1960s and 1970s, boosted by the presence of many American servicemen on 'rest and recreation' leave from the Vietnam War. Since then, the 'sex industry' has continued with the women, and men, workers supporting poor families back in their villages, or in some cases using their income to gain consumer goods. However, in the north, where many prostitutes come from, Abbot Phra Thepkavī Kusalō has set up a foundation aimed particularly at training young women in traditional handicrafts so as to empower them and protect them from the economic lure of prostitution (Swearer, 1995: 123).

Lands of Eastern Buddhism

In the lands of Eastern Buddhism, Confucianism has been the dominant influence on social ethics. In this, women have been seen as inferior, and were bound to obey first their father, then their husband, and then their grown-up son, if they were widowed, though a woman could gain power through her sons. Sons have been preferred to daughters, for only they could carry out the rites for the family ancestors. On marriage, a woman entered her husband's extended family as its most junior member. A man had seven grounds on which he could divorce his wife, but a woman had no grounds on which she could divorce her husband (Kelleher, 1987: 143).

The egalitarian strains of Mahāyāna Buddhism often softened this discrimination, but it did not remove it. In nineteenth-century China, there was a movement among financially independent women of rural Canton who wished to improve the lot of women, their patron being the *Bodhisattva* Kuan-yin. They either refused to marry, living in nun-like groups, or postponed the consummation indefinitely, through staying in their own family's home. Their aim was to avoid loneliness or oppression in marriage, lack of financial independence, or the pain of childbirth.[30]

In Japan, also, the influence of Confucian and Shintō social ethics put women in an inferior position, and set up strong sex-role differentiations. As in China, Mahāyāna Buddhism partly adapted to this, while also keeping up some more egalitarian emphases. In the Heian period

---

[30] Topley, 1975; Reed, 1992: 169; Carmody, 1989: 104.

(794–1185 CE), when Buddhism was particularly strong, there were a number of notable women writers, including the author of *The Tale of Genji*, the first novel in the world (Carmody, 1989: 117). In the war-torn Ashikaga period (1333–1573), though, Confucianism had a strong influence on the code of the *bushi* class of warrior-knights. While the males were expected to give their all for their feudal lord, their wives were expected to do the same for them. This included ritual suicide if their chastity was threatened, or if their husband's attention to them might compromise his devotion to his lord (Carmody, 1989: 118–19). In the Tokugawa period (1603–1867), when Neo-Confucianism was the state ideology, and Buddhism was used as an arm of the state, the position of women was at its lowest point, and women were excluded from Buddhist sacred places and mountains (Uchino, 1986: 149).

In the pre-1947 legal code, a divorce was only instituted by a man, or by his family, if they did not like the wife, or she could not give birth to a son to continue the family line. This could occur even if the couple did not want to divorce. A wife could only act in legal matters with the approval of her husband's family, and adultery was only a ground for divorce if committed by the wife (Pharr, 1980: 40). The American-influenced 1947 constitution made it illegal to discriminate against people on grounds of sex, and equalized divorce, inheritance and property rights (Maykovich, 1978: 387, 390). Since then, women have eagerly taken advantage of the greater educational opportunities that have developed. For the majority, though, this is seen to be a way of 'polishing' themselves so as to be able to win an appropriate husband (Jahan, 1982: 22). In a 1982 survey, 71 per cent of Japanese women agreed with the idea that 'woman keeps house while man works outside' (Tanaka, 1986: 70). While this is itself a narrowing of a woman's role as compared to her traditional role in agriculture and small businesses, women in some way benefit, for 79 per cent of women also said that they have the final say in how family income is spent, as compared to 37 per cent in the USA and 33 per cent in England (Tanaka, 1986: 74). In the political sphere, while a formal career in politics would once have been unthinkable, the Japanese Socialist Party has in recent years had a woman, Mrs Doi, as its leader.

Lands of Northern Buddhism

In the lands of Northern Buddhism, as in those of Southern Buddhism, Buddhism has been the dominant influence on social ethics. A Chinese anthropologist who studied Tibet in the 1940s advised his government that China might have much to learn from the Tibetans as regards:

the independence of women from male subservience; the ability of women to inherit and maintain households, lands and economic enterprises without male guardianship; the freedom of women to enter into, and to sever marriage bonds, etc. (cited in Miller, 1980: 158)

More recently, a Western anthropologist has commented:

In the Buddhist societies of Tibet and the borderlands of Nepal . . . Women enjoy as much sexual freedom as men, and both have equal rights to property. Women are not subject to the discipline and control of men, but are recognized as personalities solely responsible for their actions and moral character. (Furer-Haimendorf, 1967: 223)

While monogamy has been the most common form of marriage in Tibet (in around 70 per cent of households), polyandry has been fairly common among peasants and herdsmen of some regions (in perhaps 50 per cent of households there), and polygamy has been found among wealthy families. In the case of polyandry, a woman generally married several brothers (Bell, 1928: 192–4). Among peasants, this helped prevent the break-up of precious family lands; among nomadic herdsmen, it meant that the wife was not left alone when one of the husbands was away. In such a marriage, her power and influence were considerable (p. 159). If a man married a daughter of a family with no son, he then took her family name and was subordinate to her in management of the family estate (Bell, 1928: 156–7; Miller, 1980: 161). The family line might descend through either males or females, and a number of families consisted entirely of women: grandmother, mother and daughter (Miller, 1980: 162). As to laws of inheritance in pre-Communist Tibet, these varied between regions. In the east, only sons and brothers inherited, not wives or daughters. In central Tibet and in Bhutan, the sons inherited, though where there were none, daughters did (Bell, 1928: 87–8).

In past centuries, when Tibet was sometimes ruled by regional chiefs, some of these were women, widows or daughters of previous chiefs (Bell, 1928: 14, 160–1). Earlier this century, Bell notes that Tibetan chiefs, ministers and officials were never women, but that they often consulted their wives on official work, and that the Queen of Sikkim (an area of Tibetan culture) was more active in administration than the King (pp. 161–2). Thus women have had much political influence in forming opinions and policies (Miller, 1980: 163). Among Tibetans in exile today, there are many women in positions involving great responsibility: a woman is the moving force behind the Tibetan Homes Foundation in India (Miller, 1980: 160, 164). In Tibet itself, laywomen as well as nuns have been very active in demonstrations against the Chinese occupation of the country. Traditionally, women have also been in charge of retail trade in Tibet (Miller, 1980: 163), and men and women have shared in agricultural tasks, though the men usually do the ploughing (Bell, 1928: 158–9). In Ladakh, while men take leadership roles in the public realm, women have great power within the household-based economy, which until recently has been more important (Norberg-Hodge, 1991: 68–9).

In the West, Buddhism, to varying extents, is adjusting to feminist-influenced social norms, as it has adjusted to other social norms in Asia. Especially in North America, women are taking a very active part in it,[31] and this is having some influence on the Asian teachers establishing their centres there. In a context where people can choose between Buddhist traditions, the latter's views and practices relating to women may be a factor influencing in their choice.

CONCLUSION

Overall, one can say that the rise of Buddhism in India brought an improvement in the status of women relative to their position in Brahmanism. As Hinduism reasserted itself and influenced more aspects of Indian culture, however, less positive views of women came to be accepted in some *Jātaka* stories and early Mahāyāna texts. In turn, though, the Mahāyāna tradition sought to subvert these elements, and the Theravāda downplayed them. In the Chinese cultural area, Buddhism likewise lived alongside a tradition which broadly sought to keep women 'in their place'. While partly accommodating itself to this, Buddhism also sought to subvert it. Buddhism has, in a variety of ways, sought to improve the position of women living in discriminatory, or otherwise unfortunate, situations. Through its practices, it has also facilitated the self-confidence, empowerment and spiritual liberation of both women and men.

While most traditions have a spiritual 'glass ceiling' precluding a female from being a full Buddha, all traditions accept female *Arahat*s, and the Mahāyāna accepts advanced female *Bodhisattva*s, and occasionally female Buddhas. Within the monastic setting, while Buddhism has had

---

[31] See: Boucher, 1993; Friedman, 1987; Gross, 1994; Hopkinson et al., 1986; Lenore, 1987; Tsomo, 1995; Shasta Abbey, 1981; also Carmody, 1989: 84–5, 88–9, and Spring Wind, 1986: 52.

ordained women from the time of the Buddha, some traditions did not
overcome difficulties in transmitting their ordination-line, or let it lapse,
and nuns have been in a number of ways junior partners to the monks.
Yet the role of ordained women has been strengthened in the twentieth
century. Moreover, amongst laywomen, in societies where Buddhism has
been the dominant religion, women's freedoms, rights and status have
often been compared favourably with those in many others in Asia or,
until recently, the West.[32]

[32] My thanks to my colleague Dr Pamela Anderson, and my research student Liz Williams, for
comments on a draft of this chapter. They raised issues that I had not thought of, though my
final view may not agree with theirs.

CHAPTER 10

Homosexuality and other forms of 'queerness'

His Holiness opposes violence and discrimination based on sexual orientation.
On the Dalai Lama in San Francisco, 1997

The word 'homosexuality' derives from the Greek *homos*, 'same', rather than the Latin *homo*, 'man', so it refers to sex between either men or women. Nevertheless, 'lesbianism' is usually used to refer to sexual relations between females (Herdt, 1987: 445). Same-sex relationships span a spectrum from brotherly or filial affection, which is universally admired, to affectionate respect for a spiritual teacher, or strong bonds of friendship, likewise generally admired, to erotic feelings for those of the same sex, to sexual activity with those of the same sex, to a person's conscious self-identification as 'homosexual', 'gay' or 'lesbian'. In modern Western culture, any man who engages, or has engaged, in homosexual activity has tended to be identified as 'a homosexual', though this way of identifying a person based on his or her sexual orientation is not found in other cultures. Gilbert Herdt identifies three forms of the cultural structuring of what is now seen as 'homosexual' activity (usually of males) across different cultures:

(1) age-structured homosexuality, in which people of the same sex but of different ages are sexually involved; (2) gender-reversed homosexuality, wherein a person adopts the dress, mannerisms, and sexual activities of the opposite sex; and (3) role-specialized homosexuality, in which a person, by virtue of his or her social and religious role, is entitled to engage in homosexual activity. (1987: 446)

The first type, which occurred in ancient Greece, has been the most common, and does not preclude the junior participants' later marrying and having children, though perhaps taking boy lovers also. The Greeks, however, strongly condemned passive homosexuality in adults, i.e. being penetrated, rather than being the 'active' penetrator (Herdt, 1987: 447). Early Christianity was antagonistic to homosexuality, but was then ambiguous on it until the eleventh century. It was strongly condemned from the time of Thomas Aquinas, and came to be punishable by the stake.

411

Herdt holds that

the modern social category and erotic identity signified by the term *gay* is not the same as the homosexual organizations or roles found in ancient times and in other cultures . . . it is in several respects a unique development in human society. This suggests a change from a predominantly gender-reversed feminization to a more frequent masculinization of overt homosexuality in popular culture. (1987: 452)

The term 'gay pride' has positively affirmed an overt homosexual identity, and in America, this has also led to 'gay, lesbian, bisexual, and transgendered (and/or transsexual)' people to appropriate positively the once abusive term 'queer' to refer to themselves as a group (Corless, 1995: 1).

In order to gauge the attitude(s) of Buddhism to homosexuality, 'homosexuals' and others who now call themselves 'queer', it is first necessary to examine its understanding of and attitude to those of non-standard sexuality.

SEX-CHANGE

Early Buddhist texts refer to the sex of a person as something that can change within one life, as well as between lives. In the *Vinaya*, there is reference to a monk in whom the sexual characteristics of a woman appeared, and a nun in whom the sexual characteristics of a man appeared.[1] In both cases, the Buddha appears to accept this and simply say that the ex-monk nun should follow the rules of the nuns, and the ex-nun monk should follow the rules of the monks. In commentarial literature, the sex of a person is seen as determined at conception, but as subject to possible change (*Asl.* 322).[2] Causes of sex-change are seen as karmic in nature. The *Dhammapada* commentary tells of a man instantly turning into a woman when he is sexually attracted to a monk; after marrying and giving birth, she then turns back to a man when she asks the monk's forgiveness, and goes on to become an *Arahat* (*Dhp. A.* 1.325–32; cf. *AKB.* IV.55a–b). Sex-change, then, is not seen as limiting spiritual potential.

HERMAPHRODITES

While men and women can both be ordained, and attain enlightenment, even if they change sex, this is not the case with a hermaphrodite, one 'having the sexual characteristics of both sexes' (*ubhato-byañjanaka*).

In the *Vinaya*, it is said that because of the possibility of a hermaph-

---

[1] *Vin.* III.35; cf. *Miln.* 267 and *AKB.* IV.13c and 38.
[2] Biologically, sexual identity is manifested at ten weeks' gestation.

rodite enticing a fellow monk or nun into having sex, hermaphrodites should not be ordained (*Vin.* I.89; *Vin.* II.271). The Theravādin commentator Buddhaghosa held that there were female hermaphrodites, who could both impregnate and give birth, and male ones, who could not give birth, and that either type could be sexually attracted to both men and women (*Asl.* 322–3). In this, he perhaps conflates hermaphroditism and bisexuality (Zwilling, 1992: 206).

As to the karmic causes of hermaphroditism, in the seventh century *Ta-ch'eng tsao-hsiang kung-te ching*, composed in China or Central Asia, these are (for a man):

(1) Uncleanness where there should be reverence and respect; (2) lust for the bodies of other men; (3) the practice of lustful things upon his own body; (4) the exposure and sale of himself in the guise of a woman to other men. (Beyer, 1974: 53)

Just as Buddhaghosa sees hermaphrodites as bisexual, this sees homosexual activity as leading to hermaphroditism. The text holds, though, that such results can be avoided if a person has deep repentance and faith, and builds a Buddha image.

The *Milindapañha* sees hermaphrodites as among those who are 'obstructed' and so cannot attain understanding of *Dhamma*, even if they practise correctly. No reason is given, but the others who are also obstructed are *paṇḍaka*s (see below), ghosts, one of false view, a cheat, one who has done one of the five heinous acts, a self-ordained person, a monk or nun who has gone over to another sect, the seducer of a nun, one who has committed an offence entailing the formal meeting of the *Saṅgha*, and a child under seven years (*Miln.* 310). Apart from the young child, ghost and *paṇḍaka*, these are clearly those with moral failings.

PAṆḌAKAS

A *paṇḍaka*, or 'one without testicles' (Zwilling, 1992: 204), is often discussed in similar contexts to the hermaphrodite. The term has generally been translated as 'eunuch' – i.e. someone deliberately castrated – in the past, but Leonard Zwilling argues that this equation is wrong, as eunuchs were virtually unknown in pre-Muslim India. Rather, he holds, it and its synonyms were used in a metaphorical way, 'as we do in English when it is said of a weak or pusillanimous person that he (or even she) "has no balls"' (1992: 204). Indeed, they are said, like women, to cry when a prince is banished (*J.* VI.502).

Before discussing what exactly the term refers to, it is useful to point out that it is applied to a man who lacks the normal characteristics of maleness, or occasionally (*Vin.* II.271) to a woman who lacks the characteristics of femaleness. In outlining the variety of sexual types, whether among humans or animals, the *Vinaya* talks of females, males, hermaphrodites and *paṇḍaka*s (*Vin.* III.28). While the hermaphrodite has the sexual characteristics of *both* genders, it appears that the *paṇḍaka* is seen as one who has the characteristics of *neither* gender. This accords with a set of four logical possibilities often referred to in Buddhist texts: that something is *x*, or not *x*, or both (in part) *x* and (in part) not *x*, or neither *x* nor not *x*, where '*x*' refers to a certain characteristic. A common commentarial gloss for *paṇḍaka* is *napuṃsaka*, the 'non-male', and the usage of the term shows that it refers to someone who is neither a normal male nor a normal female, i.e. a 'neuter'. In the discussion of various monastic offences of a sensual nature for a nun, the *Vinaya* states that the act, if done in relation to a human male, is a full offence, and a lesser offence if it is done in relation to a non-human male, or in relation to a *paṇḍaka*, who is thus seen as non-male human (*Vin.* IV.215, 233, 269). Zwilling points out, in fact, that the pre-Buddhist *Artharva Veda* distinguishes *paṇḍaka*s from ordinary males and females, and implies that they were transvestites (Zwilling, 1992: 205).

Buddhaghosa sees a particular kind of mind-consciousness, accompanied by neutral feeling, as occurring at the time of conception, and thereafter as the background, resting state of consciousness (*bhavaṅga*), for 'the blind, the deaf, the foolish, the mad, a hermaphrodite, a neuter (*napuṃsaka-*)' born as humans (*Asl.* 264–5), or simply for '*paṇḍaka*s etc.' among humans (*Vism.* 457). Thus a person is seen as a non-male, or *paṇḍaka*, from the time of conception: being one is not a this-life choice, or a result of castration.

Buddhaghosa also describes five types of *paṇḍaka*:[3]

(1)   the 'sprayed (*āsitta*)-*paṇḍaka*': one who quenches his lust by fellating another man to ejaculation;

(2)   the 'jealous (*usūya*)-*paṇḍaka*': 'one who, through the arising of jealousy, quenches his lust through watching others have intercourse': a voyeur;

(3)   the 'by-a-means (*opakkamika*)-*paṇḍaka*': one for whom 'semen is expelled using some special means';

(4)   the 'fortnight (*pakkha*)-*paṇḍaka*': one who, because of past karma, is a

---

[3]   At *Vin. A.* v.1015–16, commenting on the *Vin.* 1.85–6 prohibition of ordaining a *paṇḍaka*; cf. Zwilling, 1992: 204.

paṇḍaka only for half the lunar month; the other half, he can quench his lust;

(5) the 'non-male (*napuṃsaka*)-*paṇḍaka*': one who, from the time of conception, is lacking.

Here, it seems that types (1)–(3) can only attain sexual arousal by some unusual method and type (4) is one who is impotent for part of the month, while type (5) is perhaps one who cannot attain ejaculation as he has been 'lacking' since before birth; Vasubandhu sees this type as having an 'incomplete body [*ātmabhāva*]' (*AKB.* IV.97b–c). This could perhaps refer to a 'male' born without testicles, or one whose testicles remain undescended, so as to appear absent. In the *Mahāvastu*, *paṇḍaka*s are among various people such as 'hunchbacks, dwarfs, and pigmies' (*Mvs.* II.469; cf. II.47) who attend a king in his palace. They are also among a small group of people allowed to enter the women's apartment, and even the apartment of the chief queen (II.469). This seems to imply that they are somehow deformed, and are regarded as no sexual threat to a king's wives or harem. Zwilling sees the term as signifying 'those with a variety of sexual dysfunction' who all 'share the common quality of being "*napuṃsaka*", "lacking maleness". That is, for one reason or another they fail to meet the normative sex role expectation for an adult male' (1992: 205).

The female *paṇḍaka* is mentioned on a few occasions also. In the *Vinaya*, two passages imply that a 'female *paṇḍaka*' cannot be a sexual partner for a man (*Vin.* III.129, 144). Zwilling says that the term, 'by analogy with the male *paṇḍaka*, would seem to be no more than the female of the species and equivalent to the *nārīṣaṇḍa*, or lesbian, of the medical literature' (1992: 208). Just to equate the female *paṇḍaka* with a lesbian is problematical, though: while she might be sexually attracted to women, she is also clearly seen as having some organic abnormality of the uterus. This is apparent from the nature of a list of those who cannot be ordained as nuns, namely those:

without sexual characteristics, and who were defective in sex, and bloodless, and with stagnant blood, and who always wore a menstrual cloth and were dripping and deformed, and female-*paṇḍaka*s, and man-like women (*vepurisikā*), and those (whose anus and vagina) were run-together, and those who were hermaphrodites. (*Vin.* II.271)

Sexual behaviour of paṇḍakas

The Buddha is said to have prohibited the ordination of any *paṇḍaka*s, and required the disrobing of any who were already ordained, because of the following situation (*Vin.* 1.85–6). A *paṇḍaka* monk approached some young monks, then some fat novices, then some mahouts and grooms, asking each in turn to 'defile' him. While the first two groups sent him away, the last group agreed to his request. They then spread it about that Buddhist monks were *paṇḍakas*, or that those who were not *paṇḍakas* nevertheless 'defiled' *paṇḍakas*.

This indicates that a *paṇḍaka* was seen as some kind of promiscuous passive homosexual. That (male) *paṇḍakas* were seen as potentially sexually available to men is clearly indicated by its being said that even a good monk is mistrusted and suspected if he goes for alms to the haunts of prostitutes, widows, coarse young girls, *paṇḍakas* or even nuns (*A.* III.128; cf. *Vin.* 1.70). Thus Buddhaghosa sees them, like prostitutes and coarse young girls, as dominated by lust and longing for friendship with anyone (*Vin. A.* v.991–2). They are 'non-males (*napuṃsakā*) who are full of defilements, with unquenchable lust'. Accordingly, a monk should not sit down in a private place with a *paṇḍaka*, though this is a lesser offence than sitting in such a place with a woman (*Vin.* IV.96). Zwilling affirms that in the *Vinaya*, *paṇḍakas* are nearly always referred to in the context of sexual, specifically homosexual, behaviour (1992: 205). He sums up his views by describing them as 'a socially stigmatised class of passive, probably transvestite, homosexuals' (1992: 209).

To have such people in a celibate male community would be seen as problematic, hence the bar on their ordination. For a monk to penetrate any being, including another man or a *paṇḍaka* (*Vin.* III.28), with his penis, in any orifice, was an offence entailing expulsion. Interestingly, this disjunction implies that being penetrated by another man did not necessarily mean that a man was a *paṇḍaka*. It may perhaps be that he was raped, though the seventh-century *Ta-ch'eng tsao-hsiang kung-te ching* even distinguishes between one reborn as a *paṇḍaka* and one 'with the lusts and desires of a woman, and enjoys being treated as a woman by other men', through such past karmic causes as having despised other men or enjoyed dressing as a woman. Thus not even all passive homosexuals are classified as *paṇḍakas*. Moreover, in the *Vinaya*, penetrating another man or a *paṇḍaka* was not seen to make a man a *paṇḍaka*. In the Hindu *Kāmasūtra* also, it was 'atypical gender behavior and coital role' – i.e. being penetrated – that were crucial in seeing a man as 'queerly different' (Sweet and Zwilling, 1993: 595).

Zwilling sees the ordination-bar as simply a 'practical concession to prevailing conventions' (1992: 209); but

Because the classical definitions of sexual misconduct mirror the taboos and concerns of pre-modern Indian society, might they not be reformulated based on a relativistic and situational appraisal of contemporary social mores? The textual sources surveyed here are at least consonant with a contemporary view of homosexuality as a probably organically or genetically based orientation, with the same moral significance (or insignificance) of [*sic*] heterosexuality. (1992: 210)

On this, one can say that Buddhism, except perhaps certain strands in Japan and America, does not follow a 'relativistic and situational' ethic. It is true that the Indian sources surveyed above see a *paṇḍaka* as something one is *born* as, though the term only covers certain types of *passive* homosexuals. It is true that penetration of a man or a *paṇḍaka* is seen as no worse an offence for a monk than penetrating a woman, i.e. 'homosexual' penetration is seen as no *worse* than 'heterosexual' penetration, for a celibate male. Yet the state of being a (passive-homosexual) *paṇḍaka* is seen as one with various spiritual disabilities, as will now be seen.

The psychological nature and limited potential of paṇḍakas

Milindapañha 310 sees *paṇḍaka*s, like hermaphrodites, as among those who are spiritually obstructed from attaining understanding of *Dhamma* even though they are practising correctly. The Theravādin commentator Buddhaghosa holds that *paṇḍaka*s, hermaphrodites and those of fixed wrong view are those who are described at *Vibh.* 341 as 'hindered by defilement': they cannot develop 'any meditation subject at all' (*Vism.* 177). Among others likewise hindered are those who have committed a heavy evil act having an immediate effect on rebirth ('hindered by karma'): all such are incapable of entering into the certainty of rightness in wholesome states. Likewise, in his *Abhidharma-kośa-bhāṣya*, Vasubandhu sees *paṇḍaka*s as subject to the 'obstacle of the defilements' because they suffer from chronic, continual defilements:

Defilements which surge up from time to time, even if their impulse is strong, can be overcome, but not continual defilement, even though it is at rest. The person in whom this is found does not find the time to make an effort to overcome it. From being small, they become medium sized; and from medium sized, they become strong: thus they form an obstacle. (*AKB.* iv.96)

This means that *paṇḍaka*s are obstructed from attaining insight into the Noble Path and from those acts preparing for this.

Vasubandhu also holds that, while *paṇḍaka*s and hermaphrodites can

do ordinary good deeds (such as acts of generosity), they are not susceptible to either discipline (*saṃvara*) or indiscipline (*AKB.* iv.43a–d; cf. ii.1b).
The first is:

Because they possess, to an extreme degree, the defilements of the two sexes;
because they are incapable of the reflection necessary to combat these
defilements; and because the vigour of self-respect and concern for consequences is absent in them.

The second is:

Because the intention of committing transgression [*pāpāśaya*] is not strong
among them; because indiscipline is opposed to discipline; and only one who is
susceptible to discipline is susceptible to indiscipline . . . their bodies are similar
to soil saturated with salt wherein there can neither grow wheat, nor bad herbs.

However, in the Tibetan tradition, sGam-po-pa (1079–1153), founder of
the bKa'brgyud school, holds that the *paṇḍaka* and what Guenther translates as 'the impotent'[4] can practise the discipline of the *Bodhisattva*, consisting of not harming others, and positively benefiting them, if not that
of the monk or nun (Guenther, 1959: 107).

Vasubandhu also holds that *paṇḍaka*s and hermaphrodites are counted
among sensualists, whose basis (*āśraya*) is in movement, unfirm like those
in bad rebirths, so that they cannot cut off the roots of good (*AKB.*
iv.80a–b). Likewise, the *Milindapañha* says that *paṇḍaka*s, because of their
'uncertainty', cannot keep a secret (*Miln.* 92–3). Again, Vasubandhu says
that if they kill their mother or father, it is not as heinous as if anyone
else did this, because of the 'mediocrity of their kindness and respect':

because their parents, having given to the *paṇḍaka* only an incomplete body
[*ātmabhāva*] and having only a mediocre affection for their son, are mediocre
benefactors; because, on the other hand, the *paṇḍaka* does not experience strong
respect for his parents the destruction of which would render him guilty of
mortal transgression. (*AKB.* iv.97b–c)

The above passages thus portray the *paṇḍaka* as one who can do ordinary good deeds, but is obstructed from success in meditation, understanding *Dhamma* or gaining insight into the Path, because of continual
mental defilements. He has a sensual, shameless nature replete with the
defilements of both sexes, but is uncertain and wavering, and cannot
reflect on his defilements. He is incapable of spiritual discipline and so
cannot be blamed as if he were being undisciplined intentionally. He is
unloved by his parents.

---

4 Tib. *za.ma*, Skt *ṣaṇḍha.*

Paṇḍakas and rebirth

Being 'neither a man nor a woman' is among a string of karmic effects in certain cases of adultery (*Thig.* 436–47; *J.* VI.237–9), while the *Pravrajyāntarāya Sūtra* says that if a layman hinders someone from ordaining, reviles the *Dhamma*, or is angry at monks or brahmins, then, if he is 'addicted to' these, various bad forms of rebirth may follow, including being a *paṇḍaka* (cited at *Ss.* 73–4). The *Ta-ch'eng tsao-hsiang kung-te ching* says that rebirth as a *paṇḍaka* has four karmic causes:

(1) castrating another man; (2) laughingly scorning and slandering a recluse that keeps the precepts; (3) transgressing the precepts himself because of lustful desires; (4) not only transgressing the precepts himself but also encouraging others to do the same.

However, awakening faith and building a Buddha image will prevent the result of these acts, and he will always be a man 'with all his faculties intact' (Beyer, 1974: 53). Again, Vasubandhu holds that a *paṇḍaka* who saves bulls from being castrated will regain the sexual characteristics of a man (*AKB.* IV.55a–b).

In a less judgemental context, the American Zen priest Rōshi Daizui MacPhillamy says that the 'traditional Buddhist' explanation for homosexuality is that the immediately previous lives of a homosexual were as members of the opposite sex, and that certain inclinations or memories carry over from these to colour the present life (1982: 29). Moreover, Ian Stevenson, in his study of children who seem to have detailed knowledge of past personalities of whom they claim to be rebirths, has some interesting cases relating to gender-identity. He says that he has investigated many cases in which the previous personality was of the opposite sex, and in each of five such cases about which he has written, 'the subject as a child showed traits characteristic of the opposite sex', including a partiality for its clothes and mode of play. In most cases, such behaviour fades as the child grows older, but there are exceptions, such as a Burmese woman, who claims to have been a Japanese soldier in Burma in the Second World War and who 'has remained intransigently masculine in her conduct and outlook up to her middle 20s' (1977: 318).

HOMOSEXUAL ACTS

As has been seen above, the monastic code punishes a monk with expulsion if he penetrates any orifice of any being with his penis. Any other

sexual or sensual act, with a woman, *paṇḍaka* or man, is treated less
severely. Nevertheless, many rules are designed to avoid such acts, or
those entailing expulsion. Masturbation is a serious offence for a monk,
and this includes emitting semen on another person (*Vin.* III.113), a monk
getting a novice to masturbate him, or himself masturbating a sleeping
novice (*Vin.* III.117), which could be seen to include homosexual acts. It
is a lesser offence, of expiation, for nuns 'tormented with dissatisfaction'
to slap each other's genitals with their palms or any object, with the
slapper 'enjoying the contact' (*Vin.* IV.260–1). It is similarly an offence of
expiation for two nuns to lie together on one couch (*Vin.* IV.288–9), which
could also be seen to pertain to potential homosexual behaviour
(Wijayaratna, 1990: 95). It is a lesser offence, of wrong-doing, for monks
to eat from the same dish, or share one couch (*Vin.* II.124), which is elsewhere seen as sensual behaviour by 'depraved monks' with women (*Vin.*
II.10). Lastly, at *A.* III.270, the Buddha warns that a monk should not be
excessively devoted to another monk as 'dear and pleasing', otherwise
he will have no devotion to other *Saṅgha* members, be offended if the
Saṅgha disciplines his favourite, and not listen to *Dhamma* from any other
monk. Zwilling sees this as a warning against having 'homoerotic feelings' for another monk (1992: 208).

In all of this, rules relevant to homosexual activities or feelings are
simply part of those aimed at minimizing *any* expressions of sexuality by
monks or nuns. Homosexuality is not picked out for any *special* condemnation. Zwilling is thus correct for the monastic context when he says
'when homosexual behaviour is not ignored in Indian Buddhist writings
it is derogated to much the same degree as comparable heterosexual
acts' (Zwilling, 1992: 209). It would be wrong, though, to regard the
Vinaya as seeing homosexual relationships as *more condonable* for monks
and nuns than heterosexual ones, as John G. Jones does (1979: 79). He
does so as the *Vinaya* has more to say on heterosexual activity than homosexual activity, and because homosexual relationships could not lead to
children. However, the larger amount of attention given to heterosexual
activity can simply be seen as due to the fact that it is more common.
Moreover, if a monk having sex with a man was condonable as no children would ensue, then it is unlikely that *paṇḍaka*s would actually have
been barred from being ordained.

When it comes to homosexual feelings or activities between lay
people, the even-handed opposition to both heterosexuality and homosexuality breaks down. José Cabezón is thus wrong in his generalization
on Buddhist attitudes to homosexuality when he says that homosexual-

ity has been condemned only because homosexual activity breaches celibacy, not because it goes against the norm of heterosexuality (1993: 82). In the Theravāda tradition, Buddhaghosa regards 'desire and attachment in men for men, in women for women' (*D. A.* 853) as the meaning of 'wrong practices' (*micchā-dhammo*) at *D.* III.70, which says that these began to occur at a certain time in the past as part of the moral decline of society. In the Mahāyāna tradition, Śāntideva's *Śikṣā-samuccaya* cites the *Saddharma-smṛtyupasthāna Sūtra* thus:

Likewise, endless varieties of punishments [in a future life] are described for the wrong deed of sexual intercourse between two men. The one who commits misconduct with boys sees boys being swept away in the Acid River who cry out to him, and owing to the suffering and pain born of his deep affection for them, plunges in after them.[5]

Roger Corless points out, however, that the *Śikṣā-samuccaya* is 'an anthology which has preserved other oddities such as the prediction that one who wipes snot on a sacred text will be reborn as a book . . . Such statements are hardly mainline Dharma' (1995: 3). Even in the condemnation, though, there is a hint of sympathy for the karmic plight of the paederast.

To what extent is homosexual sex seen as breaking the third precept, on sexual misconduct? In the Theravāda tradition, Buddhaghosa sees transgression of this precept as 'the will, carried out through the body by an immoral means, to transgress against those whom one should not go into'. While Conze's translation (1959: 71) of the relevant passage (*M. A.* 1.199) says 'By "those whom one should not go into", first of all, men are meant', this is in fact incorrect; the passage is simply saying that 'for men', intercourse with various categories of females breaks the precept. The *Upāsaka-janālaṅkāra*, a popular guide to Buddhism written in twelfth-century Sri Lanka, where Buddhaghosa worked, also explains the third precept (pp. 178–9) simply by discussing the categories of women with whom a layman should not have sex. Zwilling holds that, among the Indian commentators, only Buddhaghosa (which the above shows is debatable) and the anonymous author of the commentary on the *Abhidharma-samuccaya* included men among the forbidden sexual objects for men (1992: 207). This may simply be due to an oversight, in which the texts concentrate on the most common ways of breaking the third precept, rather than a positive acceptance of homosexual acts. Even so,

[5] See *Ss.* 80, but this translation draws on the partial translation given by Zwilling, 1992: 209.

it shows that most Indian Buddhist commentators did not have a particular bee in their bonnet about condemning such acts. On sexual acts
between women, Indian Buddhist texts are in fact completely silent,
other than alluding to them in the *Vinaya*.

In Tibet, though, sGam-po-pa (1079–1153) includes homosexuality in
his discussion of the third precept in his *Jewel Ornament of Liberation*. After
discussing various forms of sexual misconduct of a man with a woman,
in a way which seems partly derived from the *Abhidharma-kośa-bhāṣya* –
which omits reference to homosexual acts (see pp. 72–3) – he adds 'It also
means to have intercourse with a male or in a *paṇḍaka*'s mouth or anus'
(Guenther, 1959: 76).

In his study of the *Jātaka* stories, John G. Jones says:

When one remembers the enormous amount that is said in warning of the
dangers of forming heterosexual relationships in the Jātaka stories, it is quite
remarkable that there is not one word warning of the dangers of a homosexual
relationship. The only reservation ever expressed is with regard to the corrupting influence of an evil friend. (Jones, 1979: 115)

The stories certainly do give many examples of suffering arising from
heterosexual relationships, while warmly affirming close friendship
between men. In this, Jones sees 'a good deal of homosexual emotion
operating' (1979: 113). Even though the Indian tradition would not
describe it in this Westernized way, it 'has never seen warm, tender,
loving feelings between males as anything but good so long as the males
concerned were mutually motivated towards the good' (p. 113). Yet in
looking for accounts relating to homosexual *practice*, all Jones can come
up with are the following three stories (1979: 113–15). In story 211, a
young boy becomes the attendant of a king, and then a very dear favourite: Jones *assumes* that as kings were little given to sexual restraint, the
relationship would have been sexual. Story 253 concerns an ascetic who
values the close affection (*sineha; J.* II.283) of a serpent in human form,
though there is no reference to sexual passion (*pariḷāha*); if there had
been, the story would have had the ascetic concerned over his breaking
of celibacy. Story 346 refers only to friendly affection between a brahmin
and his aged teacher. One text which Jones cites (1979: 107) and Cabezón
takes up as 'homoerotically suggestive' (1993: 89) is story 498, on two
deer who always went about together, 'ruminating and cuddling
together, very happy, head to head, nozzle to nozzle, horn to horn' (*J.*
IV.392). Cabezón overlooks the fact, however, that the two are described
as *brothers*, so here there is only an example of brotherly affection!

Consequently, while the *Jātaka*s can be seen to affirm close friendship, there seems to be no positive evidence of a moral acceptance of homosexual acts.

HOMOSEXUALITY IN BUDDHIST CULTURES

Cabezón claims that history shows Buddhism to have been 'ambivalent' about homosexuality, and that 'the evidence seems to suggest that as a whole Buddhism has been for the most part neutral' on it (1993: 82). He sees this 'essential neutrality' as having enabled Buddhism to adapt to the sexual mores of different cultures, so that its attitudes have ranged from condemnation of homosexuality (without advocating persecution of homosexuals) through condonement to active praise, as in Japan (p. 82). This, however, depends on the doubtful notion of there being an overall 'essence' of Buddhism. Let us look at the evidence, then.

Lands of Southern Buddhism

The contemporary teacher of a form of Insight meditation, N. Goenka, an Indian by birth, 'feels that homosexuality is dangerous because it mixes what he regards as male and female energies' and that prolonged meditation means that 'the homosexuality will go away'.[6] Phra Chao, leader of the Thai *Saṅgha* at the beginning of this century, saw the prohibition on ordaining *paṇḍaka*s as applying to homosexuals.[7] The Thai social critic Sulak Sivaraksa, however, has claimed that 'the Buddha never mentioned homosexuality and only said that we should not use sex harmfully'.[8] Gay clubs do exist in Bangkok, and homosexuality may be contributing to Thailand's mounting AIDS crisis, though prostitution must surely be playing its part here. In Burma, Melford Spiro reports that monks are mostly scrupulous in keeping their vows of celibacy, avoiding both heterosexual and homosexual digressions from it. Lay people expect the monks to keep to the *Vinaya*, and the openness of monasteries to visitors makes illicit sexual acts hard to hide. Nineteenth-century Christian observers also remarked on the good discipline of the monks (Spiro, 1971: 366–8).

Spiro also reports that, when in Sri Lanka, he was told that homosexuality was not infrequent in the *Saṅgha*: between monks, monks and

---

[6] Corless, 1995: 4, citing personal communications dated 1994 and 1995.
[7] *The Entrance to the Vinaya* (Bangkok: Mahamukutarajavidyalaya, 1969), vol. 1, p. 57, cited in Zwilling, 1992: 213.
[8] Corless, 1995: 6, citing a personal communication from Eric Kolvig, 1994.

novices, and monks and laymen (Spiro, 1971: 368). Martin Southwold, though, found that Buddhist lay people in Sri Lanka reacted with hilarity to the suggestion that most monks had latent homosexuality as a character trait. In their experience, the average monk enjoys the company of women and seems to find them attractive (1983: 38). It should perhaps be noted that ordination in Sri Lanka, unlike in Thailand and Burma, is usually for life, so it is socially unacceptable to disrobe even if there are difficulties in dealing with sexual desire. This *may*, of course, lead to some monks' sexuality being diverted to being expressed in relation to other men, however much this breaks key monastic rules.

Tibet

Among Tibetan laity, homosexuality is seen in a very negative light, and it seems to have been confined almost exclusively to the *lDab ldob*s: irregular monks who saw to the physical running of the larger monasteries, took part in athletic competitions, and acted as policemen (Goldstein, 1964; Cabezón, 1993: 93). Melvyn Goldstein describes them as monks who did not readily fit into the discipline of monastic life, but who did not wish to lose the prestige and economic security of being a monk by returning to lay life. They were potential deviants whom the monastic system tamed by allowing them to exist on its edge, before absorbing them into the body of more disciplined monks. In larger monasteries, they might comprise up to 10 per cent of the population (1964: 125, 137–8, 140). The *lDab ldob*s were known to engage in sexual acts with boys, yet avoided committing an offence entailing expulsion by not penetrating any orifice. Rather, they attained stimulation by insertion of the penis between the legs of the partner from behind (Goldstein, 1964: 134; Cabezón, 1993: 93). Young monks or lay youths might sometimes be abducted by *lDab ldob*s, but the victim would keep quiet about this from fear of both *lDab ldob* retaliation and the stigma of having been a homosexual partner (Goldstein, 1964: 135). *lDab ldob*s sometimes also fought for the favours of a voluntary partner, and for this they were often punished by the monastic authorities, both for fighting and homosexuality (Goldstein, 1964: 135). Their failings, however, have not prevented them from being respected by laity and monks alike, because of their contributions to society, and for their non-attachment to wealth and people (Goldstein, 1964: 138). While they are recognized as bad monks, they are not seen as the worst kind: one who hypocritically hides his bad behaviour behind a screen of piety (Goldstein, 1964: 138–9). The *lDab ldob* is at least seen to have the virtue of honesty, which is prized by Tibetans.

Lands of Eastern Buddhism

In China, records from the mostly pre-Buddhist Han period (206 BCE–220 CE) show that certain emperors took male lovers. Male prostitution and transvestism were common in the Sung period (960–1279), though corporal punishment and a fine was decreed for male prostitutes around 1111, and homosexuality was sporadically discouraged by laws thereafter (Wawrytko, 1993: 200–1; Faure, 1991: 254). Sexual repression was more noticeable in the Ch'ing dynasty (1644–1912), and Western ideas then added to this, but the harsh treatment, even execution, by the present Communist government is unprecedented (Wawrytko, 1993: 206).

When non-Buddhist Chinese of the pre-modern period have expressed reservations about homosexuality, it has been due to a Confucian concern with the stability and continuity of the family and the corruption of those in power, or Taoist-related concern for a healthy use of sexual energies, especially for men (Wawrytko, 1993: 204–10). Nevertheless, Confucianism tended not to condemn homosexuality except where it compromised family or social obligations. There is even reference, in the Ming dynasty (1368–1644), to families giving approval to male homosexual couples living together. Lesbianism for love-starved women was seen as preferable to adultery. In the seventeenth century, Jesuit missionaries reported, with surprise, on the lack of moral outrage at homosexual behaviour. Same-sex relationships were not uncommon among actors (all male), in royal harems, between co-wives, and in brothels (Wawrytko, 1993: 201–3).

Sandra Wawrytko reports that literature of the Ming dynasty not infrequently expresses suspicion that some Buddhist nuns were lesbians. One 'lesbian classic' has the two heroines vowing to be reborn as husband and wife and invoking the Buddha as witness to their 'marriage' (1993: 203). In the nineteenth century, a Buddhist-influenced movement of financially independent silk-weaver women (see p. 406), known as the 'Golden Orchid Association', sometimes included lesbian marriages (Cabezón, 1993: 84).

In the twentieth century, prior to the Communist period, Holmes Welch reports that monks saw homosexuality in the monasteries as very rare and regarded it as 'low-taste' and pointless. However, one ex-monk reported that there was considerable emotional attachment between older and younger monks (Welch, 1967: 118). John Blofeld reports that, during his nine-month stay in a Chinese monastery, he saw no trace of any sexuality, and all were 'uninterested in homosexual attachment', though there was much attachment between friends (1972: 164). It must be remarked, in fact, that in Chinese culture, men and women have often moved in different circles, and this has encouraged close same-sex friendships. Holding hands in public is a sign of such close friendship, as in India, though not of erotic feeling, *per se* (Wawrytko, 1993: 199).

In recent years, the Ven. Master Hsüan Hua, a much-respected Chinese monk who founded monasteries in America, held that 'homosexuality . . . plants the seeds which lead to rebirth in the lower realms of existence'.[9] In the Korean tradition, which is similar to that of China, the contemporary Master Soen Sa Nim has said that homosexuality is a result of karma, but that the chanting of appropriate *mantra*s can lead to a homosexual becoming heterosexual.[10]

In Japan, while the current penal code makes no reference to homosexuality or sodomy (Wawrytko, 1993: 219), a 1987 study of male college students nevertheless found that those who were actively homosexual (4.5 per cent) tended to hide their sexual preferences because they did not want to shame their families (Wawrytko, 1993: 215), perhaps on account of Confucian influence. Moreover, Umezawa asserts that the Japanese desire not to be shamed before others explains why 'the Japanese way of thinking does not allow people to become homosexual easily' (1988: 171).

Nevertheless, as in China, the general separation of men and women in traditional Japanese culture has led to close same-sex relationships. Moreover, the indigenous religion of Shintō has encouraged a generally permissive attitude towards sexuality, as a perfectly natural aspect of humanity. Homosexual relationships have traditionally been readily tolerated so long as the partners have had commitment to and sympathy for each other. There was a high incidence of homosexuality among the *bushi* warriors, who became the ruling elite after 1192. Among them, the 'way of the young man' (*shudō*) positively affirmed age-structured homosexuality, apparently as part of male-bonding in a tight-knit military group which excluded women (Wawrytko, 1993: 212–13). Such an asso-

[9] *Buddhism: Essential Teachings*, compiled by Bhikshu Heng Shure (Talmage, Calif., City of 10,000 Buddhas, privately circulated, p. 65), cited in Corless, 1995: 4.

[10] Corless, 1995, 4, citing 'Relationships Aren't a This or a That: An Interview with Bobby Rhodes', *Turning Wheel* (Fall, 1992), 19.

ciation of manly exertion and homosexuality can also be seen in ancient Greece and among the *lDab ldob* of Tibet. In the Tokugawa period (1603–1850), homosexuality was encouraged among the *samurai* as a way for youths to learn virtue, honesty and appreciation of beauty from these older men.[11] In the Tokugawa period there is also evidence of lesbianism among prostitutes, members of harems, and neglected wives, and nineteenth-century sex-manuals include explicit passages on and illustrations of homosexual activities (Wawrytko, 1993: 213–14).

There are several connections between Buddhism and homosexuality in Japan. In a fourteenth-century text, *Chigo Kannon engi*, the *Bodhisattva* Kannon rewards a devoted monk by appearing in the form of a beautiful young novice (*Chigo*) as a male lover (Cabezón, 1993: 91). In a fifteenth-century poem, and three later texts, it is said that Kūkai, the ninth-century founder of the Tantric Shingon school of Buddhism, introduced male homosexual love from China to Japan. From the fifteenth century, various heterodox texts of the Tantric Shingon school glorified heterosexual sex as a way to enlightenment; the above-mentioned texts added homosexual love as legitimate activity for priests.[12] In the 1598 'Kōbō Daishi's Book', a vision of Kūkai gives instruction on methods of intercourse between priests and novices (Schalow, 1992: 216–20). In 1667, in a period when the celibate monastic ideal was starting to give way to that of a married priesthood (Cabezón, 1993: 92), a scholar wrote 'Rock Azaleas', a collection of homoerotic poems, mostly addressed by priests to their novice lovers. The 1687 'Great Mirror of Male Love' (*Nanshoku ōkagami*)[13] claims that Kūkai had not taught male love except in the monasteries, but that now it was becoming popular among *samurai* and merchants (Schalow, 1992: 222–8). The book is positive towards such male love, but criticizes monks of various sects for being hypocritical, in that they tried to hide the fact that they indulged in it, whether with novices or boy prostitutes. The text even complains that Rinzai Zen monks' visits to boy prostitutes had inflated their price.

In the sixteenth century, Francis Xavier, a Christian missionary to Japan, was shocked both at the incidence of 'abominations of the flesh' among Buddhist monks in particular and at the social indifference to it

---

[11] King, 1993: 146–7, citing Tsuneo Watanabe and Jun'ichi Iwata, *The Love of the Samurai: A Thousand Years of Japanese Homosexuality* (London: GMP Publishers, 1989), pp. 88, 11.

[12] Schalow, 1992: 215–16, 228; cf. Faure, 1991: 254.

[13] Translated by P. G. Schalow, *The Great Mirror of Male Love by Ihara Saikaku* (Stanford: Stanford University Press, 1989).

(Faure, 1991: 249; Wawrytko, 1993: 213). Bernard Faure summarizes his survey of homosexuality and Buddhism in China and Japan (1991: 249–57) by saying:

Most authors agree that male homosexuality was relatively well accepted in Japanese society and became a prevalent feature of Japanese monastic life. It was seen as a kind of compensation for the prohibition against the presence of women in the monasteries, a prohibition particularly enforced under the Tokugawa rule . . . its transgressive nature diminished with time, so that it was eventually perceived as a privilege of the monks. (p. 255)

Of course, by the standards of original Indian Buddhism, affirm in all Buddhist lands except Japan, (and to a certain extent Korea, through Japanese influence), any monk found to have engaged deliberately in penetrative sexual activity of any kind should automatically be expelled from the monkhood. Japanese Buddhists were not without some condemnation of homosexuality, though. In *Ōjō yōshū*, the Tendai monk Genshin (942–1017) says that homosexuals go straight to hell, because of their moral transgression and worldly attachment (Faure, 1991: 253). In the middle ages, the Tantric Tachikawa-Ryū sect, which advocated sexual yoga as a way to enlightenment, condemned homosexuality as sterile and counterproductive (Stevens, 1990: 82). Zen masters also warned that monks who had sex with novices and young boys would experience bad karmic results, and that what they taught was suspect. Ikkyū (d. 1481), though he took part in monastic homosexuality as a Zen novice, came to condemn it as leading to jealousies and strife in monasteries (Faure, 1991: 257). He preferred himself to

shun what he saw as the facade of monastic celibacy, and be openly sexually active with women. (Stevens, 1990: 97)

Western Buddhism

What of Buddhism in the West? In the UK, the Friends of the Western Buddhist Order (FWBO: see pp. 103 and 225) welcomes homosexuals, and its outreach activities to various groups in society include introductory meditation retreats for gays and lesbians.

A number of Order members live in single-sex communities, and the FWBO holds that there is a need to revive same-sex friendships, seen generally to avoid the tensions and projections that can be involved in friendship between the sexes. Same-sex friendships are seen as usually deeper, and as facilitating greater trust and spiritual communication and guidance (Subhuti, 1994: 155). Yet if men are wary of a homosexual aspect of friendship with a man, or even of just physical contact as part of such a friendship, they should face 'the fact that there may be some element of sexual attraction towards their friends' (Subhuti, 1994: 166). Though sexual contact should *not* be seen as a necessary part of same-sex friendships, people should not be afraid of the idea, and if it happens, it should be seen as perfectly ordinary (Sangharakshita, 1987: 12; Subhuti, 1994: 166).

The current FWBO attitude is that, provided the third precept is not infringed, heterosexuality, homosexuality and transvestism are all equally morally neutral (Subhuti, 1994: 172). This position of 'neutrality' seems a move away from an earlier preference, among some FWBO members, for homosexual relationships. According to Sāgaramati:

At one time – in the late 1970's/early 1980's – it was voiced that homosexual relations might be best from a 'spiritual' point of view in that they were less 'polarized' than their heterosexual equivalents, resulting in less jealousy, attachment, coercion, and other negative mental states. However, experience has shown that this is not the case: homosexual relationships are just as prone to such negative states as heterosexual ones! (I know that this is now Sangharakshita's view.)[14]

It is now held that, while 'There is nothing that makes gay sex more or less unskilful than heterosexual sex', 'For Buddhism, sexuality is something that one seeks ultimately to transcend, and contented celibacy is the ideal' (Maitreyabandhu, 1995). Celibacy is seen as an aid to non-attachment, though in the past, the FWBO has sometimes also used promiscuity as an aid to this (Subhuti, 1983: 167).

It is seen as important that sexuality is only of relatively peripheral concern to a person, so that he or she can gradually move towards full celibacy (Sangharakshita, 1987: 14). Likewise, spiritual development is seen to entail a progressive transcendence of polarized identification with a person's masculinity or femininity (Subhuti, 1994: 171). The FWBO ideal is one of androgyny, where initial gender-related self-images are overcome by men and women, each having developed, in single-sex situations, qualities normally associated with the other, and 'there is no self-identification as either a man or a woman' (Subhuti, 1994: 166). For this reason, Sangharakshita is critical of homosexuals whose self-identity is based on their sexual orientation (Sangharakshita, 1987: 12; Subhuti, 1994: 172).

[14] Letter, 21 November 1995.

A different kind of view on homosexuality is expressed by Jacqui and Alan James, UK teachers of a form of Insight meditation. They see it as a 'problem area' in which the male homosexual rejects the feminine 'facet of the life-stream' yet often imitates certain female qualities, and the lesbian does the opposite. They thus see it as:

a confusion of the desire to blend the masculine and feminine principles. It is to go on the wrong path through hatred . . . The rejection of one polarity which always accompanies homosexuality is a major stumbling block to the integration and transcendence of masculinity and femininity which signifies real progress on the meditative path. (1987: 42)

They hold, interestingly, that a 'slightly worse problem' is to take to celibacy simply out of fear of sexuality, and thus to repress it with a blind denial of its reality. Such an approach includes 'fear of the responsibility involved in trying to blend the masculine and feminine elements . . . men have to acknowledge the softer side of their nature, the compassionate side. Women need to acknowledge and develop their analytical skills and their impartiality' (pp. 43–4). Also in the UK, the Forest Sangha, which seeks to continue the traditions of Thai meditative monasticism in the West, allows ordination of homosexuals who are able and willing to be celibate, though not of those 'not completely a male' (i.e. *paṇḍaka*s).[15]

In the USA, in his research among Buddhist groups in the San Francisco Bay area, Roger Corless has found that they are either 'neutral or openly accepting' towards 'queer practitioners' (1995: 6). Likewise, José Cabezón reports that in North America, while homophobia is not unknown among Buddhists, he knows of no Buddhist institution that has marginalized its lay homosexual constituency, or required their sexual abstinence. He also knows of no Westerner being denied ordination in North America through being a homosexual (1993: 94). Broadly speaking, one can see this attitude as largely a result of the mixing of the Japanese attitude, conveyed through Zen and Pure Land teachings, and Western liberalism, which has affected both these and a largely de-traditionalized form of Theravāda Insight meditation which is now becoming popular.

Reverend Daizui MacPhillamy, a clinical psychologist and Sōtō Zen priest, has affirmed that:

homosexuality is not an impediment to Enlightenment and gay people are welcome in Buddhist training. How could it be otherwise? How could love

[15] Ajahn Sucitto, letter dated 16 November 1995.

between *any* sentient beings be contrary to the Buddha Nature . . . ? . . . The Buddhist mind understands that All is One *and* All is different. (1982: 28)

He points out that the Sōtō community at Shasta Abbey has included both gay monastics and lay people, and that 'their progress in training has been no different from that of heterosexually-oriented trainees and at least one of them has had a full *kenshō*' (p. 28). The only difference is that they have to deal with the internalized homophobia of society, which sees gays as 'evil, sick or deformed', so that they may be either ashamed or proud of being gay (p. 32). A gay trainee should be willing to give up his present sexual orientation: but only in the sense that any dedicated practitioner, gay or straight, should be *willing* to give up anything for awakening, whether or not he or she actually has to do so (pp. 29–30). Some homosexuals might be changed by the practice, others not, such as the one who had a *kenshō*.

There are various gay and/or lesbian Buddhist groups (Corless, 1995: 5, 14–17), and in 1994, a Gay Pride march in New York City included Zen Buddhists marching under a 'Zen Queers' banner.[16] Such groups aim at a sense of belonging and at mutual support in helping heal the wounds arising from internalized homophobia and the AIDS crisis. Indeed, the 'queer' Buddhists of San Francisco like to cite the Buddha's saying 'If you, monks, do not tend one another, then who is there who will tend you? Whoever, monks, would tend me, he should tend the sick' (*Vin.* 1.302) (Corless, 1995: 11). The Hartford Street Zen Centre runs Maitri, an AIDS hospice, one of the first of its kind (Corless, 1995: 5). Corless points out that the awareness of mortality attendant on the AIDS crisis has helped develop or quickened the interest of 'queers' in Buddhism (1995: 9–10). Another response to the AIDS crisis has been by Eric Kolvig, of the Insight Meditation Center, Barre, Massachusetts, who came to San Francisco in 1993 to teach Insight meditation in a way that would help gays deal with the fear, rage and grief arising from the AIDS epidemic, and the self-hatred that they and lesbians have ingested from the surrounding society (Corless, 1995: 10–11).

Professor Taitetsu Unno, a minister of the Pure Land Buddhist Churches of America, has conducted ceremonies of commitment between Buddhist gay couples (Corless, 1995: 6). The Japanese-based Sōka Gakkai International, which at first saw homosexuality as something to be overcome by a heterosexual marriage, announced in 1995

---

[16] *Indra's Network* newsletter (October/November 1995), 11, reproducing an edited article by Arline Klatte, 'Mindful Warriors', from the American *Trends* magazine.

that it would conduct same-sex marriages, as its former advice was not working (Corless, 1995: 5). In the Tibetan tradition, Dzigar Kongtrul Rinpoche agreed to the marriage of a gay Buddhist to a gay Catholic in a joint Buddhist-Christian ceremony.[17]

The current Dalai Lama, when asked about homosexuality, at first alluded to the traditional Tibetan view that oral and anal intercourse are wrong, then said that 'homosexual conduct is not a fault as long as both partners agree to it, neither is under vows of celibacy, and the activity does not harm others'.[18] Nevertheless, in 1996, he published a book, *Beyond Dogma*,[19] in which he said that 'A sexual act is proper when the couples use the organs created for sexual intercourse and nothing else.'[20] This concerned some liberal American Buddhists, especially gays, who had thought that Buddhism was non-judgemental on sexual matters. In June 1997, the Dalai Lama visited San Francisco, where a large number of gay people live, and said in an address to followers and the press:

We have to make a distinction between believers and unbelievers . . . From a Buddhist point of view, men-to-men and women-to-women is generally considered sexual misconduct. From society's viewpoint, mutually agreeable homosexual relations can be of mutual benefit, enjoyable and harmless.[21]

This did not go down well with his listeners, with Steve Peskin, co-founder of the Buddhist AIDS project in San Francisco, criticizing the Dalai Lama for contributing to anti-gay attitudes.[22] The Dalai Lama also discomforted both heterosexual and gay followers by saying:

Sexual misconduct for men and women consists of oral and anal sex . . . Even with your wife, using one's mouth or other hole is sexual misconduct. Using one's hand, that is sexual misconduct,

though 'To have sexual relations with a prostitute paid by you and not by a third person does not constitute improper behaviour.' Given their concern at the Dalai Lama's remarks, the lesbian, gay, bisexual and transgender (LGBT) Buddhist community asked for a private meeting with him to discuss the issue of homosexuality, and he accordingly met

---

[17] Corless, 1995: 6, citing Jeff Logan-Olivas, 'Story of a Gay Wedding', *Turning Wheel* (Fall 1992), 20.   [18] Corless, 1995: 6, citing Scott Hunt, 'Hello Dalai', *Out* (February/March 1994), 102.

[19] (Berkeley, Calif.: North Atlantic Books).

[20] *The Sunday Times* newspaper, 15 June 1997, 'Gays Rail at Straight Talk by Dalai Lama'.

[21] *San Francisco Chronicle*, 11 June 1997, as cited by David S. da Silva Cornell, 'More re: Dalai Lama and Sex' posting to 'Buddhist' Internet discussion forum, 7 July 1997. See also *The Sunday Times* newspaper, 15 June 1997, 'Gays Rail at Straight Talk by Dalai Lama'.

[22] *The Sunday Times* newspaper, 15 June 1997, 'Gays Rail at Straight Talk by Dalai Lama'.

a delegation on 11 June. After this, he gave out a short press release which said that he

> was greatly concerned by reports made available to him regarding violence and discrimination against gay and lesbian people. His Holiness opposes violence and discrimination based on sexual orientation. He urges respect, tolerance, compassion, and the full recognition of human rights for all . . . Since these matters [of sexuality] are complex and require careful consideration, His Holiness welcomes the invitation and suggestion for further study and discussion on human sexuality to be organised by some of the meeting participants.[23]

The LGBT Buddhists, who were heartened by the meeting, also gave out a press release:

> In a warm, relaxed meeting, the Dalai Lama sought to clarify his understanding of traditional Buddhist texts concerning sexuality . . . He expressed his willingness to consider the possibility that some of these teachings may be specific to a particular cultural and historical context. He stressed that he does not have the authority to unilaterally reinterpret Buddhist scriptures, but urged those present to build a consensus among other Buddhist traditions and communities to collectively change the understanding of the text for contemporary society. His Holiness expressed interest in the insights of modern scientific research and its value in developing new understandings of these texts.
>
> His Holiness . . . was characteristically open and non-judgemental.[24]

Subsequently, LGBT Buddhists in the USA and Hong Kong started to reflect on how to build a new consensus, and embarked on setting up an Internet discussion forum with this in view.[25] One gay Buddhist went on to note that the Dalai Lama had previously said that a problem with oral, anal and manual sex was that they disturbed the inner energy channels which are central to tantric meditation. Accordingly, said the Buddhist, they *could* be seen as acceptable for those Buddhists not involved in such practices.[26]

CONCLUSION

While close friendships have been accepted in monasteries, homosexual activity has not been, except in Japan and, in a moderated form, among

---

[23] David S. da Silva Cornell, 'Official Press Releases from Lesbian and Gay Meeting with Dalai Lama' posting to 'Buddhist' Internet discussion forum, 7 July 1997.   [24] Ibid.

[25] David S. da Silva Cornell, 'After HHDL's Meeting w/LGBT Buddhists' posting to 'Buddhist' Internet discussion forum, 27 June 1997. For those who are interested, Cornell's e-mail address is: cornelld@hayboo.com.

[26] David S. da Silva Cornell, 'Re: Dalai Lama and Sex-Reply' posting to 'Buddhist' Internet discussion forum, 7 July 1997.

irregular monks in Tibet. In the case of the type of sexually dysfunc-
tional passive homosexual known as a *paṇḍaka*, ordination has been
barred, and the spiritual potential in the present life of such people seen
as limited. In Japan, which has had some influence on American
Buddhism, resistance to the ideal of monastic celibacy, which culminated in the development of a married priesthood, led to a toleration
and even advocacy of homosexual activity in the monasteries.
Homosexual activity among lay people has been sporadically condemned as immoral in Southern and Northern Buddhism, but there is
no evidence of persecution of people for homosexual activities. An attitude of unenthusiastic toleration has existed. In China, there has been
more tolerance, and in Japan positive advocacy.

Glossary and details of historical figures and texts

P = Pali, S = Sanskrit, E = English

Abhidhamma (P); *Abhidharma* (S): third section of early Buddhist Canon, on systematized teachings, psychology, philosophy.

Abhidharma-kośa (S): a key text of the Sarvāstivāda school, by Vasubandhu. *Abhidharma-kośa-bhāṣya* is his own commentary on this, mainly from the point of view of the Sautrāntika school.

Arahat (P); *Arhat* (S): a fully liberated saint who has experienced *Nirvāṇa* by uprooting and destroying his or her attachment, hatred and delusion.

Asaṅga: fourth- or fifth-century CE Indian author of a number of Mahāyāna treatises, especially of the Yogācāra school.

Asoka (P); Aśoka (S): Buddhist ruler (*c.* 268–239 BCE) of a large Indian empire; left many stone-carved edicts indicating his rule according to Buddhist social ethics.

Bodhi-caryāvatāra (S): a work of Śāntideva on the path of the *Bodhisattva*.

Bodhisatta (P); *Bodhisattva* (S): a being-for-enlightenment: one fully dedicated to becoming a perfect Buddha. In the Theravāda, mainly used for Gotama in many of his past lives, as described in the *Jātaka*s. In the Mahāyāna, a being, human or divine, on the long *Bodhisattva*-path.

Bodhisattva-bhūmi (S): a text, by Asaṅga, on the stages of the *Bodhisattva*-path, with a substantial section on ethics.

Brahmanism: early form of Hinduism.

brahmin (E) (P and S *brāhmaṇa*): a Hindu priest, member of the highest of four social classes in the Hindu system.

Buddhaghosa: famous Indian commentator on texts of Theravāda school. Active in fifth-century CE Sri Lanka.

Cakkavatti (P); *Cakravartin* (S): a 'wheel-turning' king: a compassionate and just emperor. Seen as a secular parallel to a Buddha.

Candrakīrti: late sixth-century CE Indian writer and commentator of the Mahāyāna Madhyamaka school.

Conditioned Arising (E) (P *paṭicca-samuppāda*; S *pratīya-samutpāda*): also known as Dependent Origination. The doctrine that all mental and physical states arise from and depend on conditions. A common application of this principle is a series of twelve conditions, including spiritual ignorance and craving, culminating in the arising of *dukkha*.

435

Dalai Lama: the current political leader of the Tibetan people in exile, and former ruler of Tibet. Seen as one in a line of Dalai Lamas, each of whom is regarded as both a reincarnation of the last one and a re-manifestation of the compassionate *Bodhisattva* Avalokiteśvara.

Dhamma (P); *Dharma* (S): the Buddha's teachings, the path of Buddhism, and the experiences attained by practising that path, culminating in *Nirvāṇa*. In a socio-moral sense, non-violence, justice and compassion. Also the natural law-orderliness of the world.

Dhammapada (P): part of the *Sutta* section of the Pali Canon. A collection of 423 verses, many of an ethical nature.

*dhamma*s (P); *dharma*s (S): basic patterns/processes, whether mental or physical, seen in the *Abhidhamma* to be the interacting component processes making up the world.

dukkha (P); *duḥkha* (S): 'suffering', or general 'unsatisfactoriness' or 'imperfection' of everything but *Nirvāṇa*.

emptiness (E) (S *śūnyatā*): Mahāyāna idea of the lack of inherent nature in anything, on account of everything being conditioned and interrelated.

Eastern Buddhism: form of Buddhism mediated by Chinese culture, i.e. Buddhism of China, Taiwan, Korea, Japan, Vietnam, Singapore and parts of Malaysia. A form of Mahāyāna Buddhism.

Gotama (P); Gautama (S): family name of the historical Buddha, *c.* 480–400 BCE.

Jātaka (P and S): a 'birth story' purporting to be about a past life of the Buddha as a *Bodhisattva*. A text relating such a story.

karmic fruitfulness (P *puñña*, S *puṇya*): the auspicious power of good actions to purify the mind and bring good karmic fruits. Often translated as 'merit'.

knowledge, the threefold (E) (P *tevijjā*; S *traividyā*): memory of past lives; the 'divine eye', i.e. seeing how other beings are reborn according to their karma; experience of *Nirvāṇa* and full insight into the other Noble Truths.

knowledges, the six (E) (P *abhiññā*; S *abhijñā*): psychic power over matter; the 'divine ear', i.e. hearing sounds – human and divine – at great distances; thought reading; and the 'threefold knowledge' – see last entry.

Mahāyāna (S): the 'Great Vehicle'. Form of Buddhism which puts much emphasis on the *Bodhisattva*-path to Buddhahood, for the sake of all beings. Found mainly in China, Korea, Japan, Vietnam, Tibet and Mongolia.

mantra (S): a sacred phrase, word or syllable that is used to tune into a particular holy being and its power.

Mantrayāna (S): 'Vehicle of Sacred Words'. More or less equivalent to Vajrayāna.

Māra (P and S): An evil tempter-deity, seen as the embodiment of desire and death, dwelling in the highest of the sense-desire-realm heavens.

merit: *see* karmic fruitfulness.

Milindapañha (P): a post-canonical Theravādin text, of around the first century CE, purporting to record dialogues between King Milinda (155–130 BCE) and the monk Nāgasena.

mudra (S): a ritual gesture, often used to amplify the efficacy of a *mantra*.

Nāgārjuna (c.150–250 CE): Indian founder of Mahāyāna Madhyamaka school.

Nibbāna (P); *Nirvāṇa* (S): literally 'extinction', in the sense of the going out of the 'fires' of attachment, hatred and delusion, which cause *dukkha*, and the end of *dukkha* itself. The goal of Theravāda Buddhism, attained initially in life, then finally entered at death.

Noble One (P *ariya*; S *ārya*): one who has gained a first glimpse of ultimate reality, so as to be at least a Stream-enterer (Theravāda) or first-stage *Bodhisattva* (Mahāyāna).

Northern Buddhism: form of Buddhism mediated by Tibetan culture, i.e. Buddhism of Tibet, North-west China, Mongolia, Bhutan, and parts of Nepal and the far north of India. Is a form of Mahāyāna and Vajrayāna.

observance day (P *uposatha*; S *(u)poṣadha*): a type of 'sabbath' day on the full-moon, new-moon or one of two half-moon days, when lay people's visits to a temple are more common and observance of precepts more assiduous.

Pali: language in which the Theravādin texts are preserved, also used for chanting.

Pali Canon: Theravādin collection of scriptures, consisting of sections on *Vinaya*, *Sutta* and *Abhidhamma*, the first two of which substantially date from the time of the Buddha. Passed on by communal recitation until first written down in around 80 BCE.

precepts, five: undertaking to avoid: intentional harming of any living being; theft and cheating; sexual misconduct; lying; unmindful states due to alcohol or drugs.

refuges, three: the Buddha, *Dhamma* and (Noble) *Saṅgha*, seen as inspiring focuses of inspiration and inner strength, and thus as uplifting objects of devotion.

renunciant (P *samaṇa*; S *śramaṇa*): one who has renounced lay life to become a celibate religious practitioner who lives by alms. The term is applied to non-Brahmanical religious wanderers such as Buddhist and Jain monks and nuns.

saṃsāra (P and S): 'wandering on': the round of rebirths and, more generally, the conditioned world, as contrasted with the unconditioned, *Nirvāṇa*.

Saṅgha (P); *Saṃgha* (S): the monastic community, and in the highest sense, the community of anyone, monastic or lay, who is a Noble One.

Sanskrit: language in which many of the texts of Mahāyāna Buddhism came to be written. These now mainly exist only in Tibetan and Chinese translations.

Śāntideva: seventh-century CE Indian Mahāyāna poet.

Sarvāstivāda (S): a non-Mahāyāna school of early Buddhism, once very successful in northern India.

Sarvāstivādin (S): follower of the above school.

Sarvōdaya Śramadāna: name of a Gandhian-influenced Sri Lankan Buddhist rural development movement.

Śikṣā-samuccaya (S): a compilation, from various Mahāyāna *Sūtra*s, by Śāntideva.

Southern Buddhism: form of Buddhism particularly mediated by Sri Lanka, i.e. Buddhism in Sri Lanka (Ceylon), Burma, Thailand, Cambodia, Laos, parts of south Vietnam. Theravāda with a little residual influence from Mahāyāna.

Śrāvaka-yāna (S): 'Vehicle of the Disciples/Listeners (*śrāvakas*)': a Mahāyāna term for followers of non-Mahāyāna schools, for example Theravādins and Sarvāstivādins: those who follow the Buddha's teachings so as to be able to become *Arhats*.

Stream-enterer (P *sotāpanna*; S *srotāpanna*): first grade of sainthood, attained by first glimpse of *Nirvāṇa*.

Sutta (P); *Sūtra* (S): a discourse attributed to the Buddha, or a similar teaching taught by a disciple of his and approved of by him.

Tantra (S): a 'system' of meditation and ritual, preserved in a text (also called a *Tantra*) used in Vajrayāna Buddhism.

Theravāda (P): the 'Ancient teaching' or 'Way of the Elders' school, one of the major pre-Mahāyāna schools of Buddhism, and the only one to survive into the modern day, found mainly in Sri Lanka, Burma, Thailand, Cambodia and Laos.

Theravādin (P): a follower of the Theravāda school.

Upāsaka-śīla Sūtra (S): a Mahāyāna text, popular in China, on lay ethics.

Vajrayāna (S): 'Diamond Vehicle' form of Mahāyāna dominant in Tibet and Mongolia, emphasizing the visualization of holy beings and the use of *mantra*s, or sacred words of power.

Vasubandhu: fourth-century CE author of the *Abhidharma-kośa* and its *bhāṣya* (commentary). An author of the same name, who may be the same person, was the half-brother of Asaṅga, both of whom wrote a number of works of the Mahāyāna Yogācāra school of philosophy.

Vinaya (P and S): The monastic discipline, including a code of rules and how to conduct monastic business. The texts containing this.

Visuddhimagga (P): a work of Buddhaghosa outlining the whole Theravāda path of training in moral conduct, meditation and wisdom.

References

Ackroyd, J., 1987, 'Bushidō', in Eliade, 1987: vol. II, pp. 581–4.

Aitken, R., 1984, *The Mind of Clover: Essays in Zen Buddhist Ethics*, San Francisco, North Point Press.

1985, 'Lessons from Shaku Soen', in Eppsteiner, 1988: 145–9.

Allione, T., 1986, *Women of Wisdom*, London, Arkana.

Anderson P., 1992, 'Good Death: Mercy, Deliverance, and the Nature of Suffering', *Tricycle: The Buddhist Review*, 2 (2), 36–42.

Ariyaratne, A. T., 1974, 'Buddhism and Sarvodaya', *Buddhist Quarterly* (journal of the London Buddhist Vihāra), 7 (2), 3–9.

1979, 1980, *Collected Works*, vol. I and vol. II, The Netherlands, Sarvodaya Research Institute.

1995, 'Buddhist Thought in Sarvodaya Practice', paper given at the Seventh International Seminar on Buddhism and Leadership for Peace, Department of Philosophy, University of Hawaii, Honolulu, 17 pages.

Aronson, H. B., 1980, *Love and Sympathy in Theravāda Buddhism*, Delhi, Motilal Banarsidass.

Ash, C., 1994, 'Buddhist Economics: Scope and Method' paper given at the Contemporary Buddhism: Text and Context conference, University of Leeds, April 1994: handout, plus oral presentation, unpublished.

Badiner, A. H., ed., 1990, *Dharma Gaia: A Harvest of Essays in Buddhism and Ecology*, Berkeley, Calif., Parallax Press.

Bapat, P. V. and Hirakawa, A., 1970, *Shan-Chien-P'i-P'o-Sha, a Chinese Version by Saṅghabhadra of Samantapāsādikā: Commentary on Pali Vinaya Translated into English for the First Time*, Poona, Bhandarkar Oriental Research Institute.

Barber, A. W., 1991, '*Prātimoka, Bodhi-citta,* and *Samaya*', in Fu and Wawrytko, 1991: 81–91.

Barnard, C., 1978, 'A Case for Euthanasia', in G. C. Oosthuizen, H. Shapiro and S. A. Strauss (eds.), *Euthanasia*, Cape Town, Oxford University Press, pp. 197–212.

Bartholomeusz, T., 1992, 'The Female Mendicant in Buddhist Srī Lankā', in Cabezón, 1992: 37–61.

1994, *Women Under the Bo Tree: Buddhist Nuns in Sri Lanka*, Cambridge, Cambridge University Press.

1999, 'In Defence of Dharma: Just-War Ideology in Buddhist Sri Lanka', *Journal of Buddhist Ethics*, 6, pp. 1–11.

Basham, A. L., 1967, *The Wonder that was India*, London, Sidgwick & Jackson, reprinted 1971 by Fontana.

1982, 'Asoka and Buddhism: A Re-examination', *Journal of the International Association of Buddhist Studies*, 5 (1), 131–43.

Batchelor, M. and Brown, K., eds., 1992, *Buddhism and Ecology*, London and New York, Cassell (sponsored by the World Wide Fund for Nature).

Becker, C. B., 1990, 'Buddhist Views of Suicide and Euthanasia', *Philosophy East and West*, 40 (4), 543–55.

Bell, C., 1924, *Tibet Past and Present*, reprinted 1992, Delhi, Asian Educational Services.

1928, *The People of Tibet*, Oxford, Clarendon Press.

Bellah, R. N., 1957, *Tokugawa Religion: The Values of Pre-Industrial Japan*, New York, The Free Press; London, Collier Macmillan.

1963, 'Reflections on the Protestant Ethic Analogy in Asia', *Journal of Social Issues*, 19, pp. 52–60.

Beyer, S., 1973, *The Cult of Tara: Magic and Ritual in Tibet*, Berkeley, Calif., University of California Press.

1974, *The Buddhist Experience – Sources and Interpretations*, Encino, Calif., Dickenson.

Blackstone, K. R., 1998, *Women in the Footsteps of the Buddha: Struggle for Liberation in the Therīgāthā*, London, Curzon Press.

Blofeld, J., 1972, *The Wheel of Life – The Autobiography of a Western Buddhist*, London, Rider.

Bloss, L. W., 1987, 'The Female Renunciants of Sri Lanka: The Dasasilamattawa', *Journal of the International Association of Buddhist Studies*, 10, pp. 7–31.

Bodhi, Bhikkhu, 1984, *The Noble Eightfold Path*, Kandy, Sri Lanka, BPS.

1993, *A Comprehensive Manual of Abhidhamma: The Abhidhammattha Sangaha of Acariya Anuruddha*, Kandy, BPS (translation).

Bollée, W. B., 1970, *Kuṇālajātaka: Being an Edition and Translation*, London, Luzac & Co.

Bond, G. D., 1988, *The Buddhist Revival in Sri Lanka – Religious Tradition, Reinterpretation and Response*, Columbia, University of South Carolina Press.

1995, 'The Sarvodaya Movement's Quest for Peace and Social Awakening', paper given at Seventh International Seminar on Buddhism and Leadership for Peace, Department of Philosophy, University of Hawaii, Honolulu, 12 pages.

1996, 'A. T. Ariyaratne and the Sarvodaya Shramadana Movement in Sri Lanka', in Queen and King 1996: 121–46.

Boucher, S., 1993, *Turning the Wheel: American Women Creating the New Buddhism* (updated and expanded edition of original 1988 edition), Boston, Mass., Beacon Press.

Brear, A. D., 1974, 'The Nature and Status of Moral Behaviour in Zen Buddhism', *Philosophy East and West*, 24 (4), 429–41.

Broido, M. M., 1988, 'Killing, Lying, Stealing and Adultery: A Problem of

Interpretation in the Tantras', in D. S. Lopez (ed.), *Buddhist Hermeneutics*, Kuroda Institute Studies in East Asian Buddhism 6, Honolulu, University of Hawaii Press.

Brooks, A. P., 1981, 'Mizuko Kuyō and Japanese Buddhism', *Japanese Journal of Religious Studies*, 8 (3–4), 119–47.

Bunnag, J., 1973, *Buddhist Monk, Buddhist Layman: A Study of Urban Monastic Organization in Central Thailand*, Cambridge, Cambridge University Press.

Burns, D. M., 1977, *The Population Crisis and Conservation in Buddhist Perspective*, Bodhi Leaf pamphlet no. B.76, Kandy, Sri Lanka, BPS.

Burr, R., 1995, 'Buddhist Conflict Management' (on the Sarvōdaya Śramadāna movement), paper given at the Seventh International Seminar on Buddhism and Leadership for Peace, Department of Philosophy, University of Hawaii, Honolulu, 19 pages.

Cabezón, J. I., ed., 1992, *Buddhism, Sexuality and Gender*, New York, State University of New York Press.

1993, 'Homosexuality and Buddhism', in A. Swidler (ed.), *Homosexuality and World Religions*, Valley Forge, Penn., Trinity Press International, pp. 81–101.

1996, 'Buddhist Principles in the Tibetan Liberation Movement', in Queen and King, 1996: 295–320.

Carlson, Rōshi Kyogen, 1982, 'The Meaning of Celibacy', *Journal of Shasta Abbey*, 9 (1978), reproduced in *Sexuality and Religious Training*, a 1982 booklet of Throssel Hole Priory, near Hexham, England, pp. 34–9.

Carmody, D. L., 1989, *Women and World Religions*, 2nd edn, Englewood Cliffs, N.J., Prentice-Hall.

Carrithers, M., 1983, *The Forest Monks of Sri Lanka: An Anthropological and Historical Study*, Delhi, Oxford University Press India.

Causton, R., 1988, *Nichiren Shōshū Buddhism: An Introduction*, London, Rider.

Chang, G. C. C., ed., 1983, *A Treasury of Mahāyāna Sūtras: Selections from the Mahāratnakūṭa Sūtra* (a translation from the Chinese by The Buddhist Association of the United States), University Park, Pennsylvania State University Press.

Chappell, D. W., 1995, 'Searching for a Mahayana Social Ethics', paper given at the Seventh International Seminar on Buddhism and Leadership for Peace, Department of Philosophy, University of Hawaii, Honolulu, 13 pages.

Chapple, C., 1992, 'Nonviolence to Animals in Buddhism and Jainism', in Kraft, 1992: 49–62.

Chapple, K. C., 1993, *Non-violence to Animals, Earth, and Self in Asian Traditions*, New York, State University of New York Press.

Ch'en, K., 1964, *Buddhism in China*, Princeton, N.J., Princeton University Press.

Ch'en, K. K. S., 1973, *The Chinese Transformation of Buddhism*, Princeton, N.J., Princeton University Press.

Ching, Yu-ing, 1995, *Master of Love and Mercy: Cheng Yen*, Nevada City, Calif., Blue Dolphin Publishing.

Clasquin, M., 1992, 'Contemporary Theravāda and Zen Buddhist Attitudes to

Human Sexuality: An Exercise in Comparative Ethics', *Religion*, 22, pp. 63–83.

Cleary, T., 1986, *Shōbōgenzō: Zen Essays by Dōgen*, Honolulu, University of Hawaii Press (translation).

Cone, M. and Gombrich, R., 1977, *The Perfect Generosity of Prince Vessantara*, Oxford, Clarendon Press (translation).

Conze, E., 1959, *Buddhist Scriptures*, Harmondsworth, Penguin (anthology of translations).

1967, *Thirty Years of Buddhist Studies*, Oxford, Cassirer.

1968, *Selected Sayings from the Perfection of Wisdom*, London, The Buddhist Society (anthology of translations).

1973, *The Perfection of Wisdom in Eight Thousand Lines and its Verse Summary*, Bolinas, Four Seasons Foundation (translation).

Conze, E., Horner, I. B., Snellgrove, D. and Waley, A., 1954, *Buddhist Texts Through the Ages*, Oxford, Cassirer; 1964, London, Luzac & Co., New York, Harper & Row (anthology of translations).

Cook, F., 1989, 'The Jewel Net of Indra', in J. B. Callicott and R. T. Ames (eds.), *Nature in Asian Traditions of Thought: Essays in Environmental Philosophy*, Albany, State University of New York Press, pp. 213–30.

Corless, R., 1995, 'Coming Out in the Sangha: Queer Community in American Buddhism', pre-publication version of a paper now in C. S. Prebish and K. Tanaka (eds.), *The Faces of Buddhism in America*, Berkeley, University of California Press, 1998, pp. 253–65, 328–33.

Cousins, L. S., 1974, 'Ethical Standards in World Religions: III. Buddhism', *The Expository Times*, 85, pp. 100–4.

1996, 'Good or Skilful? *Kusala* in Canon and Commentary', *Journal of Buddhist Ethics*, 3, pp. 136–64.

Davis, W., 1989, 'Buddhism and the Modernization of Japan', *History of Religions*, 28 (4), 304–39.

Dayal, H., 1932, *The Bodhisattva Doctrine in Buddhist Sanskrit Literature*, London, Routledge & Kegan Paul; reprinted 1970, Delhi, Motilal Banarsidass.

de Bary, W. T., ed., 1972, *The Buddhist Tradition in India, China and Japan*, New York, Vintage Books (selected translations, with comments).

De Groot, J. M. M., 1893, *Le Code du Mahāyāna en Chine: son influence sur la vie monacle et sur la monde laïque*, Amsterdam, J. Müller; reprinted New York, Garland Publishers, 1980 (translation and discussion of the *Brahmajāla Sūtra*).

Demiéville, P., 1957, 'Le Bouddhisme et la guerre: postscriptum à "L'Histoire des moines guerriers du Japon" de G. Renondeau', *Mélanges*, Vol. 1, Paris, L'Institut des Hautes Etudes Chinoises, Presses Universitaires de France, pp. 347–85. Reprinted in his *Choix d'études bouddhiques (1929–1970)*, Leiden, E. J. Brill, 1973, pp. 261–99. On Buddhist non-violent ideals, Buddhism and armed conflict in Chinese and then Japanese history, and Buddhist 'justifications' for this.

de Silva, K. M., Duke, P., Goldberg, E. S. and Katz, N., eds., 1988, *Ethnic Conflict in Buddhist Societies: Sri Lanka, Thailand and Burma*, London, Pinter; Boulder, Colo., Westview Press.

de Silva, L., 1994, *Ministering to the Sick and the Terminally Ill*, Kandy, Sri Lanka, BPS.

De Silva, P. 1975, *The Search for Buddhist Economics*, Kandy, Sri Lanka, BPS.

    1976, *Value Orientations and Nation Building*, Colombo, Sri Lanka, Lake House Investments Ltd.

Dewaraja, L. S., 1981, *The Position of Women in Buddhism*, Wheel pamphlet no. 280, Kandy, Sri Lanka, BPS.

Dhammika, S., 1993, *The Edicts of King Asoka*, Wheel pamphlet no. 386–7, Kandy, Sri Lanka, BPS (translation).

Dharma Realm Buddhist University, 1981, *The Buddha Speaks the Brahma Net Sūtra*, Talmage, Calif., Buddhist Text Translation Society (translation).

Dharmasiri, G., 1989, *Fundamentals of Buddhist Ethics*, Antioch, Calif., Golden Leaves Publ. Co.

Dowman, K., 1984, *Sky Dancer: The Secret Life and Songs of the Lady Yeshe Tsogyel*, London, Routledge & Kegan Paul.

Duus, P., 1976, *The Rise of Modern Japan*, Boston, Mass., Houghton Mifflin.

Ekvall, R. B., 1964, *Religious Observances in Tibet*, Chicago and London, University of Chicago Press.

Eliade, M., ed., 1987, *The Encyclopaedia of Religion*, 16 vols., New York, Macmillan; London, Collier Macmillan.

Eppsteiner, F., ed., 1988, *The Path of Compassion: Writings on Socially Engaged Buddhism*, Berkeley, Calif., Parallax Press.

Evans, D., 1987, 'A Note and Response to "The Buddhist Perspective on Respect for Persons"', *Buddhist Studies Review*, 4 (2), 97–8.

Evans-Wentz, W. Y., 1951, *Tibet's Great Yogī Milarepa: A Biography from the Tibetan*, 2nd edn, London, Oxford University Press (translation).

Falk, N. A., 1980, 'The Case of the Vanishing Nuns: The Fruits of Ambivalence in Ancient Indian Buddhism', in N. A. Falk and R. M. Gross (eds.), *Unspoken Worlds: Women's Religious Lives in Non-Western Cultures*, San Francisco, Harper & Row, pp. 207–24.

    1990, 'Exemplary Donors of the Pāli Tradition', in Sizemore and Swearer, 1990: 124–43.

Faure, B., 1991, *The Rhetoric of Immediacy: A Cultural Critique of Chan/Zen Buddhism*, Princeton, Princeton University Press.

Fenn, M. L., 1991, 'Unjustified Poverty and Karma (Pali Kamma)', *Religious Studies and Theology* (Alberta), 11 (1), 20–6.

    1996, 'Two Notions of Poverty in the Pāli Canon', *Journal of Buddhist Ethics*, 3, pp. 98–125.

Florida, R. E., 1991, 'Buddhist Approaches to Abortion', in *Asian Philosophy*, 1 (1), 39–50.

    1993, 'Buddhist Approaches to Euthanasia', *Studies in Religion/Sciences Religieuses*, 22 (1), 35–47.

    1998, 'Abortion in Buddhist Thailand', in Keown, 1998: 11–29.

Fox, D. A., 1971, 'Zen and Ethics: Dōgen's Synthesis', *Philosophy East and West*, 21 (1), 33–41.

French, R. R., 1995, 'The Cosmology of Law in Buddhist Tibet', *Journal of the International Association of Buddhist Studies*, 18 (1), 97–116.

Friedman, L., 1987, *Daughters of Lion's Yawn: Women Teachers of Buddhism in America*, Boulder, Colo., Shambhala.

Fu, C. W. and Wawrytko, S. A., eds., 1991, *Buddhist Ethics and Modern Society: An International Symposium*, New York, Greenwood Press.

Fujii, N., 1980, *Buddhism for World Peace*, Tokyo, Japan-Bharat Sarvodaya Mitra Sangha.

Furer-Haimendorf, C. von, 1967, *Morals and Merit*, Chicago, University of Chicago Press.

Geiger, W., 1929, *Cūḷavaṃsa*, Parts I and II, 2 vols., London, PTS (translation).

   1980, *The Mahāvaṃsa or Great Chronicle of Ceylon*, London, PTS (translation).

Ghosananda, Maha, 1992, *Step by Step: Meditations on Wisdom and Compassion*, ed. J. S. Mahoney and P. Edmonds, Berkeley, Calif., Parallax Press. Selections from the teachings of this Cambodian monk-activist for peace, with an introduction discussing his life in context.

Gokhale, B. G., 1966, 'Early Buddhist Kingship', *Journal of Asian Studies*, 26 (1), 15–22.

Goldstein, M. C., 1964, 'A Study of the *Ldab ldob*', *Central Asian Journal*, 9, pp. 123–41.

Gombrich, R. F., 1971a, *Precept and Practice: Traditional Buddhism in the Rural Highlands of Ceylon*, Oxford, Clarendon Press.

   1971b, 'Merit Transference in Sinhalese Buddhism', *History of Religions*, 11, pp. 203–19.

   1988, *Theravāda Buddhism: A Social History from Ancient Benares to Modern Colombo*, London and New York, Routledge & Kegan Paul.

Gombrich, R. and Obeyesekere, G., 1988, *Buddhism Transformed: Religious Change in Sri Lanka*, Princeton, N.J., Princeton University Press.

Gomez, L. O., 1992, 'Nonviolence and the Self in Early Buddhism', in Kraft, 1992: 31–48.

Gosling, D., 1984, 'Discussion Notes: Buddhism for Peace', *Southeast Asian Journal of Social Science*, 12 (1), 59–70.

   1985, 'Thailand's Bare-headed Doctors', *Modern Asian Studies*, 19 (4), 761–96.

Goulet, D., 1981, *Survival with Integrity: Sarvodaya at the Crossroads*, Colombo, Marga Institute.

Griffiths, P. J., 1986, *On Being Mindless: Buddhist Meditation and the Mind–Body Problem*, La Salle, Ill., Open Court.

Gross, R. M., 1994, *Buddhism After Patriarchy: A Feminist History, Analysis, and Reconstruction of Buddhism*, Albany, N.Y., State University of New York Press.

Guenther, H. V., 1959, *sGam-po-pa's Jewel Ornament of Liberation*, London, Rider; reprinted Berkeley, Calif., Shambhala, 1971 (translation).

Hall, F., 1902, *The Soul of a People* (on nineteenth-century Burma), London, Macmillan.

Hall, R. E., ed., 1970, *Abortion in a Changing World*, New York and London, Columbia University Press.

Hämmerli, U. P., 1978, 'A Definition from the Viewpoint of a Physician', in G. C. Oosthuizen, H. Shapiro and S. A. Strauss (eds.), *Euthanasia*, Cape Town, Oxford University Press, pp. 180–96.

Hanks, L. M. & J. R., 1963, 'Thailand – Equality Between the Sexes', in B. Ward (ed.), *Women in the New Asia*, Paris, UNESCO, pp. 424–51.

Harris, E. J., 1994, *Violence and Disruption in Society: A Study of the Early Buddhist Texts*, Wheel booklet no. 392/393, Kandy, BPS.

1998, *What Buddhists Believe*, Oxford, Oneworld.

Harris, I., 1991, 'How Environmentalist is Buddhism?', *Religion*, 21, pp. 101–14.

1994a, 'Causation and *Telos*: The Problem of Buddhist Environmental Ethics', *Journal of Buddhist Ethics*, 1, pp. 45–56.

1994b, 'Buddhism', in J. Holm and J. Bowker (eds.), *Attitudes to Nature*, London, Pinter, pp. 8–27.

1995a, 'Buddhist Environmental Ethics and Detraditionalization: The Case of EcoBuddhism', *Religion*, 25, pp. 199–211.

1995b, 'Getting to Grips with Buddhist Environmentalism: A Provisional Typology', *Journal of Buddhist Ethics*, 2, pp. 173–90.

1997, 'Buddhism and the Discourse of Environmental Concern: Some Methodological Problems Considered', in M. E. Tucker and D. R. Williams (eds.), *Buddhism and Ecology: The Interconnection of Dharma and Deeds*, Cambridge, Mass., Harvard University Center for the Study of World Religions, pp. 377–402.

Harrison, E. G., 1998, '"I Can Only Move my Feet towards *Mizuko Kuyō*." Memorial Services for Dead Children in Japan', in Keown, 1998: 93–120.

Harvey, P., 1987, 'The Buddhist Perspective on Respect for Persons', *Buddhist Studies Review*, 4 (1), 31–46.

1990a, *An Introduction to Buddhism: Teachings*, History and Practices, Cambridge, Cambridge University Press.

1990b, 'Venerated Objects and Symbols of Early Buddhism', in K. Werner (ed.), *Symbols in Art and Religion: The Indian and the Comparative Perspectives*, London, Curzon Press; Glenn Dale, Md., The Riverdale Company, pp. 68–102.

1993, 'The Dynamics of Paritta Chanting in Southern Buddhism', in K. Werner (ed.), *Love Divine: Studies in Bhakti and Devotional Mysticism*, Richmond, Surrey, Curzon, pp. 53–84.

1995, *The Selfless Mind: Personality, Consciousness and Nirvāṇa in Early Buddhism*, London, Curzon Press.

1999, 'Vinaya Principles for Assigning Degrees of Culpability', *Journal of Buddhist Ethics*, 6, pp. 271–91.

Havnevik, H., 1991, *Tibetan Nuns Now: History, Cultural Norms and Social Reality*, Oslo, Norwegian University Press.

Herdt, G., 1987, 'Homosexuality', in Eliade, 1987: vol. VI, pp. 445–53.

Hirakawa, Akira, 1982, *Monastic Discipline for the Buddhist Nuns: An English*

Translation of the Chinese Text of the Mahāsāṃghika-Bhikṣunī-Vinaya, Patna, Kashi Prasad Jayaswal Research Institute.

1995, 'The Formation of the Pañca-śīla in Early Buddhism', *World Fellowship of Buddhists Review*, 32 (3), 8–23.

Hopkinson, D., Hill, M. and Kiera, E., eds., 1986, *Not Mixing Up Buddhism: Essays on Women and Buddhist Practice* (extracts from *Kahawai Journal of Women and Zen*), Fredonia, N.Y., White Pine Press.

Horner, I. B., 1930, *Women Under Primitive Buddhism: Laywomen and Almswomen*, London, Routledge & Kegan Paul; reprinted 1975, Delhi, Motilal Banarsidass.

Hoshino, Eiki and Takeda, Dōsho, 1987, 'Indebtedness and Comfort: The Undercurrents of *Mizuko Kuyō*', *Japanese Journal of Religious Studies*, 14 (4), 305–20.

Huxley, A., 1995a, 'Buddhism and Law: The View from Mandalay', *Journal of the International Association of Buddhist Studies*, 18 (1), 47–95.

1995b, 'The Vinaya: Legal System or Performance Enhancing Drug?', paper given to the Buddhist Forum series of seminars at the Department of Religious Studies, School of Oriental and African Studies, London, 25 January 1995.

1995c, 'The Kurudhamma: From Ethics to Statecraft', *Journal of Buddhist Ethics*, 2, pp. 191–203.

1997, 'Studying Theravāda Legal Literature', *Journal of the International Association of Buddhist Studies*, 20 (1), 63–91.

Ikeda, D., 1981, *A Lasting Peace*, Tokyo, Weatherhill.

1994, *Unlocking the Mysteries of Birth and Death: Buddhism in the Contemporary World*, London, Warner Books.

Inada, K., 1995, 'A Buddhist Response to the Nature of Human Rights', *Journal of Buddhist Ethics*, 2, pp. 55–66.

Ingersoll, J., 1966, 'Fatalism in Village Thailand', *Anthropological Quarterly*, 39 (3), 200–25.

Ives, C., 1992, *Zen Awakening and Society*, Honolulu, University Press of Hawaii.

Jackson, R. R., 1992, 'Ambiguous Sexuality: Imagery and Interpretation in Tantric Buddhism', *Religion*, 22, pp. 85–100.

Jahan, R., ed., 1982, *Women in Asia* (includes information on Sri Lanka, South Korea and Japan), London, Minority Rights Group.

Jaini, P. S., 1991, *Gender and Salvation: Jaina Debates on the Spiritual Liberation of Women*, Berkeley, Calif., University of California Press.

James, J. and A., 1987, *Modern Buddhism*, Box, Wiltshire, Aukana.

Jayatilleke, K. N., 1972, *Ethics in Buddhist Perspective*, Wheel booklet no. 175/176, Kandy, Sri Lanka, BPS.

Jhingran, S., 1989, *Aspects of Hindu Morality* (see pp. 91–9 for a useful survey on the position of women), Delhi, Motilal Banarsidass.

Jones, J. G., 1979, *Tales and Teachings of the Buddha: The Jātaka Stories in Relation to the Pali Canon*, London, George Allen & Unwin.

Jones, K., 1989, *The Social Face of Buddhism*, London, Wisdom.

Juergensmeyer, M. 1990, 'What the Bhikkhu Said: Reflections on the Rise of Militant Religious Nationalism' (in Sri Lanka), *Religion*, 20, pp. 53–75.

Kabilsingh, C., 1986, 'The Future of the Bhikkhunī Samgha in Thailand', in D. L. Eck and D. Jain (eds.), *Speaking of Faith: Cross-cultural Perspectives on Women, Religion and Social Change*, London, The Women's Press, pp. 147–63.

1988, 'How Buddhism can Help Protect Nature', *World Fellowship of Buddhists Review*, 25 (2), 17–24.

1991, *Thai Women in Buddhism*, Berkeley, Calif., Parallax Press.

Kalupahana, D., 1976, *Buddhist Philosophy: A Historical Analysis*, Honolulu, University of Hawaii Press.

Kammer, R., 1978, *Zen and Confucius in the Art of Swordsmanship: The Tengu-geijustsu-ron of Chozam Shissai*, London, Routledge & Kegan Paul (translation).

Kantowski, D., 1980, *Sarvodaya: The Other Development*, New Delhi, Vikas.

Kapleau, Roshi P., 1981, *To Cherish All Life: A Buddhist View of Animal Slaughter and Meat Eating*, Rochester, N.Y., The Zen Center.

Karunatilake, H. N. S., 1976, *This Confused Society*, Colombo, Sri Lanka, Buddhist Information Centre.

Kasulis, T. P., 1981, *Zen Action, Zen Person*, Honolulu, University of Hawaii Press.

Kato, B., Tamura, Y. and Miyasaka, K., 1975, *The Threefold Lotus Sutra* (translated from the Chinese), New York, Weatherhill; Tokyo, Kosei.

Katz, N., 1982, *Buddhist Images of Human Perfection: The Arahant of the Sutta Piṭaka Compared with the Bodhisattva and Mahāsiddha*, Delhi, Motilal Banarsidass.

1986, 'Social and Political Attitudes of Sri Lankan Monks', *South Asia Report*, November 1988.

1988, 'Sri Lankan Monks on Ethnicity and Nationalism', in de Silva et al., pp. 138–52.

Kawanami, H., 1990, 'The Religious Standing of Burmese Nuns (*Theḷa-shin*): Ten Precepts and Religious Honorifics', *Journal of the International Association of Buddhist Studies*, 13, pp. 17–39.

Kelleher, T., 1987, 'Confucianism', in A. Sharma (ed.), *Women in World Religions*, Albany, State University of New York Press, pp. 135–59.

Kemper, S., 1990, 'Wealth and Reformation in Sinhalese Buddhist Monasticism', in Sizemore and Swearer, 1990: 152–69.

Kennett, Roshi J., 1972, *Selling Water by the River: a Manual of Zen Training*, New York, Random House; 2nd edition, *Zen is Eternal Life*, Berkeley, Calif., Dharma, 1976.

1982, 'Abortion and the Buddha Nature', *Journal of Shasta Abbey*, 9 (1978), reproduced in *Sexuality and Religious Training*, a 1982 booklet of Throssel Hole Priory, near Hexham, England, pp. 17–20.

Keown, D., 1992, *The Nature of Buddhist Ethics*, London, Macmillan.

1995a, *Buddhism and Bioethics* (an analysis of Buddhist views relating to abortion, euthanasia and criteria of death), London, Macmillan and New York, St Martin's Press.

1995b, 'Are there "Human Rights" in Buddhism?', *Journal of Buddhist Ethics*, 2, pp. 3–27.

1996, 'Buddhism and Suicide – the Case of Channa', *Journal of Buddhist Ethics*, 3, pp. 8–31.

ed., 1998, *Buddhism and Abortion*, London, Macmillan, which includes, by him, the introduction (pp. 1–9) and 'Buddhism and Abortion: Is there a "Middle Way"?' (pp. 199–218).

Keown, D. V., Prebish, C. S. and Husted, W. R., eds., 1998, *Buddhism and Human Rights*, London, Curzon Press.

Kern, H., 1884, *The Saddharma-puṇḍarīka Sūtra or the Lotus of the True Law*, Sacred Books of the East, vol. XXI, Oxford, Clarendon Press; 1968, Delhi, Motilal Banarsidass (translation).

Keyes, C. F., 1978, 'Political Crisis and Militant Buddhism in Contemporary Thailand', in Smith, 1978: 147–64.

1983, 'Merit-Transference in the Kammatic Theory of Popular Theravāda Buddhism', in C. F. Keyes and E. V. Daniel (eds.), *Karma: An Anthropological Inquiry*, Berkeley, University of California Press, pp. 261–86.

1990, 'Buddhist Practical Morality in a Changing Agrarian World: A Case from Northeastern Thailand', in Sizemore and Swearer, 1990: 170–89.

Khantipalo, Bhikkhu, 1979, *Banner of the Arahants: Buddhist Monks and Nuns from the Buddha's Time till Now* [in ancient and Southern Buddhism], Kandy, Sri Lanka, BPS.

1986, *Aggression, War and Conflict*, Bodhi Leaf pamphlet no. B.108, Kandy, Sri Lanka, BPS.

Khoroche, P. (tr.), 1989, *Once the Buddha Was a Monkey: Ārya Śūrya's Jātakamālā*, Chicago and London, University of Chicago Press (translation).

King, S. B., 1996, 'Thich Nhat Hanh and the Unified Buddhist Church: Nondualism in Action', in Queen and King, 1996: 321–65.

King, W. L., 1964, *In the Hope of Nibbana: An Essay on Theravada Buddhist Ethics*, La Salle, Ill., Open Court.

1981, 'A Christian and a Japanese Buddhist Work Ethic Compared', *Religion*, 11, pp. 207–26.

1993, *Zen and the Way of the Sword: Arming the Samurai Psyche*, Oxford and New York, Oxford University Press.

Kirsch, A. T., 1975, 'Economy, Polity and Religion in Thailand', in G. W. Skinner and A. T. Kirsch (eds.), *Change and Persistence in Thai Society*, London, Cornell University Press, pp. 172–96.

Koya, Yoshio, 1954, 'A Study of Induced Abortion in Japan and its Significance', *Milbank Memorial Fund Quarterly*, 32, pp. 282–93.

Kraft, K., ed., 1992, *Inner Peace, World Peace: Essays on Buddhism and Nonviolence*, Albany, N.Y., State University of New York Press.

Krishan, Y., 1986, 'Buddhism and the Caste System', *Journal of the International Association of Buddhist Studies*, 9 (1), 71–83.

Kübler Ross, E., 1989/90, 'The Good Death', in *Raft – The Journal of the Buddhist Hospice Trust*, no.2 (special issue on euthanasia), 5–6.

LaFleur, W., 1973–4, 'Saigyō and the Buddhist Value of Nature', in *History of Religions*, 13 (2), 91–126 and 13 (3), 227–48. Reprinted, in a condensed form, in J. B. Callicott and R. T. Ames (eds.), *Nature in Asian Traditions of Thought:*

Essays in Environmental Philosophy, Albany, State University of New York Press, 1990, pp. 183–212.

1992, *Liquid Life: Abortion and Buddhism in Japan*, Princeton: Princeton University Press.

1995, 'Silences and Censure: Abortion, History, and Buddhism in Japan – A Rejoinder to George Tanabe', *Japanese Journal of Religious Studies*, 22, pp. 185–96.

Lamotte, E., 1949, *Le Traité de la grande vertu de sagesse de Nāgārjuna (Mahāprajñāpāramitāśāstra)*, Bureaux du Muséon, Louvain, vol. II (translation).

1976, *The Teachings of Vimalakīrti*, London, PTS (translation).

1987, 'Religious Suicide in Early Buddhism', *Buddhist Studies Review*, 4 (2), 105–18.

1988, *History of Indian Buddhism* (translated from French (1958) by S. Boin-Webb), Leuven, Belgium, Peters Press.

Law, B. C., 1973, *Heaven and Hell in Buddhist Perspective*, Delhi, Bhartiya Publ. House.

Lee, O., 1978, *Legal and Moral Systems in Asian Customary Law: The Legacy of the Buddhist Social Ethic and Buddhist Law* (focusing on South-east Asia, particularly Burma), San Francisco, Chinese Materials Center.

Legge, J., 1886, *A Record of Buddhist Kingdoms: Being an Account by Chinese Monk Fa-Hien of his Travels in India and Ceylon (A.D. 399–414)*, Oxford, Clarendon Press; reprinted 1965, New York, Paragon Book Reprint Corp. and Dover Publications (translation).

Lenore, F., 1987, *Meetings with Remarkable Women: Buddhist Teachers in America*, Boston, Mass., Shambhala.

Lesco, P. A., 1986, 'Euthanasia: A Buddhist Perspective', *Journal of Religion and Health*, 25 (1) (Spring), 51–57.

1987, 'A Buddhist View of Abortion', *Journal of Religion and Health*, 26 (3), 214–18.

Lester, R. C., 1973, *Theravada Buddhism in Southeast Asia*, Ann Arbor, University of Michigan Press.

Levering, M. L., 1982, 'The Dragon Girl and the Abbess of Mo-Shan: Gender and Status in the Ch'an Buddhist Tradition', *Journal of the International Association of Buddhist Studies*, 5 (1), 19–35.

1992, 'Lin-chi Rinzai Ch'an and Gender: The Rhetoric of Equality and the Rhetoric of Heroism', in Cabezón, 1992: 137–56.

Levine, S., 1992, 'No Second-Guessing: An Interview with Stephen Levine', *Tricycle: The Buddhist Review*, 2 (2), 48–50.

Lindbeck, V., 1984, 'Thailand: Buddhism Meets the Western Model', *The Hastings Center Report*, 14 (December), 24–6 (on bioethics).

Ling, T. O., 1969, 'Buddhist Factors in Population Growth and Control: A Survey Based on Thailand and Ceylon', *Population Studies*, 23 (1), 53–60.

1973, *The Buddha: Buddhist Civilization in India and Ceylon*, London, Temple Smith.

1979, *Buddhism, Imperialism and War: Burma and Thailand in Modern History*, London, George Allen & Unwin.

1980a, *Buddhist Revival in India: Aspects of the Sociology of Buddhism*, London, Macmillan.

1980b, 'Buddhist Values and Development Problems: A Case Study of Sri Lanka', *World Development*, 8, pp. 577–86.

Lipner, J. J., 1991, 'The Classical Hindu View on Abortion and the Moral Status of the Unborn', in H. G. Coward, J. J. Lipner and K. K. Young (eds.), *Hindu Ethics: Purity, Abortion and Euthanasia*, Delhi, Sri Satguru Publications, pp. 41–69.

Little, D. and Twiss, S. B., 1978, *Comparative Religious Ethics: A New Method*, New York, Harper & Row.

Luk, C., 1972, *The Vimalakīrti Nirdesa Sutra*, Berkeley and London, Shambhala (translation).

MacAndrews, C. and Sien, C. L., 1979, *Developing Economies and the Environment: The Southeast Asian Experience*, New York, McGraw-Hill.

McConnell, J. A., 1995, *Mindful Mediation: A Handbook for Buddhist Peacemakers*, Bangkok, jointly published by: Buddhist Research Institute (Mahachula Buddhist University); Spirit in Education Movement; Wongsanit Ashram; Foundation for Children.

McDermott, J. P., 1984, *Development in the Early Buddhist Concept of Kamma/Karma*, New Delhi, Munshiram Manoharlal.

1998, 'Abortion in the Pāli Canon and Early Buddhist Thought', in Keown, 1998: 157–82.

McFarlane, S. 1986, 'Buddhism', in E. Laszlo and J. Y. Yoo (eds.), *World Encyclopaedia of Peace*, Oxford, Pergamon Press, vol. 1, pp. 97–103.

1990, '*Mushin*, Morals and Martial Arts: A Discussion of Keenan's Yogācāra Critique', *Japanese Journal of Religious Studies*, 17 (4), 397–432.

1994, 'Fighting Bodhisattvas and Inner Warriors: Buddhism and the Martial Traditions of China and Japan', in *The Buddhist Forum, Volume III, 1991–1993*, ed. T. Skorupski and U. Pagel, London, School of Oriental and African Studies, pp. 185–210.

1995, 'Skilful Means, Moral Crises and Conflict Resolution', paper given at Seventh International Seminar on Buddhism and Leadership for Peace, Department of Philosophy, University of Hawaii, Honolulu.

MacPhillamy, Rōshi D., 1982, 'Can Gay People Train in Buddhism?', *Journal of Shasta Abbey*, 9 (1978), reproduced in *Sexuality and Religious Training*, a 1982 booklet of Throssel Hole Priory, near Hexham, England, pp. 27–32.

MacQueen, G., 1981, 'The Conflict between External and Internal Mastery: An Analysis of the *Khantivādi Jātaka*', *History of Religions*, 20 (3), 242–52.

Macy, J., 1983, *Dharma and Development: Religion as Resource in the Sarvodaya Self-help Movement*, West Hartford, Conn., Kumarian.

1991, *World as Lover, World as Self*, Berkeley, Calif., Parallax Press (collected essays).

Mahāmakuṭ Rājavidyālaya Press, 1990, *Pāli Chanting – With Translations*, Bangkok.

Mahasi Sayadaw, 1981, *Sallekha Sutta: A Discourse on the Refinement of Character*, Hinsdale, Ill., Buddhadharma Meditation Center.

Maitreyabandhu, 1995, 'Homosexuality: Has Everyone Got it Wrong?', *Golden Drum* (journal of the Friends of the Western Buddhist Order), No. 37 (May/July), 28.

Malalasekera, G. P., 1967, '"Transference of Merit" in Ceylonese Buddhism', *Philosophy East and West*, 17, pp. 85–90.

Maliszewski, M., 1987, 'Martial Arts', in Eliade, 1987: vol. IX, pp. 224–8.

Mannari, Hiroshi, 1996, 'The Social Background of Japanese Business Leaders: 1880, 1920 and 1960', Inaugural Professorial Lecture at the University of Sunderland, UK, 2 May 1996, 21 pages. Professor Mannari is President of Kibi International University, Okayama, Japan.

Manogaran, C., 1987, *Ethnic Conflict and Reconciliation in Sri Lanka*, Honolulu, University of Hawaii Press.

Maung, M., 1964, 'Cultural Change and Economic Change in Burma', *Asian Survey*, 4, pp. 757–64.

—— 1970, 'The Burmese Way to Socialism Beyond the Welfare State', *Asian Survey*, 10, pp. 533–51.

Maykovich, M. K., 1979, 'The Japanese Family', in M. S. Das and P. D. Bardis (eds.), *The Family in Asia*, London, Allen & Unwin, pp. 381–410.

Metraux, D. A., 1996, 'The Soka Gakkai: Buddhism and the Creation of a Harmonious and Peaceful Society', in Queen and King, 1996: 365–400.

Mettānando Bhikkhu, 1991, 'Buddhist Ethics in the Practice of Medicine', in Fu and Wawrytko, 1991: 195–213.

Miller, B. D., 1980, 'Views of Women's Roles in Buddhist Tibet', in A. K. Narain (ed.), *Studies in the History of Buddhism*, Delhi, B. R. Publishing Corp., pp. 153–66.

Misra, G. S. P., 1984, *Development of Buddhist Ethics*, New Delhi, Munshiram Manoharlal.

Mitomo, R., 1991, 'The Ethics of Mahāyāna Buddhism in the *Bodhicaryāvatāra*', in Fu and Wawrytko, 1991: 15–26.

Moore, C., 1981, *Paraprofessionals in Village-level Development in Sri Lanka: The Sarvodaya Shramadana Movement*, Ithaca, Rural Development Committee, Cornell University.

Morgan, F. B., 1973, 'Vocation of Monk and Layman: Signs of Change in Thai Buddhist Ethics', in B. L. Smith (ed.), *Tradition and Change in Theravada Buddhism*, Leiden, Brill, pp. 68–77.

Mullin, G. H., 1987, *Death and Dying: The Tibetan Tradition*, London, Arkana (translated texts, plus introductions).

Murcott, S., 1991, *The First Buddhist Women: Translations and Commentary on the Therigatha*, Berkeley, Calif., Parallax Press.

Nakasone, R. Y., 1990, *Ethics of Enlightenment: Essays and Sermons in Search of a Buddhist Ethic*, Fremont, Calif., Dharma Cloud Publishers (a Pure Land view.

Ñāṇamoli Thera, 1958, *The Practice of Loving-kindness: Mettā*, Wheel booklet no. 7, Kandy, Sri Lanka, BPS.

Nash, J. and M., 1963, 'Marriage, Family and Population Growth in Upper Burma', *Anthropology*, 19, pp. 251–66.

Nash, M., 1965, *The Golden Road to Modernity*, New York, John Wiley and Sons (on Burma).

Nattier, J., 1991, *Once Upon a Future Time: Studies in a Buddhist Prophecy of Decline*, Berkeley, Calif., Asian Humanities Press.

Nhat Hanh, Thich, 1967, *Vietnam: The Lotus in the Sea of Fire*, London, SCM Press; New York, Hill & Wang.

  1975, *The Miracle of Mindfulness: A Manual on Meditation*, revised edition, translated by Mobi Ho, Boston, Mass., Beacon Press, reprinted 1987.

  1987, *Being Peace*, London, Rider; New York, University of New York Press.

Nhat Hanh, Thich et al., 1993, *For a Future to be Possible: Commentaries on the Five Wonderful Precepts*, Berkeley, Calif., Parallax Press.

NIBWA: *Newsletter on International Buddhist Women's Activities*, 1988, 'Buddhist Views on Abortion', no. 17 (October–December), 6–14.

Nikam, N. A. and McKeon, R., 1959, *The Edicts of Asoka*, Chicago and London, University of Chicago Press; Midway reprint, 1978 (translation).

Nishiyama, K. and Stevens, T., 1975, *Shōbōgenzō: The Eye and the Treasure of the True Law*, vol. 1, Sendai, Japan, Daihokkaikaku (translation).

Niwano, N., 1977, *A Buddhist Approach to Peace*, Tokyo, Kosei Publishing Co.

Norberg-Hodge, H., 1991, *Ancient Futures: Learning from Ladakh*, London, Rider.

Nyanaponika, 1978, *The Roots of Good and Evil*, Wheel booklet no. 251/253, Kandy, Sri Lanka, BPS.

Nyanasobhano (Leonard Price), 1989, *A Buddhist View of Abortion*, Bodhi Leaf booklet no. 117, Kandy, Sri Lanka, BPS.

Obeyesekere, G., 1988, *Meditation on Conscience*, Social Scientists' Association of Sri Lanka, Occasional Papers, Colombo, Navamaga.

Obeyesekere, G. and Reynolds, F., 1972, *The Two Wheels of Dhamma: Essays on the Theravada Tradition in India and Ceylon*, Chambersburg, Penn., American Academy of Religion.

Odzer, C., 1998, 'Abortion and Prostitution in Bangkok', in Keown, 1998: 31–52.

Ornatowski, G. K., 1996, 'Continuity and Change in the Economic Ethics of Buddhism: Evidence from the History of Buddhism in India, China and Japan', *Journal of Buddhist Ethics*, 3, pp. 198–240.

Otani, G., 1991, 'Nichiren's View of Ethics', in Fu and Wawrytko, 1991: 105–15.

Pagel, U., 1995, *The Bodhisattvapiṭka: Its Doctrines, Practices and their Position in Mahāyāna Literature*, Tring, Institute of Buddhist Studies.

Patrul Rinpoche, 1994, *The Words of my Perfect Teacher: Kunzang Lama'i Shelung*, translated by the Padmakara Translation Group, Sacred Literature Trust Series, San Francisco and London, HarperCollins.

Paul, D. Y., 1979, *Women in Buddhism: Images of the Feminine in Mahāyāna Tradition*, Berkeley, Calif., Asian Humanities Press (translations and discussion).

  1980, 'Portraits of the Feminine: Buddhist and Confucian Historical Perspectives', in A. K. Narain (ed.), *Studies in the History of Buddhism*, Delhi, B. R. Publishing Corp., pp. 209–21.

Payutto, Bhikkhu P. A. [also known as Phra Rājavaramuni], 1993, *Good, Evil and*

Beyond: Kamma in the Buddha's Teaching, Bangkok, Buddhadhamma Foundation Publications.

1994, *Buddhist Economics: A Middle Way for the Market Place*, Bangkok, Buddhadhamma Foundation.

Perera, L. P. N., 1993, *Sexuality in Ancient India: A Study Based on the Pali Vinayapiṭāka*, Kelaniya, Sri Lanka, Postgraduate Institute of Pali and Buddhist Studies.

Pfanner, D. E. and Ingersoll, J., 1962, 'Theravada Buddhism and Village Economic Behaviour: A Burmese and Thai Comparison', *Journal of Asian Studies*, 21, pp. 341–61.

Pharr, S. J., 1980, 'The Japanese Woman: Evolving Views of Life and Role', in S. A. Chipp and J. J. Green (eds.), *Asian Women in Transition*, University Park and London, Pennsylvania State University Press, pp. 36–61.

Piburn, S., ed., 1990, *The Dalai Lama; A Policy of Kindness: An Anthology of Writings By and About the Dalai Lama*, Ithaca, N. Y., Snow Lion.

Piker, S., 1973, 'Buddhism and Modernization in Contemporary Thailand', in B. L. Smith (ed.), *Tradition and Change in Theravāda Buddhism*, Leiden, Brill, pp. 51–67.

Prasad, C. S., 1979, 'Meat-eating and the Rule of *Tikoṭipariśuddha*', in A. K. Narain (ed.), *Studies in Pāli and Buddhism*, Delhi, B. R. Publishing Corp., pp. 289–95.

Prebish, C. S., 1975, *Buddhist Monastic Discipline: The Sanskrit Prātimokṣa Strūas of the Mahāsāṃghikas and Mūlasarvāstivādins*, University Park and London, Pennsylvania State University Press.

1980, 'Vinaya and Pratimoksa: The Foundations of Buddhist Ethics', in A. K. Narain (ed.), *Studies in the History of Buddhism*, Delhi, B. R. Publishing Corp.

Premasiri, P. D., 1972, *The Philosophy of the Atthakavagga* (on *Sn.* 766–975), Wheel pamphlet no. 182, Kandy, Sri Lanka, BPS.

Pye, M., 1978, *Skilful Means: A Concept in Mahāyāna Buddhism*, London, Duckworth.

1983, 'Suffering and Health in Mahāyāna Buddhism', in D. Goodacre (ed.), *World Religions and Medicine*, Oxford, The Institute of Religion and Medicine, pp. 24–32.

Queen, C. S., 1996, 'Introduction: The Shapes and Sources of Engaged Buddhism', in Queen and King, 1996: 1–44.

Queen, C. S. and King, S. B., eds., 1996, *Engaged Buddhism: Buddhist Liberation Movements in Asia*, Albany, State University of New York Press.

Rahula, W., 1974, *The Heritage of the Bhikkhu: A Short History of the Bhikkhu in the Educational, Cultural, Social, and Political Life*, New York, Grove Press, 1974 (revised version of the original 1956 translation from Sinhalese).

1978, 'Self-cremation in Mahāyāna Buddhism', in his *Zen and the Taming of the Bull*, London, Gordon Frazer, pp. 111–14.

Rājavaramuni, Phra [also known as Bhikkhu P. A. Payutto], 1990, 'Foundations of Buddhist Social Ethics', in Sizemore and Swearer, 1990: 29–53.

Ratanakul, P., 1986, *Bioethics: An Introduction to the Ethics of Medicine and Life Sciences*, Bangkok, Mahidol University.

1988, 'Bioethics in Thailand: The Struggle for Buddhist Solutions', *Journal of Medicine and Philosophy*, 13, pp. 301–12.

1990, 'Thailand: Refining Cultural Values', *Hastings Center Report*, 20 (2) (March/April), 25–7.

1998, 'Socio-Medical Aspects of Abortion in Thailand', in Keown, 1998: 53–66.

Ray, R., 1980, 'Accomplished Women in the Tantric Buddhism of Medieval India and Tibet', in N. A. Falk and R. M. Gross (eds.), *Unspoken Worlds: Women's Religious Lives in Non-Western Cultures*, San Francisco, Harper & Row, pp. 227–42.

Reed, B. E., 1992, 'The Gender Symbolism of Kuan-yin Bodhisattva', in Cabezón, 1992: 159–80.

Renondeau, G., 1957, 'Histoire des moins guerriers du Japon', in *Mélanges*, vol. I, Paris, L'Institut des Hautes Etudes Chinoises, Presses Universitaires de France, pp. 159–346.

Reynolds, F. E., 1990, 'Ethics and Wealth in Theravāda Buddhism', in Sizemore and Swearer, 1990: 59–86.

Reynolds, F. E and M. B., 1982, *Three Worlds According to King Ruang: A Thai Buddhist Cosmology*, Berkeley Buddhist Studies Series 4, Berkeley, Asian Humanities Press (translation).

Rhys Davids, C. A. F. and Norman, K. R., 1989, *Poems of Early Buddhist Nuns (Therīgāthā)*, London, PTS (translation).

Richman, P., 1992, 'Gender and Persuasion: The Portrayal of Beauty, Anguish, and Nurturance in an Account of a Tamil Nun', in Cabezón, 1992: 111–36.

Rojanaphruk, Phra, 1995, 'A Man on the March' (on Mahā Ghosānanda), *World Fellowship of Buddhists Review*, 32 (1) (January–March), 67–70. Reprinted from *The Nation* newspaper, Bangkok, 4 December 1994.

Rouner, L. S., ed., 1988, *Human Rights and the World's Religions*, Notre Dame, University of Indiana Press.

Ruegg, D. S., 1980, '*Ahiṃsā* and Vegetarianism in the History of Buddhism', in S. Balasooriya et al., (eds.), *Buddhist Studies in Honour of Walpola Rāhula*, London, George Fraser, pp. 234–41.

Saddhatissa, H., 1970, *Buddhist Ethics: Essence of Buddhism*, London, George Allen & Unwin.

1971, *The Buddha's Way*, London, George Allen & Unwin, reprinted 1985; New York, Brazillier, 1972.

Saddhatissa, H. and Webb, R., 1976, *A Buddhist's Manual*, London, British Mahābodhi Society.

Sandell, K., ed., 1987, *Buddhist Perspective on the Ecocrisis*, Wheel booklet no. 346–8, Kandy, Sri Lanka, BPS.

Sangharakshita, 1987, 'Buddhism, Sex and Spiritual Life' (an interview), *Golden Drum* (journal of the Friends of the Western Buddhist Society), no. 6 (October), 4–14.

Saniel, J. M., 1965, 'The Mobilization of Traditional Values in the Modernization of Japan', in R. N. Bellah (ed.), *Religion and Progress in Modern Asia*, London, Collier Macmillan, pp. 124–49.

Santikaro Bhikkhu, 1996, 'Buddhadasa Bhikkhu: Life and Society through the Natural Eyes of Voidness', in Queen and King, 1996: 147–94.

Sarkisyanz, E., 1978, 'Buddhist Backgrounds of Burmese Socialism', in Smith, 1978: 87–99.

Satha-Ananda, Suwanna, 1995, 'Ethics of Wealth: Buddhist Economics for Peace', paper given at the Seventh International Seminar on Buddhism and Leadership for Peace, Department of Philosophy, University of Hawaii, Honolulu, 9 pages.

Schalow, P. G., 1992, 'Kūkai and the Tradition of Male Love in Japanese Buddhism', in Cabezón, 1992: 215–30.

Schmithausen, L., 1991a, *The Problem of the Sentience of Plants in Earliest Buddhism*, Tokyo, The International Institute for Buddhist Studies.

1991b, *Buddhism and Nature: The Lecture delivered on the Occasion of the EXPO 1990, An Enlarged Version with Notes*, Tokyo, The International Institute for Buddhist Studies.

1997, 'The Early Buddhist Tradition and Ecological Ethics', *Journal of Buddhist Ethics*, 4, pp. 1–74.

Schumacher, E. F., 1973, *Small is Beautiful: A Study of Economics as if People Mattered*, London, Blond and Briggs, pp. 48–56: 'Buddhist Economics', which first appeared in G. Wint (ed.), *Asia: A Handbook*, London, Anthony Blond, 1966.

Schuster, N., 1981, 'Changing the Female Body: Wise Women and the Bodhisattva Career in Some *Mahāratnakūṭasūtras*', *Journal of the International Association of Buddhist Studies*, 4 (1), pp. 24–69.

1985, 'Striking a Balance: Women and Images of Women in Early Chinese Buddhism' in Y. Y. Haddas and E. B. Findly (eds.), *Women, Religion and Social Change*, Albany, State University of New York Press, pp. 87–111.

Schuster Barnes, N., 1987, 'Buddhism', in A. Sharma (ed.), *Women in World Religions*, Albany, State University of New York Press.

Shaner, D. E., 1989, 'The Japanese Experience of Nature', in J. B. Callicott and R. T. Ames (eds.), *Nature in Asian Traditions of Thought: Essays in Environmental Philosophy*, Albany, State University of New York Press, pp. 163–82.

Shasta Abbey (publisher: no editor named), 1980, *Buddhism and Respect for Animals*, Mt Shasta, Calif., Shasta Abbey Press.

1981, *Women in Buddhism* (booklet on women in Zen), Mt Shasta, Calif., Shasta Abbey Press.

Shaw, M., 1985, 'Nature in Dōgen's Philosophy and Poetry', *Journal of the International Association of Buddhist Studies*, 8 (2), 111–32.

Shōhei, I., 1987, 'Buddhist Martial Arts', in Eliade, 1987: vol. IX, pp. 228–9.

Sivaraksa, S., 1986, *A Buddhist Vision for Renewing Society – Collected Articles by a Concerned Thai Intellectual*, Bangkok, Tienwan Publishing House.

1991, 'Buddhist Ethics and Modern Politics: A Theravāda Viewpoint', in Fu and Wawrytko, 1991: 159–66.

1992, *Seeds of Peace: A Buddhist Vision for Renewing Society*, Berkeley, Calif., Parallax Press.

Sizemore, R. F. and Swearer, D. K., eds., 1990, *Ethics, Wealth and Salvation: A Study in Buddhist Social Ethics*, Columbia, S.C., University of South Carolina Press.

Smart, N., 1972, 'Creation, Persons and the Meaning of Life', in Ralph Ruddock (ed.), *Six Approaches to the Person*, London and Boston, Mass., Routledge & Kegan Paul.

Smith, B. L., ed., 1978, *Religion and Legitimation of Power in Thailand, Laos, and Burma*, Chambersburg, Penn., Anima Books.

Smith, B., 1992, 'Buddhism and Abortion in Contemporary Japan: Mizuko Kuyō and the Confrontation with Death', in Cabezón, 1992: 65–90, a revised version of a 1988 article of the same title in the *Japanese Journal of Religious Studies*, 15, pp. 3–24.

Smith, H. E., 1979, 'The Thai Rural Family', in M. S. Das and P. D. Bardis (eds.), *The Family in Asia*, London, George Allen & Unwin, pp. 16–46.

Sogyal Rinpoche, 1992, *The Tibetan Book of Living and Dying*, London, Rider.

Southwold, M., 1983, *Buddhism in Life: The Anthropological Study of Religion and the Sinhalese Practice of Buddhism*, Manchester, Manchester University Press.

Spiro, M. E., 1966, 'Buddhism and Economic Action in Burma', *American Anthropologist*, 68, pp. 1163–73.

1971, *Buddhism and Society: A Great Tradition and its Burmese Vicissitudes*, London, George Allen & Unwin.

Sponberg, A., 1992, 'Attitudes towards Women and the Feminine in Early Buddhism', in Cabezón, 1992: 3–36.

Spring Wind Buddhist Cultural Forum, 1986, *Women and Buddhism*, Toronto, Zen Lotus Society (a special issue of *Spring Wind – Buddhist Cultural Forum* 6 (1), (2) and (3)). This includes 'Buddhist Views on Abortion', 166–72.

Stevens, J., 1990, *Lust for Enlightenment: Buddhism and Sex*, Boston, Mass. and London, Shambhala.

Stevenson, I., 1977, 'The Explanatory Value of the Idea of Reincarnation', *Journal of Nervous and Mental Diseases*, 164 (5), 305–26.

Story, F., 1976, 'The place of Animals in Buddhism', in his *Dimensions of Buddhist Thought: Collected Essays Vol. III*, Kandy, Sri Lanka, BPS, pp. 363–73: a reprint of his *The Place of Animals in Buddhism*, Bodhi Leaf pamphlet no. B.24, Kandy, Sri Lanka, BPS, 1964.

Stott, D., 1986, *A Circle of Protection for the Unborn*, Bristol, Ganesha Press.

1992, 'Buddhadharma and Contemporary Ethics: Some Notes on the Attitude of Tibetan Buddhism to Abortion and Related Procedures', *Religion*, 22, pp. 171–82.

Subhuti, Dharmachari, 1983, *Buddhism for Today: A Portrait of a New Buddhist Movement*, Shaftesbury, Dorset, Element Books.

1994, *Sangharakshita: A New Voice in the Buddhist Tradition*, Birmingham, Windhorse Publications.

Sucitto Bhikkhu, 1988, *On Death and Dying*, Newport, Buddhist Hospice Trust.

Suksamran, S., 1977, *Political Buddhism in Southeast Asia: The Role of the Sangha in the Modernization of Thailand*, London, Hurst.

1982, *Buddhism and Politics in Thailand*, Singapore, Institute of Southeast Asian Studies.

Suu Kyi, Aung San, 1995, *Freedom from Fear and Other Writings*, 2nd edn, Harmondsworth, Penguin.

Suzuki, D. T., 1930, *Studies in the Lankavatara Sutra*, London, Routledge & Kegan Paul.

1932, *The Lankavatara Sutra*, London, Routledge & Kegan Paul (translation).

1959, *Zen and Japanese Culture*, New York, Bollingen Foundation.

Swan, B., 1983, 'Sri Lanka: Constraints and Prospects in the Pursuit of Rural Development', in D. A. M. Lea and D. P. Chaudhri (eds.), *Rural Development and the State*, London and New York, Methuen, pp. 127–60.

Swearer, D. K., 1973, 'Community Development and Thai Buddhism', *Visakha Puja*, Bangkok, Buddhist Association of Thailand, pp. 59–67.

1989, *Me and Mine: Selected Essays of Bhikkhu Buddhadāsa*, New York, State University of New York Press.

1995, *The Buddhist World of Southeast Asia*, New York, State University of New York Press.

1996, 'Sulak Sivaraksa's Buddhist Vision for Renewing Society', in Queen and King, 1996: 195–235.

Sweet, M. J. and Zwilling, L., 1993, 'The First Medicalization: The Taxonomy and Etiology of Queerness in Classical Indian Medicine', *Journal of the History of Sexuality*, 3 (4), 590–607.

Tähtinen, U., 1976, *Ahimsa – Non-violence in the Indian Tradition*, London, Rider.

Tambiah, S. J., 1973, 'Buddhism and This-worldly Activity', *Modern Asian Studies*, 7 (1), 1–20.

1976, *World Conqueror and World Renouncer – A Study of Buddhism and Polity in Thailand against a Historical Background*, Cambridge, Cambridge University Press

1984, *The Buddhist Saints of the Forest and the Cult of Amulets (as in Thailand)*, Cambridge, Cambridge University Press.

1992, *Buddhism Betrayed? Religion, Politics and Violence in Sri Lanka*, Chicago and London, University of Chicago Press.

Tanabe, G. J., 1994, review of LaFleur's *Liquid Life* in *Japanese Journal of Religious Studies* 21, pp. 437–40.

Tanaka, M., 1986, 'The Myth of Perfect Motherhood: Japanese Women's Dilemma', in D. L. Eck and D. Jain (eds.), *Speaking of Faith: Cross-cultural Perspectives on Women, Religion and Social Change*, London, The Women's Press, pp. 69–76.

Tangwisuttiji, N., 1990, 'An Environmentalist Monk', *World Fellowship of Buddhists Review*, 27 (2), 53–5.

Taniguchi, Shoyo, 1987, 'Biomedical Ethics from a Buddhist Perspective', *The*

Pacific World: Journal of the Institute of Buddhist Studies, New Series no. 3, pp. 75–83.

Tarthang Tulku, 1985, *Mother of Knowledge: The Enlightenment of Ye-shes mTsho-rgyal*, Berkeley, Calif., Dharma Publishing.

Tatz, M., 1986, *Asanga's Chapter on Ethics, with the Commentary of Tsong-Kha-Pa*, Studies in Asian Thought and Religion, vol. 4, Lewiston/Queenston, Edwin Mellen Press (translations from Asaṅga's chapter on ethics (*śīla*) in his *Bodhisattva-bhūmi*, in Sanskrit, and Tsong-kha-pa's *Basic Path to Awakening*, in Tibetan).

1994, *The Skill in Means (Upāyakauśalya) Sūtra*, Delhi, Motilal Banarsidass (translation).

Tedesco, F., 1998, 'Abortion in Korea', in Keown, 1998: 121–55.

Terweil, B. J., 1979, *Monks and Magic: An Analysis of Religious Ceremonies in Central Thailand*, 2nd rev. edn, London, Curzon Press.

Thanissaro Bhikkhu (G. DeGraff), 1994, *The Buddhist Monastic Code: The Patimokkha Training Rules Translated and Explained*, printed for free distribution. Available from: The Abbot, Metta Forest Monastery, PO Box 1409, Valley Center, CA 92082, USA.

Tharchin, S. G. L., 1984, *King Udrayana and the Wheel of Life – The History and Meaning of the Buddhist Teaching of Dependent Origination*, Howell, N. J., Mahayana Sutra and Tantra Press.

Thitsa, K., 1980, *Providence and Prostitution: Image and Reality for Women in Buddhist Thailand* (booklet), London, Change International Reports.

Thomas, E. J., 1949, *The Life of the Buddha as Legend and History*, 3rd rev. edn, London, Routledge & Kegan Paul.

Thurman, R. A. F., 1981, 'The Emptiness that is Compassion', *Religious Traditions*, 4 (2), 11–34.

1985, 'Nagarjuna's Guidelines for Buddhist Social Action', in Eppsteiner, 1988: 120–44.

Timmerman, P., 1995, 'Defending Materialism', *People and the Planet*, magazine of the World Wide Fund for Nature, 4 (1), pp. 30–1.

Topley, M., 1975, 'Marriage Resistance in Rural Kwangtung', in M. Wolf and R. Witke (eds.), *Women in Chinese Society*, Stanford, Stanford University Press.

Toynbee, A. and Ikeda, D., 1989, *Choose Life: A Dialogue*, Oxford, Oxford University Press.

Tsai, K. A., 1994, *Lives of the Nuns: Biographies of Chinese Buddhist Nuns from the Fourth to Sixth Centuries* (a translation of *Pi-ch'iu-ni chuan*), Honolulu, University of Hawaii Press (translation).

Tsomo, Karma Lekshe, ed., 1988, *Sakyadhītā: Daughters of the Buddha* (a record of the first International Conference of Buddhist Nuns, Bodh-Gayā, 1987), Ithaca, N.Y., Snow Lion.

1995, *Buddhism through American Women's Eyes*, New York, Snow Lion.

Tsunoda, R., de Bary, W. T. and Keene, D., 1964, *Sources of Japanese Tradition*, 2 vols., New York and London, Columbia University Press (translations and comments).

Tucci, G., 1980, *The Religions of Tibet*, London, Routledge & Kegan Paul.

Tworkov, H., 1992, 'Anti-abortion/Pro-choice: Taking Both Sides', *Tricycle: The Buddhist Review*, 1 (3), 60–9.

Uchino, K., 1986, 'The Status Elevation Process of Sōtō Sect Nuns in Modern Japan', in D. L. Eck and D. Jain (eds.), *Speaking of Faith: Cross-cultural Perspectives on Women, Religion and Social Change*, London, The Women's Press, pp. 149–63.

Umezawa, K., 1988, 'Medical Ethics in Japan', *Biomedicine and Pharmacotherapy*, 42, pp. 169–72.

Upadhyaya, K. N., 1971, *Early Buddhism and the Bhagavad Gītā*, Delhi, Motilal Banarsidass.

van der Tak, J., 1974, *Abortion, Fertility, and Changing Legislation: An International Review*, Lexington, Mass., and London, Lexington Books.

Van Loon, L., 1978, 'A Buddhist Viewpoint', in G. C. Oosthuizen, H. Shapiro, and S. A. Strauss (eds.), *Euthanasia*, Cape Town, Oxford University Press, pp. 71–9.

Victoria, B., 1997, *Zen at War*, New York, Weatherhill.

Von Hinüber, O., 1995, 'Buddhist Law According to the Theravāda-Vinaya: A Survey of Theory and Practice', *Journal of the International Association of Buddhist Studies*, 18 (1), 7–45.

Walters, J. S., 1995, 'Gotamī's Story', in D. S. Lopez (ed.), *Buddhism in Practice* (an anthology of translations), Princeton, N. J., Princeton University Press, pp. 113–38 (translation of pp. 529–43 of the *Therī-apadāna*, from the Pali Canon (story no. 17)).

Warren, H. C., 1896, *Buddhism in Translations*, Harvard Oriental Series; reprinted 1987, Delhi, Motilal Banarsidass (anthology of translations).

Wawrytko, S. A., 1991, 'On the Path of Ultimate Awakening: Women's Liberation in the Context of Taoism and Ch'an/Zen', in Fu and Wawrytko, 1991: 265–80.

1993, 'Homosexuality and Chinese and Japanese Religions', in A. Swidler (ed.), *Homosexuality and World Religions*, Valley Forge, Penn., Trinity Press International, pp. 199–230.

Wayman, A., 1991, *Ethics of Tibet: Bodhisattva Section of Tsong-Kha-Pa's Lam Rim Chen Mo*, Albany, State University of New York Press (translations).

Weber, M., 1951, *The Religion of China: Confucianism and Taoism*, New York, The Free Press, and London, Collier-Macmillan.

1958, *The Religion of India: The Sociology of Hinduism and Buddhism*, New York, The Free Press, and London, Collier Macmillan.

1963, *The Sociology of Religion*, Boston, Mass., Beacon Press.

Welch, H., 1967, *The Practice of Chinese Buddhism, 1900–1950*, Cambridge, Mass., Harvard University Press.

1972, *Buddhism Under Mao*, Cambridge, Mass., Harvard University Press (pp. 267–97 discusses attempts to find Buddhist textual support for killing class and foreign enemies).

WFBR: *World Fellowship of Buddhists Review*, 1981, 'News and Views: Abortion Bill', 18 (6), 19–35, 52–3.

WFBR: *World Fellowship of Buddhists Review*, 1983, editorial: 'Another Buddhist's View on Buddhists Eating Meat', 20 (3), appendix, pp. 1–8.

WFBR: *World Fellowship of Buddhists Review*, 1984, 'Buddhists Concerned for Animals', 21 (4), pp. 73–9.

Whitmyer, C., ed., 1994, *Mindfulness and Meaningful Work: Explorations of Right Livelihood*, Berkeley, Calif., Parallax Press.

Wijayaratna, M., 1990, *Buddhist Monastic Life: According to the Texts of the Theravāda Tradition*, Cambridge, Cambridge University Press.

Williams, P., 1989, *Mahāyāna Buddhism: The Doctrinal Foundations*, London, Routledge.

   1998, *Altruism and Reality: Studies in the Philosophy of the Bodhicaryāvatāra*, London, Curzon Press.

Willis, J., ed., 1989, *Feminine Ground: Essays on Women and Tibet*, Ithaca, N.Y., Snow Lion.

Willson, M., 1986, *In Praise of Tārā: Songs to the Saviouress*, London, Wisdom.

Wilson, B. and Dobbelaere, K., 1994, *A Time to Chant – The Soka Gakkai Buddhists in Britain*, Oxford, Oxford University Press.

Wiltshire, M., 1983, 'The "Suicide" Problem in the Pāli Canon', *Journal of the International Association of Buddhist Studies*, 6 (2), 124–40.

Yampolsky, P. B., 1990, *Selected Writings of Nichiren*, edited with an introduction by Yampolsky; translated by Burton Watson and others, New York, Columbia University Press.

Young, K. K., 1987, 'Hinduism', in A. Sharma (ed.), *Women in World Religions*, Albany, State University of New York Press, pp. 59–103.

Yün-hua, J., 1965, 'Buddhist Self-immolation in Medieval China', *History of Religions*, 4, pp. 243–68.

Yuthok, Karma Gelek, 1995, 'The Five Precepts and the Vajrayāna', *World Fellowship of Buddhists Review*, 32 (3), 45–56.

Zwilling, L., 1992, 'Homosexuality as Seen in Indian Buddhist Texts', in Cabezón, 1992: 203–14.

Useful addresses

(correct at time of going to press)

INTERNET RESOURCES

Journal of Buddhist Ethics:
   UK address: http://jbe.gold.ac.uk
   US address: http://jbe.la.psu.edu
'Buddha-L' or 'Buddhist Academic Discussion Forum'
   to subscribe, send an e-mail message to: listserv@listserv.louisville.edu
   with the message:
   subscribe buddha-l [your name here]
'Buddhist' or 'Forum on Indian and Buddhist Studies'
   to subscribe, send an e-mail message to:
   listserv@lists.mcgill.ca
   with the message:
   subscribe buddhist [your name here]

ENGAGED BUDDHISM

Angulimala, Buddhist Prison Chaplaincy Organisation, The Forest Hermitage, Lower Fulbrook, Warwick, CV35 8AS, England.
International Network of Engaged Buddhists Secretariat, 127 Soi Santipap, Nares Road, Bangkok 10500, Thailand.
Network of Engaged Buddhists, Plas Plwca, Cwmrheidol, Aberystwyth, Wales, SY23 3NB.

NATURE

The Buddhist Perception of Nature Project, c/o Miss Nancy Nash, International Co-ordinator, 5 H Bowen Road, 1st Floor, Hong Kong. Telex: 72149 SIDAN HX.

WAR AND PEACE

Buddhist Peace Fellowship, PO Box 4650, Berkeley, CA 94704, USA. $25 membership fee, which includes quarterly newsletter.

APPROACHING DEATH

Raft – The Journal of the Buddhist Hospice Trust, c/o Ray Wills, 5 Grayswood Point, Norley Vale, Roehampton, London, sw15 4BT, England. £2 per issue.

WOMEN AND BUDDHISM

Yasodhara: Newsletter on International Buddhist Women's Activities, c/o Dr Chatsumarn Kabilsingh, Faculty of Liberal Arts, Thammasat University, Bangkok 10200, Thailand. $10 per annum. From her, for $35 including postage, one can get her Kabilsingh's *A Comparative Study of Bhikkhunī Pāṭimokkha* (200 pages).

Sakyadhītā, the International Association of Buddhist Women: Sakyadhita International, c/o Mather/ Vincenty, 1143 Piikoi Place, Honolulu, Hawaii 96822, USA. $30 ($15 for nun, student or unemployed) per annum for subscription, which includes a newsletter.

Kahawai Journal of Women and Zen, Diamond Sangha, 2119 Kaloa Way, Honolulu, Hawaii 96822, USA.

Index of Buddhist texts, schools, cultural areas, movements and organizations

Śrāvakayāna (non-Mahāyāna)

123, 131, 134, 136, 140, 142, 144, 147, 314, **437**
Edicts of Asoka (who was close to both
Theravāda and Sarvāstivāda), **116–17**, 157,
158, 166, 167, 173, 177, 188, 253, 346, 353,
392
Jātaka-mālā (Khoroche, 1989), 105n, 172n, 291
Mahā-vastu (Mvs.) (of Lokottaravāda school),
110n, 115, 198, 199, 373, 385, 386, 415
Maṇimēkalai, 393
Sarvāstivāda school, 6, 12, 83, 151, 161, 254,
312, 368, 386, 371; Mūla-, 93, 387, 399, 437;
Sautrāntika (a related school), 83
Sarvāstivāda texts: *Abhidharma-kośa-bhāṣya*
(AKB.) (of Vasubandhu; AK is Sarvāstivada,
and B. is a Sautrāntika commentary on it),
6, 19, 23, 24, 25n, 26n, 46, 52n, 57, 72–3, 74,
75, 78, 79, 84, 85, 150, 151, 166–7, 174, 254,
296, 298, 308, 312, 318, 339, 368, 371, 378,
390, 412, 412n, 415, 417–18, 419, 422, 435;
Madhyamāgama, 386; *Vibhāṣā*, 296
schools other than Theravāda and
Sarvāstivāda: Dharmaguptaka, 83, 93, 386,
397; Haimavata, 386; Lokottaravāda, 115;
Mahā-saṃghika, 83, 386; Mahīśāsaka, 83,
289, 386

Theravāda texts of the Pali Canon

4–5, 6, 42, 43, 61, 68, 83, 232, 254, 358, 367,
368, 401, **437**
Abhidhamma Piṭaka, 5, 25n, 43, 175, 312, 326,
362, 368, 435; *Dhamma-saṅgaṇi (Dhs.)*, 308,
368; *Kathāvatthu (Kvu.)*, 12, 20n, 44n, 66, 92n,
298; *Puggala-paññatti (Pug.)*, 13; *Vibhaṅga*
(Vibh.), 14, 24, 40n, 48, 52, 306n, 312, 318,
368, 372, 417
Aṅguttara Nikāya (A.), 10, 11, 15, 16, 17, 18, 19, 21,
22, 23, 24, 25, 30, 31, 34, 38, 39, 41, 44n, 47,
48, 52, 56, 57, 61, 62, 63, 66, 67, 68, 71, 75,
78, 83, 89, 92n, 97, 101n, 102, 103, 110n, 115,
152, 157, 160, 170, 172, 176, 187, 188, 189,
190, 191, 191n, 196, 200, 204, 209, 239, 240,
249, 252, 291, 292, 356, 357, 358, 371, 372,
379, 380, 381, 383, 390, 401, 402, 416, 420;
Kālāma Sutta, 10, 47
Dīgha Nikāya (D.), 16n, 19, 22, 24, 26n, 30, 41,
43, 47, 48, 52, 58, 61n, 65, 66, 67, 68, 69, 71,
77, 91, 96, 99–100, 110n, 111, 117n, 152, 153n,
173, 174, 183, 188, 189, 197, 197n, 203, 240,
241, 252, 254, 287, 311, 312, 313n, 346, 357,
369, 371, 372, 379, 385, 389, 403, 421;
Aggañña Sutta, 114, 118, 153, 218, 224n, 252,
346, 421; *Cakkavatti-sīhanāda Sutta*, 114, 197,
201, 252, 346, 403; *Kūṭadanta Sutta*, 157, 198,
202, 232, 240, 241; *Mahā-sudassana Sutta*, 198;
Sigālovāda Sutta, 70, 77, **97–8**, **99–100**,
109–10, 155, 109, 188, 189–90, 232, 389
Khuddaka Nikāya: Buddhavaṃsa (Bv.), 373, 385;
Cariya-piṭaka (Cp.), 63n, 378; *Dhammapada*
(Dhp.), 9, 15, 25, 29, 31, 34, 42, 43, 56, 62, 66,
67, 68, 92n, 104, 107, 156, 195, 196, 242, 243,
247, 250, 280, 401, 436; *Itivuttaka (It.)*, 18, 25,
44, 50, 61n, 62, 191; *Jātaka* (and its
commentary) *(J.)*, 5, **9**, 20, 25, 29, 53, 54, 74,
89, 99, 101, 107, 115, 115n, 150, 158, 162, 170,
172, 176, 190, 204, 209, 241, 242, 315, 343–4,
369, 370, 372, 373, **376–9**, 383, 392, 402,
409, 413, 419, 422–3, 436; *Khanti-vādi Jātaka*,
105–6, 243; *Kunāla Jātaka*, 377; *Kurudhamma*
Jātaka, 54; *Vessantara Jātaka*, 63–4, 98, 100,
403; *Khuddaka-pāṭha (Khp.)*, 12, 19, 29, 46, 98;
Khp: Karaṇīya-metta Sutta, 104–5, 170, 372;
Khp: Maṅgala Sutta, 98, 188, 232; *Niddesa*
(Nd.), 368; *Paṭisambhidā-magga (Ps.)*, 312n;
Petavatthu (Pv.), 65, 315, 368, 369; *Sutta-nipāta*
(Sn.), 34, 43, 68, 69, 70, 71, 76, 77, 87n, 99,
110, 110n, 111, 160, 188, 189, 240; *Sn:*
Parābhava Sutta, 232; *Theragāthā (Thag.)*,
154–5, 390; *Therī-apadāna*, 360–1; *Therīgāthā*

463

Eastern Buddhism

Index of concepts

Abhidhamma, 5, 43, 60, 78, 175, 308, 312, 368, 435; *and see* index of Buddhist texts and schools
abortion, **311–52**; in Buddhist cultures, 328–42; and Buddhist principles, 313–26; in China, 332; and contraception, 326–8; and euthanasia, 323; in Japan, 332–41; karmic results of, 315, 325, 338; law and morality on, 342–50; laws on in Buddhist countries, 332–3, 339, 349, 350; possible grounds for, 319–26; rates of, 330–1, 333; in Sri Lanka, 329; in Thailand, 330–2; among Tibetans, 328–9
acknowledgement of fault, 26–8, 56, 247, 248
actions: criteria for moral assessment of, 43, **46–9**; four kinds of, 44, 58 and intention, 17, 52–4, 55, 58; karmic fruits of, 2, 10, 11, **14–16, 24–6**, 59, 287; mental, 17, 48, 56, 57, 66, 341, 345; and motive/root, 17, **28–31**, **46–7**, 49, 57, 58, 89, 135, 239, 288; right, 37–9, 74; as shaping character, 58; ten unwholesome, 48, 74; wholesome/ unwholesome, **10, 42–3**, 60–1, 67, 134, 288, 296, 370; wrong, 17, 56, 59, 74
adoption, 322, 324, 326, 329, 350, 351
adultery, 71–3, 407
ahiṃsā (non-injury), 69, 156
AIDS/HIV, 319, 323, 349, 423, 431, 432
alcohol and intoxication, 54, 77–9, 91, 141, 142, 344
alms-giving, 61–4, 192, 381
androcentrism, 357, 390, 391
androgyny, 364, 375
anger, 36, 244–6, 250, 262–3, 301, 351
animals: and euthanasia, 173, 195; experimentation on, 168–70; help for, 170–4; husbandry of, 166; non-harming of, 114, 156–7, 344, 346, 348; place and nature of, 24, 150–1, 156; sacrifice of, 157, 168

apology, 247, 341
*Arahat*s, 26, 39, 40, 43, 45, 67, 111, 360, 373, 375, 390, 435; and *Bodhisattva*s, 129, 134; as Buddhist teachers, 233; female, 357–61, 372, 373, 384, 409; as incapable of killing, 254; as beyond karmic fruitfulness, 43–4; among laity, 92; wilderness meditators among, 154
Arahatship, 41, 92, 123, 134, 291, 359; as Theravāda goal, 361
army chaplains, 255
asceticism, 355; and misogyny, 357, 360, 378; and wariness of the opposite sex, 379–83
aspiration, 41, 361
assemblies, four, 88, 356
attachment, 67, 122, 147, 293, 297, 325, 353, 382, 428; to body, 380; to female form, 379; to 'I', 244; as lesser fault than hatred or delusion, 90; to material things, 239; to sense-pleasures, 73, 89, 90, 303; to virtues and vows, 40, 45,160

'baby and chimpanzee test', 321, 322, 323, 325, 326, 350
beings: as close friends or relatives in past life, 29, 35, 120, 121, 127, 163, 244, 369; inter-relationship of all, 185; sentient, 56, 253, 315
between lives state, 312–13
bodhi-citta, 'thought of enlightenment', 126–8, 133, 361, 374, 375
*Bodhisattva*s (beings-for-enlightenment), **4**, 163, 361, 373, **435**; compassion of, 124, 135–7; counterfeit, 133; ethics of, 130–2, 144; and evil deeds, 27; female, 361, 363, 366, 373–6, 399, 409; generosity of, 63, 64, 158, 291, 403; heavenly, 27, 81, 130, 134, 363; interaction with in Mahāyāna, 27, 81, 127, 128; lay, 139, 140, 146, 147, 148, 191, 194, 195; Noble, 128, 140; *paṇḍaka* as able to be, 418; path of, 4, 5, 123–6, 128, 133, 134, 135, 141, 147, 373, 374, 376; perfections of, 63, 74, 128–30, 134, 274,

Index of concepts

Index of names

478

Index of names

Sri Lanka, 5, 7, 9, 158, 166, 167, 173, 174, 178, 179, **225–7**, 233, 327, 421; abortion, views of in, 266, 316, 320, 329, 343, 351; animals' treatment in, 171; 'Buddhist economics', views on in, 216–17; commercial roles in, 208, 210; contraception in, 326, 328; ethnic conflict in, 255–60, 275–7, 282, 283, 328; giving in, 192; homosexuality in, 423–4; kings in, 117, 201, 231; law tradition in, 343; laywomen in, 404, 405; meateating in, 161, 162; monks and monasticism in, 118, 205, 423, 424; mothers in, 98; nuns in, 395, 396, 397, 398, 400; precepts in, 71, 72, 79, 80, 82, 88; 'Protestant Buddhism' in, 112, 161; psychological repression in, 263; suicide, attitude to in, 299; *and see* Sarvōdaya Śramadāna in index of Buddhist texts and schools

Stott, David, 314, 315, 318, 319, 324, 326, 327, 328, 329

Taiwan, 7, 84, 393, 394, 397
Tambiah, Stanley, 115, 207, 218, 260, 275
Tamils, 255–60, 276, 328, 393
Taniguchi, Shoyo, 297, 303, 322, 325
Taoism, 269, 425
Tārā, 'Saviouress', 361, 363, 366, 376
Thailand, 7, 166, 167, 169–70, 174, 178, 180, 196, 225, 275, 327, 329; abortion and views on it in, 316, 317, 321, 322–3, 330–2, 333, 340, 343, 344–5, 351; AIDS in, 423; animals, treatment of in, 171; Brahmanism in, 404; 'Buddhist economics', views on in, 216–19; care of the dying in, 297, 304; class system in, 112; commercial roles in, 208; Communism, fear of in, 260–1; conflict in, 260, 262–3; Confucianism in, 237; contraception in, 326; economy and development in, 118, 208, 225, 237; environmentalism in, 181–2; euthanasia, views on in, 297; generating karmic fruitfulness in, 194; giving in, 96, 192, 194–5; homosexuality in, 423; kings in, 117, 260; laywomen in, 404–6; marriage in, 101–3; meateating in, 161; military in, 254; nuns in, 208, 394, 395–8; ordination in, 424; precepts in, 70, 72, 77, 78, 82, 88; prostitutes in, 405, 406; religious expenditure in, 192–3; social

relationships in, 98, 99, 214, 404; slavery in, 188–9; smoking in, 79
Tibet and Tibetans, 7, 165, 166, 167, 178, 437; on abortion, 14, 328–9, 343, 351; animals, treatment of in, 176; commercial roles in, 208; compassionate killing in, 140; female deities and incarnations in, 361, 365, 399; female saints of, 399; gambling in, 70; holy beings in, 364; homosexuality in, 418, 422, 424–5, 432, 434; law tradition in, 343; laywomen in, 399, 407–9; marriage in, 102; monasticism in, 149, 206, 424–5, 427; Mūla-Sarvāstivādin code in, 67, 93; non-violence in, 284; nuns in, 399–400; on precepts, 83, 288; on rarity of human life in, 29; smoking in, 79; on suicide, 288; tantric practice in, 137; trading by monks in, 206; views of particular Lamas, 73, 301–2, 320, 326, 328, 329n, 364; *and see* Dalai Lama, sGam po pa, Yeshe Tsogyel
Tilopa (tenth-century Indian tantric adept), 142
Toda, Josei, 273
Tsong-kha-pa (1357–1410), 132, 139, 140
Tworkov, Helen, 342, 348

United Kingdom, 165, 292, 302, 307, 320, 331, 407; views on homosexuality of Buddhists in, 428–30
Utilitarianism, 49–50, 51

Vajra-vārāhī, 399
Vasubandhu (fourth century), 6, 24, 166, 254, 374, 415, 417, 418, 419, **438**
Vietnam, 7, 260, 284, 294, 394
Vietnam War, 109, 255, 260, 278, 292, 406
Vimalakīrti, 148, 195
Visākhā, 191, 401

Weber, Max, 206–7, 210, 214–15
Wu, Emperor (502–40), 158, 164

Yeshe Tsogyel (eighth century; Tibetan Yeshes mTsho-rgyal), 129, 365, 399

Zanskar valley, 54, 167–8
Zwilling, Leonard, 413, 414, 415, 416, 420, 421